METALWORK
TECHNOLOGY AND PRACTICE

METALWORK
TECHNOLOGY AND PRACTICE

OSWALD A. LUDWIG
Formerly Department Head
Vocational Education
Henry Ford High School
Detroit, Michigan

Revised by:
WILLARD J. McCARTHY
College of Applied Science
and Technology
Illinois State University
Normal, Illinois

McKNIGHT & McKNIGHT
Publishing Company
Bloomington, Illinois

"No matter what a man's work,
he can do it better if he is well informed."

—Dr. Frank Crane

Preface

This book presents instruction and information in the following basic areas of metalwork: bench metalwork, sheet metalwork, forging, heat treatment, foundry work, welding, finishing and quality control, machine tool theory and practice, and numerical control machining.

The previous fourth edition has been carefully and completely reviewed and brought up-to-date. Many units are expanded significantly to reflect current industrial and technological practice. A number of sections are completely rewritten, and additional new units have been added.

New materials included at the beginning of the book are: an introduction to metalwork, occupational information, and information concerning project planning. The following units are expanded considerably: hand tools, cutting fluids, fits and fitting, rivets, fasteners, screw threads, threading tools, abrasives, grinding wheels, power sawing, drill-press operations, and quality control and inspection. The unit on heat treatment has been completely rewritten. New units concerning hardness testing and numerical control machining have been included.

This fifth edition includes the information necessary for an introductory course in machine shop theory and practice. The lathe unit includes the basic lathe operations through threading, and additional units cover the use of the shaper, milling machines, and grinding machines. A new unit on numerical control machining provides a basic understanding of the principles and practices of this important and widely used machine control method.

Simple language and abundant illustrations have been used throughout the book. A comprehensive vocabulary list is included at the end of each unit. It is important to learn the meanings of technical words in each unit, especially the words which are italicized. Review questions also are included at the end of each unit. The questions may be used as an aid in guiding your study or for review purposes after demonstrations or during class discussions. A revised *Study Guide* (workbook) is also available for use with this new edition.

This fifth edition was prepared to meet the objective so clearly expressed by Oswald A. Ludwig in the preface of the previous edition:

Shop courses often emphasize the "doing" or skill aspects of metalwork and neglect the information that constitutes a very real part of every process and operation. Shop courses must emphasize the training and educational values that are the result of gaining information as well as of making things. This book fills the needs of shop theory, technology, technical information, and shop science classes. It also supplies the information about tools, machines, materials, and operations so badly needed in drafting classes.

Metalwork Technology and Practice provides a broad introduction to the theory and practice of metalworking. Metals are basic to our industrial and technological progress and development.

Willard J. McCarthy

Acknowledgments

Acknowledgment and appreciation is expressed by the publishers and the present coauthor to the following people who provided helpful criticism, information, and suggestions used in the preparation of previous editions: Mr. F. R. Kepler, Mr. Harry M. Dextor, Mr. Floyd C. Allison, and Mr. Carnot Iverson. Mrs. Oswald A. Ludwig participated unstintingly in the preparation of previous editions, and Mr. Earl A. Ludwig provided assistance in the fourth edition.

The new fifth edition was prepared with extensive help from many individuals and industrial firms. Appreciation is expressed to Mrs. McCarthy for typing the manuscript and the necessary correspondence. Howard T. Davis prepared new drawings used in the book.

Sincere appreciation is expressed to the following industrial firms and organizations who provided numerous illustrations and technical material used in the book:

Adjustable Clamp Company
AJAX Electric Company
Aluminum Company of America
American Gas Company
American Iron and Steel Institute
American Machinist
American Screw Company
American Society for Metals
Ames Precision Machine Works
Anaconda Company
Armstrong Brothers Tool Company
Barber-Colman Company
Bausch & Lomb, Inc.
Bridgeport Machines, Inc.
Brown & Sharpe
   Manufacturing Company
Buick Division, General
   Motors Corporation
Cadillac Division, General
   Motors Corporation
Carboloy Metallurgical Products
   Dept., General Electric Company
Carburundum Company
Chevrolet Division, General
   Motors Corporation
Chicago Rivet & Machine Company
Chrysler Corporation
The Cincinnati Lathe
   & Tool Company
The Cincinnati Milling Machine
   Company
The Cincinnati Shaper Company
The Cincinnati Tool Company
Clausing Division,
   Atlas Press Company
The Cleveland Twist Drill Company
Detroit Power Screwdriver Company

Eugene Dietzgen Company
Henry Disston & Sons Company
DoALL Company
Eclipse Counterbore Company
Federal Products Corporation
Fellowcrafters, Inc.
The Foot-Burt Company
Friden, Inc.
General Motors Corporation
Goodell-Pratt Company
G. A. Gray Company
Great Lakes Screw Corporation
Greenfield Tap & Die Corporation
Hobart Brothers Company
The Holo-Krome Screw Corporation
Hughes Industrial Systems Division,
   Hughes Aircraft Company
Inland Steel Company
International Business Machines
C. E. Johansson Gage Company
Johnson Gas and Appliance Company
Linde Air Products Company
Link-Belt Company
McEnglevan Heat Treating &
   Manufacturing Company
McGraw-Hill Book Company, Inc.
Miller Electric Company
National Bureau of Standards
National Cash Register Company
National Cylinder Gas Company
National Machine Tool Builders
   Association
National Twist Drill & Tool Company
Niagara Machine & Tool Works
Norton Company
Oldsmobile Division, General
   Motors Corporation

Oliver Machinery Company
Pontiac Division, General
   Motors Corporation
Pratt & Whitney Company
Precision Tool & Manufacturing
   Company
Reynolds Metals Company
The Rigid Tool Company
Rockwell Manufacturing Company,
   Power Tool Instructor
George Scherr Company
Sheldon Machine Company, Inc.
Shore Instrument &
   Manufacturing Company
South Bend Lathe, Inc.
The L. S. Starrett Company
Taft-Pierce Manufacturing Company
Tempil° Corporation
Thermolyne Corporation
Thompson Products Company
TOCCO Division, Park-Ohio
   Industries, Inc.
Today, International Harvester
   Company
Union Carbide Corporation
Union Drawn Steel Company
Union Twist Drill Company
U. S. Electrical Manufacturing
   Company
U. S. Pipe & Foundry Company
United States Steel Corporation
Waldes Kohinoor, Inc.
The Walton Company
J. H. Williams & Company
World, International Harvester
   Company
Youngstown Sheet and Tube
   Company

Content

List of Tables

How to Use This Book

Textbook or Reference Book

This book may be used as a text for regular study and reading assignments or it may be used for reference purposes.

Demonstration Aid

The teacher may use this book as a guide in planning his demonstration; the student may use it to prepare for the demonstration so that he may observe it more intelligently. It may also be used to follow up the demonstration, for the student can go on with his project with greater confidence and gain skill more quickly if he has the necessary information at hand to help him with details.

Table of Contents

The Table of Contents may be used as a *course outline*.

Units

Each unit is arranged as an instruction sheet. The units have been arranged as much as possible in order of learning difficulty. They may, however, be arranged in other sequences. Those units, or sections, which best meet the needs of the student should be selected.

Occupational Information

Since the philosophy of the *general metal shop* is to provide tryout experiences and to help the student decide upon the occupation he is to follow, certain occupational information has been woven into the text. Unit 2 explains many different kinds of metalworking occupations, including engineers, technicians, skilled occupations, and semiskilled occupations.

Safety

Unit 3 explains general safety practices in the metal shop. Other safety topics are explained throughout the text.

Section Numbers

In this book a *section* is a part of a *Unit*. These sections are numbered throughout the book for ready reference. The sign § means *section;* §§ means *sections*. Many references are made to sections which give more information on certain topics.

Preparing Job Sheets

In planning and using job sheets, the student may be referred to this book for information. This can be done by inserting on the job sheet the number of the section in the book which gives the necessary information. This eliminates including on the job sheet the information about a certain tool or process and simplifies the sheet.

Review Questions

The review questions which follow each unit may be used to guide the student's study and for class discussion of each unit. The questions also may be used after demonstrations to review and establish the points covered in the demonstrations.

Coordination

The Coordination of *related subjects* at the end of each unit suggests assignments which may be made to give application to other school subjects.

Words to Know

There are about 2000 or more words in this book which are new to many students. The meanings of the words in *italics* must be learned to understand the lessons and to aid in developing a *technical vocabulary. Definitions* of words appear in the footnotes and in the context.

Machine Tools

Units 57 through 62 are longer units concerning Machine Tools and their operation. These units include the lathe, shaper, horizontal and vertical milling machines, and grinding machines. Power saws and their operation are included in Unit 12. The drill press, drilling accessories, and drilling procedures are included in Units 25 through 30. These units concerning machine tools and their operations include sufficient content for a beginning course in machine shop theory and practice.

Index

The book is indexed in detail to make it useful as a handbook or reference book as well as a text. The teacher should help the student form the habit of using the Index. It is the best way to find valuable information.

Study Guide

Metalwork Technology and Practice is complete. However, a *Study Guide* has been prepared and published separately which helps the student to think through the lessons, do them in the least time, and keep them in an orderly manner. The teacher can quickly check the knowledge and progress of the student.

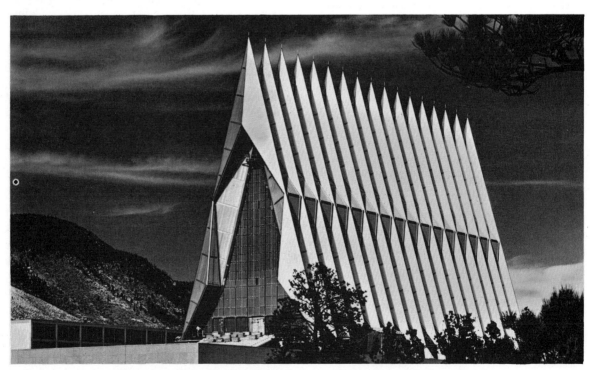

Chapel at U.S. Air Force Academy — Many Men with Specialized Abilities Work in Many Occupations to Make Possible this Building with its Aluminum Tetrahedrons
(Courtesy Aluminum Company of America)

Introduction to Metalwork

1. Metals Are Important

Have you ever thought about the importance of metals in our industrial society and in our daily lives? The value of finished metal products exceeds the value of the products of any other industry in America. A large proportion of the labor force is employed in metalworking occupations. The work force in metalworking occupations includes classifications of workers with various levels of knowledge and skills. It includes engineers, technicians, skilled craftsmen, and semiskilled workers in many areas of specialization.[1] You will learn about these and other metalworking occupations in Unit 2. At this time, however, you will want to know about the uses of metals and how metals are classified and selected for different products.

Metals are used everywhere around us. They are used in the production of transportation vehicles, including automobiles, trucks, railroad cars, aircraft, space craft, ships, submarines, and motor scooters. Structural steel and other structural metals are used in the construction of bridges and large buildings.

Many different kinds of metals are used in the production of appliances for the home. These items include stoves, refrigerators, TV sets, washing machines, air conditioners, and lawn mowers. Metals are used in the manufacture of industrial machinery, including farm machinery, road building machinery, machine tools, and hand tools. Metals are used for sporting equipment such as golf clubs, outboard motors, and fishing boats. The more valuable or precious metals are used in making coins, jewelry, tableware and cutlery.

2. Metals Have Different Properties

Metals have different characteristics, and these characteristics are called *properties*.[2] When an engineer or product designer selects the metals which are to be used in a modern metal product, he selects them on a basis of their properties. Several common properties of metals include the following:

Density refers to the weight of the metal. The density may be indicated in pounds per square inch (p.s.i.) or pounds per square foot. The density of steel is 0.284 p.s.i. Aluminum, which is much lighter in weight, has a density of 0.097 p.s.i. Hence, steel is nearly three times

---

[1]The following is a very good source for information concerning all types of occupations including metalworking occupations: U.S. Department of Labor, Bureau of Labor Statistics, *Occupational Outlook Handbook* (Washington, D.C.: U.S. Government Printing Office, 1968-69 Edition), 763 pages. A revised edition is printed every 2 years.

[2]The student should learn the meanings of all *italicized* words.

as dense or as heavy as aluminum of the same volume.

Corrosion resistance is the ability to resist rusting or other chemical action. Aluminum, stainless steel, and copper are far more corrosion resistant than ordinary steel.

Hardness means resistance to penetration. Steel is much harder than lead or pure aluminum. Some steels, however, can be hardened by heat-treatment processes. (See §§ 951 and 952.) They can be made so hard that they will penetrate or cut other metals. Examples of steels which are hardened by heat-treatment processes include files, hacksaw blades, drills, and other metal cutting tools.

Toughness in metal refers to its ability to withstand shock or heavy impact forces without fracturing. A metal ranking high in toughness will generally bend or deform before it fractures or breaks. When steel is extremely hardened by heat treatment, it loses some of its toughness. Files or drills, which are hardened by heat treatment, will usually break before they bend significantly. Very often toughness is more important than hardness in steel. It is more important for steering knuckles, bumpers, springs, and other parts of an automobile chassis to rank high in toughness than to rank too high in hardness. The durability of a product is related to the combination of toughness and hardness properties.

Brittleness refers to the ease with which metals will fracture without bending or deforming greatly. Glass is very brittle. Hardened tool steels and gray, cast iron are relatively brittle when compared with ordinary, unhardened steels.

Tensile strength means resistance to being pulled apart. It is the force necessary to pull apart a piece of metal which has one square inch of cross sectional area. Tensile strength is generally expressed in terms of thousands of pounds per square inch. For example, pure soft aluminum has a tensile strength of about 13,000 p.s.i. Soft, low-carbon steel has a tensile

strength of about 69,000 p.s.i. The tensile strength of certain kinds of tool steels and alloy steels can be increased to about 200,000 p.s.i. by heat-treatment processes. (See No. C1095 steel in Table 9, p. 154.)

Metals have a number of other important properties. You will probably be studying these later. (See § 358.)

Different metals are selected for different products because of their *properties*. Each kind of metal may be considered as having a personality of its own. For example, aluminum is lighter in weight and is more corrosion resistant than steel. On the other hand, since most types of steel possess greater tensile strength, they are much stronger than most of the common grades of aluminum.

3. Classification of Metals

Pure Metals

Metals are classified as *pure metals* or as *alloys*. A pure metal is a single chemical element which is not combined with any other chemical element. Examples of metals which are available as pure metals are iron, aluminum, copper, lead, tin, and zinc. Pure metals, such as pure iron, pure copper, or pure aluminum, are generally too soft, lack high strength, or rank low in some other desired property. Thus their use in the pure state is limited to few practical construction applications.

Alloys

The properties of a pure metal may be changed by melting and mixing one or more pure metals with it; this procedure produces a new metal which is called an *alloy*. An alloy may have characteristics very different from either of the original pure metals from which it was formed. Stainless steel is a familiar alloy steel composed of iron, nickel, and chromium. It is strong, tough, and very corrosion resistant.

An alloy, therefore, may be defined as a metallic substance composed of a combination of two or more metallic elements, one of which must be intentionally added to the base metal. Nonmetallic elements may also be included in alloys.

Metals may be classified further as either *ferrous* metals or as *nonferrous* metals. The word ferrous is derived from the Latin word *ferrum* which means iron. The principal element in all steel is iron. Thus all steels are called ferrous metals. Examples of nonferrous metallic elements are aluminum, copper, lead, tin, and zinc.

The many kinds of alloys also may be classified as either *ferrous alloys* or *nonferrous alloys*. Alloys are named after the principal metal, called the *base metal*. Thus steels which have alloys intentionally alloyed with iron, such as nickel, chromium, or tungsten, are called *alloy steels*. Metallic alloying elements are alloyed with aluminum to form *aluminum-base* alloys. They may also be alloyed with copper to form *copper-base* alloys or with zinc to form *zinc-base* alloys. Aluminum-base alloys, copper-base alloys, and other alloys of nonferrous base metals are called nonferrous alloys. Whether a metal is a pure metal or an alloy, it is still called a *metal*.

4. Selection of Metals

Engineers, industrial product designers, technicians, and skilled craftsmen in metalworking occupations must know about various metals and their properties. There are hundreds of different grades of structural steels, alloy steels, tool steels, and special steels available for selection. More than 60 different aluminum-base alloys and more than 60 copper-base alloys are available.

Many other kinds of nonferrous alloys are also available for industrial use today. There are more than 100 different metals used in the manufacture of a modern automobile. There are about 12,000 metal parts used in the average modern automobile. In fact, more than 1000 different kinds of metals or alloys

are available for the design and production of metal products in modern industry.

You will be learning more about the different metals, their properties, and how they are produced in other chapters of this book. At this time, however, it is important to know that there are many different kinds of metals. Each kind of metal was developed to acquire certain properties which are demanded in the design and production of various metal products. You will want to know the principal properties of the common metals when you design, work with, and construct metal projects in your metalworking course.

The reasons for selecting metals on a basis of properties can be understood when you consider several modern industrial products. Aluminum is used in the construction of items such as aircraft, small engines, lawn furniture, storm windows, and fishing boats. It is a desirable metal for these items because of its lightness in weight, its corrosion resistance, and its strength. Special grades of aluminum have a tensile strength rating which is as great as that for ordinary low-carbon steel. (See Table 10.)

Steels which can be hardened by heat-treatment processes must be selected for making cutting tools which are used to cut other metals. Steels of this type are called *tool steels*. Files, hacksaw blades, drills, chisels, and threading dies are made of tool steels. You will have an opportunity to learn more about heat-treatment processes when you study other units (see Unit 46).

5. How To Profit From the Study of Metalwork

The following are a few of the many ways in which you can profit from the study of metals and metalworking processes:

(1) It will provide knowledge and skills which are necessary in seeking employment in many metalworking occupations.

(2) Metalworking will provide knowledge and skills necessary in many occupations involving the care, servicing, and maintenance of metal products. These kinds of occupations include auto mechanics, appliance repairmen, millwrights, factory maintenance workers, and maintenance workers for many kinds of machines and equipment.

(3) Metalworking will provide experiences valuable in other kinds of occupations where mechanical ability and a knowledge about metals are important. These kinds of occupations include most engineering occupations, dentistry, industrial designers, laboratory technicians, scientists, and technical specialists.

(4) Metalworking will provide information and experience which will enable you to understand, care for, and repair metal products around your home. You will be spending a large portion of your lifetime income on metal products which must be maintained and cared for.

(5) You will have opportunities to work with common metalworking tools, machines, materials, and processes. The range of experience which you acquire in metalwork, of course, will depend on the length of the course or the amount of time spent in studying metals.

(6) You will learn how to plan, construct, inspect, and evaluate the quality of metal projects which you produce.

(7) You will apply your knowledge of mathematics, science, and drawing on practical metal projects or exercises. You will be solving problems such as planning projects, calculating bills of materials, and calculating cutting speeds and feeds for machine tools. You will apply scientific theory in understanding the internal changes which take place in steel when it is hardened and tempered during heat-treatment processes.

(8) You will learn to work safely with tools and machines. In the technical and mechanical age in which we live, these experiences will always be valuable. You can apply these kinds of experiences to the development of mechanical hobby interests and do-it-yourself jobs.

(9) You will have the opportunity to develop an understanding of the metalworking industry, its workers, its products, and many of its processes.

6. Developing a Basic Knowledge of Metalwork

Basic knowledge and skills in metalworking can be acquired through systematic study. *Metalwork technology* is sometimes called *general metalwork*, or just *metalwork*. It is a broad subject, covering many different areas of metalworking materials, processes, and activities. The following are some of the important areas of activity included:

(1) Designing and planning metalwork projects or jobs, which includes reading drawings, making sketches, and making a bill of materials.

(2) Sawing and bench work, which includes use of hand tools and power sawing.

(3) The study of various metals, alloys, and their properties.

(4) Care of equipment.

(5) Drill press work and drilling operations.

(6) Threads, dies, taps, and threading.

(7) Fitting and assembling metals.

(8) Sheet metalwork.

(9) Hot metalworking processes such as soldering, brazing, welding, forging, heat treatment of steel, molding, and casting.

(10) Tool sharpening.

(11) Finishing and inspecting.

(12) Machine tools such as the lathe, shaper, milling machines, and grinding machines.

You will have the opportunity to study and work in several of the basic areas of metalwork listed above. The number of areas in which you work during your course will depend on your grade level and the length of time devoted to your study of metalwork. It will also depend to a large extent on the kinds of equipment included in your metalworking shop or laboratory.

7. Getting the Most From Metalwork

The following hints will help you get the most out of your metalworking course:

(1) Learn the rules and procedures established for your metalworking shop or laboratory as soon as possible, and then follow them carefully.

(2) Your instructor will probably demonstrate the safe use of each machine before you are permitted to use the machine. Then use your textbook for review or further study about that type of machine and its accessories.

(3) One of the distinguishing characteristics about a good craftsman is that he knows the principal parts of the machines which he operates. Learn the correct name for each tool and machine. Also learn the principal parts of each tool or machine.

(4) Learn the properties of the common metals. You will probably be using some of these metals in the construction of projects or exercises in the shop. Some metals are hard and brittle, while others are soft and bend easily. Some metals are lightweight while others are much heavier. Some steels can be increased in hardness and strength by heat treatment, while others do not respond to heat treatment. Remember, each kind of metal has a personality of its own.

(5) Make an effort to learn as much as possible about different kinds of metalworking industries. Study about the different occupational opportunities available in metalworking industries. Visit metalworking plants whenever the opportunity occurs.

(6) Your textbook includes basic information concerning many kinds of metals, tools, machines, and metalworking processes. For further information, or for more advanced information, you will want to study other metalworking books. A suggested bibliography of reference books for further study is listed on page 607. You may be able to find some of these books in your school library, in your shop library, or in a public city library.

Review Questions

1. Why are metals important in our daily lives?

2. List ten important items made of metals.

3. In what kinds of occupations are workers employed in the metalworking industry?

4. Explain what the word *properties* means, as applied to metals.

5. What is meant by the *density* of metals?

6. Explain the meaning of *corrosion resistance*.

7. Explain the importance of hardness in metals.

8. List several metal products where toughness is sometimes more important than hardness.

9. Explain the meaning of the term *tensile strength* as applied to metals.

10. List the approximate tensile strength for the following:
   a. Pure aluminum
   b. Low-carbon steel

11. List several metals which are available as pure metals.

12. What is an alloy?

13. What is the principal metal or base metal used in producing ferrous metals?

14. List several nonferrous metals.

15. What is meant by the *base* metal in an alloy?

16. List several common base metals which are used to make groups of alloys.

17. List two common classifications for the many different kinds of alloys.

18. List several kinds of occupations in the metalworking industry where the worker must know about various metals and their properties.

19. About how many different kinds of metals are used in the production of a modern automobile?

20. About how many different kinds of metals and alloys are available for the design and construction of metal products?

21. Why were so many different kinds of metals developed?

22. List several metal products commonly made of aluminum.

23. List several properties of aluminum.

24. What kind of steels is used in making tools which cut metals?

25. List several ways in which you can profit from the study of metals.

26. List several occupations, other than metalwork occupations, in which the study of metalwork is important.

27. List some ways in which you can apply knowledge of mathematics, drawing, and science in metalwork.

28. List several different areas of metalworking processes which are included in the study of the broad area of *metalwork technology.*

29. List several ways in which you can plan to get the most out of your study of metalwork.

Coordination

Words to Know

alloy
aluminum
corrosion
density
ferrous metal
metallic element
nonferrous metal
occupation
properties of metal
tensile strength
tool steel

Mathematics

1. When the automobile industry in the United States assembles 24,500 automobiles each day for 1 year (365 days), how many automobiles are produced during the year?

2. If a skilled worker loses 20 days work due to a serious industrial accident, and his usual wage was $4.25 per hour, 8 hours per day, how much money has he lost in wages?

3. The tensile strength of a common type of low-carbon steel is 80,000 p.s.i. (pounds per square inch). What maximum tension load will be required to pull a bar of this kind of steel apart if its cross sectional size is ⅛″ x 1″?

Social Science

1. Write a story in which you tell the kind of society we would probably be living in if metals had not been developed for useful purposes in making machinery or consumer goods.

2. Write a story which tells how transportation vehicles, machinery, household utensils, or tools were made before mass-production methods were developed.

3. Make a list of 100 items which are made largely of metals. Which are used in or around your home?

Occupational Information

1. Write a story telling how automobiles are mass produced in great quantities today.

2. Select some very common metal product with which you are familiar and tell how it is mass produced.

3. If you have ever visited a manufacturing plant which produces metal products, write a story telling about it. Explain how the product was made and the kinds of work you saw being done.

Industrial Consultants to Public Education Inform Students of Career Opportunities
(Courtesy International Harvester Co.)

Descriptions of Metalworking Occupations

10. Factors To Consider in Selecting an Occupation

You may say that you want to be an engineer, a technician, a machinist, a tool-and-die maker, an auto mechanic, a lathe operator, or a drill-press operator. Regardless of which occupation or trade you choose, what do you really know about that occupation or trade? Let us take the machinist's trade as an example.

Do you know what a machinist does?

How much does he earn?

How many hours a day does he usually work?

Does he have work all year-round?

How long does it take to learn to be a machinist?

Can you learn all of it in school?

Is the machinist's work dangerous?

What is the difference between a machinist, toolmaker, diemaker, diesinker, millwright, etc.?

Are you healthy and strong enough for the trade?

Is your eyesight good?

What are your chances of getting a job after you have learned the trade?

Will you still be able to work at that job when you are 40 years old; will you still want to do it then?

These are questions which you should think over carefully. Try to get answers for them. Ask your parents, friends, relatives, and teachers about them. Read about them. This unit gives some information about many metalworking jobs. It is entirely possible that you will live and work for 30 to 60 years after completing school. Your income, living, home, pleasures, happiness, and success depend on your choice of work. In fact, everything and anything that you may mention depends upon your job.

It is important that you know all about the job that you select and that you check on whether or not you will be able to do the work. This unit should help you to get this information and thus give you happiness and success in your work.

11. Meaning of Skill and Knowledge

Skill is the training of your hands to do certain things. *Knowledge* comes from the word *know*. To learn a trade or to become a technician (see § 18) you must acquire both *skills* and *knowledge*. A worker in a skilled trade must be able to apply *knowledge* effectively to the tasks which he performs. To learn a trade, to become a *technician,* or to become an *engineer* (see § 17), you must *know* something about mathematics, drawing, science, and other subjects. You must know *why* things are done in a certain way. You also need to know much of the information in this book for the purpose of communicating with and understanding the people that work in various metalworking industries.

12. Hours and Wages

Men in metalworking jobs usually work 7 to 8 hours each day. It is difficult to state here how much pay workers get because it changes from time to time and is different for various jobs and in the various sections of the country. Remember that the most highly skilled workers, or those with the most education and training, generally get the highest pay. Extra pay is usually received for overtime. A highly skilled worker in any occupation or trade is seldom without work, but it may require constant study to keep up with the changes in machines and methods.

13. Classification of Occupations

An *occupation* is the kind of job or work at which one is employed in earning a living. An *occupation* has the same meaning as a *job* or *vocation*. There are many kinds of occupations or jobs at which one can earn a living. There are actually more than 20,000 different occupational titles, or job titles, described in the *Dictionary of Occupational Titles*.[1] Hundreds of the occupational titles described are metalworking occupations, trades, or jobs.

The amount of education and training required for different metalworking occupations may vary considerably. The training period may range from a period of several days to 5 years or longer. For example, a drill press operator may be trained to perform simple drilling operations, with a small drill press, during a period of several days in a school shop or in an industrial plant. On the other hand, a training period of 4 years is generally

[1] U.S. Department of Labor, Bureau of Employment Security, *Dictionary of Occupational Titles*, Vol. 1, *Definition of Titles* (Washington, D.C.: U.S. Government Printing Office, 1965), 809 pages.

required for training an all-around machinist. (See § 19.)

General Classifications

Metalworking occupations and the workers employed in these occupations are often classified under broad classifications which are based upon the knowledge, skill, and length of training needed to perform the required work. The following are several common broad occupational classifications used:

    (1)   Unskilled workers
    (2)   Semiskilled workers
    (3)   Skilled workers
    (4)   Engineers
    (5)   Technicians

These very broad and general occupational classifications will be explained in the following sections.

14. Unskilled Workers

This classification includes workers requiring little or no special training for the tasks they perform. Examples of jobs in this classification include common laborers who handle and move materials by hand. Other examples include floor sweepers, dish washers, and domestic workers who perform tasks requiring little thought or little application of knowledge. The percentage of unskilled workers in the total labor force is decreasing and will probably continue to decrease in the years ahead.

15. Semiskilled Workers

This classification includes workers in occupations or jobs requiring some special training for the tasks they perform. A broad range of occupations or jobs is included in this classification. Thousands of different kinds of jobs may be classified as semiskilled jobs. The training period for semiskilled jobs, in most instances, may range from several days to about 1 year. The training may be provided in a school shop, or it may be provided on the job by the employer. In some instances, however, the training period may require as long as 2 years. Examples of metalworking jobs in the semiskilled classification include assembly-line workers in factories, machine tool operators, inspectors, maintenance mechanics, painters, spot welders, and punch-press operators.

Machine tool operators are generally included in the semiskilled classification. This group includes drill press operators, lathe operators, milling machine operators, planer and shaper operators, and operators of nearly every kind of specialized production machine tool. A machine tool operator is generally employed to operate one kind of machine tool. As he becomes skilled, he can perform all of the operations which can be performed on the machine.

Some machine tool operators require training periods of only several days. Many require up to 6 months or 1 year of training. A few high ranking semiskilled machine tool operators require up to 2 years of on-the-job training and experience in order to become fully qualified to set up and operate a complex production-type machine tool.

Because of the variation in skill and training required, semiskilled workers, such as machine tool operators, are further classified for job promotion and pay purposes. It is common practice to classify machine tool operators as *Class A, Class B,* or *Class C* operators. The Class A operator generally possesses more knowledge, skill, and experience than the Class B or Class C operator.

Hourly pay rates vary considerably for machine tool operators in various parts of the United States. However, during 1965 a survey indicated that a large group of Class A machine tool operators averaged about 34¢ an hour more than Class B operators, and about 74¢ an hour more than Class C operators.

Highly competent machine tool operators are able to make all necessary machine setups on the machines they operate. They are able to make all calculations and adjustments, including the determination of cutting speeds and feeds. Frequently they must be able to read blueprints, use precision measuring tools, and machine parts accurately.

Experience in high school or vocational school metalwork or machine shop classes is valuable for securing employment and advancing more rapidly as a machine tool operator. This kind of experience is also valuable in securing employment in many kinds of semiskilled jobs in the metalworking industry.

There will be some increase in the number of machine tool operators during the 1970's. More than 10,000 job openings will be available because of deaths and retirements alone. With the continued development of automated machinery, the production rate per worker will continue to increase. And the number of jobs available may also be affected. However, a machine tool operator with good educational qualifications can adjust easily to technical change and secure a new job more easily.

16.   Skilled Workers

Workers under this classification include those employed in the skilled trades. A *trade* is a job or work which generally requires from 2 to 5 years to learn. It requires both *knowledge* and *skill*. One generally learns a skilled trade through a combination of shop instruction, classroom instruction, and on-the-job training. The classroom instruction generally includes mathematics, blueprint reading, technical theory, science, and any other necessary instruction required in the trade.

Examples of skilled trades included under metalworking occupations include the following: machinist, layout man, tool-and-die maker, instrument maker, boilermaker, welder, sheet metalworker, molder, and heat treater. Descriptions of these trades, the nature of the work involved, and educational training requirements are explained later in section 19. Further information concerning skilled trades and other occupations is also included in the *Occupational Outlook Handbook.*[2]

A skilled *tradesman,* also called a skilled *craftsman,* must be able to perform all of the jobs or tasks which are common in his trade or craft. For example, a *machinist* is a skilled worker. He must be able to set up and operate all of the machine tools used in his trade. He must know shop mathematics, how to read blueprints, and how to use precision measuring tools.

Apprenticeship Method

This is one highly recommended method for learning a skilled trade. An *apprentice* is one who is employed to learn a trade in a systematic order under a master of the trade or under the direction of a company. The length of the apprenticeship training period may vary for different trades, anywhere from 2 to 6 years. The apprenticeship period for becoming a machinist or tool-and-die maker, for example, is usually 4 or 5 years. Upon completion of an apprenticeship one becomes a *journeyman,* a worker who has met minimum qualifications for entrance into his trade.

When an apprentice completes his term of training, he generally receives a written document which shows that he has satisfactorily completed his apprenticeship training program. The document specifies the trade or occupation in which the worker is qualified. This document is recognized by many employers and labor unions throughout the country as qualification for entrance into the trade. The new journeyman in a trade must continue studying the tools, processes, and procedures in his trade if he wishes to become highly skilled, and if he wishes to advance more rapidly in his trade.

[2]U.S. Department of Labor, Bureau of Labor Statistics, *Occupational Outlook Handbook* (Washington, D.C.: U.S. Government Printing Office, 1968-69 Edition), 858 pages. A revised edition is printed every 2 years.

To qualify for apprenticeship training in a skilled metalworking trade, one must generally be a high school graduate, or he must have equivalent trade or vocational school education. He must have better than average mechanical ability. High school or vocational school graduates with a good background in science, mathematics, English, drafting, and metalwork or machine shop courses are frequently sought after as apprentices for skilled metalworking trades or occupations.

An apprentice earns while he learns a trade. His wage scale is graduated so that his earnings increase, periodically, with his increase in experience.

Pickup Method

This is a second way in which many workers acquire the broad knowledge and experience required for employment as a skilled tradesman. This method involves working on different kinds of semiskilled jobs, within one occupational area, until one acquires sufficient broad knowledge and experience to gain employment as a skilled worker in that occupational area.

For example, many workers have learned the machinist's trade (see § 19) by the pickup method. They acquired the broad knowledge and skill required of the machinist by working at different semiskilled jobs, on many different machine tools, until they could set up and operate all of the common machine tools.

Workers who choose to learn the machinist trade or any other skilled trade by the pickup method will find that it generally takes longer than serving an apprenticeship. Frequently they must attend vocational or technical schools to learn blueprint reading, shop mathematics, and technical theory relating to the trade which they are learning.

It is becoming increasingly difficult to learn and enter skilled metalworking occupations by the pickup method. The apprenticeship method is generally recommended and recognized as a more efficient method for learning and entering a skilled trade.

17. Engineers

Engineers plan, design, and direct the building of skyscrapers, roads, bridges, tunnels, canals, waterworks, city sewers, dams, mines, automobiles, airplanes, ships, railroads, power plants, electrical appliances, electronic equipment, radio stations, machinery, and engines. Engineers must have college degrees, must like mathematics and drawing, and know a lot about physics[3] and chemistry.[4]

Engineers frequently specialize in some particular phase of engineering such as mechanical, electrical, or chemical engineering. Many kinds of engineers design metal products, develop and supervise the manufacturing procedures and processes for metal products, or utilize metals in the products they design. The following are some phases of engineering in which the engineer works directly or indirectly with metals in his work; therefore, engineers who specialize in these areas of engineering must know and understand the properties of metals and metalworking processes:

(1) *Architectural engineers:* Design all types of buildings ranging from small homes constructed largely of wood, to factories and large buildings constructed largely of structural metals and masonry.

(2) *Aviation engineers:* Develop new designs for aircraft, missiles, and space vehicles.

(3) *Civil engineers:* Design highways, bridges, dams, waterways, and sanitary systems.

(4) *Electrical engineers:* Design and develop electrical machinery, electrical switches, controls for machines and appliances, radios, television, automatic controls for industrial machin-

ery, electric power generators, electric distribution systems, and many other electronically controlled products.

(5) *Marine engineers:* Develop new designs for commercial and military ships, submarines, and other types of marine equipment.

(6) *Mechanical engineers:* Design many different kinds of machines, appliances, and mechanical equipment, including both industrial and consumer products.

(7) *Metallurgical engineers:* Develop processes and methods of extracting metals from their ores, refining them, and preparing them for practical use. They develop new alloys with improved properties, as required for many kinds of metal products.

(8) *Tool and manufacturing engineers:* The tool and manufacturing engineer generally starts with the model of an industrial or consumer product created by a product engineer. He plans and organizes men, materials, and machines for the complete and economical mass production of the product. This involves analyzing and planning the industrial processes involved. It involves designing the special manufacturing machines, equipment, assembly line, and any packaging system required. It involves supervision of the construction and installation of the equipment needed for the entire production of the product. And it involves the supervision and control of production through all phases, from the raw material to the finished and packaged product.

The tool and manufacturing engineer works with manufacturing prob-

---

[3]*Physics* is the science of measuring force or energy and everything that occupies space.

[4]*Chemistry* is the science of mixing and separating substances, sometimes heating and cooling them, finding out what they are made of, and observing how they react.

lems ranging from mass-production techniques required for producing new kinds of breakfast cereal to the mass-production techniques required for producing new kinds of automobiles.

Other Kinds of Engineers

Another kind of engineer is one who runs a railroad locomotive, an engine on a steamship, or one who runs the machinery for heating, ventilating, and supplying power for a factory or large building. Some engineers work indoors while others work outdoors. This kind of an engineer should have at least a high school education, or better, depending upon the work. It takes from 2 to 5 years to learn the work. He must pass an examination before being qualified for the job.

18. Technicians

Technician occupations are among the fastest growing occupational groups in the United States. Technicians include workers whose jobs generally require the application of scientific and mathematical theory. Their work generally involves helping to translate scientific ideas into useful products or services. They frequently work directly under scientists, engineers, or industrial managers. It has been estimated that industry needs several technicians for every professional engineer.

In general, the educational and training requirements for technicians include high school graduation and 2 years of post-secondary school training. This type of technical training is available in various types of schools including technical institutes, junior colleges, community colleges, area vocational or technical schools, armed forces schools, technical-vocational high schools, private technical schools, and extension divisions of colleges and universities.

The term *technician* does not have a generally accepted definition. It is used by different employers to include many kinds of workers, in a variety of jobs, with various backgrounds of education and training. In some instances it is used to designate workers performing routine technical work confined within a limited sphere. More frequently, however, the term is used to designate employees who perform tasks requiring greater breadth of technical knowledge and experience, such as assisting engineers and scientists.

In general, technician occupations in modern industrial establishments require technical education and training which rank between that required of the skilled tradesman and the engineer. The technician usually must possess more theoretical knowledge of drafting, mathematics, science, and technical writing than a skilled craftsman or tradesman. However, he is not expected to know as much about these subjects as the engineer.

Technicians very often train in only one area of technology, such as the following common areas of specialization: mechanical technology, tool technology, industrial or manufacturing technology, aeronautical technology, automotive technology, electrical technology, chemical technology, civil engineering technology, metallurgical technology, instrumentational technology, and safety technology. Technicians of one specialty may require greater familiarity with one or more of the skilled trades than technicians of other specialties. However, they are not required to perform as skilled craftsmen. Some kinds of technicians are expected to know about many kinds of industrial machines, tools, and processes. This is particularly true in the case of *industrial* or *manufacturing technicians* who are employed to supervise skilled and semi-skilled workers in modern metals manufacturing establishments.

Technicians often perform the tasks which would otherwise be done by engineers. They often perform the supervisory tasks required to carry out the plans of scientists and engineers. In this capacity they must understand the work and many of the problems which concern semiskilled and skilled workers on the production line. And they also must understand some of the work and many of the problems of concern to the scientist and engineer.

Very often technicians are required to serve as technical sales representatives for manufacturers. In this capacity they may give advice on the installation of machines or equipment. They also give advice on maintenance of the machines, equipment, or products which they represent.

Some of the duties performed by several kinds of technicians who specialize in various areas of technological study are explained in the following description of the various kinds of technicians and their work.

Aeronautical Technology

Technicians in this area work with engineers and scientists by assisting with problems involving the design, production, and testing of aircraft, rockets, helicopters, missiles, and spacecraft. They aid engineers by preparing layouts of structures, by collecting information and making calculations, by checking drawings, and by the performance of many other duties.

Chemical Technology

Chemical technicians work mainly with chemists or chemical engineers in the development, production, utilization, or sale of chemical products. The chemical field is so broad that technicians in this area specialize in the chemical problems involved in one industry, such as the food processing, electroplating, or paper industry.

Civil Engineering Technology

Technicians in this area assist civil engineers with the many tasks involved in the planning and construction of highways, bridges, dams, viaducts, and other structures which civil engineers design. The technician helps in the planning stage of a structure by assisting with surveying, drafting, and the preparation of specifications for materials. When a structure or project is under construction, the technician works with the engineer and the contractor in scheduling construction activities. He also inspects the construction to determine that the workmanship and materials conform to blueprint specifications.

Electronics Technology

This field includes work in the following areas of radio, television, other kinds of communications equipment, electric motors, and electronic controls on many types of electrical machines. This field also involves many kinds of electronic measuring and recording devices, such as missile and spacecraft guidance devices. In the broad field of electronics technology, a technician generally specializes in one phase of the work, such as television, electric motors, or electronic controls.

Heating, Air Conditioning, and Refrigeration Technology

Technicians in this field often specialize in one of the areas of work, such as air conditioning. They may further specialize in one activity such as the design of layouts for air conditioning. In the manufacture of air conditioning equipment they may be assigned the problem of analyzing production procedures. They may also be assigned problems such as devising methods for testing air-conditioning equipment.

Industrial Technology

Technicians in this area are often called *industrial technicians, manufacturing technicians,* or *production technicians*. Industrial technicians assist industrial engineers, manufacturing engineers, and tool engineers in a wide variety of problems in many different industries. Industrial technicians are particularly important in metals manufacturing industries. They assist engineers who generally start with a product which has been designed and which must be mass produced.

Their work involves assisting engineers with problems which involve efficient use of men, materials, and machines in the production of goods and services. These problems involve plant layout, development and installation of special production machinery, planning the flow of raw materials or parts, developing materials handling procedures, and controlling inventories. They are also concerned with problems involving time-and-motion studies, analysis of production procedures and costs, quality control of finished products, and packaging methods.

Industrial technicians often acquire experience which enables them to advance into specialized areas of work. These areas include industrial safety, industrial job supervision, and industrial personnel work which involves interviewing, testing, hiring, and training employees.

Instrumentation Technology

This area is more recent and is expanding rapidly with improved mechanized, industrial production methods. The *instrumentation technician* assists engineers in designing, developing, and making many different kinds of special measuring instruments and gages. Such instruments and measuring devices are used for automatic regulation and control of machinery; measurement of weight, time, temperature, and speed of moving parts; measurement of volume, mixtures, and flow; and the recording of data.

Mechanical Technology

This is a broad term which often includes such areas as tool design technology, machine design technology, production technology, automotive technology, and diesel technology.

Technicians employed in the above areas of technology assist engineers with problems involved in the design and development of machine tools, production machinery, auto-

motive engines, diesel engines, and other kinds of machinery. Technicians assist engineers in making sketches and drawings of machine parts; estimating costs for materials, estimating production costs; solving design problems involving surface finish, stress, strain, and vibration; and developing and performing test procedures on machines or equipment.

When making performance tests on machines and equipment, technicians use many kinds of measuring instruments and gages. They also prepare written reports of test results, including graphs, charts, and other data concerning the performance and efficiency of the equipment.

The *tool designer* is a well-known specialist included under the area of mechanical technology. The *tool design technician* designs and draws tools, jigs, fixtures, and holding devices for use on many kinds of production machines. He may also supervise others in making the tools which he designs.

Metallurgical Technology

The metallurgical technician generally works with a metallurgist, assisting him with various metallurgical problems. He assists the metallurgist in testing samples of metals for their chemical content, hardness, tensile strength, toughness, corrosion resistance, durability, and machinability. He assists the metallurgists in problems which involve the development of improved methods of extracting metals from their ores. He also assists in the development of new metals that have properties that are different and not yet established.

Other Kinds of Technicians

In addition to specialization in the above areas of technology, technicians also specialize: *mathematical technicians* work with and assist scientists, engineers, and mathematicians by performing many kinds of computations. *Agricultural technicians* work with agricultural scientists in the improvement of farm products, foods, and soils. Other kinds of technicians include medical and x-ray technicians, dental technicians, optical technicians, and petroleum technicians.

19. Descriptions of Occupations

The following descriptions of many common skilled and semiskilled metalworking jobs or occupations are arranged in alphabetical order:

Aircraft-and-Engine Mechanic

An aircraft-and-engine mechanic repairs, inspects, and overhauls airplanes. He may do either emergency repairs or major repairs and frequent inspections. He should be able to measure with *micrometers* (see Unit 10), use *hand tools,* and run such *machine tools*[5] as the *drill press* (see Units 25-30) and the *grinder* (see Units 49-51). The work is greasy, dirty, and some work has to be done outdoors.

An aircraft-and-engine mechanic should have a high school education and should attend a school or technical institute. He will learn drafting (see § 27), electricity-electronics, physics, and other subjects which he will need in his trade. If he does not attend trade school, he may learn these in night school. It takes a minimum of 4 years to learn the trade.

An *auto mechanic* may wish to become an aircraft-and-engine mechanic. He must pass tests to get a license from the *Federal Aviation Agency;* without this license, he may be a *helper.*

The airplane mechanic must guard against gasoline fumes and explosions and the danger of inhaling poisonous carbon monoxide gas.[6]

Annealer

An annealer softens metal so that it can be cut easily (see § 955). He should have at least

a high school education and must know much about the metals with which he works. Annealing is hot work; there is a danger, too, of being burned by hot materials.

Assembler

An assembler puts together the finished parts of a machine, automobile, engine, typewriter, lock, watch, etc. (see § 679). Such work may be very simple or it may call for much skill.

Auto Mechanic

An auto mechanic services and repairs mechanical, electrical, and body parts of not only cars but buses, trucks, and various gasoline-powered vehicles, too. He should be able to measure with *micrometers* (see Unit 10), use many *hand tools,* run the *drill press* (see Units 25-30), and the *grinder* (see Units 49-51). A skilled auto mechanic can also repair trucks and tractors; he may also wish to become an *aircraft-and-engine mechanic.* The work is greasy and dirty and some work may be done outdoors.

An auto mechanic should have at least a high school education. He will learn the trade and progress quicker if he is a technical school or trade school graduate and is good at mathematics and drafting (see § 27). If he does not attend a technical school or trade school, he may learn these in night school. It takes 3 to 4 years, and sometimes even longer, to learn the trade. A man who has done metalwork, such as can be learned from this book, may learn the trade more quickly. He would be a much better auto mechanic if he also had some of the training of a *machinist.*

The auto mechanic must guard against gasoline fumes and explosions and the danger

---

[5]*Hand tools* are tools which are held and used by the hands, as hammers, wrenches, screwdrivers, and files. A *machine tool* is a machine used for cutting metal.

[6]*Carbon monoxide* is a gas made of one part *carbon* and one part *oxygen.* It is the same gas which comes from the exhaust pipe of an automobile. Only 2% carbon monoxide in the air of a room will make a person unconscious in half an hour.

of inhaling the poisonous *carbon monoxide gas*.

Bench Mechanic

A bench mechanic works at a bench with hand tools, and he must read *blueprints* (see § 28). His primary function is the repair of parts that have been disassembled from a machine or vehicle such as carburetors, transmission, and engines.

Blacksmith

The blacksmith works with hot iron to make or repair metal, machine parts, tools, and other metal articles. The blacksmith also repairs many iron implements, does *welding, hand forging,* and *heat treating* (see Units 43-46). He must know much about iron and steel and know how to read *blueprints* (see § 28).

It takes 3 to 4 years to learn the trade as an *apprentice*. Blacksmithing is hot and heavy work which must be done by a strong, healthy man. A blacksmith must beware of being burned by hot metal. The number of blacksmiths in the United States is decreasing, but rural areas will have need for this type of work for many years. The blacksmith's and *ornamental ironworker's* trades are closely related. (See also *hammerman* and *welder*.)

Boilermaker

The boilermaker assembles prefabricated parts of boilers, tanks, and machines out of iron and *steel plates* (see § 329) and can also repair them. He must drill and punch holes, use machines for cutting and bending the plates, drive hot *rivets* (see § 716), and read *blueprints* (see § 28). The boilermaker must be strong because the work is heavy and hot. Boilermakers work at the site where the boiler, tank, or machine is to be assembled. He must be skilled in using tools and equipment for installation and repair. There is the danger of being burned by hot boilers and rivets. A young man should be 18 years old when he begins to learn this trade. It takes about 4 years as a helper to become a boilermaker.

Case Hardener

A case hardener *hardens* the surface of metal. (See § 957.) The case hardener must know much about iron and steel and should have at least a high school education. Case hardening is hot work; there is danger of being burned with hot material, and poisonous fumes must be guarded against.

Coremaker

A coremaker makes *cores* used to form holes or hollow parts in *castings* which make them lighter so that less metal will have to be cut away afterwards (see § 975).

He must be healthy and have a good mind and skill. The coremaker should learn mathematics and also learn how to read *blueprints* (see § 28). A young man may learn the trade in a *foundry* during an apprenticeship of about 4 years.

The work is usually steady. The coremaker's job is closely related to the *molder's* trade but is lighter work than molding.

Diemaker

The diemaker makes metal forms or patterns, called *dies*, which are used in *punch presses*[7] to stamp out forms in metal. Automobile fenders are made with such dies. These dies must be exact or the many hundreds or thousands of pieces made with them would be wrong. (See also *die* for drawing wire in Fig. 286.) The diemaker can set up and run any machine and use any tool in the shop. He must read *blueprints,* make sketches (see §§ 28 and 39), use *layout tools,* and measure with *micrometers* (see Units 6-8, 10).

The diemaker uses most of the information given in this book. He must have good eye-

---

[7]A *punch press* is a powerful machine which punches holes of different shapes in metal as easily as you punch a ticket. It may also be used to press a flat sheet of metal into a certain shape or form, such as an automobile body or fender.

sight to make fine measurements. He should have at least a high school education but will learn the trade and progress faster if he is a technical school or trade school graduate and is good at mathematics and drafting (see § 27). A prospective diemaker can learn mathematics and drafting in night school if he did not attend a technical school or trade school. Technical training may bring a promotion to the rank of foreman or superintendent. It takes at least 4 to 5 years to learn the trade as an *apprentice.*

A diemaker is seldom without work and is one of the last persons to be laid off. The diemaker's, *diesinker's,* and *toolmaker's* trades are closely related.

Diesinker

The diesinker makes the metal dies which are used in *drop hammers* to hammer hot steel into the form. The object thus made is called a *drop forging* and the dies are called *drop forging dies* (see § 912).

A *drop hammer* is a large, powerful machine which has a heavy weight that acts as a hammer. The weight has a *die* fastened to its bottom side. The hot, soft metal is laid upon another die which is fastened on the base or anvil. The weight then drops on the hot metal and hammers it into both dies. This forms the metal into the shape of the dies. A drop hammer which is run by steam is a *steam hammer.*

Besides tools, many automobile and machine parts which must have great strength are hammered out this way. Automobile axles and many wrenches are drop forgings. The dies must again be exact or the many hundreds or thousands of pieces made with them would be wrong.

The diesinker must have good eyesight, read *blueprints,* make *sketches* (see §§ 28 and 39), use *layout tools,* and measure with *micrometers* (see Units 6-8, 10). He uses most of the information given in this book. He can set up and run any machine and use any tool in the shop. He should have the same educational preparation as the *diemaker.*

A diesinker is seldom without work and is one of the last to be laid off. The diesinker's, *diemaker's,* and *toolmaker's* trades are closely related.

Drill Press Operator

A drill press operator earns his living by running a *drill press.* Units 25-30 give complete information about drill presses and how to run them. A drill press operator can do many different operations on the drill press, set up the work, and sometimes sharpen *drills.* A boy can learn to run a drill press in a week or at most in a few months. (See also *machine operator.*)

Electrician

This is often called the *Age of Electricity and Electronics.* Electrical devices are in the home, office, factory, store, on ships, automobiles, farms, streets, and elsewhere. Electricity furnishes light, heat, and power; it carries messages and gives us entertainment; it controls machines, does difficult mathematical jobs, and keeps records. Electrical things are installed and repaired by an electrician. He uses much of the information given in this book.

An electrician should be at least a high school or trade school graduate before he may learn the trade as an *apprentice,* which takes 4 years. An *electrician* must know mathematics and *physics,* how to read *blueprints,* know something about metals (see Units 18-21), *drills* and *drilling, assembly tools* (see Unit 35), *pipe, pipe-fitting tools, tubing* (see Unit 38), and *soldering* (see Unit 42). An electrician must know the *National Electrical Code* which tells the correct way to install wires, switches, etc. (see § 446). He must guard against electrical shock.

Some electricians work indoors while others work outdoors. The electrician who works outdoors putting up poles, wires, and cables and maintains them, is called a *lineman*. The electrical field is large and includes many kinds of work. A good electrician is one who may find himself lost in another type of electrical work. For example, an electrician doing *house wiring* may not be able to work on motors in a factory without additional training. The electrician's and *radio serviceman's* trades are closely related. (See also *electrical equipment* in Unit 24.)

Electroplater

The electroplater covers metal articles with a protective, attractive surface coat of chromium, nickel, silver, gold, or another metal by using *electricity* (see §§ 1117-1118). He must know something about electricity and *chemistry*, and if possible he should be a high school or trade school graduate. Some of the work is damp, there is danger of getting *acid burns*, and the worker must guard against poisonous fumes.

Forgeman

See *hammerman*.

Founder

See *molder*.

Gagemaker or Instrument Maker

The gagemaker, sometimes called an *instrument maker*, makes and repairs all kinds of *gages*. (The meaning of the word *gage* is explained in section 1145.) He is a type of *toolmaker*. To do this he must be able to set up and run any machine in the shop. He must also make accurate measurements; therefore, his eyesight must be good. The gagemaker must read *blueprints*, make *sketches*, and *lay out* his work (see § 56), and he uses most of the information given in this book.

He will learn the trade much quicker and progress faster is he is a technical school or trade school graduate that is good at mathematics and drafting (see § 27). If he does not attend a technical school or trade school, he may learn these skills in night school. Technical school or trade school training will help him get promoted to foreman or superintendent. It takes at least 4 years to learn the trade.

A gagemaker is seldom without work and is one of the last to be laid off. However, the danger of being cut by sharp tools is ever present.

Gas Fitter

A gas fitter measures, cuts, fits, and connects *gas pipes*, and *pipe fittings* (see § 768). He also installs gas stoves, gas heaters, gas meters, and other gas equipment. The gas fitter's trade is closely related to the *plumber's* trade.

Grinding Machine Operator

A grinding machine operator sharpens tools or polishes them on a *grinding machine* (see Units 49-51). The *universal tool-and-cutter grinder* is described in section 1291. Some of the work is damp and dusty. A young man can learn to run a grinding machine in 3 to 6 months. (See also *machine operator*.)

Gunsmith

A gunsmith makes and repairs firearms.

Hammerman

A hammerman, also called a *forgeman*, runs a *drop hammer* (see *diesinker*) on which he forges automobile axles, wrenches, etc. The difference between *hand forging* and *drop forging* is explained in section 912. The hammerman must have a knowledge of *iron* and *steel* (see Units 18-20) and must be able to read *blueprints* (see § 28). He should have at least a high school education and must be strong and healthy. The work is hot, heavy, dirty, noisy, and the danger of being burned by hot metal is ever present. (See also *blacksmith*.)

Hardener

A hardener *hardens* steel by heating and cooling it. (See § 951.) This work is usually learned by working in the heat-treatment department of a factory. A hardener should at least have a high school education. It is hot work and there is danger of being burned by hot metal and hot liquids. Poisonous fumes must be guarded against.

Inspector

An inspector checks or examines materials, parts, or articles while they are being made or immediately after they are finished (see § 1133). He must read *blueprints* (see § 28), know the different kinds of *fits* (see § 667), and use all kinds of measuring tools. An inspector should have at least a high school or trade school education.

Jeweler

The jeweler makes high-grade jewelry of platinum, gold, and silver. The quality of his work requires good eyesight, even though most of it is done while he looks through an eye *loupe* or magnifying glass. The jeweler must know how to run a *jeweler's lathe* and other small hand and machine tools. (See § 1179.) If possible, he should have a high school or trade school education and learn the trade as an *apprentice*.

Journeyman

A journeyman is one who has learned a *skilled* trade (see § 16).

Lathe Operator

A lathe operator uses the *lathe* described in Unit 57. He can do different operations on it, set up the work, and sharpen the tools he needs. A young man can learn to run a lathe in 3 months to a year. He should have a high school or trade school education. Lathes are more abundant in this country than any other metalworking machine tool. (See also *machine operator*.)

Layout Man

A layout man reads the dimensions given on the *blueprint*, and then with fine measuring and marking tools he draws lines and marks on the metal surface to show where to cut or form the metal. He must know mathematics, how things are made in the shop, and the properties of various metals.

The layout man is a *diemaker, diesinker, machinist, toolmaker,* or *sheet metalworker* who is chosen to do all the layout work. More information about *layout work* is given in sections 56, 98, 562, and 792.

Machine Operator

A machine operator earns his living by adjusting and running only one machine. He has *specialized* in the operation of that machine. If he runs a *drill press*, he is a *drill press operator* (see Fig. 417); if he runs a *lathe* (see Unit 57), he is a *lathe operator*. Thus, there are also *shaper operators, planer operators, milling machine operators,* and *grinding machine operators* (see Units 60-61).

A young man can learn to run any one of these machines in 3 to 6 months. It may take a year to specialize on some of them. He should have a high school education. A machine operator should be able to read *blueprints* (see § 28) and *micrometers* (see Unit 10). There is the danger of getting hands caught in the machine and of being cut by sharp tools. Some of the work is greasy and dirty. (See also *machinist*.)

Machine Setup Man

The machine setup man specializes in getting machine tools ready for operation and instructs *machine operators* in their use. He keeps an eye on the machines run by the machine operators and keeps them adjusted. The machine setup man may have learned how to set these machines by observing them while he was a machine operator, or he may be a fully qualified machinist. He should be able to read blueprints and to use all kinds of measuring tools and gages.

Machinist

A machinist repairs and constructs machine tools. He does *fitting* (see § 665), sets up and runs any machine, is able to use any tool in the shop, must read *blueprints,* make *sketches,* use *layout tools,* and measure with *micrometers* (see Units 6-8, 10). He uses most of the information given in this book.

He must have good eyesight because he must make fine measurements, superior judgment of depth and distance, and good coordination. A high school education is preferred. He will learn the trade quicker and progress faster if he is a technical school or trade school graduate and is good at mathematics and drafting. If he does not attend a high school or trade school, he may learn these skills in night school. Technical school or trade school training will help him to be promoted to foreman and superintendent. It takes 4 years to learn the trade as an *apprentice.*

A machinist is seldom without work. There is the danger of being cut by sharp tools and some of the work is greasy and dirty. (See also *machine operator.)*

Mechanic or Machine Repairman

A mechanic is skilled in working with machines and in shaping and uniting materials by using tools and instruments. *Preventive maintenance* is a major part of his job. He inspects the equipment, oils and greases the machines, and cleans and repairs any of its parts. He thus *prevents* any breakdowns or work delay.

If major breakdowns do occur, he must completely disassemble the machine in order to make the necessary repairs.

Metallurgist

The metallurgist has studied the art and science of separating metals from the rocks and earth in which they are found and of preparing them for use. (See *metallurgy* in section 296.) He knows how to mix different metals and make new metals (the meaning of *alloys* is explained in section 343). The metallurgist aids progress with every new metal discovered. The metallurgist must study chemistry. He must have a college education.

Metal Patternmaker

The metal patternmaker makes the *metal patterns* which are used to make molds in the *foundry* (see §§ 962 and 991). He prepares these patterns from metal stock, rough castings of the original work pattern, wax, or ceramics. He must read *blueprints,* make *sketches,* and use the same hand tools and machines that are in a *machine shop.*[8] Precision and accuracy are the keynotes of his job.

A patternmaker should complete high school or trade school. It takes about 5 years to learn the trade as an *apprentice.*

The work is interesting and usually steady. There is a danger of being cut by sharp tools.

Metal Spinner

A metal spinner forms bowls, cups, trays, saucers, vases, pitchers, etc. by pressing flat pieces of soft sheet metal over forms which turn in the *lathe* (see Fig. 1090). *Metal spinning* is explained in Unit 58. The metal spinner must have skill, read drawings (see § 29), and should have a high school education. His wages are usually high. There is danger of being cut by sharp tools.

Milling Machine Operator

A milling machine operator can do many different operations and set up the work on a *milling machine.* A young man can learn to run a milling machine in 3 months to a year. He should have a high school education. (See also *machine operator.)*

Millwright

A millwright moves and installs heavy machines and equipment in shops (see Fig. 598),

---

[8]A *machine shop* is a place where pieces of metal are formed, cut, polished, and finished by machines into tools, parts of machines, etc.

and constructs any special foundation for them. He must read *blueprints,* and lubricate, dismantle, or repair the machinery he installs. A young man with at least a high school education may learn the trade as an *apprentice.* The millwright's and *erector's* trades are closely related.

Molder

The molder makes *molds* and *castings* by packing sand around the pattern of a metal part to be copied (See §§ 962, 991, and Fig. 825.) He must be healthy, strong, and skilled. The molder needs a high school education. He should learn mathematics and know how to read *blueprints.* It takes about 4 years to learn the trade as an *apprentice.*

Molders get higher pay than men in most other trades. The work is hot, dusty, dirty, much of it is heavy lifting and working with damp sand. There is the danger of being burned by hot metal and sparks. It is usually steady work. The molder's and *coremaker's* trades are closely related.

Ornamental Ironworker

The ornamental ironworker makes beautiful iron lamps, lanterns, door knockers, fireplace tools, railings, fences, gates, doors, and hinges. Some of his art can be seen in museums, libraries, churches, banks, and many fine buildings. He must know mathematics, drafting, *sketching* (see §§ 27, 39), *forging* (see § 912), and should have a high school education. The ornamental ironworker's trade is closely related to the *blacksmith's* trade.

Parts Programer

A parts programer analyzes and schedules, on a program sheet, the operations involved in machining many kinds of metal parts which are to be machined on *numerically controlled* machine tools. Numerically controlled machine tools process parts automatically, with little effort or control on the part of the machine tool operator. The operator loads parts into the machine, replaces worn tools, and removes parts from the machine.

The parts programer reads and interprets the blueprint or drawing of a part to be machined. He analyzes and lists on a program sheet, in proper sequence, the machining operations involved in machining the part. The operations are listed in coded form on the program sheet. The coded information is placed on magnetic tape, or it may be punched into the tape with a tape writing machine similar to a typewriter. The tape is then inserted into the machine's electronic control device. When the *start* button is pressed, the machine tool will machine the required part automatically.

The programer must indicate the kinds of operations to be performed, the tools to be selected and used, the correct cutting speeds and feeds, and when cutting fluids are to be used. Hence, a parts programer must have a good knowledge of mathematics, blueprint reading, and machine shop operations. With large, complex, multipurpose machine tools, he must have a knowledge of mathematical computers and how to use them.

The parts programer is a relatively new metalworking occupation. The need for workers in this field is increasing rapidly. For entrance in this field one must be a high school graduate with broad knowledge and experience in machine tool operations. Special training and experience in the programing and operation of numerically controlled machine tools are available in technical schools, junior colleges, vocational schools, and in *on-the-job* training programs in industry. Industrial plants frequently select competent machinists or machine tool operators for training as parts programers. They also select competent graduates of machine tool training programs in high schools, vocational schools, technical schools, and junior colleges.

Pipe Fitter

A pipe fitter measures, cuts, fits, and connects pipes and *pipe fittings* (see § 768) for gas, air, oil, or water. He should know something about *steam fitting*, and read blueprints. The pipe fitter's, *plumber's,* and *steam fitter's* trades are closely related.

Planer Operator

A planer operator can set up work on the planer and sharpen his tools. A young man can learn to run a planer in 3 to 6 months. (See also *machine operator.*)

Plumber

The plumber installs and repairs sewer and drain pipes, water pipes, gas pipes, meters, sinks, bathtubs, showers, faucets, tanks, etc., and works with *lead* (see § 375). He helps to keep our homes, schools, and other buildings clean and free from sickness by keeping the sewers, water systems, and heating in order.

A plumber should have a high school or trade school education. He must learn mathematics, read *blueprints,* and know something about *steam fitting* and building in general. He goes from job to job; the work is often dirty and disagreeable but quite steady. It takes 5 years to learn the trade as an *apprentice.* State examinations must be passed before a license can be obtained. The plumber's, *pipe fitter's,* and *steam fitter's* trades are closely related. (See also Units 38 and 42.)

Polisher and Buffer

A polisher and buffer uses *grinding wheels* (see Unit 49) to polish metals and *buffing wheels* for *buffing* (see Unit 52). It is dusty and dirty work.

Radio-and-Television Serviceman

A radio-and-television repairman must read drawings (see § 29) and have training in electricity. He should have at least a high school education. The radio-and-television serviceman's and *electrician's* trades are closely related.

Riveter

A riveter spreads the small end of a hot *rivet* into the form of a head by hammering. (See § 714.) He does this with a hammer that works with air forced through a hose and a trigger to start and stop. It is called an *air hammer.* The riveter works in a shipyard, boiler shop, or on the steel frame of a railroad car, bridge, big building, or skyscraper. It is heavy work. The riveter who works on ships, bridges, and skyscrapers must work outdoors, winter and summer, and must travel from job to job. There is the danger of falling from high places. It is necessary that he be careful and strong. The riveter's work is closely related to the *boilermaker's* and *structural ironworker's* trades.

Salesman of Machines, Tools, or Materials

A salesman of machines must know how to demonstrate the use of various machines. He must be able to answer questions about the goods he is selling and show others how to use them. It is also necessary to know how they are made.

A salesman of machines or tools has often worked at a trade such as *diemaker, diesinker, machinist,* or *toolmaker.* Often he is a college graduate. He must also know something about advertising, how to show or display his goods, and how to write contracts for the things he sells. The salesman must have a knowledge of the goods made by his company's competitors in order that he may be able to compare these goods with those he is trying to sell. There are courses in *salesmanship* which he can study. He must be neat and pleasant; he must know what people need and want. The salesman must also speak good English. He must know when to talk and when to be silent. Some salesmen travel over a large territory and are away from home for long periods.

Sheet Metalworker

A sheet metalworker makes and repairs such things as stoves and furnace pipes, furnaces, ventilators, signs, eave troughs, metal roofs and ceilings, metal doors and windows, metal furniture and lockers, automobile and airplane bodies, etc. which are made out of *sheet metal* (see § 789). He may work in a factory, on buildings, or on ships.

The sheet metalworker must know how to *rivet* (see § 714) and *solder* (see §§ 847 and 859). He must read *blueprints* (see § 28) and have a high school or trade school education. The sheet metalworker must know *geometry*,[9] drafting and how to make *patterns* (see § 792). This trade takes at least 3 to 4 years to learn.

Spring and fall are the busy seasons for outdoor work. Factory work is more steady. The work is noisy at times and there is the danger of falling from high places and of being cut by sharp edges of metal. The sheet metalworker must also guard against *lead poisoning* caused by solder made of *lead* and *tin* (see § 851). The sheet metalworker's and *tinsmith's* trades are closely related.

Steam Fitter

A steam fitter measures, cuts, fits, and connects pipes and *pipe fittings* for steam and hot water heating systems. (See § 768.) He must read *blueprints* (see § 28) and know how to *weld* (see § 874). The work is dirty and at times requires heavy lifting. A young man should have a high school or trade school education. It takes 4 to 5 years to learn the trade. The steam fitter's, *pipe fitter's,* and *plumber's* trades are closely related.

Structural Ironworker

You have seen the great steel frames which form the skeletons of large buildings or skyscrapers. Fastening the many *steel beams* and

[9]*Geometry* is the branch of mathematics which deals with points, lines, surfaces, and angles.

frames together is called *structural ironwork.* You may have seen a structural ironworker stand on a steel beam and swing high in the air. He also builds bridges and ships. The structural ironworker fastens the big parts together with welding or hot *rivets,* and he must read *blueprints.* It is necessary that he be a careful and strong outdoor worker and a good climber. There is the danger of falling from high places. (See also *riveter.*)

Temperer

A temperer *tempers* metal as explained in section 954. He must know a great deal about the metals with which he works. It is hot work and there is the danger of being burned by hot metal and hot liquids. Poisonous fumes must be guarded against.

Toolmaker

The toolmaker makes and repairs all kinds of special tools, cutting tools, *jigs* (see § 549), and *gages* (see § 1145). These must be measured with fine instruments and therefore his eyesight must be good. The jigs must be exact or the many hundreds or thousands of pieces held in them, to be drilled or otherwise cut, would be wrong. The toolmaker can set up and run any machine and use any tool in the shop. He must read *blueprints,* make *sketches,* (see §§ 28 and 39), use *layout tools,* and measure with *micrometers* (see Units 6-8, 10). He uses most of the information given in this book.

The toolmaker should have at least a high school education, but he will progress faster if he is a technical school or trade school graduate. He must know mathematics and drafting. He may learn these subjects in night school. Technical school or trade school training will help him to be promoted to the positions of foreman and superintendent. It takes 4 to 5 years to learn the trade as an *apprentice.*

A toolmaker is seldom without work and is one of the last persons to be laid off. There is the danger of being cut by sharp tools if he is not careful. The toolmaker's, *diemaker's, diesinker's,* and *gagemaker's* trades are closely related.

Welder

The welder joins metal parts by melting the parts together with the use of the oxyacetylene welding process (see § 887) or with the use of the electric-arc welding process (see § 889). He also melts new metal onto old metal and cuts metal by burning it with a cutting torch. There are many different kinds of welding processes used in industry (see Fig. 705). A highly skilled welder knows how to utilize a number of the different welding processes, and he is able to weld many different metals.

The welder should know about metals and how to read *blueprints*. A beginner can learn to do simple welding jobs in a month. To become skilled in welding with several different processes may take from 6 months to several years, or longer. Welders must be licensed in many states.

The welder is very important in industry today, and he will become increasingly important in future years. There is some danger of being burned by the torch or hot metal if one is not careful. (See *steam fitter.*)

Review Questions

1. List several factors which you should consider in selecting your occupation.

2. Explain the meanings of *skill* and *knowledge.*

3. List several school subjects which you should know if you wish to learn a trade, become a technician, or become an engineer.

4. Define the meaning of *occupation.*

5. List five broad, metalworking, occupational classifications which are based upon the knowledge, skill, and length of training required.

6. List several kinds of unskilled jobs.

7. List several kinds of semiskilled metalworking jobs.

8. What is the length of the training period for most semiskilled metalworking jobs?

9. What kinds of tasks do machine tool operators perform?

10. List three classifications often used for classifying machine tool operators. Which class possesses the most skill and knowledge?

11. What is a *trade?*

12. List several skilled metalworking trades.

13. What subjects do many skilled tradesmen study in the classroom phase of their training?

14. In what book can one find further information about skilled trades or other occupations?

15. Describe the kind of work which a machinist does, and the kinds of knowledge which he must possess.

16. Describe the apprenticeship method of learning a trade.

17. What is a *journeyman?*

18. Of what significance is the written document which an apprentice receives upon completion of his training program?

19. What qualifications must one generally have in order to qualify for an apprenticeship?

20. Describe the pickup method for learning a skilled trade.

21. What are the educational qualifications for becoming an engineer?

22. List eight kinds of engineers who must know about metals and metalworking processes.

23. Describe the kinds of work performed by tool and manufacturing engineers.

24. What is a technician?

25. Explain, in a general way, the education and training requirements for becoming a technician.

26. Describe the kinds of work performed by technicians who specialize in the area of industrial technology.

27. List ten different kinds of technician occupations.

Coordination

Words to Know

acid burn	lathe operator
Age of Electricity	layout man
air hammer	lead poisoning
aircraft-and-engine mechanic	lineman
annealer	machine operator
apprentice	machine setup man
assembler	machine shop
auto mechanic	machine tool
bench mechanic	machine tool operator
blacksmith	machinist
boilermaker	mechanic
carbon monoxide	metallurgist
casehardener	metal patternmaker
chemistry	metal spinner
coremaker	milling machine operator
diemaker	millwright
diesinker	molder
drill press operator	ornamental ironworker
drop forging	physics
drop forging die	pipe fitter
drop hammer	planer operator
electrician	plumber
electroplater	polisher
engineer	punch press
forgeman	radio-and-television serviceman
founder	riveter
foundry	salesman
gage maker	semiskilled worker
gas fitter	sheet metalworker
geometry	silversmith
grinding machine operator	skill
gunsmith	skilled worker
hammerman	steam fitter
hand tool	steam hammer
hardener	structural ironworker
helper	technician
house wiring	temperer
inspector	toolmaker
instrument maker	trade
jeweler	unskilled worker
journeyman	welder

Science

1. Of what importance is physics in industrial occupations?

2. Of what importance is chemistry in industrial occupations?

Mathematics

1. Of what importance is mathematics in industry?

Drafting

1. Of what importance is drafting in industry?

Occupational Information

1. Write a story entitled, "Why I Picked the Metalworking Course."

2. Choose five metalworking jobs and get information to fill in a form like the one shown at bottom of this page.

3. Describe fully the occupation that you intend to follow:

   (a) What things are made by doing that work?
   (b) Is the work seasonal?
   (c) What are the wages earned?
   (d) What are the number of hours of work per day?
   (e) How long does it take to learn the trade?
   (f) Where can you learn the trade?
   (g) Is the work dangerous?
   (h) Are good health, strength, and good eyesight needed for the work?
   (i) What chances are there of getting a position?
   (j) What possibilities are there for promotion?
   (k) What chances are there for you to keep the job after you are 40 or 50 years old?
   (l) What education is required?

4. Think of a person who has worked at the occupation which you intend to learn.

You may call him Mr. Smith and write all that you know about him:

(a) What kind of work does he do?

(b) How long has he done this kind of work?

(c) Does he earn a comfortable living?

(d) Does he live in a comfortable home?

(e) What do his friends and neighbors think of him?

(f) Do they respect him?

(g) How much education does he have?

(h) How long did it take him to learn his trade?

(i) How much does he earn in a week? In a year?

(j) Is he often out of work?

SUMMARY OF SELECTED METALWORKING JOBS

	Job	Wages	Kind of Work	Hours	Training Needed	Dangers Involved	Where Can It Be Learned
1.							
2.							
3.							
4.							
5.							

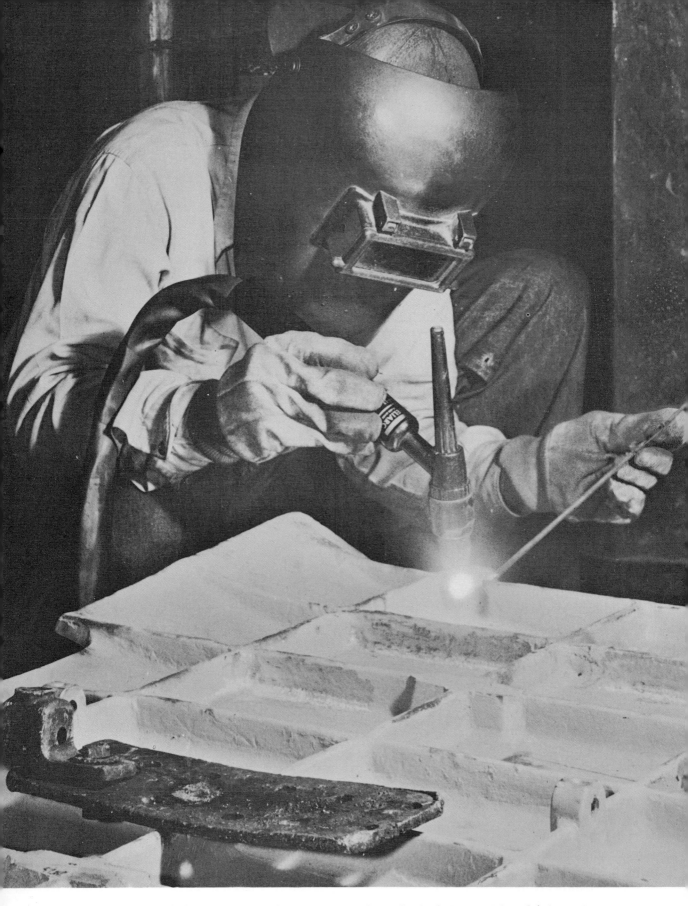

Welding Is Typical of Many Types of Work which Require Careful Attention
to Safe Practices — This Man is Welding an Aluminum Alloy Casting
Using the Tungsten Inert Gas (TIG) Process
(Courtesy Aluminum Company of America)

Safety in Metalworking

22. Dressing Safely for Work

Be Clean and Neat

A worker who keeps himself clean and neat is usually a *safe worker* and ordinarily does clean, neat work. Loose or torn clothing should not be worn, especially around machines. Loose clothing may be caught by a moving part of the machine and pull the worker into gears or blades.

Apron

Wear a clean apron made of heavy *canvas*. It should hang down to the knees as shown in Fig. 1. *Apron strings* should be strong and long enough so that they can be tied properly at the back. Strings tied in front may be caught in a machine. The apron should fit snugly on the chest and fit closely around the waist; apron strings that cross on the back fit best because they pull the apron up close to the chest and snugly around the body. *Pockets* should be sewed on properly; a torn pocket may get caught in a machine.

Aprons should be washed regularly. An apron is for keeping clothing clean, not for wiping dirty hands. It is best to own two aprons; one may be worn while the other is being washed. A sweater should be removed because it overheats the worker.

Sleeves

Sleeves should be rolled up or cut off above the elbows (see Fig. 1). Sew the sleeves, if they are cut off, so that there will be no loosely hanging threads. Loose or torn sleeves, or sleeves that are not rolled up, may get caught in a machine.

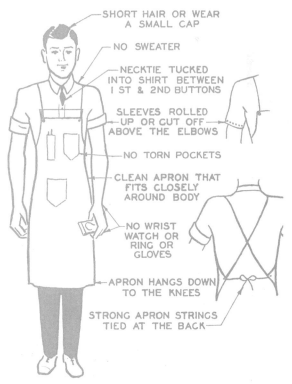

SHORT HAIR OR WEAR A SMALL CAP

NO SWEATER

NECKTIE TUCKED INTO SHIRT BETWEEN 1ST & 2ND BUTTONS

SLEEVES ROLLED UP OR CUT OFF ABOVE THE ELBOWS

NO TORN POCKETS

CLEAN APRON THAT FITS CLOSELY AROUND BODY

NO WRIST WATCH OR RING OR GLOVES

APRON HANGS DOWN TO THE KNEES

STRONG APRON STRINGS TIED AT THE BACK

Fig. 1. Dressed Safely for Work

Necktie

The long or *flowing necktie* should be removed entirely or tucked into the shirt between the first and second buttons; the first button is the collar button (see Fig. 1). This will keep it from getting tangled in a machine.

Gloves

Gloves should never be worn around a machine because they may get caught.

Hair

Long hair may be tangled in a machine. The worker who insists on having long hair should wear a small cap; *goggles*, with an elastic band, may be used to hold the hair back. (See Fig. 836.)

Wristwatches and Rings

Wristwatches and rings sometimes get caught in machines. They should be removed while working around machinery.

23. General Safety for Metalworking

Safe work practices and safe work habits result when you use machines, tools, and materials correctly. You also must follow commonly recognized safety rules and safety practices in order to avoid possible accidents or personal injury. The following safety rules, safety precautions, and safety procedures should be followed:

(1) Always notify the instructor immediately when you are injured in the shop or laboratory, no matter how slight the injury.

(2) Always have proper first aid applied to minor injuries. Always consult a physician for proper attention to severe cuts, bruises, burns, or other injuries.

(3) Safety goggles or a face shield of an approved type should be worn at all times in shop or laboratory.

(4) Oil or grease on the floor is hazardous and can cause slipping; hence it should always be cleaned up immediately.

(5) Place oil rags or other inflammable wiping materials in the proper containers.

(6) Keep aisles and pathways clear of excess stock, remnants or waste. Store long metal bars in the proper storage area.

(7) Return all tools or machine accessories to the proper storage areas after use.

(8) Operate machines or equipment only when authorized to do so by your instructor.

(9) Avoid needless shouting, whistling, boisterousness, or play when in the shop or laboratory. Give undivided attention to your work.

(10) Never touch metal which you suspect is hot. If in doubt, touch the metal with the moistened tip of your finger to determine whether it is hot.

(11) When you approach someone who is operating a machine, wait until he has finished that particular operation or process before you attract his attention.

(12) Avoid touching moving parts of machinery.

(13) Do not lean on a machine which someone else is operating.

(14) Do not operate a machine until the cutting tools and the workpiece are mounted securely.

(15) Be sure that all of the safety devices, with which a machine is equipped, are in the proper location and order before using the machine.

(16) If more than one person is assigned to work on a certain machine, only one person should operate the controls or switches.

(17) Never leave a machine while it is running or in motion.

(18) A machine should always be stopped before oiling, cleaning, or making adjustments on it.

(19) Always use a brush or a stick of wood to remove metal chips from a machine. Otherwise you may be cut by sharp chips.

(20) Do not try to stop a machine such as a drill press spindle or a lathe spindle with your hands.

(21) Do not touch moving belts or pulleys.

(22) Always be certain that the machine has stopped before changing a V-belt.

(23) Before starting a machine be sure that it is clear of excess tools, oil, or waste.

(24) Request help from a fellow worker when it is necessary to lift a heavy machine accessory or other heavy object. Always lift with your legs, not your back.

(25) Do not work in restricted areas which are marked off as safety zones.

(26) Be sure that everyone around you is wearing approved safety goggles or a safety shield if you are permitted (by your instructor) to blow metal chips from a machine with compressed air.

(27) Know the location of the nearest fire alarm in the building in case of fire. Also learn the location of the nearest fire extinguisher and ask your instructor to explain how it is operated.

(28) Always place inflammable materials, such as paint thinners, lacquers, and solvents, in a metal cabinet away from open flames.

24. Safety with Hand Tools

The following safety rules or safe work practices should be followed in using hand tools:

(1) Use the right tool for the job to be performed (see Fig. 2).

(2) See that tools and your hands are clean and free of grease or oil before use.

(3) Cutting tools should be sharp when using them. Dull tools cause accidents because of the greater forces required to use them.

(4) Sharp edge tools should be carried with their points and cutting edges pointing downward.

(5) Heads of cold chisels and punches should not be allowed to mushroom or crack; they should be properly dressed or repaired. (See Fig. 188.)

(6) When using a chisel, always chip in a direction which will prevent flying chips from striking others.

(7) Use the correct type of a wrench for the job and use it properly. You can injure your knuckles or hand if the wrench slips. (See Fig. 3.)

(8) When using a file be sure that it is equipped with a snug-fitting handle. Otherwise, the sharp tang on the file could injure your hand.

(9) When you hand tools to others, give them with the handle first.

(10) Always report damaged tools to the instructor. Damaged tools can cause injuries.

160,000 ACCIDENTS ... NEARLY 8% INVOLVED THE USE OF HAND TOOLS

Fig. 2. Many Accidents Happen in Using Hand Tools (Courtesy J. H. Williams Co.)

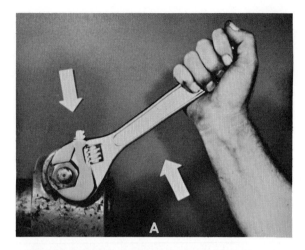

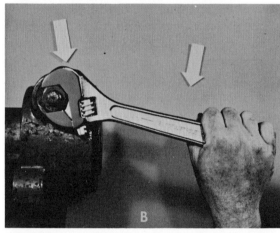

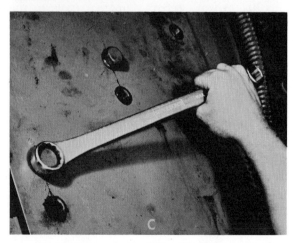

Fig. 3. Use a Wrench Properly
(Courtesy J. H. Williams Co.)

A. Wrong: Do not push on the handle.
B. Right: Pull on the handle.
C. Use offset box wrench on bolts and nuts in
   locations like this

(11) Tools should always be wiped free of grease or dirt after use, and they should be returned to the proper storage location.

25. Other Safety Rules

Other safety rules are given throughout the book as each machine, tool, or operation is explained.

Review Questions

1. Should loose clothing be worn around machinery? Why?

2. Why should aprons be clean?

3. Describe an apron for use in the shop.

4. Should a sweater be worn around machinery? Why?

5. Why should sleeves be rolled up above the elbows?

6. How may a loosely hanging necktie cause an accident?

7. Should gloves be worn in the shop? Why?

8. How may you keep long hair from getting caught in a machine?

9. How may a wristwatch or a ring cause an accident?

10. Dress as a safe worker and be inspected by the teacher.

11. List two safety rules or safe practices regarding first aid and the reporting of injuries.

12. Why should oil or grease be removed from the floor or cleaned from hand tools?

13. List several safety rules or safe work practices which should be followed in the metals shop or laboratory.

14. List several safety rules or safe practices to be followed in the use and care of hand tools in the metals shop or laboratory.

Coordination

Words to Know

apron pocket   canvas
apron string   dressing safely

loose clothing   shop apron
safe worker

Mathematics

1. If a worker, earning $16.97 a day, loses 13½ days' work, due to an accident, how much pay does he lose?

Social Science

1. Why is it important that a worker keep himself clean and neat?

2. What is meant by workmen's compensation?

Occupational Information

1. How should a man who works around machinery be dressed to do work well and safely?

2. What age must a worker be to receive old-age benefits under the Social Security Law?

Careful Planning
Saves Time and Material
— This Toolmaker Is
Laying Out the Base
for a Jig (Courtesy **Today**,
International Harvester
Co.)

Part **1**

Planning the Job

Reading Drawings and Making Sketches

26. Why Are Drawings Needed?

You have at some time seen a picture of a lamp, bookend, tie rack, camp stool, ash tray, waste basket, hammer, or package rack for a bicycle which you wished to make either for yourself or as a gift for your dad or brother. When you decided to make it you hardly knew how to start because sizes and kinds of materials were not given. As an example, see the picture of a hook in Fig. 6. You need a *working drawing*,[1] giving a better description and more information than this.

Often it is necessary to have an object or part made by someone else or to order one from a factory. The working drawing gives all the information needed by the workman who is to make the object.

Read also the reasons for *sketching* in Section 39.

27. What Is a Working Drawing?

Jobs in the shop are made from *working drawings*. A working drawing is a description of an object with all the information needed to make it; it is a drawing from which you work. When given to different shops exactly the same object can be made. Automobile parts are made in different parts of the coun-

[1] The pupil should carefully learn the meanings of all *italicized* words.

try. When brought together they fit perfectly (see interchangeability in § *1140*). The working drawing makes this possible. It must show:

(1) Shape of every part of the object.
(2) Sizes of all parts.
(3) Kind of material.
(4) Kind of finish.
(5) How many pieces of each part are wanted.

A *mechanical drawing* is a working drawing made with mechanical drawing instru-

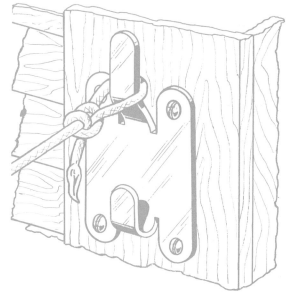

Fig. 6. Hook

ments. It is usually made by the *draftsman* in the *drafting room.*

Drafting includes mechanical drawing and *sketching.* (See § 39.)

28. What Is a Blueprint?

The draftsman often makes a tracing of a working drawing on *translucent*[2] paper or cloth, so that several copies can be made quickly. The *diazo printer* in Fig. 7 makes an exposure through the tracing to light-sensitive paper using a bright light. The paper is developed using ammonia fumes to make a copy called a *blueprint,* or simply "print." Diazo copies are on white paper rather than blue as blueprints.

29. Reading Working Drawings

A *working drawing* is the language of all mechanical occupations, the shop, the drafting room, and the *industrial world.*

To *read* a working drawing one must know what certain kinds of lines, signs, and *abbreviations* mean. To become a *mechanic,* a person must first learn to read this language.

30. Parts of a Circle

It is very important that the beginner learn the names of the different parts of a *circle,* Fig. 8.

The *circumference* is the length of the curved line which forms the circle.

[2] *Translucent* is something through which you can see outlines, as frosted glass or tissue paper.

The *diameter* is a straight line drawn through the *center* of a circle, both ends touching the circumference. When we speak of a 2″ circle, we mean that 2″ is the diameter of the circle.

The *radius* is one-half of the diameter.

An *arc* is any part of the circumference of a circle.

A *chord* (pronounced cord) is a straight line connecting the two ends of an arc or connecting two points on the circumference of a circle.

A *semicircle* is a half circle.

Tangent (pronounced *tanjent*) means touching at only one point; thus a *tangent line* touches an arc or the circumference of a circle at one point.

There are 360 *degrees* in a circle, hence a *degree* is $\frac{1}{360}$ of a circle. The *area* is the amount of surface inside the circumference.

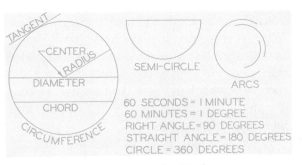

Fig. 8. Parts of a Circle

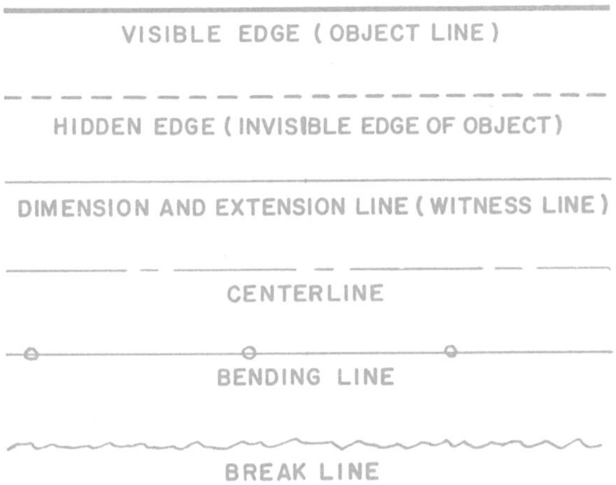

Fig. 7. Diazo Printer and Developing Tube
(Courtesy Eugene Dietzgen Co.)

VISIBLE EDGE (OBJECT LINE)

HIDDEN EDGE (INVISIBLE EDGE OF OBJECT)

DIMENSION AND EXTENSION LINE (WITNESS LINE)

CENTERLINE

BENDING LINE

BREAK LINE

Fig. 9. Lines Used on Working Drawings

31. Lines on Working Drawings

The lines on working drawings which the beginner must know are shown in Fig. 9.

A *visible line* is a thick line used to show all edges that can be seen (see Figs. 9-13).

A *hidden line,* sometimes called an *invisible edge* or a *dotted line,* is made of ⅛″ dashes ¹⁄₁₆″ apart. It is used to show hidden edges, just as if one could look right through the object (see Figs. 9, 12, 600, 601, and 819).

An *extension line, or witness line* as it is also called, is a thin line. It is drawn from the edge from which the measurement is to be made. Note that the extension line does not touch the object; it should be about ¹⁄₃₂″ from the object and extend about ⅛″ past the *arrowhead* (see § 34). (See Figs. 9 and 13.)

A *dimension line* is also a thin line; it is drawn between the extension lines about ¼″ from the object. The *dimension* is in the opening in the dimension line. (See Figs. 9 and 13.)

Whenever we talk about the distance from one hole to another, we mean from the *center* of the one hole to the *center* of the other. Dimensions between holes should always be given from *center to center* because the workman in the shop measures that way. (See Fig. 13.) Measurements are always made from the center of a circle or *arc* (see § 30). *Centerlines,* Figs. 9 and 13, locate the center of a circle or arc. They are the foundation lines for measuring and must be drawn before the circle or arc is drawn. The centerline, for short, is also used to show the *axis* of an object and to locate slots. A centerline is a thin line made up of a ⅝″ line, then a ¹⁄₁₆″ dash, a ⅝″ line, a dash again, with ¹⁄₁₆″ space between the lines and dashes. It is drawn *horizontally*[3] *and vertically*[4] through the center of every circle and arc. The ¹⁄₁₆″ dashes should

[3] *Horizontal* comes from the word *horizon* which is the line where the earth and sky seem to meet. A *horizontal line* is one that lies in the same direction as the horizon line; a line that is level.

[4] *Vertical* means upright, perpendicular, plumb.

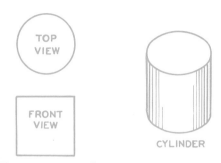

Fig. 10. Front and Top Views of Cylinder

Fig. 11. Front and End Views of Cylinder

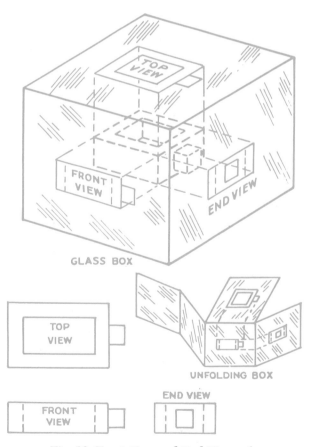

Fig. 12. Front, Top, and End Views of a Hollow Block

cross at the center of the circle or arc (see Fig. 13 again). If a rounded, metal object is to be made, the layout (see § 56) on the metal surface is started with centerlines. Dimensions given between the centerlines on the drawing are thus used; they should be located with reference to centerlines or finished surfaces. See also how centerlines are used in layout work in Figs. 43, 83, 86, 98, 444, and 658. Centerlines are also used to show the centers of slots and grooves (see Fig 13).

Bending lines are shown in Figs. 9 and 634;

Table 1
ABBREVIATIONS AND SYMBOLS[5]
USED ON DRAWINGS
(See section 32)

'	Feet, or Minutes
"	Inches, or Seconds
°	Degrees
±	Plus or minus; more or less
₵	Centerline
D or Dia	Diameter
R or Rad	Radius
P	Pitch
RH	Right Hand
LH	Left Hand
USF	United States Form
USS	United States Standard
SAE	Society of Automotive Engineers
USAS	United States American Standards Institute
Thds.	Threads
NC	National Coarse
NF	National Fine
UNC	Unified National Coarse
UNF	Unified National Fine
CS	Carbon Steel
HRS	Hot Rolled Steel
CRS	Cold Rolled Steel
HSS	High-Speed Steel
√	Finish
Csk	Countersink

[5] A *symbol* is a mark or sign that is used instead of writing out one or more words, as, the symbol ± is used instead of the words "plus or minus."

a small circle is drawn by hand at each end of the line.

A *break line* is a wavy line; it is used to show that a part is broken off as in Figs. 6, 122, and 333.

32. Lettering

It is often necessary to add short notes, words, or *abbreviations* of words to give all the necessary information on a working drawing (see Fig. 18). All these must be *lettered*, freehand, neatly and plainly because lettering can be read easier by everyone. Table 1 gives a list of abbreviations and *symbols*[5]

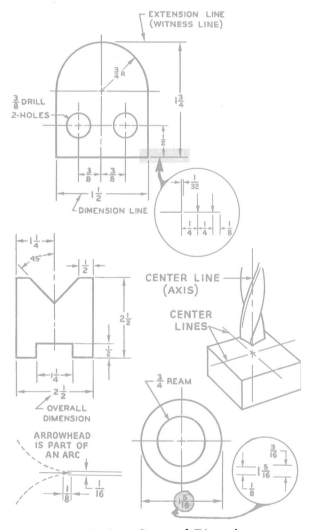

Fig. 13. Centerlines and Dimensions

used on drawings. Abbreviate only when there is not enough space for the whole word.

33. Views

On a working drawing each view shows the outline or shape of the object as seen from that side. To show an object completely, two or more views are usually necessary. Some objects can be described with only one view. No more views than are necessary should be drawn. A working drawing of a *cylinder* needs only two views, the *front view* and *top view*, Fig. 10, or the *front view* and *end view* when the cylinder lies on its side as in Fig 11. Some objects need three views: a front view, a top view, and an end (or side) view. It will help you to draw these views if you can imagine that the object is in a glass box, Fig. 12, with the views drawn on the front, top, and end of the box. When the box is unfolded, the views will be in their correct positions.

34. Dimensions

Dimensions are the most valuable part of a working drawing because they give the size of the object. The *dimension lines* and dimensions are drawn as in Fig. 13. Draw long, narrow *arrowheads* that touch the *extension lines* which extend from the object to show the distances given by the dimensions.

Dimensions most often read from the bottom or right side of the sheet. Some drafting rooms make all dimensions read from the bottom of the sheet as in Figs. 13 and 14. *Fractions* must be made with a *horizontal line* (see section *31*), as $\frac{1}{2}''$, $\frac{3}{4}''$. When all dimensions are in inches, the *inch marks* ($''$) can be omitted.

Give the *diameter* of a circle rather than the *radius* (see § *30*). The diameter should be marked *D* or *Dia* except when it is plain that the dimension is the diameter. The radius of an *arc* should be marked *R* or *Rad*. Dimensions between holes should always be given from *center to center* (see § *31*).

A dimension should be repeated only when there is a special reason for doing it. If the space is too small for a dimension, use one of the ways shown in Fig. 14. Always give *over-all dimensions* which are the dimensions that give the total length, width, and height or thickness of the object (see Fig. 13). Additional examples of dimensions are given in Figs. 634 and 848.

35. What Is Meant by the Scale of a Drawing?

Oftentimes, an object is too large to draw *full-size* on a sheet of paper. It is, therefore, drawn *half-size, quarter-size,* etc., or it is drawn *to scale* which means that it is drawn so that ⅛″ equals 1 foot, ¼″ equals 1 foot, etc. The dimensions are placed on such a drawing the same as if the drawing were full-size. (See Fig. 634.) If the drawing is other than full-size, the scale that is used must be given in a note on the drawing, as "Scale: ¾″ = 1 Foot."

36. What Is a Cross Section?

The part of a working drawing that shows the object as if it were cut is called a *cross section* or simply *section*. It shows the inside shapes of holes and the thicknesses of parts,

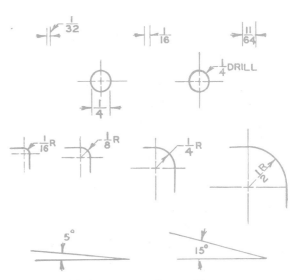

Fig. 14. Dimensions for Small Spaces

(see Figs. 15 and 509). The cut metal is often shown by *parallel lines*[6] called *section lines*. (See also cross sections of files in Fig. 203 and a blast furnace in Fig. 260.)

37. Quick Way to Draw Screw Threads

Section *602* describes *screw threads*. A quick way to draw screw threads is shown in Figs. 16 and 17. The lines may be made either slanted or straight across.

A *hole* that has threads in it is a *tapped hole* and it may be shown as in Fig. 17. The note, ½″-13NC-2, means that the screw or bolt which must screw into the hole is ½″ in diameter and has 13 threads per inch, the kind of thread is *American (National) Coarse Thread*, and has a *Class 2, Free Fit*. (See also #12-24NC-2 in Fig. 18.)

Sections *615-620, 642,* and *649* give more information about *threads* and *taps*.

38. Meaning of Design

The word *design* means to plan something. It is usually done by *drawing* or *sketching* (see §§ *26* and *39*).

39. Meaning and Reasons for Sketching

Often the step to a better job for a young man is to be able not only to *read drawings*, but to be able to make them. (See § 29.) The *mechanic* must not only know how to read the language of the industrial world but must know also how to write it. He must be able to give his own ideas and describe an object to someone else. It is often necessary to make a part for a machine for which there is neither time to make a drawing with instruments nor to have a draftsman make a drawing.

Sometimes only one piece of a machine part is to be made and, therefore, it would be too expensive to have the draftsman make a mechanical drawing. Very often the mechanic

[6]*Parallel lines* are lines that run in the same direction and are always the same distance apart, such as railroad tracks. Theoretically, parallel lines will never intersect.

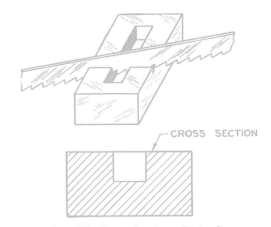

Fig. 15. Cross Section of Metals

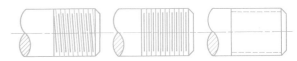

Fig. 16. Quick Ways to Draw Screw Threads

Fig. 17. Looking Into a Hole that has Threads in It

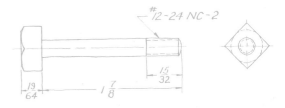

Fig. 18. Sketch of Bolt

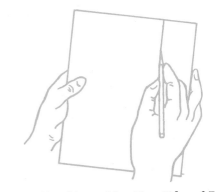

Fig. 19. Sketching a Line Near Edge of Paper

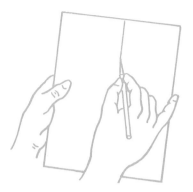

Fig. 20. Sketching a Line Near Center of Paper

Fig. 21. Sketching a Line Along Upper Edge of Paper

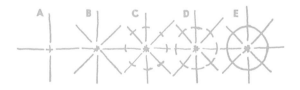

Fig. 22. Steps in Sketching a Circle

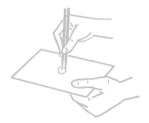

Fig. 23. Sketching a Small Circle with Two Pencils

in the shop has ideas of his own about the *design* of an object. Then too, in the shop there are no mechanical drawing instruments handy. In such cases the workman must make his own *freehand drawing* in the shop with the tools he has at hand. These are usually only paper and pencil. With these tools he can, in a very short time, make a working drawing that will answer the purpose. Even when a rule is handy, the experienced mechanic often does not use it. This working drawing made in the shop is called a *sketch*. A sketch of a bolt is shown in Fig. 18.

Sketches are valuable because they show ideas and dimensions of a machine part. The cleverest idea, however, may result in serious mistakes if the sketch is poorly made. The greatest joy in making things lies in planning and making them yourself. The beginner should practice making clean sketches that give all the information needed and that can be read easily by others as well as by himself.

40. Sketching Lines

The straight edges of a paper pad may help to sketch straight lines near the edge of the paper by moving the third finger as a guide along the edge of the pad as in Fig. 19. Straight lines near the center of the paper may be sketched by moving the little finger as a guide along the edge of the pad as in Fig. 20. Straight lines along the upper edge of the paper may be sketched by bending the wrist as shown in Fig. 21. Straight lines near the lower edge of the paper may be sketched by using the back of the little finger as a guide.

41. Sketching Circles

One way to sketch circles is shown in Fig. 22.

A. Draw *centerlines* through the point that is to be the center of the circle. (See § *31*.)

B. Draw two *diagonal*[7] lines.

[7]*Diagonal* means slanting, sloping, crosswise.

C. Mark the *radius* (see § 30) of the circle on each of the lines.

D. Draw short *arcs* (see § 30) through the marks.

E. Finish circle.

Another easy way to sketch circles is to use two pencils like a *compass*[8] and turn the paper under the pencils. Fig. 23 shows how to sketch a small circle this way. The pencils should be held as in Fig. 24 for larger circles. Large circles may also be sketched by turning the paper under the pencil and middle finger, Fig. 25.

Review Questions

1. What is a working drawing?
2. Who uses working drawings?
3. What is a mechanical drawing?
4. What is a tracing?
5. What is a blueprint?
6. Draw samples of the different lines used on working drawings and name them.
7. What do the following abbreviations mean: Dia, √, RH, LH, R, USS, SAE, Thds., NC, NF, UNC, UNF, USAS?
8. What view appears directly below the top view?
9. What is an overall dimension?
10. What is the scale of a quarter-size drawing?
11. What is a cross section?
12. What does design mean?
13. What is a sketch?
14. Who makes sketches?

Coordination

Words to Know

abbreviation	axis
American (National)	bending line
Coarse Thread	blueprint
arc	break line
area	center
arrowhead	centerline

center to center	front view
chord	full-size
circle	half-size
circumference	hidden line
compass	horizontal line
cross section	industrial
cylinder	invisible edge
degree	lettering
design	mechanical drawing
developer	minute
diagonal	overall dimension
diameter	parallel lines
diazo printer	printer
dimension	quarter-size
dimension line	radius
drafting room	scale
draftsman	screw thread
drawing	second
end view	semicircle
extension line	sketching
freehand drawing	symbol

Fig. 24. Sketching a Large Circle with Two Pencils

Fig. 25. Sketching a Circle with Pencil and Middle Finger

---

[8]A *compass* is an instrument used to draw a circle.

tangent line   vertical
top view   visible line
tracing   witness line
transparent   working drawing

Mathematics

1. What is the diameter of a 1½″ circle?
2. What is the circumference of a 3½″ circle?
3. What is the diameter of a circle that has a circumference of 7.346″?
4. What is the radius of a circle that has a circumference of 10.479″?
5. How long is an arc that equals $\frac{1}{12}$ of the circumference of a 4″ circle?
6. Which has more degrees, a small circle or a large circle?
7. How many degrees are there in $\frac{2}{15}$ of a 4″ circle? Of a 1½″ circle?

8. What is the area of a 3⅛″ circle?
9. What is the scale of a drawing that is $\frac{1}{16}$ size?

Drafting

1. Make a sketch of the first job that you are expected to make in the shop.
2. What is the scale of an eighth-size drawing?
3. What is the difference between "quarter size" and "¼″ = 1 ft."?

Occupational Information

1. Explain in writing why working drawings are the language of the shop, the drafting room, and the industrial world.
2. Of what use is a draftsman in an industrial plant? Explain in writing.
3. In which of the jobs discussed in Unit 2 is a knowledge of reading working drawings and sketching important?

Planning a Project

46. Making a Job Plan

Before attempting to construct a project of your own design, you should prepare a *job plan*. A job plan generally includes the following items:

(1) A working drawing of the project (see § 27); this may be a carefully sketched freehand drawing.

(2) A bill of materials.

(3) A list of tools and equipment needed.

(4) A list of the steps of procedure, in proper order, for making the project.

(5) Approval by your instructor (if required) before making the project.

It is often easier to prepare a job plan if you use a *form sheet* designed for this purpose. A form sheet of the type shown in Fig. 33 may be used, unless your instructor provides you with a form sheet. The *working drawing* should be attached to the completed *form sheet*, thus completing the *job plan*, as shown in Figs. 34 and 35.

When you prepare a job plan for a project which you wish to construct, you will be using procedures similar to those used in industry. Every item of hardware around you, ranging from a ball-point pen to a modern automobile, must be carefully planned before it is produced. Working drawings must be made for each part of each product. The proper materials must be selected for each part, and the costs must be analyzed. Tools, ma-

chinery, and equipment must be provided. Then the procedures must be carefully analyzed for most economical production. Your job plan, therefore, involves some of the kinds of activities which are performed by manufacturing engineers (see § 17), industrial technicians (see § 18), and skilled workers (see § 16).

47. What Is a Bill of Materials?

You must have metal before you can make a metal object. It is necessary to know how to

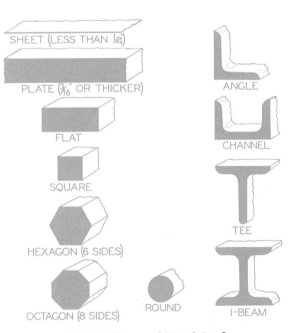

Fig. 32. Shapes of Metal Stock

JOB PLAN FORM SHEET

Name: _____   Grade: _____

Project: _____   Hour: _____

Source of project idea, if not your own design: _____

_____

Estimated Time: _____   Actual Time: _____   Approved: _____

BILL OF MATERIALS

Part No.	No. of Pieces	Size			Material	Unit Cost: (Per sq. ft., lb., etc.)	Total Cost
		T	W	L			

Total Cost _____

TOOLS AND EQUIPMENT:

STEPS OR PROCEDURE:

    1. Select stock
    2. Mark out stock to length or overall size
    3. Cut out the stock
    4. Make part No. 1
        a.
        b.
        c.
        d. Etc.
    5. Make part No. 2
        a.
        b.
        c.
        d. Etc.
    6. Make part No. 3
        a.
        b. Etc.
    7. Etc.
    8. Etc.
    9. Assemble the project
        a.
        b. Etc.
  10. Inspect
  11. Apply the finish

Fig. 33. Job Plan Form Sheet
A form like this may be used for
planning your project.

order the metal. The *working drawing* (see § 27) gives all the information needed to make a *bill of materials* (see Fig. 34). The bill of materials should be made in the form shown in Fig. 33.

It should show:

(1) The parts, identified by numbers or alpha-letters.

(2) The number of pieces needed for each part.

(3) The size of the material (§ 49).

(4) The shape (see Fig. 32), and the kind of material (see Table 1).

(5) The unit cost of the material: (the cost per foot, per square foot, per pound, etc.)

(6) The total cost of the object.

48. What Is a Standard Part?

A *standard part* is a part that is the same no matter who makes it. *Hardware* and *standard parts* as bolts, screws, nuts, washers, etc., that have uniform sizes and shapes should also be listed (see § 730). Use *catalogs* to get information about standard parts and materials.

49. Meaning of Stock

Rough material that is to be made into finished articles is called *stock*. Steel as it comes from the *steel mill*[1] is stock. The different shapes are shown in Fig. 32.

50. Measuring Stock

Remember that the size given on the bill of materials is the size of the *rough metal* that you will order or buy. The size given on the working drawing is the *finished size*. The size of any part, as given on the working drawing, must have added to it extra metal which must be cut away in making the object. Give the sizes of metal as follows:

---

[1]A *steel mill* is a place where steel is made into sheets or different shapes of bars such as round or square.

Flat Piece of Metal

Thickness x width x length, as follows:
⅛″ x 1¾″ x 4¼″ long

Square Piece of Metal

Thickness x width x length, as:
1″ x 1″ x 4¼″ long

Round Piece of Metal

Diameter x length, for example:
2″ Dia. x 4″ long

Hexagonal[2] Piece of Metal

Distance across flat sides x length, as:
1¼″ *across flats* x 4″ long

Section 793 tells how *sheet metal* is measured (see also § 789). The length of the metal needed to make a curve, *scroll,* or *spiral* (see §§ 941 and 942) may be measured by first making the shape out of soft wire, then straightening it out and measuring the length. Or, it may be measured with a *divider* as explained in section 109.

Review Questions

1. What is a job plan, and what items are generally included on it?

2. What is a bill of materials and what information should be on it?

3. Where may the information for making out a bill of materials be found?

4. What are standard parts?

5. Should the size given on the bill of materials be that of the rough metal or of the finished part?

6. What dimensions should be given on the bill of materials for flat metal? For square metal? For a round piece of metal? For hexagonal metal?

7. How can the length of a curve or scroll be measured?

8. Make out a bill of materials for the first job that you will make in the shop.

---

[2]*Hexagonal* means six-sided.

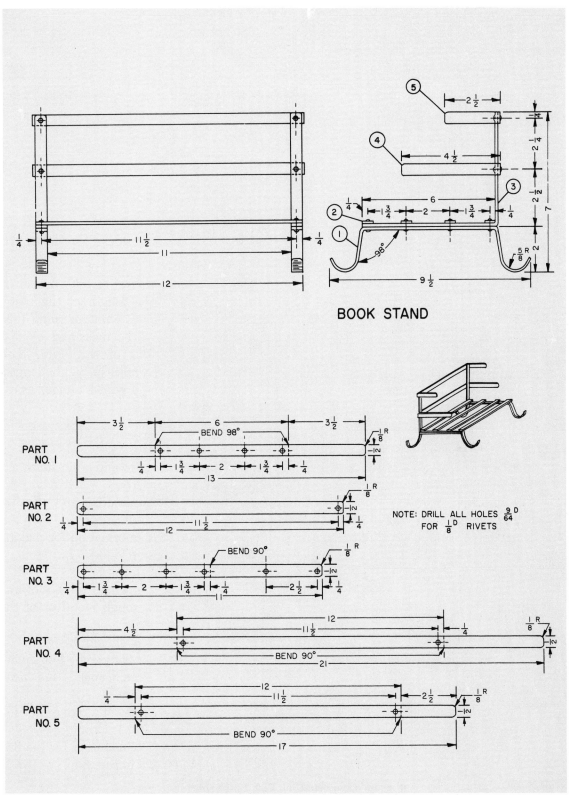

BOOK STAND

NOTE: DRILL ALL HOLES $\frac{9}{64}$ D
FOR $\frac{1}{8}$ D RIVETS

Fig. 34. Working Drawing of a Book Stand

COMPLETED JOB PLAN FORM SHEET

Name: Dale, Brent _____   Grade: _____9_____

Project: __Book stand_____   Hour: __3rd Period__

Source of project idea, if not your own design: _____

_____

Estimated Time: __8 hours__ Actual Time: __10 hours__ Approved: ____J. K. Doakes____

BILL OF MATERIALS

Part No.	No. of Pieces	Size			Material	Unit Cost: (Per sq. ft., lb., etc.)	Total Cost
		T	W	L			
1	2	1/8	1/2	13	H. R. Flat steel		
2	4	1/8	1/2	12	H. R. Flat steel bar		
3	2	1/8	1/2	11	H. R. Flat steel bar		
4	1	1/8	1/2	21	H. R. Flat steel bar		
5	1	1/8	1/2	17	H. R. Flat steel bar		
	8	1/8		9/16	R. H. Iron rivets		
	4	1/8		7/16	R. H. Iron rivets		
					Flat black paint		

Total Cost _____

TOOLS AND EQUIPMENT:

  24" steel rule, scriber, center punch, machinist's hammer, hack saw, vise, combination square, divider, drill press, 9/64" drill, rivet set, riveting hammer, bending fork, file, and 1" paintbrush.

STEPS OR PROCEDURE:

1. Select stock, $\frac{1}{8}$" x $\frac{1}{2}$" hot-rolled, flat steel bars.
2. Lay out parts to overall length, as indicated in bill of materials.
3. Cut out all parts.
4. Make Part 1.
    a. Lay out bend lines.
    b. Lay out and center punch locations for holes.
    c. Drill holes.
    d. File 1/8" radii on ends.
    e. Bend legs to 98° angles in vise.
    f. Bend curved ends of legs with bending fork.
5. Make Part 2.
    a. Lay out and center punch locations for holes.
    b. Drill holes on one end of each part.
    c. With one rivet dropped through the drilled holes, clamp the four parts together and drill the holes in the opposite ends.
    d. File radii on the ends.
6. Make Part 3.
    a. Lay out and center punch for holes.
    b. Drill holes; be certain that the holes align with those in Part 1.
    c. File radii on ends.
    d. Lay out bend lines and bend.
7. Make Part 4.
    a. Lay out bend lines.
    b. Lay out and center punch for holes.
    c. Drill the holes; the holes should be the same distance apart as the holes in Part 2.
    d. File radii on ends.
    e. Make bends.
8. Make Part 5.
    a. Lay out bend lines.
    b. Lay out and center punch for holes.
    c. Drill the holes; the holes should be the same distance apart as the holes in Part 2.
    d. File radii on ends.
    e. Make bends.
9. Assemble the project.
    a. Rivet Parts 1, 2, and 3 together.
    b. Rivet Part 4 to Part 3.
    c. Rivet Part 5 to Part 3.
10. Check project for squareness; adjust as necessary by bending in vise.
11. Apply finish: flat black paint, or other desired finish.

**Fig. 35. Completed Job Plan Form Sheet for a
Book Stand**

Coordination

Words to Know

across flats	hexagon
bill of materials	I-beam
catalog	octagon
divider	plate
hardware	round
hexagonal	sheet
job plan	square
order	tee
scroll	spiral
shapes of metal stock	standard part
angle	steel mill
channel	stock
flat	

Drafting

1. Make a sketch of a project that you expect to make in the shop.

2. Make a complete job plan for a project that you expect to make in the shop.

Checking Work Against the Blueprint
(Courtesy Thompson Products Co.)

Laying Out Parallel and Perpendicular Lines, Using a
Combination Square and a Surface Plate
(Courtesy Delta Div., Rockwell Mfg. Co.)

Layout Tools

56. What Is Meant by Laying Out?

Laying out is the marking of lines, circles, and *arcs* (see § 30) on metal surfaces; such work is called *layout work*. It is the transferring of information from a *working drawing* to metal surfaces to show the workman at the machine or bench how much metal should be cut away. In many ways laying out on metal is the same as making a *mechanical drawing* on paper (see §§ 27 and 98).

57. Layout Tools

The tools used for making a drawing on metal are *layout tools*. They are different from those used for making a mechanical drawing because lines must be scratched or cut slightly into the metal. Descriptions of the layout tools that are most often used and their uses are given in the sections that follow.

Fig. 38. Surface Plate

58. Who Uses Layout Tools

The layout tools described in this unit are used in many trades. They are used by the *auto mechanic, bench mechanic, diemaker, diesinker, gage maker, inspector, layout man, machine operator, machinist, metal pattern-maker, ornamental ironmaker,* and *toolmaker.* Some of them are used by the *blacksmith, coppersmith,* and *sheet metalworker.* These trades are described in Unit 2.

59. Surface Plate

The surface plate is a large iron plate with a very flat surface, Fig. 38. It is cut on a machine and then carefully *ground* or *scraped.* (For *surface grinding* see § 1291, for *scraping* see §§ 260-266.) The surface plate is thus an expensive tool. It may be placed on the bench and used as a foundation or table upon which rests the work, gages, and other tools used to lay out work as shown in Figs. 64 and 65.

The surface plate should be handled with care so that the finished surface will not be nicked or scratched. A small nick will keep the work or layout tools from laying perfectly flat and might cause the layout to be wrong. Protect the finished surface, when not in use, with a *wooden cover* or case. If it is not to be used for a long time, keep it from rusting by covering it with oil. (See also Fig. 926 and § 1137.)

60. Machinist's Hammer

The *head* of a machinist's hammer has a ball-shaped *peen;* thus it is called a *ball peen hammer,* Fig. 39. The *face* and peen are *hardened* (see § 951); the middle, containing the *eye*, which is the hole, is left soft. The *face* should be rounded a little so that it will not make marks. Machinist's hammers weigh from 1 ounce to 3 pounds, without the handle. A hammer weighing ¾ to 1¼ pounds is used for ordinary work around the shop. A light hammer is better for layout work; one weighing from 2 to 6 ounces can be handled easily since only very light blows are necessary. *Peening* is explained in sections 831 and 833. (See also § 686.)

61. Hammer Handle

The *hammer handle* is made of a kind of wood called *hickory*. It is thinner near the middle to make it springy so that the shock of the blow will not hurt the wrist. The length of the handle depends upon the size of the hammer. The handle should fit the eye which is smaller in the middle than at the outside. This helps to keep the head from slipping off the handle after it is fastened with steel *wedges*.[1]

A new hammer handle is dry and *brittle*.[2] It will last longer and will be easier to handle if it is treated as follows immediately after it has been fitted: Put the entire hammer in *lubricating oil* (see § 394) so that the oil will cover it completely for about 2 weeks. Then remove the hammer from the oil, wipe it clean, and put on a coat of *white shellac*[3] to

prevent swelling and shrinking, the main cause of loose handles. (See also § 796.)

62. Scriber

The scriber is a piece of *hardened steel* (see § 951) about 6″ to 10″ long, pointed on one or both ends like a needle, Fig. 40. It is held like a pencil to scratch or *scribe* lines on metal (see Figs. 77-79, 95, 106, and 108.) The bent end is used to scratch lines in places where the straight end cannot reach. Sharpen the points on an *oilstone* (see § 1074).

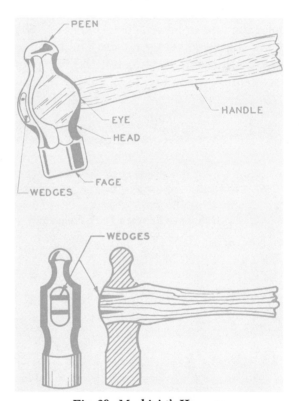

Fig. 39. Machinist's Hammer

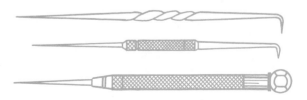

Fig. 40. Scribers

---

[1]*A wedge* is a piece of metal or wood which tapers to a thin edge.

[2]*Brittle* means easily and suddenly broken, such as glass or chalk.

[3]*Shellac* is an orange or yellow gum from the trees of Asia. *Shellac varnish,* often just called shallac, is made by putting the gum in alcohol; it is also known as *orange shellac*. After the color is removed, it is called *white shellac*. Shellac dries as the alcohol evaporates. Since water cannot pass through a coat of shellac, it is used to make articles waterproof.

63. Prick Punch

The prick punch is a sharply pointed tool of *hardened steel*, Fig. 41. It is used to make small *punch marks* on layout lines in order to make them last longer. (See §§ 105 and 562.)

64. Center Punch

The center punch looks like a prick punch (see Fig. 41). It is usually larger than the prick punch; it has a 60° or 90° point while the prick punch has a sharper point. It is also made of *hardened steel.*

The center punch is used only to make the prick-punch marks larger at the centers of holes that are to be drilled (see §§ 562-563); hence the name center punch. The beginner may use a *center gage* to test the 60° point (see *center gage* in Fig. 189).

65. Divider

The divider is a two-legged, steel instrument with hardened points, Fig. 42. Its size is measured by the greatest distance it can be opened between the two points. Thus a 4″ divider opens 4″ between the points, a 6″ divider opens 6″ between the points, etc. Dividers are used to scribe circles and parts of circles (see Fig. 83), to lay off distances (see Fig. 84), and to measure distances (see § 109 and Figs. 85 and 86). Both points should be even in length; sharpen on an *oilstone* (see § 1074). The wing divider is shown in Fig. 637.

66. Trammel

A large circle or an *arc* having a large *radius* (see § 30) may be made with a tool called a *trammel,* Fig. 43. It is sometimes

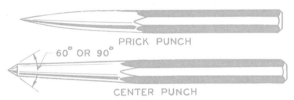

Fig. 41. Difference Between Prick Punch and Center Punch

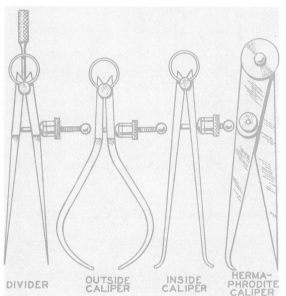

Fig. 42. Divider and Calipers

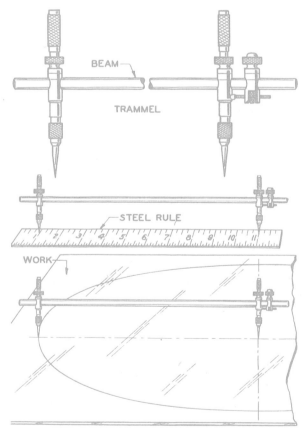

Fig. 43. Trammel

called a *beam compass* or *beam trammel* and may also be used to measure distances in the same way that a divider is used (see § 109). The size of the circle or arc that may be made or the distance that may be measured depends on the length of the *beam*.

67. Outside Caliper

An outside caliper is a two-legged, steel instrument with its *legs* bent inward. (See Fig. 42.) Its size is measured by the greatest distance it can be opened between the legs. It is used to measure the outside diameters of round objects and to measure widths and thicknesses as is shown in Fig. 44. The distance between the legs is then measured with a rule as in Fig. 45.

68. Fine Measuring
with Outside Caliper

Fine measurements with an outside caliper depend upon the sense of *touch* and *feel* in the finger tips. The caliper should, therefore, be held gently with the finger tips. It should be moved back and forth over the work and set until both legs just touch the sides. It is very easy to force the legs over the work and so get a wrong measurement. The correct touch or feel is obtained only through much practice.

69. Setting Outside Caliper

To set an outside caliper to a certain size, hold a steel rule in the left hand and, with the right hand, place one leg of the caliper against the end of the steel rule (see Fig. 45). Place the finger behind the end of the steel rule to keep the leg from slipping off while setting the other leg of the caliper to the size wanted.

70. Inside Caliper

An inside caliper is a two-legged, steel instrument with its legs bent outward (see Fig.

42). It is used to measure the diameters of holes or to measure spaces as in Fig. 46; it is then measured on the rule as in Fig. 47.

71. Fine Measuring
with Inside Caliper

Fine measurements with an inside caliper depend upon the sense of *touch* or *feel* in the finger tips. The caliper should, therefore, be held gently with the finger tips and moved back and forth in the hole until both legs just touch the sides. It is very easy to spring the

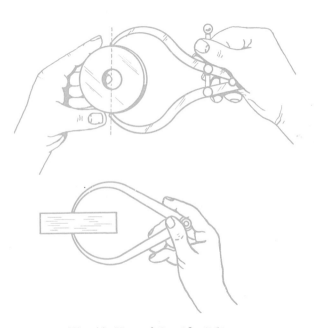

Fig. 44. Uses of Outside Caliper

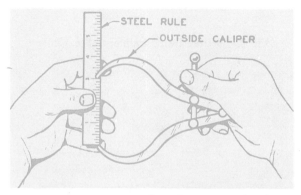

Fig. 45. Setting Outside Caliper to Steel Rule

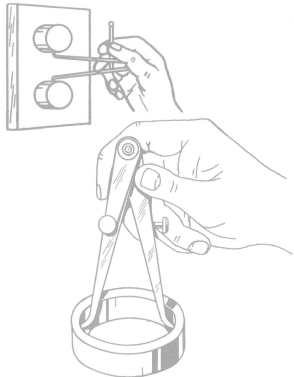

Fig. 46. Uses of Inside Caliper

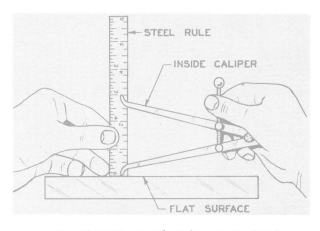

Fig. 47. Setting Inside Caliper to Steel Rule

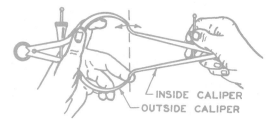

Fig. 48. Transferring a Measurement from
One Caliper to Another

legs and thus obtain a wrong measurement. (See also § 146.)

72. Setting Inside Caliper

To set an inside caliper to a certain size, hold the end of the steel rule against a flat metal surface and then set the caliper as in Fig. 47.

73. Transferring a Measurement from One Caliper to Another

To transfer a measurement from an inside caliper to an outside caliper, or from an outside caliper to an inside caliper, hold the caliper which already has the measurement in the left hand and the one which is to be set in the right hand. Set the caliper in the right hand to the size of the one in the left hand as in Fig. 48. You should feel the points touching slightly.

74. Hermaphrodite Caliper

The hermaphrodite caliper has one pointed leg like a divider and one bent leg (see Fig. 42). It is used to find the center on the end of a round bar (see Fig. 94) and to scribe lines *parallel* to the edge of a piece of work (see § 120 and Fig. 101).

80. Steel Rule

The steel rule, Fig. 54, also called *machinist's rule*, is made in many thicknesses, widths, and lengths from ¼″ to 4′. The most commonly used steel rule is 6″ long. A steel rule is used to measure and should be handled with care to keep the edges from becoming nicked or worn round.

The edges of steel rules are divided by fine lines into different parts of an inch, such as 8ths, 16ths, 32nds, and 64ths of an inch (see § 141). The smallest division is $\frac{1}{64}''$, the next larger is $\frac{1}{32}''$, the next is $\frac{1}{16}''$, then ⅛″, ¼″, and ½″. Some rules are divided into 100ths of an inch. The divisions are called *graduations*. Some rules have divisions on the ends to make measurements in small spaces. It will help a beginner to recognize ⅟₆₄″, ⅟₃₂″, ⅟₁₆″, etc. and to learn to read a steel rule if the rule is placed on Fig. 54.

A thin, springy rule is called a *flexible steel rule* and is used to measure curves, Fig. 55. The use of a *hook rule* is shown in Fig. 76. It is also useful in setting an *inside caliper*. (See Fig. 47.) Section 135 explains the *decimal rule,* and the *shrink rule* is explained in section 964. Section 103 gives more information about measuring with a steel rule.

81. Combination Set

The combination set, Fig. 56, is the most commonly used set of tools in the *machine shop*. The set includes a *square head, center head, bevel protractor, spirit level, steel rule,* and *scriber*. The rule or blade may be fastened quickly to each of the first three; the beginner should ask how it is done so that the small parts will not be lost or damaged.

Figures 57, 78, 95, and 106 show a few of the uses that can be made of the steel rule when the head (or stock), bevel protractor, or center head are fastened to it.

82. Combination Square

The combination square has many uses, Fig. 57. (See Figs. 56, 64, and 79.) Note that 45° and 90° can be measured with it. Its *squareness* should be tested as explained in section 88.

83. Center Head

The center head may be used to extend a line around a corner, Fig. 58.

The center head with the steel rule fastened to it is called a *center square*. It is used to find the center of a round piece (see Fig. 95).

84. Bevel Protractor

The bevel protractor (see Fig. 56) is divided into *degrees* (see § 30), and with the rule fastened to it any *angle*[4] can be measured, Fig. 59. (See Figs. 78 and 222.)

[4]An *angle* is the opening between two intersecting straight lines.

85. Spirit Level

A *spirit level* is usually fitted into the *bevel protractor*, Fig. 59, and the *head* of the com-

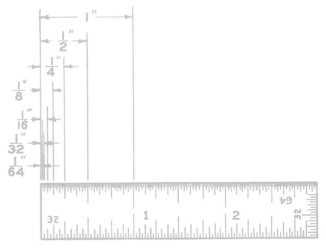
Fig. 54. Divisions of One Inch (Actual Size)

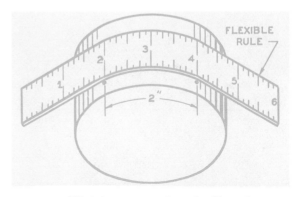
Fig. 55. Measuring with a Flexible Rule

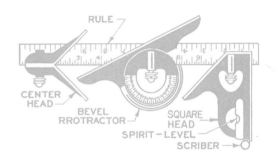
Fig. 56. Combination Set

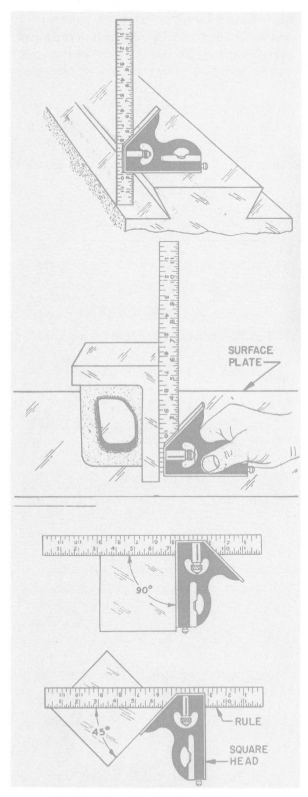

Fig. 57. Uses of a Combination Square

bination square to help in *leveling* the work or setting it at an *angle*. (See Fig. 598.)

86. Double Square

A double square, Fig. 60, has a *head* and a *rule* that slides in the head the same way that the steel rule slides in the *combination square* (see Fig. 57). It is called a double square because the *squareness* of work can be tested at either side of the head. The double square is usually smaller than the combination square and so is handier, especially for small work.

87. Solid Steel Square

The solid steel square is made in one piece, both *blade* and *beam*, Fig. 61. It is made of *hardened steel* (see § 951) and is more exact than the *combination square* with its sliding parts which may be worn, dirty, or nicked.

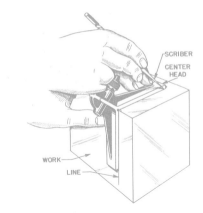

Fig. 58. Extending a Line Around a Corner with a Center Head

Fig. 59. Setting Work at an Angle with a Spirit Level on a Bevel Protractor

The uses of the solid steel square are shown in Fig. 62. (See Fig. 220.)

88. Testing Squareness of a Square

The squareness of any square may be tested by placing the *beam* of the square against a *straightedge* with the *blade* resting on a smooth surface, Fig. 63. While holding the square in this position, scribe a line along the

edge of the blade. Then turn the square over as shown by the dotted lines and see if you have the same line. Both inside and outside edges of the blade should be tested this way.

89. Surface Gage

The surface gage has a heavy, flat *base* carrying a *spindle* which may be set at any angle, Fig. 64. A *scriber*, which may also be

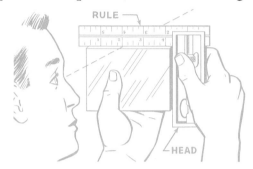

Fig. 60. Testing Squareness (90°) of Work with a Double Square

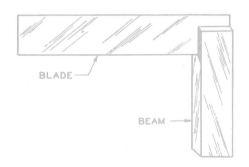

Fig. 61. Solid Steel Square

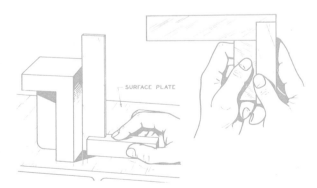

Fig. 62. Uses of Solid Steel Square

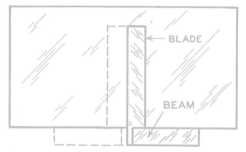

Fig. 63. Testing Squareness of a Square

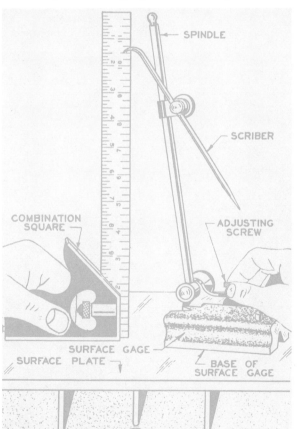

Fig. 64. Setting the Height of a Surface Gage

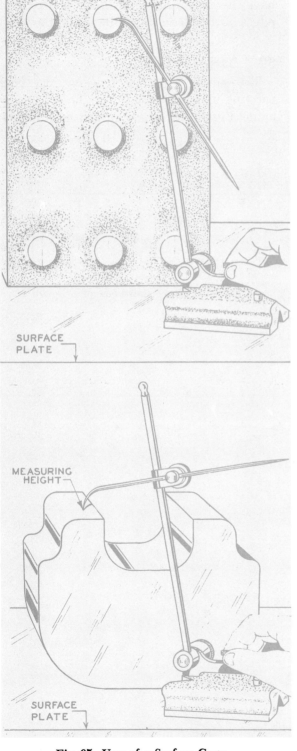

SURFACE PLATE

MEASURING HEIGHT

SURFACE PLATE

Fig. 65. Uses of a Surface Gage

set at any angle or at any height, is clamped to the spindle. The surface gage scribes a line *parallel* (see § 120) to a surface or another line and is often used as a *height gage*. It is often placed on a *surface plate* and used as shown in Figs. **64, 65,** and 944. The *adjusting screw* is used for fine setting. The height of the point of the scriber may be measured with a rule as in Fig. 64. The V-shaped grooves at one end and at the bottom make it useful on or against round work.

90.   Angle Plate

The angle plate, also called *toolmaker's knee,* has two *planed surfaces* at a *right angle* to each other, Fig. 66. It is often necessary to clamp the work that is to be laid out to the angle plate, Fig. 68. (See also Figs. 428-429.)

91.   Parallel Clamp

The *parallel* clamp, also called a toolmaker's clamp, Fig. 67, is often used to hold parts to-

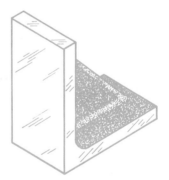

Fig. 66. Angle Plate

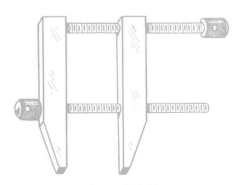

Fig. 67. Parallel Clamp

gether or to hold the work against an *angle plate* while laying out as in Fig. 68. The jaws should always be kept *parallel*. (See §§ 539 and 683.)

92. V-Block

The V-block is a block of steel with V-shaped grooves, Fig. 69. It is used to hold round work for laying out. (See § 544.)

Review Questions

1. Why are layout lines put on metal?

2. For what is a surface plate used?

3. Why is the surface plate an expensive tool?

4. How should the surface plate be protected when not in use? Why should it be protected?

5. Describe a ball peen hammer.

6. What is a scriber? For what is it used?

7. How may a scriber be sharpened?

8. What is the difference between a prick punch and a center punch? For what is each used?

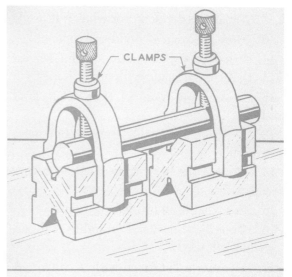

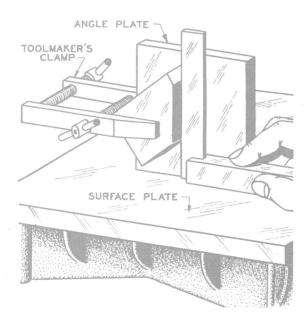

Fig. 68. Uses of Parallel Clamp and Angle Plate in Layout Work

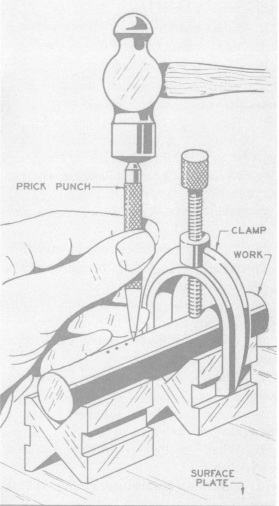

Fig. 69. Uses of V-Blocks in Layout Work

9. What is a divider? For what is it used?

10. How far can a 4″ divider be opened?

11. What is the diameter of the largest circle that can be made with a 6″ divider?

12. Describe a trammel. For what is it used?

13. Describe an outside caliper. For what is it used?

14. How is the size of an outside caliper measured?

15. For what is an inside caliper used?

16. Describe the hermaphrodite caliper. For what is it used?

17. Measure a flat piece with a caliper. A round piece. A round hole.

18. Set an outside caliper for measuring a shaft that is to fit in the hole of a pulley.

19. Name ten layout tools.

20. What is the smallest division on a machinist's rule?

21. How many 16ths are there in 1″? In ¼″? How many 32nds in 1″? In ⅜″? How many 64ths in ½″? In ⅛″? In ¼″?

22. Draw lines of the following lengths: 3½″, 4⅞″, 1¾″, $2^{13}/_{16}$″, $1^{21}/_{32}$″, $1^{53}/_{64}$″.

23. Write in numbers: six feet seven and three-quarters inches.

24. Name the parts of the combination set.

25. What two angles can be made with a combination square?

26. What is the use of the spirit level on the bevel protractor?

27. Why is a solid steel square more exact than a combination square?

28. Describe the surface gage. What is its use?

29. Of what use is the adjusting screw on the surface gage?

30. What is an angle plate? How is it used in layout work?

31. Describe a parallel clamp. For what is it used?

32. Describe the V-block. What is its use?

33. Locate the center on the end of a round piece of stock with a center square.

34. Set the bevel protractor at 40°. What other angle can be measured with this setting?

35. Test the squareness of a square.

Coordination

Words to Know

angle plate	machinist's hammer
ball peen hammer	machinist's rule
beam compass	orange shellac
brittle	outside caliper
center gage	parallel
center punch	parallel clamp
combination set	peening
bevel protractor	planed surface
center head	prick punch
rule	punch mark
spirit-level	right angle
square head	scrape
combination square	scraped surface
decimal rule	scriber
double square	shellac
flexible steel rule	shrink rule
graduation	solid steel square
hardened steel	squareness
height gage	steel rule
hermaphrodite caliper	straightedge
hickory	surface plate
hook rule	toolmaker's clamp
inside caliper	trammel
layout tool	V-block
layout work	wedge
leveling	white shellac
lubricating oil	

Drafting

1. What instrument is used in the drafting room as the scriber is used in the shop? The divider? The surface plate?

2. What tool or instrument is used in the drafting room as the steel rule is used in the shop? The bevel protractor? The steel square?

3. Draw circles of the following diameters: 1½″, 3¼″, 2⅝″, 3⁹⁄₁₆″, 1¹⁹⁄₃₂″.

Occupational Information

1. In which of the jobs in Unit 2 are most of the layout tools in Unit 6 used?

2. Describe in detail how a planed surface is produced.

Mathematics

1. How many 64ths are there in ⅜″? In ⅝″? In ⅞″? In ¹⁵⁄₁₆″? In ²¹⁄₃₂″?

2. How much larger is ⅛″ than ¹⁄₁₆″?

3. Does ½ of ⅛″ equal ¼″?

4. Is ½ of ¾″ a quarter inch?

5. Is half of ½″ a quarter inch?

6. Draw lines of the following lengths: 5½″, 4¾″, 2⅝″, 1¹¹⁄₁₆″, 3²⁷⁄₃₂″, 2⁴⁹⁄₆₄″.

7. What part of a circle is 15°?

Before plant facilities are changed, thorough planning and model layouts are analyzed for the purposes of: (1) insuring the most effective and efficient use of floor space, (2) minimizing the required manpower in making adjustments in the location of equipment, and (3) to communicate the planners' ideas to the people that will do the moving. (Courtesy International Harvester Co.)

Laying Out

98. Why Is Layout Work Important?

Greater ability is needed to lay out work than to run a machine (see § 56). A *blueprint* (see § 28) gives dimensions without the drawing itself being exact, while the lines on the metal must be laid out exactly because there are no dimensions given as on a mechanical drawing or blueprint. A small mistake in the layout means that the work may be cut incorrectly and spoiled, which may be very expensive. Check and recheck all measurements and dimensions carefully and often before going ahead too far. (See *layout man*, sections *19* and *562*.)

99. Coloring Metal for Layout

The first step in layout work is to color the surface upon which the lines are to be made. Some surfaces are rough while others are smooth and bright. To see the lines on the surface easily, it is necessary to color it. Rough surfaces may be covered with white chalk or a white paint. The chalk should be rubbed in with the fingers until smooth.

Iron and steel surfaces that are smooth and bright may be coated with *layout dye* or *copper sulfate solution.*[1]

[1] A *solution* is made by dissolving a solid, liquid, or gas in another substance, usually a liquid.

100. Layout Dye

A *layout fluid* that comes in different colors may be bought for coloring metal surfaces for laying out. The metal is first rubbed clean and then the fluid is put on with a brush or sprayed on, Fig. 75. It dries quickly. This dye is better, easier, and safer to use than *copper sulfate solution*. It may also be used on copper, brass, aluminum, and tin.

Layout fluid is recommended, particularly for beginners. Some plants still use the dangerous copper sulfate solution described in section *101*.

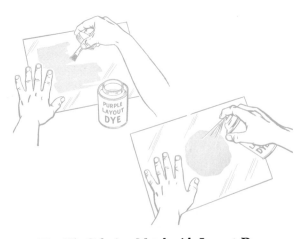

Fig. 75. Coloring Metal with Layout Dye

101. Making Copper Sulfate Solution

Copper sulfate solution, also known as *blue vitriol*, gives iron and steel a copper look. It is made by adding *copper sulfate crystals*, also called *bluestone*, to 4 ounces of pure water. There should be more crystals than the water will *dissolve*,[2] some crystals being left at the bottom. Then add 10 drops of *sulfuric acid*.[3] *It is very important to put the acid in last, or an explosion will result.*

Copper sulfate crystals are blue in color and are *poisonous*. Sulfuric acid and the resulting copper sulfate solution are also poisonous; it eats holes in cloth. The copper sulphate solution should be kept in a glass bottle, closed with a *glass stopper*. (See § 1117.)

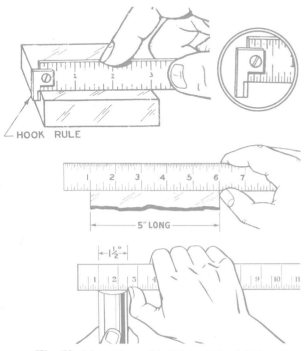

HOOK RULE

5" LONG

1½"

Fig. 76. Measuring with Edge of Steel Rule

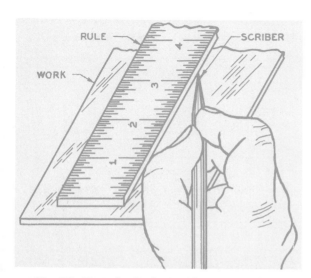

Fig. 77. Slant the Scriber so the Point Follows the Lower Edge of the Rule

102. Putting Copper Sulfate Solution on Metal

The metal surface should first be *polished* clean and free of all grease (see §§ 287-288). The solution should be put on the metal with a piece of clean cloth. After the surface has turned to a copper color, it should be rubbed with a drop of oil to stop the acid from eating further into the metal. After coloring, the surface is ready for the layout.

Copper sulfate solution should not touch the layout tools because it rusts them. If some does get on a tool, rub it off immediately and wipe the tool with oil.

103. Measuring with Steel Rule

To measure with a steel rule (see § 80), stand the rule up on its *edge* on the work so that the lines on the rule touch the work, Fig. 76. (See § 610.) The *division line* on the rule has a certain thickness. Always measure to the center of the line. Measure from the 1″ mark because the end of the rule may be worn. Fig. 55 shows how to use a *flexible steel rule*.

104. Scribing Lines

After the metal surface has been colored (see § 99), it is ready for the layout. To draw

[2]*Dissolve* means to melt, such as sugar or salt in water.
[3]*Sulfuric acid* is a heavy, oily, poisonous liquid. It is yellowish, but when pure it is colorless. It is made by uniting hydrogen, sulfur, and oxygen. When added to water it is used to clean metals. (See #1097.)

a straight line, place the steel rule, square, or *bevel protractor* in the correct position and hold it against the work with the left hand, Fig. 78. Hold the *scriber* with the right hand just as you hold a pencil and lean it to one side so that the point will draw along the lower edge of the rule, Figs. 77-79, 95, 106, and 108. Scratch one line. Use a sharp scriber; sharpen it on an oilstone (see § *1072*).

105. Prick Punching

The *coloring* (see § 99) and the scribed lines of a layout wear off in the handling of the work. The lines should be *prick punched* to make them last longer, Fig. 80. The point of the prick punch should be placed exactly on the line, held squarely on the surface, and struck lightly with the hammer. The *prick-punch marks* should be about 1/16″ apart. The lines appear as in Fig. 81 after cutting. Note that one-half of the punch marks is left when the correct amount of metal has been cut away. (See also §§ *119* and *562*.)

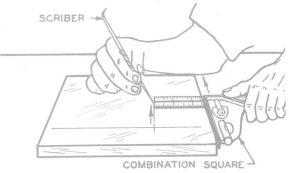

Fig. 79. Scribing a Line, Using a Combination Square

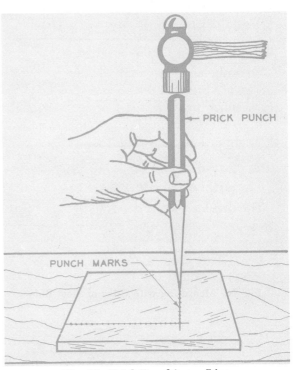

Fig. 80. Prick Punching a Line

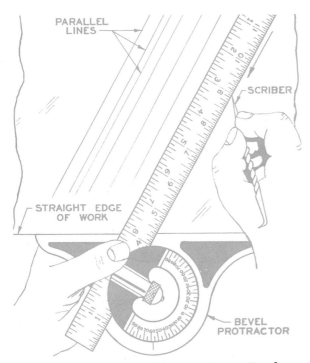

Fig. 78. Scribing 57° Lines, Using a Bevel Protractor

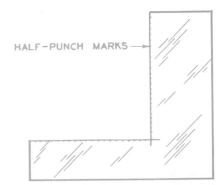

Fig. 81. Half-Punch Marks Prove that the Correct Amount of Metal has been Cut Away

106. Setting a Divider

To make a circle, set the divider to the size of the *radius*, half of the *diameter* (see § 30). For example, if the circle is to be 2″ in diameter, the divider should be set at 1″. Setting a divider to a certain size is shown in Fig. 82. Place one point of the divider into one of the lines of the steel rule, usually the 1″ line, then move the other point until it exactly splits the other line at which the divider is to be set. The V-shape of the lines helps to set the divider points correctly by feeling. Handle carefully to avoid springing.

107. Scribing Circle with a Divider

To scribe a circle with a divider, hold it by the *stem*, Fig. 83. Place one point in the prick-punch mark at the *intersection*[4] of the lines to keep it from slipping and swing it to the right or left. Scratch a sharp circle.

108. Laying Out Equal Distances with a Divider

The divider may be used to divide a line or circle into a number of equal parts. This is shown in Fig. 84.

[4] An *intersection* is the place at which two lines cross or meet each other.

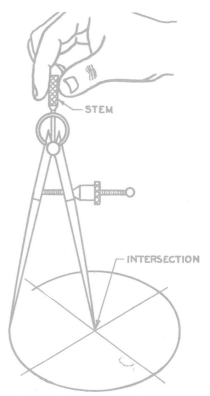

Fig. 83. Scribing a Circle with Divider

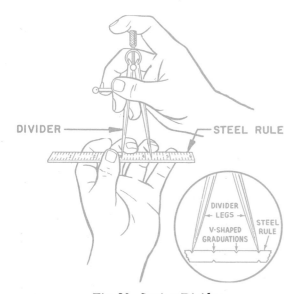

Fig. 82. Setting Divider

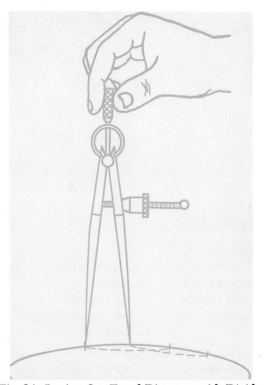

Fig. 84. Laying Out Equal Distances with Divider

109. Measuring with a Divider

The divider may be used to measure distances, Fig. 85; the distance between the divider points may then be read on the rule (see Fig. 82.)

Fig. 86 shows how the divider may also be used to measure the length of a curve or a *scroll* (see § *941*). This is done by setting the divider to a certain distance, say ½″ (see Fig. 82), and then *stepping off* along the *measuring line* or *neutral line* of the curve or scroll and counting the number of steps. When a metal curve is bent, the outside of the metal stretches and the inside squeezes together, but the measuring line does not change.

Review Questions

1. What is the result if the layout is wrong?
2. Why should the surface for a layout be colored?
3. When is chalk used on the surface?
4. For what is layout dye used? Why is it better than copper sulfate solution?
5. What is another name for copper sulfate solution?
6. What color does copper sulfate make on a steel surface?
7. Is copper sulfate poisonous?
8. How should copper sulfate solution be kept?
9. How should a steel rule be placed on the work when measuring?
10. How can lines be made to last longer on a layout?

Coordination

Words to Know

bluestone	layout fluid
blue vitriol	polish
copper sulfate	prick punching
solution	prick-punch marks
dissolve	solution
glass stopper	stepping off
intersection	sulfuric acid
layout dye	

Occupational Information

1. Why is it necessary to lay out jobs in the shop?
2. Why does the most experienced man in the shop always do the layout work? What is such a man called?

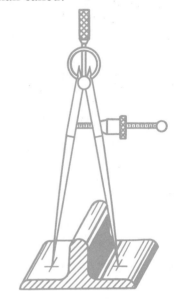

Fig. 85. **Measuring Distances with Divider**

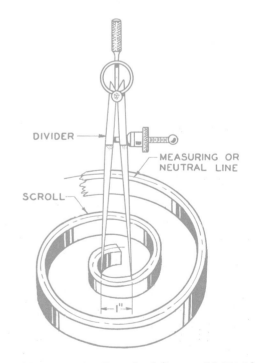

Fig. 86. **Measuring Length of Curve with Divider**

Layout Techniques

115. Finding Center of Circle

To find the center of a circle, put four small prick-punch marks on the *circumference*. Then, with the divider set to the *radius* of the circle, scribe four *arcs* as in Fig. 92. (See §§ *30* and *106*.) The center of the circle is between the four arcs, Fig. 93.

116. Finding Center on the End of a Round Bar

The center on the end of a round bar may be found in several ways. The *hermaphrodite caliper* may be used to scribe four arcs while the bar is held in a vise, Fig. 94.

Fig. 93. Center of the Circle Is Between the Four Arcs

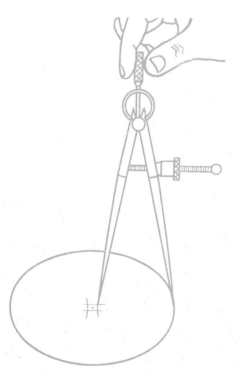

Fig. 92. Finding the Center of a Circle with Divider

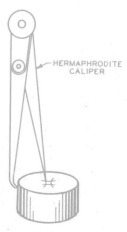

HERMAPHRODITE CALIPER

Fig. 94. Finding Center of a Round Bar with Hermaphrodite Caliper

The *center square* may be used to find the center of a round piece of metal, Fig. 95. (See § 83.) Any two lines drawn across the end of a round piece of metal with a center square will cross at the center.

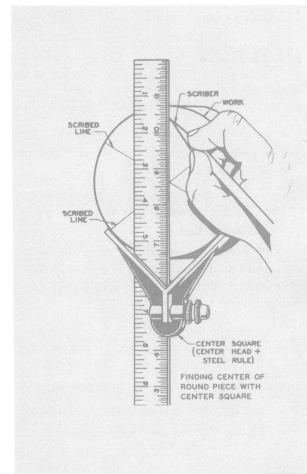

Fig. 95. **Finding the Centers of Round Pieces**

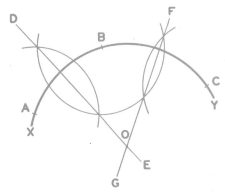

Fig. 96. **Finding the Center of an Arc**

The center of a round bar may also be found with a *surface gage*.

117. Finding Center of an Arc

Suppose that the arc *XY* in Fig. 96 is already on the metal surface and that it is necessary to locate its center. To find the center of the arc:

Step 1: Place three prick-punch marks *A*, *B*, and *C* anywhere on the arc *XY*.

Step 2: With the divider, scribe three arcs of the same size from points, *A*, *B*, and *C* (see Fig. 96).

Step 3: Scribe lines *DE* and *FG* through the *intersections* of the arcs. (See § *107*.) The intersection at *O* is the center of the arc *XY*.

118. Finding Center of Hole

Sometimes the center of a circle comes in a hole. To find the center of a circle, a bridge of soft wood can be whittled to fit across the hole, Fig. 97. A large-headed tack or a small piece of tin, with corners bent down like spurs, is then driven into the wood. The center is then located on the tin by one of the procedures explained in section *115*. Place a small prick-punch mark exactly at the center. (See § *562*.)

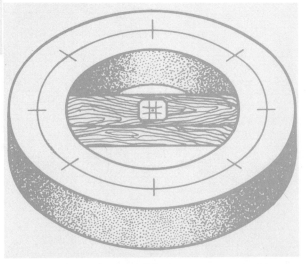

Fig. 97. **Bridging a Hole to Locate its Center for Layout**

119. Laying Out Circle

After scribing a circle, as explained in section *107*, place prick-punch marks at all *intersections* and on the circle, Figs. 98 and 99. The prick-punch marks should be spaced about ⅟₁₆″ apart. Section *562* tells how to lay out a hole that is to be drilled.

120. Laying Out Parallel Lines with Hermaphrodite Caliper

Parallel lines are lines that run in the same direction and are always the same distance apart, for example, railroad tracks, Fig. 100.

The *hermaphrodite caliper* may sometimes be used to lay out parallel lines. The bent leg is held against the edge of the work and as the caliper is moved along, the pointed leg draws a line on the surface parallel to the edge of the work, Fig. 101. It is very useful when many duplicate pieces have to be laid out alike.

121. Laying Out Parallel Lines with Dividers

Suppose that the line *AB*, Fig. 102, is already on the metal surface and that it is necessary to draw the line *CD* parallel to *AB* and at a given distance from it:

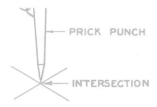

Fig. 98. Prick Punching at Intersection of Lines

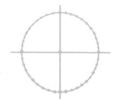

Fig. 99. Prick Punched Circle

Step 1: Place small prick-punch mark at *E* and *F* any place on line *AB*.

Step 2: Set the divider to the distance that the two lines are to be apart (see Fig. 82).

Step 3: With one leg of the divider set at *E*, draw the *arc GH*.

Step 4: With the same setting of the divider and with *F* as a center, draw the arc *KL*.

Step 5: Draw the line *CD tangent* (see § *30*) to the arcs *GH* and *KL*.

The line *CD* is parallel to the line *AB* and the given distance from *AB*.

Fig. 100. Parallel Lines

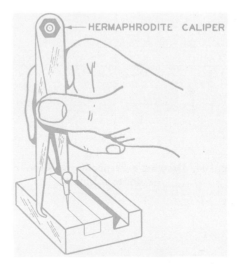

Fig. 101. Scribing Lines Parallel to Edge with Hermaphrodite Caliper

Fig. 102. Laying Out Parallel Lines

122. Laying Out a Perpendicular Line from a Point to a Line

Lines which form *right angles* (90 degrees) with each other are called *perpendicular lines,* Fig. 103. Suppose that the line *AB* and the point *C* in Fig. 104 are already on the metal surface and that it is necessary to draw a *perpendicular* to the line *AB* from point *C*:

Step 1: Prick punch point *C* lightly.

Step 2: Set the divider and make an *arc* so that it crosses the line *AB* as at *D* and *E.*

Step 3: Prick punch lightly at *D* and *E.*

Step 4: With *D* and *E* as centers, scribe arcs which cross at *F.*

The line drawn through the points *C* and *F* is perpendicular to the line *AB.*

123. Laying Out a Perpendicular Line through a Point on a Line

Suppose that the line *AB* in Fig. 105 is already on the metal surface and that it is

Fig. 103. Perpendicular Lines (All Angles Are 90°)

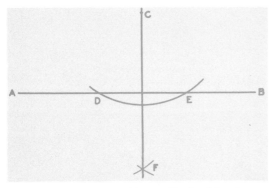

Fig. 104. Drawing a Perpendicular Line from a Point to a Line

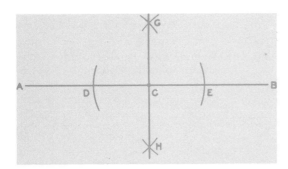

Fig. 105. Drawing a Perpendicular Line through a Point on a Line

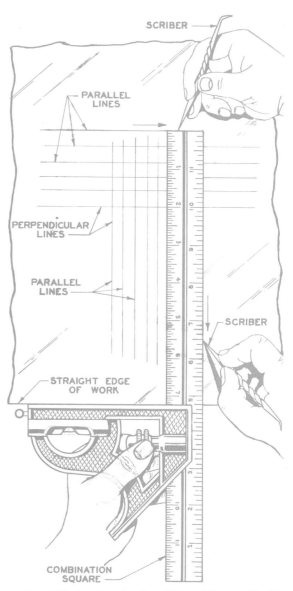

Fig. 106. Laying Out Parallel and Perpendicular Lines with a Combination Square, the Work Having Only One Straight Edge

necessary to draw a *perpendicular* through the point *C* which is on line *AB*:

Step 1: Prick punch point *C* lightly.

Step 2: With the divider set at any distance and with *C* as a center, scribe *arcs* crossing the line *AB* as at *D* and *E*.

Step 3: Prick punch lightly at *D* and *E*.

Step 4: With *D* and *E* as centers and with the divider set at a greater distance than before, scribe arcs which cross at *G* and *H*.

The line drawn through the points *G* and *H* also passes through the point *C* and is perpendicular to the line *AB*.

124. Laying Out Parallel and Perpendicular Lines with a Combination Square, the Work having only One Straight Edge

If the work has one *straight edge,* parallel lines and perpendicular lines may be laid out as in Fig. 106. (See also Fig. 78.)

125. Bisecting an Angle

Bisect means to cut or divide into two equal parts. Thus, to bisect an angle means to divide the angle into two equal parts or angles.

Suppose that the angle *AOB* in Fig. 107 is on the metal surface and it is necessary to bisect it:

Step 1: Prick punch lightly at *O*.

Step 2: With the divider set at any distance and with *O* as a center, draw *arcs* cutting the lines as at *C* and *D*.

Step 3: Prick punch lightly at *C* and *D*.

Step 4: Then with *C* and *D* as centers, draw arcs which cross each other as at *E*.

The line drawn through the points *E* and *O* bisects the angle *AOB*.

126. What Is a Template?

A *template*, also spelled templet, is a *pattern* for marking the shape of pieces of work or for marking holes, etc. It is usually made of plastic or sheet steel (see § 329) and is useful when many duplicate pieces have to be laid out alike, Fig.108. The template is laid on the work; the lines, circles, etc., are then marked with a scriber. Fewer layout tools are thus needed and time is saved by not needing to do a lot of measuring. (See § 792.)

Review Questions

1. Describe how you can locate the center on the end of a round bar with a surface gage.

2. How can you find the center of a hole?

3. Construct parallel lines.

4. Construct perpendicular lines.

5. What does bisect mean?

6. Bisect an angle.

7. What is a template? When is it most used?

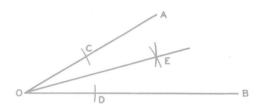

Fig. 107. Bisecting an Angle

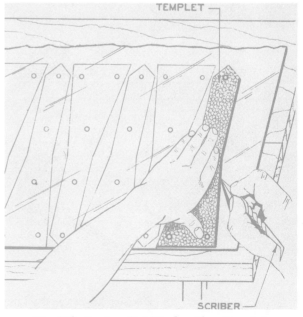

Fig. 108. Laying Out Work with a Template

Coordination

Words to Know

bisect   perpendicular line
pattern   template or templet

Mathematics

1. Tell how to find the center of a circle on a metal surface.

2. Tell four ways to find the center on the end of a round bar in the shop.

3. Locate the center of an arc drawn on the blackboard.

Drafting

1. Draw an arc with a circular object, then locate the center of the arc, using drawing instruments.

2. Construct parallel lines 1″ apart.

3. Construct a perpendicular to a line from a point outside the line.

4. Construct a perpendicular to a line through a point on the line.

5. Bisect a 45° angle.

Occupational Information

1. Tell why a layout man needs more education that a man who runs a machine.

**Precision Layout on the Template Produces Precision Cutting
in this Multiple Flame-Cutting Machine
(Courtesy Linde Air Products Co.)**

Decimal Equivalents

132. Decimal Equivalents

You must know all about *decimal fractions* to learn to read a *micrometer* in the next unit because all micrometers are read in decimal fractions, Fig. 114. You must also know how

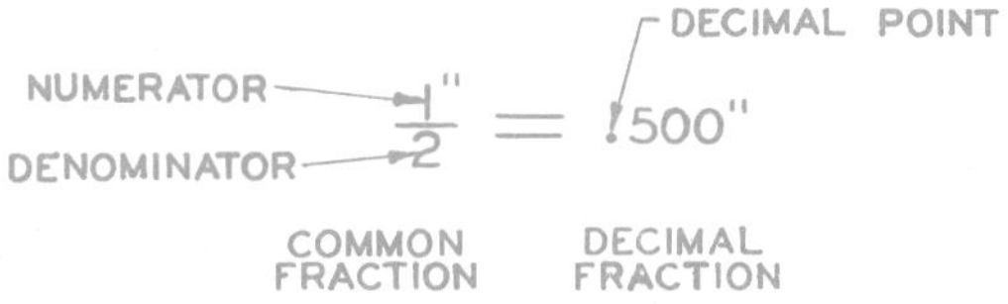

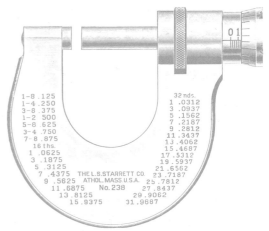

Fig. 114. **Decimal Equivalent**

to change a *common fraction* to a decimal fraction as ½″ = .5″. For example, to set a micrometer at ⅛″ which is a common fraction, it must be changed to the decimal fraction .125″. Since a micrometer is read in *thousandths of an inch*, which is three places after the *decimal point* (as .001″, .003″, etc.), all decimal fractions must be carried to three places, thus ½″ = .500″. This is done by dividing the *numerator* by the *denominator*, as 1 ÷ 2, or

$$\frac{0.500}{2\overline{)1.000}}$$

Thus 0.500″ is the *decimal equivalent* of ½″. *Equivalent* means equal in value.

In the shop, such fractions as .870″ are often read eight hundred seventy thousandths.

Likewise, .0625″ is often read sixty-two and one-half thousandths or sixty-two and five-tenths thousandths.

133. Decimal Equivalents Table

All common fractions are changed to decimal fractions and put in the form of a table to save the time of figuring. This table is called a *Decimal Equivalents Table*. It is placed on large cards; every metal shop and drafting room has one or more of these cards hanging on the walls. To save time, decimal equivalents are usually stamped on the frame of the micrometer, Fig. 115. The young mechanic should memorize the decimal equivalents of

Fig. 115. **Decimal Equivalents on the Frame of a Micrometer** (Courtesy L. S. Starrett Co.)

1/2″, 1/4″, 1/8″, 1/16″, 1/32″, and 1/64″. If he knows these, he can figure out most of the decimal equivalents which he has to use.

A shop problem often has a fraction such as 3/5 or 7/11 that cannot be measured with a *steel rule,* which has eighths, sixteenths, thirty-seconds, and sixty-fourths. (See Fig. 54.) Such fractions must be changed to the nearest eighths, sixteenths, etc., by using the decimal equivalents table. For example: 3/5 = .600 and the nearest fraction that can be measured with the steel rule is 19/32″ which equals .593″.

134. How Thick Is One Thousandth of an Inch?

To get an idea of .001″ or 1/1000″, this paper is about 3/1000″ thick and thin tissue paper is about 1/1000″ thick. A hair on your head is about 3/1000″ thick. (See §§ *672* and *1156.*)

135. Decimal Rule

The inch on a decimal rule is divided into 10 and 100 parts instead of quarters, eighths, sixteenths, etc. It is thus unnecessary to change from a common fraction to a decimal fraction. Measurements are made quicker with this rule when decimal dimensions are wanted.

The smallest divisions on some of these rules are 50 parts to an inch (Fig. 116), instead of 100 so that they can be read easily. (See also § *141.*)

Review Questions

1. Write the decimal equivalents of 1/2″, 1/4″, 1/8″, 1/16″, 1/32″, 1/64″. Say them.
2. Write the decimal equivalents of 47/64″, 13/32″, 19/64″, 15/16″, 7/8″, 57/64″. Say them.
3. Write the following numbers: six hundred twenty-five thousandths; three hundred ninety-three thousandths; seven thousandths; sixteen thousandths; one-half thousandth; one-quarter thousandth; one ten-thousandth.
4. The answer to a problem is .225″. What is the nearest decimal equivalent that can be measured with a steel rule?
5. How thick is the paper in this book? Write it. Say it.
6. How thick is a hair on your head? Write it. Say it.
7. How thick is .001″? Make a comparison.

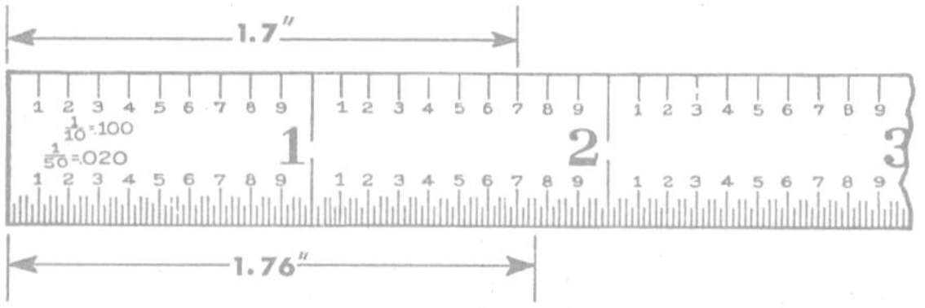

Fig. 116. Decimal Rule

Coordination

Words to Know

common fraction	denominator
decimal equivalent	equivalent
decimal equivalent table	numerator
decimal fraction	thousandth of an inch
decimal point	

Mathematics

1. Write the decimal equivalents of 7/8″, 7/16″, 5/32″, 21/64″. Say them.
2. Write the following numbers: seven hundred thirty thousandths, four hundred ninety-four thousandths, nine thousandths, twenty-four thousandths, three-quarter thousandth, five ten-thousandths.
3. Write out the following: .350″, .291″, .003″, .049″, .0005″, .00025″.
4. Memorize the decimal equivalents of 1/2″, 1/4″, 1/8″, 1/16″, 1/32″, and 1/64″. Say them. Write them.
5. Describe the metric system of measuring as compared with the English system.

Drafting

1. When should dimensions on drawings be given in common fractions and when in decimal fractions?
2. How should the following dimensions be given on drawings, changing the common fractions to decimal fractions? 1/2″, 3/4″, 7/8″, 1 1/4″, 2 1/16″, 4 5/32″, 1/64″.

Micrometers

141. What Is a Micrometer?

A micrometer, called *mike* for short, is an instrument that measures in thousandths of an inch (1/1000″). An inch on a steel rule is usually divided into 64 parts and sometimes into 100 parts (see §§ *80* and *135*). It is impossible to stamp 1000 lines per inch on the steel rule. Even if it were possible, the measurements would have to be made with a magnifying glass and even then they would be difficult to read. The micrometer, because of the way it is made, divides an inch into a thousand parts and makes fine measuring easy.

142. Parts of a Micrometer

A micrometer, Fig. 122, has a *frame, sleeve, thimble, spindle,* and *anvil.* The inside of the micrometer is shown in Fig. 122. The opening between the anvil and the spindle is made smaller or larger by turning the thimble. The size of the opening is read on the sleeve and the thimble. The *lock nut* locks the spindle so that it will not turn. The *ratchet stop* is explained in section *147*.

143. Kinds and Sizes of Micrometers

The *outside micrometer* is used the most often. (See Fig. 122.) It is used to measure the outside diameters of round objects and the widths and thicknesses of flat pieces. (See Fig. 131.)

The *inside micrometer,* Fig. 123, is used to measure the diameters of holes as in Fig. 124. The *depth micrometer* is used to measure

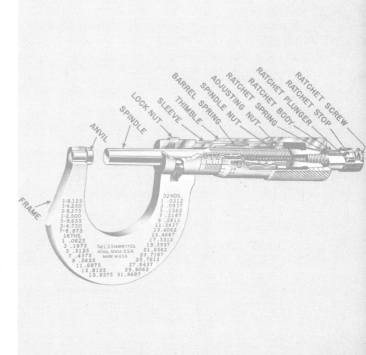

Fig. 122. **Construction of a Micrometer Caliper**
(Courtesy L. S. Starrett Co.)

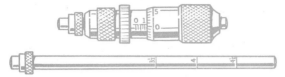

Fig. 123. Inside Micrometer

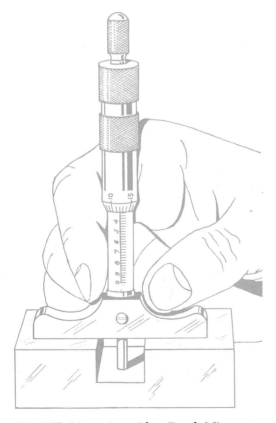

Fig. 124. Measuring with an Inside Micrometer

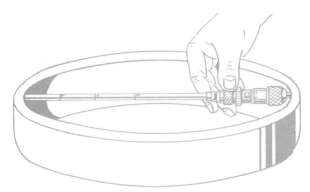

Fig. 125. Measuring with a Depth Micrometer

the depths of holes, grooves, and slots, Fig. 125.

The *screw thread micrometer*, Fig 126, is used to measure the pitch diameter of screw threads (see § *609*).

Fig. 127. They are identified by the maximum size they can measure. Thus:

A 1″ micrometer measures from 0″ to 1″.

A 2″ micrometer measures from 1″ to 2″.

144. Cost of Micrometers

The 1″ micrometer of the type shown in Fig. 122 costs about $25.35. The inside micrometer in Fig. 123 costs $34.75. The depth micrometer in Fig. 125 costs $33.10, and the screw thread micrometer in Fig. 126 costs $34.10.

145. Care of Micrometers

The micrometer is a fine instrument and should be handled as carefully as a watch. Dropping it on the floor or bench may damage its fine parts and make it useless. Keep it away from dust, grit, and grease. It should never be twirled. The spindle should not be screwed down to the anvil (as in Fig. 129) when not in use because changes in temperature cause it to *expand* (see § *721*) and shrink and thus strain it so that it will not measure correctly. (See § *1159*.) Its exactness should be tested now and then as explained in sections *148* or *149*. Micrometers should be oiled before storing away.

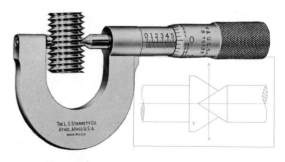

Fig. 126. Thread Micrometer Measuring the Pitch Diameter of a Screw Thread Directly
(Courtesy L. S. Starrett Co.)
Insert shows anvil and spindle position at line AB which corresponds to zero reading.

146. Touch or Feel

The exactness of most measurements depends upon the sense of touch or feel. No two persons' touches are alike. If one mechanic's touch is heavy and another mechanic's touch is light, there will be a difference in the two measurements of the same piece. The sense of touch is most delicate in the finger tips. Among skilled mechanics it is highly developed. A skilled mechanic, using the proper measuring tool, can feel 0.00025″. It can, however, only be done by holding the measuring tool delicately with the finger tips. (See Figs. 131 and 132.)

Fine measurements cannot be made where there is vibration from machinery, etc., as it destroys the sense of touch. Avoid working with a measuring tool that has been set by another man; set it yourself. The different touches of different mechanics in putting the tool on the work will cause different measurements. In making very fine measurements even the warmth of the hand will change the size of the measuring tool (see § *1159.*)

147. Ratchet Stop on Micrometer

A *ratchet stop* is placed at the end of the thimble on some micrometers so that the same tightness or *pressure* is always used, Fig. 128. The *ratchet* slips at the proper pressure.

Fig. 128. Ratchet Stop on Micrometer

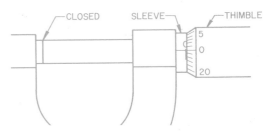

Fig. 129. Testing the Exactness of a 1″ Micrometer

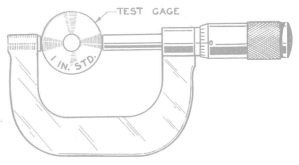

Fig. 130. Testing the Exactness of a 2″ Micrometer

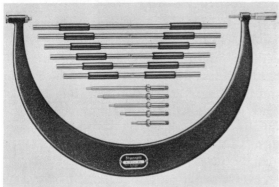

Fig. 127. Micrometer Sets, 1″ to 24″
(Courtesy L. S. Starrett Co.)

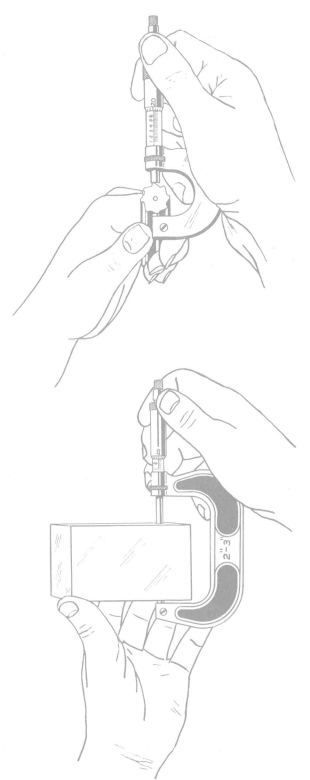

Fig. 131. Holding a Micrometer to Measure Work Held in the Hand

148. Testing Exactness of 1" Micrometer

Close the 1" micrometer completely with the correct amount of *touch*. If the micrometer is set correctly, the *O* mark on the sleeve will be in line with the *O* mark on the thimble, Fig. 129. Wear on the *anvil* and the *screw* sometimes makes it necessary to reset the micrometer. This is done by various methods, depending upon the make of the micrometer. It is best to see the manufacturer's catalog for information on how it is done.

149. Testing Exactness of 2" (or Larger) Micrometers

For testing 2" or larger micrometers, a *gage* of known size must be used and the micrometer then set to this size, Fig. 130. (See §§ *148* and *1145*.)

150. Mastering the Micrometer

To become master of the micrometer you must learn to do the following:
(1) Set the micrometer to any number.
(2) Measure articles:
    a. Hold micrometer correctly (see §§ *151-152*).
    b. Use correct touch or feel (see § *146*).
(3) Say the number.
(4) Write the number.

151. Holding Micrometer to Measure Work Held in Hand

Hold the work to be measured in the left hand. Hold the micrometer in the right hand with the third or little finger pressing the frame against the palm, Fig. 131; the thumb and first finger are free to turn the thimble. Place the work between the anvil and the spindle; then with the thumb and first finger turn the thimble until a very little pressure is felt.

It is necessary for the beginner to study his touch carefully because the measurement will not be the same when the pressure is light as when it is heavy (see § *146*); a micrometer may be sprung as much as .003″ by too much pressure. This gives the wrong measurements and damages the instrument. A *ratchet stop* on a micrometer always gives the same pressure (see Fig. 128). (See § *147*.)

152. Holding Micrometer to Measure Work not Held in Hand

Work that is not held in the hand may be measured by holding the micrometer with

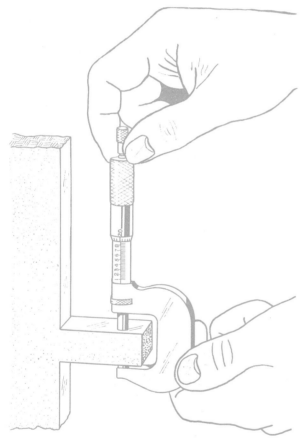

Fig. 132. Holding a Micrometer to Measure Work not Held in the Hand

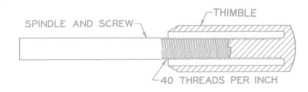

Fig. 133. Thimble is Fastened to the End of Screw

both hands as shown in Fig. 132. The frame of the micrometer is held in the left hand and the thimble turned with the right hand.

153. Micrometer Screw

All micrometers are read alike. The end of the *spindle,* inside the *thimble,* is called the screw spindle, Fig. 133. The sleeve is fastened to the end of the screw. The screw has 40 *threads* to an inch; that is, the screw must turn 40 times to move one inch. Thus, each turn of the screw equals 1/40″. Since the micrometer is read in thousandths of an inch instead of 40ths of an inch, 1/40 of an inch must be changed to thousandths of an inch by dividing the *numerator* by the *denominator* (see § *132*):

$$40 \overline{)1.000} \quad .025$$

There are also 40 lines to an inch on the *sleeve* (Fig. 122), the same as the number of threads on the screw; these lines show how many times the screw has turned. Each turn equals .025″. If one turn of the screw equals .025″, then 1/25 of a turn equals 1/25 of .025″, or .001″ (*one thousandth of an inch*). Thus, by dividing the edge of the thimble into 25 parts, it is possible to make exactly 1/25 of a turn which is .001″, or 2/25 of a turn which is .002″, etc. It makes it possible to measure in thousandths of an inch.

One-half and quarters of a thousandth can be judged as nearly as possible.

154. Explanation of Marks on Sleeve and Thimble

Turn the thimble until the *0 mark* on the thimble and the *0 mark* on the sleeve come together (see Fig. 129). This will give the smallest size that the micrometer will measure; on a 1″ micrometer it is 0; on a 2″ micrometer it is 1″; on a 3″ micrometer it is 2″.

The *marks* on the thimble are .001″ each. Turn the thimble to the next line on the thimble in the direction of the arrow, Fig. 134, and on a 1″ micrometer the *spindle* will be

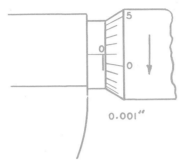

Fig. 134. One Thousandth of an Inch (.001″)

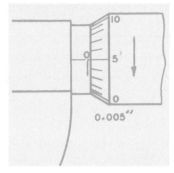

Fig. 135. Five Thousandths of an Inch (.005″)

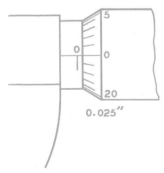

Fig. 136. Twenty-five Thousandths of an Inch (.025″)

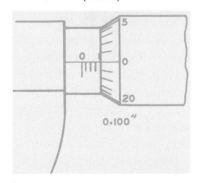

Fig. 137. One Hundred Thousandths of an Inch (.100″)

.001″ from the *anvil.* Turn the thimble to the line marked 5 on the thimble, Fig. 135, and the spindle will be .005″ from the anvil.

Note that one complete turn of the thimble is .025″ on the sleeve, Fig. 136. For each turn of the thimble, the thimble moves over one more mark on the sleeve. This means that each mark on the sleeve is .025″. Every fourth line on the sleeve is a little longer than the others and is stamped 1, 2, 3, etc., which stand for .100″, .200″, .300″, etc. (See Fig. 138.) The micrometer is set at .100″ in Fig. 137.

155. Reading a Micrometer

To find out how much the micrometer is opened (the distance between the anvil and the spindle) the marks on the sleeve may be read like any ordinary rule, remembering that the numbers 1, 2, 3, 4, etc., mean .100″, .200″, .300″, .400″, etc. To this add the thousandths that show on the thimble. For example, the readings in Fig. 138 are:

   (A) .200″ even.
   (B) .250″ (.200″ + .025″ + .025″ = .250″).
   (C) .562″ (.500″ + .050″ + .012″ = .562″).
   (D) .787½″ (.700″ + .075″ + .012½″ = .787½″ or .7875″).

Be sure to add correctly.

156. Reading a Ten-Thousandth Micrometer

Some micrometers have a *vernier,* named after the inventor, *Pierre Vernier.* A *vernier micrometer* can be read to a ten-thousandth of an inch (1/10000″ or .0001″). Each mark on the thimble is again .001″. The ten divisions on the *back of the sleeve* are the vernier; the lines are numbered 0, 1, 2, 3, 4, 5, 6, 7, 8, 9, 0 in Fig. 139. These lines have the same space as ten divisions on the thimble.

To read the vernier micrometer, first read the thousandths as on any ordinary micrometer. Suppose that this number is between

.275 and .276 as in Fig. 139. To find the fourth *decimal place*, find the line on the vernier that matches exactly a line on the thimble. In this case it is the line 4; this number 4 means 4 ten-thousandths inches (.0004″) and added to the .275″ gives the fourth decimal place. Thus the complete reading is .2754″ (.275″ + .0004″ = .2754″).

Review Questions

1. What is a micrometer?
2. Name the parts of a micrometer.
3. For what is an outside micrometer used?
4. For what is an inside micrometer used?
5. For what is a depth micrometer used?
6. For what is a screw thread micrometer used?
7. What is the largest size you can measure with a 1″ micrometer?
8. What is the smallest size you can measure with a 2″ micrometer?
9. What is the largest size you can measure with a 3″ micrometer?
10. Can you measure ½″ stock with a 2″ micrometer? Why?
11. Can you measure 1½″ stock with a 1″ micrometer? Why?
12. How much does a 1″ micrometer cost?
13. Why should the micrometer be handled with great care?
14. The sense of touch is most delicate in what part of the hand?
15. Why should you not work with a micrometer that has been set by another person?
16. What effect does the warmth of the hand have upon the measuring tool?
17. What is the use of a ratchet stop on a micrometer?
18. How many threads per inch are there on the micrometer screw?
19. Test the exactness of a 1″ outside micrometer.
20. Test the exactness of a 2″ or larger micrometer.
21. How can a micrometer be set to ⁹⁄₁₆″?

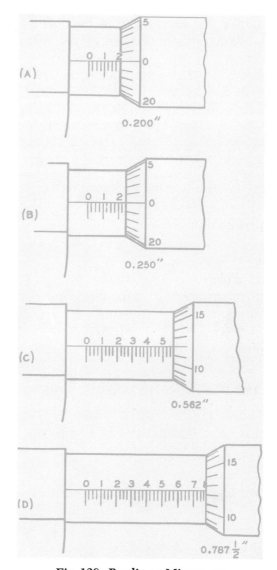

Fig. 138. **Reading a Micrometer**

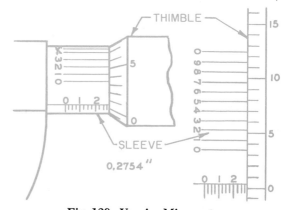

Fig. 139. **Vernier Micrometer**

22. Set the micrometer to the following sizes and have them checked by the instructor:

.001″	.772″	.4732″	.9999″
.003″	.391½″	.6837″	1.010″
.060″	.657¼″	.8133″	1.436″
.339″	.533¾″	.5633″	1.849″
.881″	.352½″	.2411″	2.112″
.999″	.3525″	.7258″	2.677″

23. What is a vernier micrometer?

Coordination

Words to Know

decimal place	frame
depth micrometer	thimble
inside micrometer	screw
micrometer	sleeve
anvil	spindle
outside micrometer	ten-thousandth
Pierre Vernier	micrometer
ratchet stop	thimble
screw thread	vernier
micrometer	vernier micrometer

Mathematics

1. Add .600″ + .050″ + .013″
2. Add .900″ + .075″ + .011½″
3. How long would an apprentice, earning $1.85 an hour, have to work to earn enough money to buy a 1″ micrometer costing $25.35?

Social Science

1. Tell how the development of fine measuring tools has helped the manufacturing industry and how humanity has benefited thereby.

Occupational Information

1. Write a biography of Pierre Vernier.

Cutting Hot Steel to Length
Prior to Rolling — Note
the Operator in the
Cab at the Right
(Courtesy U.S. Steel)

Sawing and
Bench Work

Part **II**

Hand Sawing

168. How the Hacksaw Got Its Name

It is supposed that when man first needed a cutting tool he chopped or *hacked* notches in any hard material he could find. Such a saw would make a very rough cut and may be how the *hacksaw* got its name. The hacksaw is now a greatly improved tool and is used for sawing all metals except *hardened steel* (see § 951). The cutting tool must always be harder than the material to be cut.

169. Parts of Hand Hacksaw

The parts of the hand hacksaw, Fig. 150, are the *frame, handle, prongs, tightening screw* and *wing nut*, and *blade*. The frame is

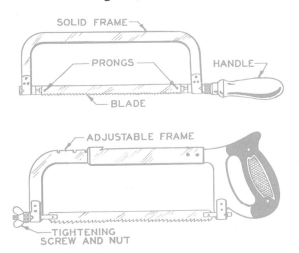

Fig. 150. Hand Hacksaws

made to hold the blade tightly. Frames are made in two styles: the *solid frame* in which the length cannot be changed and the *adjustable frame* which has a back that can be shortened or lengthened to hold blades of different lengths.

170. Hand Hacksaw Blade Selection

Hand hacksaw blades are made of thin high-grade steel which has been hardened and tempered (see §§ 951 and 954). Some blades are all *hard* and are therefore quite brittle. Other kinds of blades have hardened teeth and a softer back, and are classified as *flexible* blades. The softer back makes them springy and less likely to break. You should know the following facts about hand hacksaw blades:

Size

They are made in 8″, 10″, and 12″ lengths. The length is the distance between the centers of the holes at each end, Fig. 151. The blades are ½″ wide and 0.025″ thick.

Material

Blades are available in several kinds of material including: carbon steel, molybdenum alloy steel, tungsten alloy steel, molybdenum high-speed steel, and tungsten high-speed steel.

Number of Teeth Per Inch

A blade always has one more *point* than the number of complete teeth in 1″, Fig. 152.

(A) 14 teeth: for cutting soft steel, aluminum, brass, bronze, copper alloys, and other materials 1″ or more in thickness.

Fig. 151. Length of Blade

Fig. 152. Points Per Inch

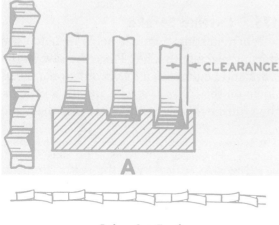

Raker Set Tooth

Wavy Set Tooth

B

Fig. 153. Profile of Blade and the Tooth Set
A. Thickness of Blade and Teeth (Enlarged)
B. Tooth Set on Metal-Cutting Saws: Upper is Raker Set; Lower is Wavy Set

(B) 18 teeth: for cutting machine steel, angle iron, drill rod, tool steel, aluminum, copper alloys, and other materials ¼″ to 1″ in thickness; for general-purpose work.
(C) 24 teeth: for cutting materials $\frac{1}{16}$″ to ¼″ thickness, iron pipe, metal conduits, light angle iron, etc.
(D) 32 teeth: for cutting materials up to $\frac{1}{16}$″ thickness, sheet metals, thin wall tubing, and thin angles or channels.

Tooth Set

Set of saw teeth refers to the way the teeth are bent to one side or the other to provide a *kerf* (the cut made by the saw) which is wider than the thickness of the saw. The wide saw kerf prevents the saw from binding, Fig. 153 (A). Two kinds of set are provided, a *raker* or *alternate* set, and *wavy* set, Fig. 153 (B). The raker set has one tooth bent to the right, one to the left, and one straight tooth in between. The wavy set has several teeth bent to the right and several teeth bent to the left, alternately. Blades with 14 and 18 teeth have the alternate set. Those with 24 or 32 teeth have the wavy set.

171. Putting Blade in Frame

When putting a new blade in the hand hacksaw, place it so that the teeth of the blade

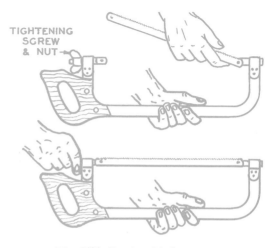

Fig. 154. Putting Blade in Frame

point away from the handle. Fasten one end of the blade to the hook at one end of the frame and the other end of the blade over the hook at the opposite end of the frame, Fig. 154. Strain the blade well as you tighten the *tightening screw;* a loose blade makes a crooked cut and is likely to break.

172.   Holding Metal for Sawing

The work should be a little below the height of the elbows or about 40″ to 44″ from

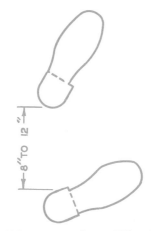

Fig. 155. Position of Feet When Sawing

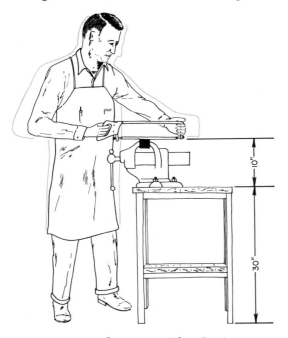

Fig. 156. Body Position When Sawing

the floor (see Fig. 156). It should be held tightly in the vise. The part to be sawed should be near the vise jaws to keep the work from *chattering*.[1] Protect polished surfaces from the rough, steel vise jaws by covering them with *vise jaw caps.* (See Fig. 534.)

173.   Body Position for Sawing

When sawing, stand with one foot ahead of the other; the left foot should point toward the bench. The arch of the right foot should be about 12″ from the heel of the left foot, Fig. 155. Face the work. The body should be positioned at about a 30° angle with the sawing stroke. Sway forward and backward on the feet in addition to slightly moving the arms, Fig. 156.

174.   Holding Hand Hacksaw

Place the right hand on the handle and the left hand firmly on the other end of the saw frame as in Fig. 157.

175.   Cutting Stroke

When starting a cut, it helps to notch the starting place with a file. Place the saw on the work and begin with a *backward stroke*. Press down on the *forward stroke* and lift a little on the *return stroke* (Fig. 158) because the blade

[1]*Chattering* is a fast, rattling noise made by the jarring, vibrating, or springing of the work or the cutting tool. It may cause nicks and notches on the work.

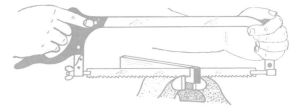

Fig. 157. Holding the Hacksaw

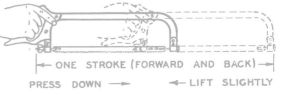

Fig. 158. One Stroke

cuts only on the forward stroke. Try to imitate the stroke of the *power hacksaw* (see Fig. 170); see how it lifts on the return stroke. Tighten the blade again after a few strokes since it will stretch when it becomes warm. Use the full blade length. Avoid jerky motions.

176. Speed

Make about 40 *cutting strokes* per minute (see Fig. 158). Sawing faster merely wears out the blade by rubbing. Make long, slow, steady strokes.

177. Pressure

Press down on the *forward stroke* and lift a little on the *return stroke* (see Fig. 158). Large pieces need more pressure than small pieces. A worn blade needs more pressure than a new blade. Rubbing, slipping, or sliding over the metal without cutting makes the cutting edges of the teeth smooth, bright, and shiny like glass. It makes the teeth blunt and dulls them. (See § 248.)

178. Wear on Sides of Teeth

The sides of the teeth wear down by the rubbing between the blade and the metal which is cut. A used blade makes a narrower cut than a new blade. A new blade, if placed in an old cut, wedges and sticks and is ruined with the first stroke because of the difference in the thicknesses of the two blades. If a cut cannot be completed with the old blade, start a new cut with a new blade.

179. Sawing Thin Metal

A thin piece of metal to be sawed should be placed in a vise with the metal gripped close to the line of the cut, so as to keep it from vibrating, springing, or *chattering*.

If the metal is thinner than the space from one tooth to the next tooth on the blade, Fig. 159 (A), it should be placed between two boards and clamped in the vise, then sawed through both wood and metal at once as in B in Fig. 159. Remember that at least three teeth should be cutting at any one time.

If there is a layout on one side of the thin metal and it is necessary to saw near a line, a *C-clamp* may be used to fasten the metal to the board, so the layout can be seen, Fig. 160.

180. Sawing Wide Pieces of Metal

To saw wide pieces of metal, it is better to set the blade at *right angles* (90°) to the frame, Fig. 161.

181. Cutting Silhouettes

A *silhouette* is the blacked-in outline of an object, similar to a shadow. A few silhouettes

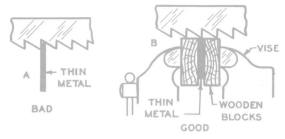

Fig. 159. Holding Thin Metal for Sawing

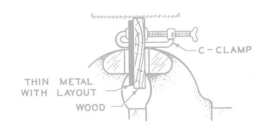

Fig. 160. Holding Thin Metal Having a Layout on One Side

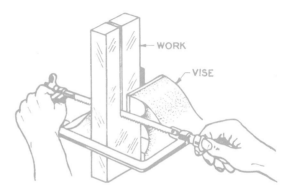

Fig. 161. Blade Set at a Right Angle to the Frame

Fig. 162. Silhouettes

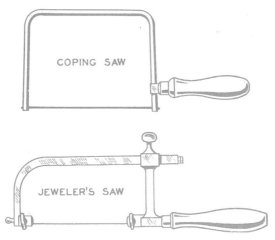

Fig. 163. Coping and Jeweler's Saws

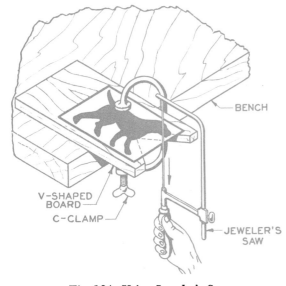

Fig. 164. Using Jeweler's Saw

are shown in Fig. 162. Silhouettes are ornamental and may be used as pins or buckles or they may be *soldered* on *hammered dishes* (see Units 41 and 42) or on dishes that have been made by *spinning.* (See Unit 58.) A small pin may be soldered to the back of a silhouette. This makes a nice ornament to be worn on a dress or on a coat.

Silhouettes, bookends, bracelets, letter openers, and other ornaments may be cut out of copper, brass, *pewter* (see § 378), or *monel metal* (see § 379). Such cuts may be made with a *coping saw* or with a *jeweler's saw,* also called a *piercing saw,* Fig. 163, because irregular holes are cut or *pierced* with this saw. *Weather vanes* can be cut out of *sheet steel* (see § 329).

Metal-cutting blades for jeweler's saws can be bought by the dozen. They have fine teeth and must be very hard in order to cut metal. The teeth of the blade should point toward the handle.

The work should be held on a *V-shaped board* laid on the edge of the bench and held down with the left hand or with a clamp. The sawing should be done with the right hand, Fig. 164. The *cutting stroke* is downward. Sometimes a hole must be drilled and the blade put through the hole and then fastened to the saw frame.

Section 799 tells of other ways to cut *sheet metal.*

182. Broken Blades

Saw blades are usually broken by:
(1) Loose blade.
(2) Loose work.
(3) Too much pressure.
(4) Blade sticking.

Review Questions

1. Can hardened steel be cut with a hand hacksaw? Why?

2. Name the hand hacksaw parts.

3. What materials are used to make hacksaw blades?

4. Is the hacksaw blade harder than the blade of a wood saw? Why?

5. How are hacksaw blades measured?

6. Which way should the teeth of a hand hacksaw blade point?

7. Why should a new blade never be used in a cut made by an old blade?

8. Does the hand hacksaw cut on the forward or return stroke? Why?

9. What should be the cutting speed of the hand hacksaw?

10. Can a hacksaw blade be sharpened with a file? Why?

11. How should sheet metal be held for sawing?

12. How can silhouettes be cut?

13. Which way should the teeth of a jeweler's saw blade point?

14. Does the jeweler's saw blade cut on the upward or downward stroke?

15. Name four causes of blade breakages.

16. Write a short story about "How the Hacksaw Got Its Name."

17. Indicate several uses for hacksaw blades with the following numbers of teeth per inch: 14, 18, 24, and 32.

18. List two kinds of tooth set on hand hacksaw blades.

Coordination

Words to Know

adjustable frame	pierce
backward stroke	piercing saw
C-clamp	point or pitch
chatter	return stroke
clearance	set
coping saw	sheet metal
cutting stroke	silhouette
feed	solid frame
forward stroke	speed
hand hacksaw	teeth
hand sawing	vise jaw cap
jeweler's saw	weather vane

Mathematics

1. On an 18 point blade, what is the distance from one tooth to the next tooth?

Power Sawing

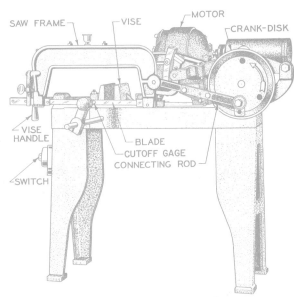

Fig. 170. Power Hacksaw and Parts

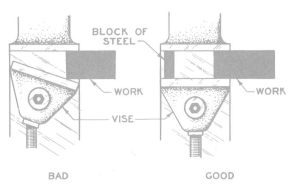

Fig. 171. Holding Short Piece of Metal in
Power Saw Vise

187. Power Sawing Machines

Three common types of power sawing machines are used for sawing metals: (1) power hacksaw, (2) horizontal band saw, (3) vertical band saw. These three power sawing machines are discussed in this unit.

188. Power Hacksaw and Its Parts

The power hacksaw, Fig. 170, is a machine for sawing all kinds of metal, except *hardened steel* (see § 951). The *blade* must always be harder than the material to be cut. The *frame* and blade move forward and backward. It is driven by an *electric motor* and *feeds*[1] and stops by itself.

189. Care of Power Hacksaw

The power hacksaw should be oiled every day with *lubricating oil*. (See §§ 394 and 413.) It should be cleaned after being used.

190. Putting Blade in Frame

When putting a blade in the power hacksaw see that the teeth point forward (away from operator). Strain the blade in the frame. It must be straight up and down. (See § 171.)

191. Holding Metal to be Sawed

To cut a piece of metal in the power hacksaw, clamp the bar to be cut tightly in the

---

[1]*Feed* is the movement of a cutting tool into the work on each stroke or revolution. (See #558.)

vise (see Fig. 170). If the bar from which a piece is to be cut is so short that it will not reach across the full width of the vise, put a piece of metal the same width as the bar at the other end of the vise, Fig. 171. The pressure on both ends of the vise must be the same. Fig. 172 shows how to hold different shapes of metal in the power saw vise. On some saws the vise may be swiveled up to 45° making angular cuts.

One end of a long bar may be supported on a *sawhorse*, Fig. 173. Both ends of the long bar should be the same height from the floor.

192. Measuring Metal to be Cut

When measuring a piece of metal to be cut in the power hacksaw, place the *edge* of the rule alongside the metal to be cut (see Fig. 76) and at the same time hold the end of the rule against the side of the saw blade, Fig. 174. While in this position move the metal to the length wanted; then tighten the vise against the metal.

193. Using Cutoff Gage

When many pieces of the same length are to be cut, the first piece may be measured as described in section 192. Additional pieces of the same length may be cut without measur-

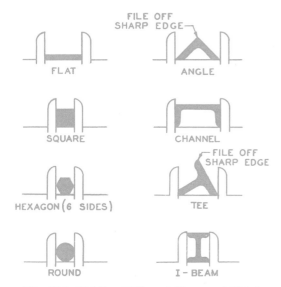

Fig. 172. Holding Different Shapes of Metal in Power Saw Vise

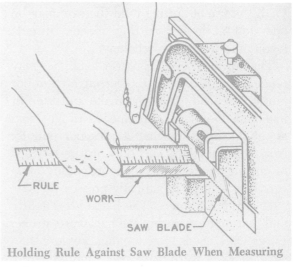

Holding Rule Against Saw Blade When Measuring

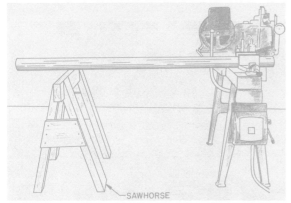

Fig. 173. Supporting End of Long Bar with Sawhorse

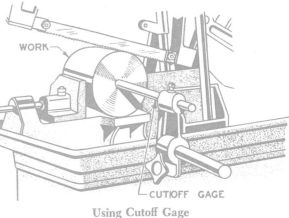

Using Cutoff Gage

Fig. 174. Measuring Metal to be Cut

ing every piece by setting the *cutoff gage* against the end of the metal, after the first piece is measured, Fig. 174.

194. Starting Power Hacksaw

Let the saw down by hand so that the blade just touches the work, Fig. 175. Next, set the saw in motion by turning on the power. If the power saw is the kind that uses *cutting fluid* (see § 406), see that it flows on the cut, Fig. 176. The blade will thus last longer.

195. Hacksaw Speed and Feed Pressure

Power hacksaws are of two basic types, *dry cutting* and *wet cutting*. With the wet cutting machines a *cutting fluid* is used (Fig. 176). With the use of cutting fluid the saw may be operated at higher cutting speeds, it cuts faster, and the blade lasts longer.

The cutting speed for power hacksaws may range from about 35 to 150 *cutting strokes* per minute, depending on the make and type of machine. Ordinarily the speeds range from about 60 to 120 cutting strokes per minute. Note that the blade cuts only on the forward or cutting stroke, while a slight feeding *pressure* or weight automatically presses the saw against the workpiece. The blade lifts slightly and does not cut during the backward stroke. Large work needs more feeding pressure than small work. A worn blade needs more feeding pressure to make it cut than a new blade, and so more pressure must be added as the blade becomes worn. Most power hacksaws are equipped with a knob or control device which may be adjusted to increase or decrease the feeding pressure exerted on the saw during the cutting stroke.

Power hacksaws may be the single-speed, 2-speed, 3-speed, or 4-speed type. They may be operated at higher cutting speeds with the application of cutting fluids than when cutting dry. Hard and tough metals, such as high-carbon steel (see § 328) or tool steel, should be cut at lower cutting speeds than ordinary

low-carbon steels (see § 326). The following are recommended cutting speeds for power hacksaws:

CUTTING SPEEDS RECOMMENDED FOR POWER HACKSAWS

MATERIAL	STROKES PER MINUTE DRY	STROKES PER MINUTE WET
Low-carbon steel	60-90	90-120
Medium-carbon steel	60	90-120
High-carbon steel	60	90
High-speed steel	60	90
Drill rod	60	90
Alloy steel	60	90
Cast iron	60-90	(cut dry)
Aluminum	90	120
Brass	60	90-120
Bronze	60	90

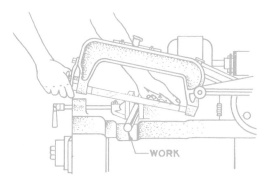

Fig. 175. Lowering Saw by Hand to Keep Blade from Breaking

Fig. 176. Cutting Fluid Flowing on Cut

Rubbing, slipping, or sliding over the metal without cutting makes the cutting edges smooth, bright, hard, and shiny like glass. It makes the teeth blunt and dulls them. The reasons for the wear on the sides of teeth and for broken blades are explained in sections 178 and 182.

196. Power Hacksaw Blades

Care must be taken in the selection of the proper hacksaw blade for a power hacksaw if the machine is to operate efficiently. Five factors which should be understood in blade selection include: (1) length, (2) thickness, (3) width, (4) tooth coarseness, and (5) the kind of material from which the blade is made.

Length

Blades are available in lengths ranging from 12″ for small machines to 30″ for very large machines. Machines of the size used in school shops generally use blades 12″ or 14″ in length.

Thickness

Blades are available in thicknesses of 0.032″, 0.050″, 0.062″, 0.075″, 0.088″, 0.100″.

Width

Blades are available in widths of ⅝″, 1″, 1¼″, 1½″, 1¾″, 2″, or 2½″.

Tooth Coarseness

The coarseness refers to the number of teeth per inch of blade length. The number of teeth per inch is also called the *pitch*. Blades are available with 3, 4, 6, 10, 14, and 18 teeth per inch. However, for most applications in the school shop, blades with 6, 10, or 14 teeth per inch are selected. Blades with 14 or 10 teeth are used for the majority of light-duty sawing operations in school shops. The 14-tooth blades are used for cutting thin wall tubing, thin angles, and other metals of less than about ¼″ thickness. The 10-tooth blades are used for general-purpose sawing applications of metals from ¼″ to about ¾″ thickness. A 6-tooth blade should be selected for effi-

[2] *A soft metal* is any metal that can be filed.

cient cuts on workpieces from about 1″ to 2″ thickness, and a 4-tooth blade for workpieces greater than 2″ in thickness.

Tooth Set

Power hacksaw blades have the *raker* tooth set, which sometimes is called the *alternate* or *regular* set. (See Fig. 153 (*B*) and also § 170.)

Blade Material

Blades are available in the following kinds of material: flexible high-speed steel, all hard high-speed steel, all hard molybdenum alloy steel, all hard tungsten alloy steel, and the *welded and composite blade* which has a hardened high-speed steel cutting edge welded to a tough alloy steel back.

Blade Selection

Blades 12″ in length are available with 10 or 14 teeth per inch, 1″ width, and 0.050″ thickness. Blades 14″ in length are available in a wide variety of specifications; they commonly are used in school shops with 1″ width, 0.050″ thickness, and with either 10- or 14-teeth per inch for light-duty cutting applications. However, for general-purpose cutting applications the 14″ blade is available in 1¼″ width, 0.062″ thickness, and with either 10- or 6-pitch teeth. For very heavy-duty applications other pitches and widths are available. As a general rule, blades with finer teeth should be used for cutting hard stock and thin sections.

197. Scroll Saw

The scroll saw, Fig. 177, also called *jigsaw*, is used to cut thin, *soft metals*[2] as well as wood, plastics, and other soft materials. It cuts curves, as in jigsaw puzzles, and is a useful tool in the home workshop.

198. Portable Band Saw

Some metal that must be sawed cannot be easily moved to the saw, so a *portable band saw*, Fig. 178, may be carried to the job. This tool has a *band saw blade* that runs continuously in one direction because the blade is a thin, flat strip of steel with a saw edge. It cuts faster than the hacksaw blade that moves back and forth cutting only on the forward stroke (see Fig. 158). It can be operated from most electrical outlets.

199. Horizontal Band Saw

The *horizontal* (see § 31) band saw, Fig. 179 (like the portable band saw explained in section 198), has a blade that runs in only one direction. It is used for cutting off metal pieces just as the power hacksaw (see § 188); it cuts faster than the power hacksaw which cuts only on one stroke and then lifts and returns

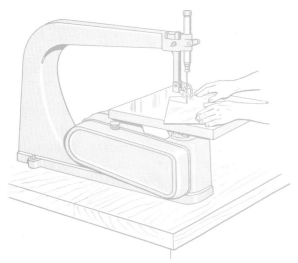

Fig. 177. Scroll Saw

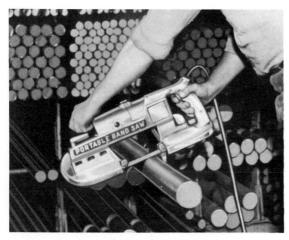

Fig. 178. Portable Band Saw
(Courtesy The DoAll Co.)

for the next cutting stroke. The frame and the blade of the horizontal band saw can be raised and lowered because it has a hinge on one end. The position of the saw blade is horizontal when in the cutting position.

Horizontal band saws may be either the *dry cutting* or the *wet cutting* type. Wet cutting machines, Fig. 179, are equipped with a cooling pump which recirculates the cutting fluid (see § 406). Some band saws are equipped with a *spray mist* system which sprays a fine mist of cutting fluid on the blade as it cuts. The use of cutting fluids permits higher cutting speeds, faster cutting, and increased saw blade life.

Kinds of Cuts

The horizontal band saw can cut off stock square or at an angle. For angular cuts, the vise may be swiveled up to 45°.

Feed Rate

The feed rate on most horizontal band saws is hydraulically controlled; therefore the danger of too rapid feeding is eliminated when the *feed rate* is properly adjusted. The feed rate should be set so that the blade may enter

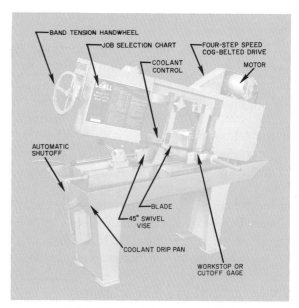

Fig. 179. Horizontal Band Saw
(Courtesy The DoAll Co.)

the work steadily and produce a steady flow of metal chips. If the feed rate is too rapid when the blade enters the work, the blade may break. When the feed rate is too slow, the blade does not cut efficiently and it will become dull more rapidly.

200. Cutting with a Horizontal Band Saw

1. See that the proper band saw blade is installed for the job.

2. See that the blade is tensioned properly. Check this with your instructor.

3. Determine that the vise is set for the type of cut desired. For a square cut it should be set at a 90° angle to the saw blade; check with a square, make a trial cut, and recheck the accuracy of the cut.

4. Select the stock, measure, and mark the point at which the cut is to be made.

5. Mount the workpiece in the saw vise in proper position for the cut (see Fig. 172). If more than one piece is to be cut, locate and set the *work stop* or *cutoff gage* at the end of the part so that additional parts may be cut to the same length without measuring each part (see Fig. 174). If the stock being cut is a long bar, support the long end on a sawhorse or stock support, Fig. 173.

6. Determine the correct cutting speed and set the machine accordingly.

7. Raise the saw frame with the handle provided, start the saw running, and adjust the feed rate; this is the rate at which the blade advances toward the work.

8. Allow the saw to make a very slight kerf, raise the blade slightly, and stop the machine. Measure the length of the stock; adjust if necessary.

9. Again start the machine, turn on the cutting fluid, and complete the cut.

10. Adjust the stock for the next cut and proceed in the usual manner.

201. Vertical Band Saw

A vertical band saw, Fig. 180, is also called a *contouring machine*. Like the horizontal band saw in Fig. 179, it has a blade which runs continuously in one direction. The blade of the vertical band saw is in a vertical position. A blade shear and a blade welder are often mounted on the saw for cutting and welding band saw blades, Fig. 180. Some manufacturers make a band saw which can be converted for use as either a horizontal- or vertical-type band saw.

Kinds of Cuts

Vertical-type band saws may be used for making either straight line cuts as in Fig. 182, angular cuts, or curved line cuts as in Fig. 182. Curved line cuts are called *contour* cuts. Hence, vertical band saws are also called *contouring machines*. The saw table may be tilted at any desired angle up to 45° for making angular cuts, Fig. 181.

When internal contour cuts are made, a hole must be drilled in the workpiece first,

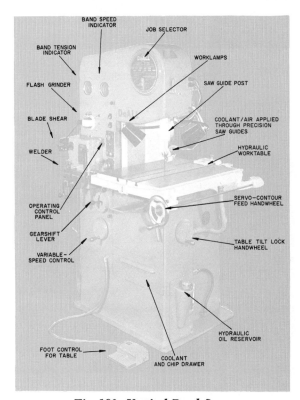

Fig. 180. Vertical Band Saw
(Courtesy The DoAll Co.)

Fig. 182. The blade is then cut with the blade shear, inserted through the drilled hole in the workpiece, and rewelded with the blade welder. Following this, the blade is installed on the machine and properly tensioned. The contour cut may then be made. Of course, the blade must again be removed from the machine and sheared in order to remove the finished workpiece.

Fig. 181. Table Tilted for Angular Cut
(Courtesy The DoAll Co.)

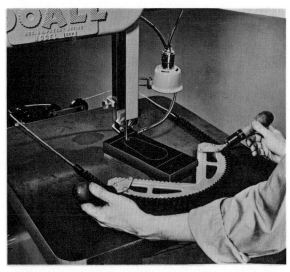

Fig. 182. Band Saw Inserted through Drilled Hole
for Internal Contour Sawing
(Courtesy The DoAll Co.)

Band Filing

Vertical band sawing machines may also be used for *band filing*, Fig. 184. A *band file* is made up of short segments of file blade which are riveted to steel tape and hooked together, Fig. 183. Band filing is much faster than hand filing. A workpiece may be band filed by simply holding it against the moving file band until the desired surface and contour are obtained.

Band Polishing

An abrasive belt may be installed on a vertical band sawing machine for band polishing. For this purpose a *guide* is mounted on the saw guide post, Fig. 185. The abrasive belt is installed on the machine and is held in position by the guide provided. Polishing is done by holding the workpiece against the moving abrasive band as shown in Fig. 185.

202. Band Saw Cutting Speeds

The cutting speed for band saws, including either the horizontal or vertical types, may be

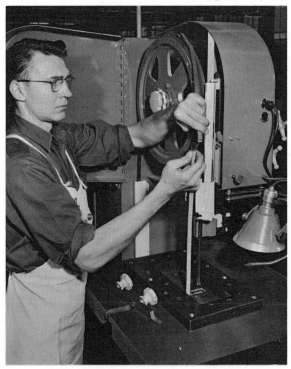

Fig. 183. Uncoupling the Band File
(Courtesy The DoAll Co.)

varied in several ways, depending on the type of motor drive system on the machine. On many horizontal band saws the speed is changed by changing the position of the V-belt on the motor and machine drive pulleys (see §§ 22 and 424). (Also see Fig. 328.) The cutting speed on some vertical band saws may be changed in a similar manner. Many vertical-type band saws have a *variable-speed drive* mechanism (see Fig. 326). With this type drive the speed of the machine may be changed to any desired speed within the speed range for the machine. However, *with the variable-speed drive mechanism, the speed of the machine can be changed only while the machine is running.*

Recommended cutting speeds vary considerably according to the following:

(1) Kind of material being cut.
(2) Hardness of the material.
(3) Thickness of the material.
(4) Whether the cutting is wet or dry.

Slower cutting speeds generally are used when cutting harder metals rather than softer metals. Slower cutting speeds are also used for cutting thick materials rather than thinner materials. Higher cutting speeds may be used for wet cutting rather than dry cutting.

The following are suggested average cutting speeds, in surface feet per minute (sfm), for cutting material ½″ to 1″ thickness with either horizontal- or vertical-type band saws:

MATERIAL	CUTTING SPEED (sfm)	
	DRY	WET
Alloy Steel (tough)	125	175
Aluminum	250	800
Bakelite	300	
Brass (soft)	500	800
Brass (hard)	200	300
Bronze	200	300
Copper	250	400
Drill Rod (annealed)	75	125
Gray Cast Iron (soft)	125	
Hard Rubber	200	
High-Speed Steel	50	75
Low-Carbon Steel	125	175
Malleable Iron	125	175
Medium-Carbon Steel	100	150

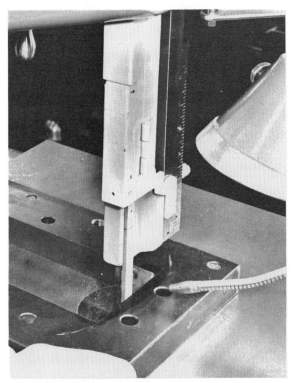

Fig. 184. Filing with a Band File (Courtesy The DoAll Co.)

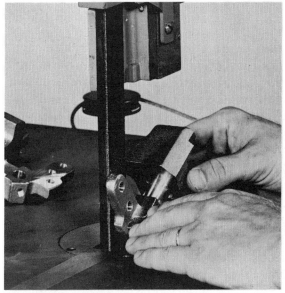

Fig. 185. Band Polishing with an Abrasive Belt on the Band Saw (Courtesy The DoAll Co.)

The above cutting speeds may be increased approximately 25% for cutting materials ¼″ or less in thickness. They should be decreased by approximately 25% for materials 2″ or more in thickness.

203. Blade Tension on Band Saw

The band saw blades on both horizontal- and vertical-type machines should be installed with the teeth pointing the direction in which the blade travels. The blade should be tightened with the proper tension, as recommended by the manufacturer of the machine. Some band saws are equipped with a *blade tension indicator* detecting when the proper tension is applied for the width of the blade installed. Ask your instructor to explain how proper blade tension is determined and applied on the band saws in your shop.

204. Band Saw Blade Selection

Blade Material

Metal-cutting, band saw blades are made from a variety of steels, including high-carbon steel, special alloy steel, and high-speed steel. The alloy steel blades and high-speed steel blades generally are designed for heavy-duty production work. The high-carbon steel blades have hardened teeth and a softer flexible back. They generally are the least expensive to purchase. Carbon steel blades are probably the most widely used on both horizontal and vertical machines in school shops, small machine shops, and maintenance machine shops.

Length

The length of band saw blades varies for different machines. Blades may be purchased in welded band for all standard machines. Blades also may be purchased in coils, 100 feet in length or longer, in a special stripout container. The blades may be cut to length and welded in the shop with a band saw blade welder, as shown on the machine in Fig. 180.

Tooth Set

Metal cutting band saw blades commonly have two kinds of set, *raker* set and *wavy* set, see *B* in Fig. 153. Both types may be used in either horizontal or vertical machines. However, generally the wavy set is recommended for most operations on horizontal machines. The raker set generally is recommended for most contouring cuts in vertical machines. The wavy set is also recommended for cutting thin metals or thin wall metals.

Blade Width

Blades generally are available in the widths shown in Table 2. A narrow width blade cuts a smaller radius than a wider blade; however, narrow width blades will break more easily when the feed rate is too great. The following shows the minimum radius which usually can be sawed with blades of various widths:

Saw Size	Radius
½″	2½″
⅜″	1¼″
¼″	⅝″
³⁄₁₆″	⅜″
⅛″	⁷⁄₃₂″
³⁄₃₂″	⅛″

Table 2
METAL-CUTTING BAND SAW SIZES

Width	Thickness	Teeth Per Inch
³⁄₃₂	0.025	18
⅛	0.025	14-18-24
³⁄₁₆	0.025	10-14-18
¼	0.025	10-14-18-24
⅜	0.025	8-10-14-18
½	0.025	6-8-10-14-18-24
⅝	0.032	8-10-14-18
¾	0.032	6-8-10-14-18
1	0.035	6-8-10-14

Blade Thickness

Blades are available in the thicknesses shown in Table 2.

Teeth Per Inch

Also called *pitch,* the "teeth per inch" refers to the coarseness of the teeth. Blades are available with various degrees of coarseness as shown in Table 2. A coarse pitch generally should be selected for sawing large sections or thicknesses and soft metals. A finer pitch usually should be selected for sawing thinner thicknesses and harder metals. There should be a minimum of *two teeth* in contact with the work at all times, except for very thin sheet metal which is cut at higher speeds. For general-purpose metal-cutting operations band saw blades of the following pitches will produce good results:

TEETH PER INCH	THICKNESS
18	up to ¼″
14	¼″ to ½″
10	½″ to 2″
8	2″ to larger

Skip-Tooth Blades

Metal-cutting band saw blades of this type have a wide space between each tooth, as though every second tooth were removed. The wide space provides extra chip clearance. These may be used for sawing nonferrous metals such as aluminum, brass, copper, lead, zinc, etc. They are also used for sawing wood, plastic, asbestos, and other nonmetallic materials. They can be used at higher operating speeds than standard blades with regular teeth and, therefore, cut many times faster. The following are general skip-tooth sawing speed recommendations:

MATERIAL	SPEED IN FEET PER MINUTE
Aluminum	2000 to 3000
Aluminum Alloys	300 to 2000
Asbestos	800 to 1500
Bakelite	2500 to 3500
Brass	400 to 1000
Copper	1000 to 1500
Formica	800 to 2000
Lucite-Plexiglas	2000 to 3000
Magnesium	3000 to 5000
Wood	2000 to 3000

Review Questions

1. Name several principal parts of a power hacksaw.

2. Can hardened steel be cut in a power saw? Why?

3. What is meant by the feed of a saw?

4. Which direction should the teeth of a power hacksaw point?

5. Explain the function of a cutoff gage on a power saw.

6. What advantages are achieved in using a cutting fluid on a power saw?

7. On which stroke does a power hacksaw blade cut?

8. How can the feed pressure be increased or decreased on power hacksaws?

9. List the recommended cutting speed for cutting low-carbon steel without cutting fluid.

10. List several factors which must be considered when selecting the proper power hacksaw blade for a job.

11. List the types of tooth set on power hacksaw blades.

12. List two types of horizontal band saws.

13. What kinds of cuts may be made on horizontal band saws?

14. What harm can result if the proper feed rate is not used on a horizontal band saw?

15. Why are vertical band saws often equipped with a shear and a blade welder?

16. What kinds of cuts or other operations can be performed on a vertical band saw?

17. How can the speed be changed on either horizontal or vertical band saws?

18. What is the necessary precaution to be observed when changing the speed on a machine equipped with a variable speed drive mechanism?

19. Recommended cutting speeds for band sawing vary according to four important factors. List them.

20. What is the recommended band saw cutting speed for low-carbon steel ¾″ thick without cutting fluid?

21. What recommendation should be followed concerning band saw blade tension?

22. What factors should be considered in the selection of a band saw blade for a vertical band saw?

23. How many teeth per inch should a band saw blade have for general-purpose sawing of carbon steel from ¼″ to ½″ thickness?

24. Explain the purposes of skip-tooth band saw blades.

Coordination

Words to Know

band saw blade
cutting fluid

feed
filing machine

horizontal band saw
jigsaw
portable band saw
power hacksaw
   blade
   connecting rod
   crank-disc
   cutoff gage

motor
saw frame
switch
vise handle
vise jaw
sawhorse
scroll saw
vertical band saw

Mathematics

1. How many 4″ pieces can be cut from a 5-foot bar, allowing ⅛″ for each saw cut?

2. By what % will the cutting efficiency be increased if cutting fluid is applied to the blade of a band saw while cutting dry medium-carbon steel?

Hydraulic Closed-Die Forging Press with 35,000-Ton Capacity Has Die Table
Twelve Feet by Twenty-Four Feet
(Courtesy Aluminum Company of America)

Chisels and Chipping

205. Meaning and Importance of Chipping

Chipping is cutting metal in small pieces with a *cold chisel* and a *hammer* (see §§ *206, 216*).

Metal can often be cut faster with a cold chisel and hammer than by machine, especially when only a small amount of metal has to be cut away. Skill is needed to hold a cold chisel, strike it with a hammer, and cut an even surface. This skill, however, comes only with much practice; the beginner should do his best to learn how to chip. Chipping is usually followed by filing. The worker who cannot do a good job of chipping must work much harder with the file.

206. Cold Chisels

Cold chisels are used to cut cold metal, hence the name. They are made of high grade steel in a number of sizes and shapes. The cutting ends are *hardened* and *tempered* (see §§ *951* and *954*) because the cutting tool must be harder than the material to be cut. A cold chisel usually has eight sides.

207. Sizes and Names of Cold Chisels

Cold chisels are usually made of steel ⅜″ to 1″ thick and from 6″ to 8″ long. The thickness and length depend upon the use of the chisel.

For fine work, the thinner and shorter chisel is used. For large work, the thicker and, usually the longer one, is used.

Cold chisels are known by the shapes of their cutting edges. Thus we have the *flat chisel, cape chisel, diamond-point chisel,* and *round-nose chisel,* Fig. 186.

208. Flat Chisel

The flat chisel has a wide *cutting edge* (see Fig. 186). It is used for chipping flat surfaces, cutting off *sheet metal* (see § 789 and Fig. 193), cutting bars and *rivets* (see Figs. 194 and 572), and for most of the ordinary chipping around the shop. It is the most commonly used chisel. (See §§ *212-213*.)

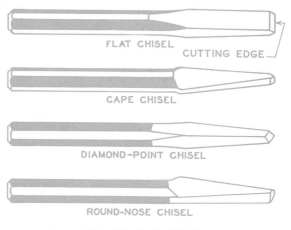

Fig. 186. Cold Chisels

209. Cape Chisel

The cape chisel has a narrow *cutting edge* and is used for cutting narrow grooves (see Figs. 186 and 190). It should be widest at the cutting edge to keep the chisel from sticking in the groove; it is thus less likely to break.

210. Diamond Point Chisel

The diamond-point chisel has a *cutting edge* shaped like a *diamond* (see Fig. 186). It is used to cut V-shaped grooves and to chip square corners.

211. Round Nose Chisel

The round-nose chisel (see Fig. 186) has a rounded *cutting edge* and is used for chipping round corners and grooves. (See Fig. 447).

212. Cutting Angle of Cold Chisels

The *cutting angle* is shaped like a wedge (see section *61*) which cuts into the metal as shown in Fig. 187.

The cutting angle on most cold chisels is from 50 to 75 degrees, depending upon the kind of metal to be cut. The softer the metal, the nearer the angle should be to 50 degrees. For cutting hard metal, the cutting angle should be more blunt. For average work it should be about 60 degrees.

213. Corners of Cold Chisels

The corners of a cold chisel are weak. They are less likely to break off or to dig into the metal while chipping if they are ground a little rounded (see Fig. 193).

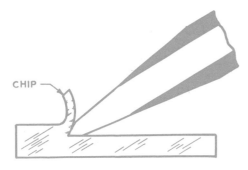

Fig. 187. Wedge Action of a Cold Chisel

214. Heads of Cold Chisels

The head of the cold chisel should be *tapered*[1] a little and rounded, as *A* in Fig. 188, but not *hardened* (see § *951*). After a cold chisel has been used for some time, the head becomes flattened like a mushroom with rough, ragged edges, as *B* in Fig. 188; it is then called a *mushroom head*. This is dangerous because when struck with the hammer one of the ragged edges may fly off and injure you or another workman. The mushroom head should be ground on the grinding wheel to the shape shown in *A* in Fig. 188.

215. Sharpening Cold Chisels

Good work can only be done with sharp chisels. Sharpen the *cutting edge* on a *grinding wheel* as explained in section *1068*. The beginner may use a *center gage* to test the *cutting angle,* Fig. 189.

216. Hammers for Chipping

The *machinist's hammer* (see § *60*) is used for ordinary chipping. It should weigh from ¾ of a pound to 2 pounds depending upon the work; use a light hammer for small work and a heavy hammer for large work. A one-pound

[1] *Tapered* means gradually narrowed toward one end.

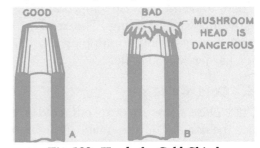

Fig. 188. Head of a Cold Chisel

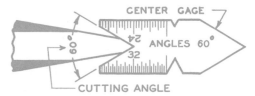

Fig. 189. Testing the Cutting Angle of a Cold Chisel with Center Gage

hammer is about right for a ¾″ chisel for ordinary chipping. It should be well balanced. The length of the *handle* should suit the arm of the man using it. The handle should be thinner near the middle to make it springy so that the shock of the blows will not hurt the wrist. The *head* should be fastened tightly to the handle.

217. Holding Chisel and Hammer

Watch an experienced mechanic at work with a cold chisel and hammer. Note his position at the bench, the way he holds the chisel, how he holds and swings the hammer, and the result. It takes much practice to do this well.

The middle of the chisel should be held loosely in the left hand, Figs. 190, 192, and 194. For small, fine work it may be held as shown in Fig. 190. The hammer handle should be grasped near the end with the right hand and held loosely to keep from tiring the arm.

218. Goggles

While chipping, wear *goggles* to protect your eyes, Fig. 191; flying *chips* cause serious injuries. Know where the chips are landing when you are chipping; many an eye has been lost by chips striking another workman. See that the chips fly against a wall or set up some kind of a *shield*.

219. How to Chip

Hold the chisel in a position that will make a chip of the right size. Keep your eyes on the cutting edge of the chisel. Swing the hammer

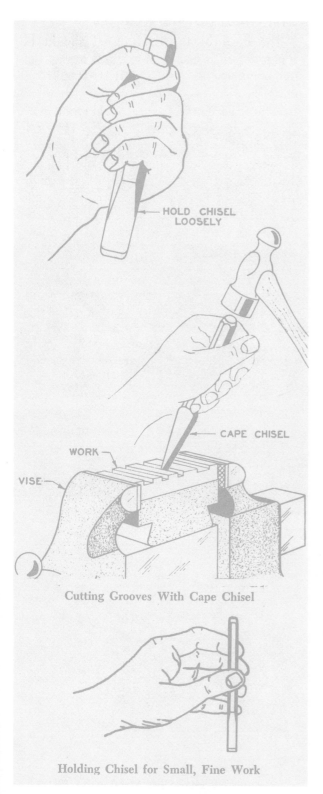

HOLD CHISEL LOOSELY

CAPE CHISEL

WORK

VISE

Cutting Grooves With Cape Chisel

Holding Chisel for Small, Fine Work

Fig. 190. Holding Chisel

Fig. 191. Goggles

over the shoulder with an easy arm movement, Fig. 192. You really throw the hammer at the chisel. Strike the head of the chisel squarely with a good, snappy blow and reset the chisel after each blow for the next cut. Cut a little at a time. This will lengthen the life of the cutting edge, the chisel will be less likely to break, and more metal will be cut in the long run.

220. Shearing

The *vise jaw* and *flat chisel* may be used together to act like a pair of scissors or *shears*. This is called *shearing*.

Thick *sheet metal* (see § 789) is often cut in a vise with a flat chisel. First, a line which is used as a guide should be made with a *scriber* (see Fig. 40). Then, clamp the metal tightly in a vise that has good edges so that the line will be just below the tops of the vise jaws. This leaves a little metal for filing to the line afterwards. Continue as in Fig. 193:

Step 1: Lay the *cutting edge* of the chisel on top of the vise jaws and against the metal.

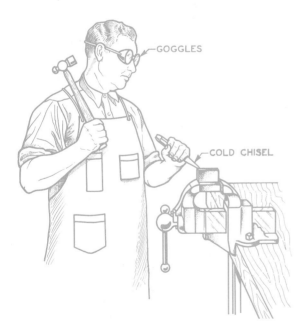

Fig. 192. Body Position, also Holding Hammer and Chisel

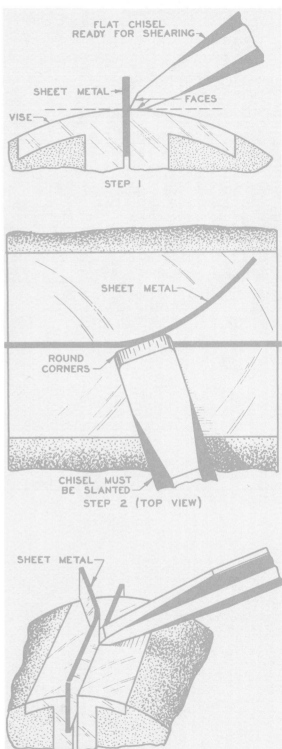

Fig. 193. Shearing Sheet Metal with a Flat Cold Chisel

Step 2: Slant the chisel a little. Make sure that the *face* of the chisel is *horizontal* as in Step 1, Fig. 193, because it is important to make a square cut.

Step 3: Start to cut.

221. Cutting Rods and Rivets

A small rod or bar may be roughly cut by nicking it on opposite sides with the flat chisel, Fig. 194, and then bending it until it breaks. Fig. 194 also shows a *rivet head* being cut off with a flat chisel. (Sec. 935 tells of other ways to cut metal.)

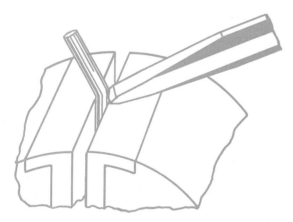

Cutting Stock in Vise with Flat Cold Chisel

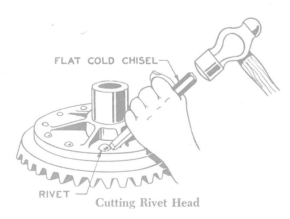

FLAT COLD CHISEL

RIVET

Cutting Rivet Head

Fig. 194. Cutting Rod and Rivet

Review Questions

1. What is meant by chipping?
2. Why should you know how to chip?
3. What shape is the bar of steel from which a chisel is made?
4. What part of the cold chisel is hardened and tempered?
5. Give the names and uses of cold chisels.
6. What is the angle of the cutting edge for average work?
7. What gage may be used to test the cutting angle of a cold chisel?
8. What size hammer should be used for chipping?
9. Where should you hold the hammer handle when chipping?
10. What part of the chisel should you watch while chipping?
11. How can you chip safely?
12. Tell of a quick way to roughly cut a rod or bar.
13. What is shearing? How is it done?

Coordination

Words to Know

bar	goggles
cape chisel	grinding wheel
chip	mushroom head
chipping	rivet
cold chisel	round-nose chisel
face	shearing
head	shield
cutting angle	tapered
cutting edge	tempered
diamond-point chisel	vise jaw
flat chisel	

Mathematics

1. What part of a circle is 60°?

Occupational Information

1. What are the dangers when using cold chisels?

Chatter Marks on Piece Machined in a Lathe (Courtesy Carboloy Co., Inc.)

Files

227. What Is a File?

A file is a *hardened* (see § 951) piece of high-grade steel with slanting rows of teeth. It is used to cut, smooth, or *fit* metal parts. (See § 665.) It cuts all metal except *hardened steel*. The cutting tool must be harder than the material to be cut.

228. Parts of File

The *tang* of a file is the pointed part which fits into the handle, Fig. 200. The *point* is the end opposite the tang. The *heel* is next to the handle. The *safe edge* or side of a file is that which has no teeth.

229. File Handles

All files should be fitted with wooden handles. Several kinds of file handles are shown in Fig. 201. Better handles have a metal insert which is self-threading on the soft tang of the file, enabling the file to be hung by its handle. Large files should have large handles while small files should have small handles. Very small files usually have ball-shaped handles that fit the palm of the hand.

The metal ring on the file handle is called a *ferrule* (see Fig. 201). It keeps the handle from splitting.

230. Fitting File Handle

To fit a common handle on a file, the handle must be drilled for the tang of the file. Drill a hole equal in diameter to the average width of the *tang* to a depth equal to the length of the tang. Next, drive the handle on the tang by striking on the bench, Fig. 202. Be very careful not to split the handle. The entire tang should fit into the handle.

Predrilled handles and types which screw onto the tang simplify the fitting.

Fig. 200. Parts of a File

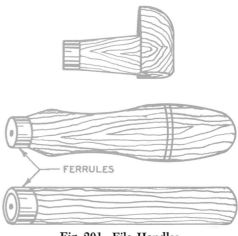

Fig. 201. File Handles

231. Sizes of Files

Files are made in many sizes. The *length*, which is always given in inches, is the distance from the *point* to the *heel*, without the *tang*. (See Fig. 200.) The common sizes of files are the 6″, 8″, 10″, and 12″ lengths.

232. Shapes of Files

The shape of a file is its general outline and *cross section* (see § 36). Files are made in hundreds of shapes. A *blunt file* is one which has the same width and thickness from the heel to the point. A *tapered file* is one which is thinner or narrower at the point. Fig. 203 and Table 3 show the most commonly used shapes. These are:

(1) *Warding.*	(7) *Round or*
(2) *Mill.*	*rat-tail.*
(3) *Flat.*	(8) *Half-round.*
(4) *Hand.*	(9) *Three-square.*
(5) *Pillar.*	(10) *Knife.*
(6) *Square.*	

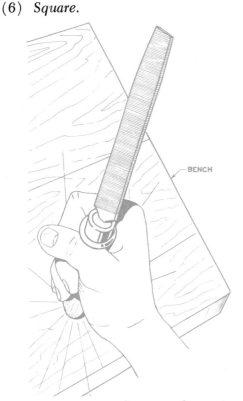

Fig. 202. Strike Handle on Bench to Drive It on the Tang

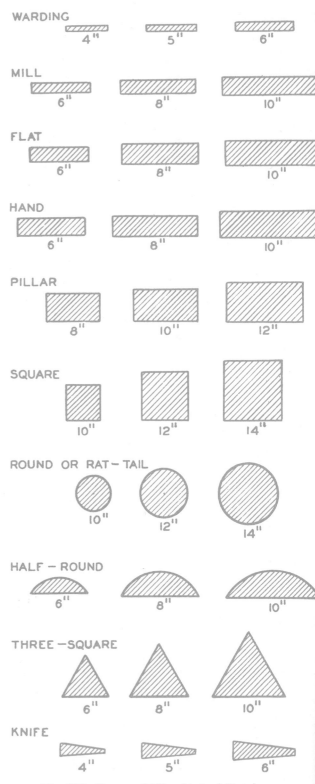

Fig. 203. Shapes of Files (Actual Sizes)

233. Cuts of Files

Cuts of files are divided into three groups as shown in Fig. 204. These groups are:

(1) *Single-cut.*
(2) *Double-cut.*
(3) *Rasp-cut.*

A *single-cut file* has single rows of cuts across the face of the file. The *teeth* are like the edge of a chisel (see § 212).

A *double-cut file* has two sets of cuts crossing each other which give the teeth the form of sharp points. These files cut faster but not as smoothly as the single-cut file.

The teeth on a *rasp-cut file* are not connected and are formed by raising small parts of the surface with a punch. The rasp-cut file is used on wood or soft metal. It is seldom used in the *machine shop.* (See § 19.)

234. Spacing Between Teeth

Single-cut and double-cut files are further divided according to the coarseness or spacing between the rows of teeth, Fig. 205. The six main kinds of spacings are:

(1) *Rough.*   (4) *Second-cut.*
(2) *Coarse.*   (5) *Smooth.*
(3) *Bastard.*   (6) *Dead smooth.*

Files with the greatest spacings between the teeth are called *rough;* those with the least spacings between the teeth are known as *dead smooth.* The teeth on the dead smooth file are very fine.

The files most often used are the bastard, second-cut, and smooth. The rough, coarse, and dead smooth files are used only on special jobs.

The coarseness of a file changes with its length. The larger the file, the coarser it is. Thus, a rough cut on a small file may be as fine as a second-cut on a large file. Compare the spacings between the teeth of different sizes of files in Fig. 206.

235. Ordering Files

One manufacturer advertises 5000 different sizes, shapes, and cuts of files. When ordering a file include the following dimensions:

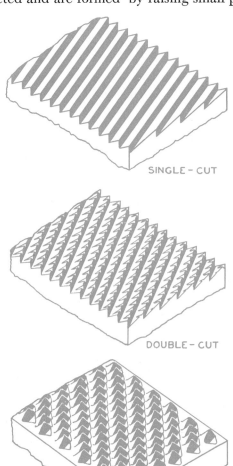

Fig. 204. Cuts of Files

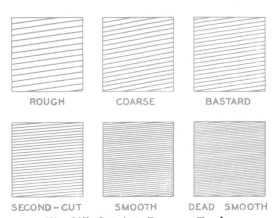

Fig. 205. Spacings Between Teeth

(1) *Length* (see § 231).
(2) *Shape* (see § 232).
(3) *Cut* (see § 233).
(4) *Spacing* between teeth (see § 234).
Example:
(1) 10-inch.
(2) Flat.
(3) Single-cut.
(4) Bastard.

236. Storing Files

Take good care of files. They should be placed where they will not rub or strike each other. Never throw them together on the bench or into a drawer with hammers, screw-drivers, cold chisels, etc. This care will save the cutting edges of the files and cause them to last longer.

Hanging files as in the upper part of Fig. 207 is good because a file with a loose handle cannot be hung up and should be started on its way for a new handle. Another good way to keep files is to place *partitions* or walls between them, Fig. 207.

237. Choosing File for Work

Table 3 on page 111 gives information about the kinds of files and their uses. Each file is made for a certain kind of work. The *double-cut hand file* cuts metal quickly. A 10″ or 12″ *bastard file* is generally used for rough filing at the bench; a *second-cut file* is used to bring the surface of the work closer to a finish. The *single-cut mill file* is used for finish cuts. The size of the work should be considered when selecting the file size to be used.

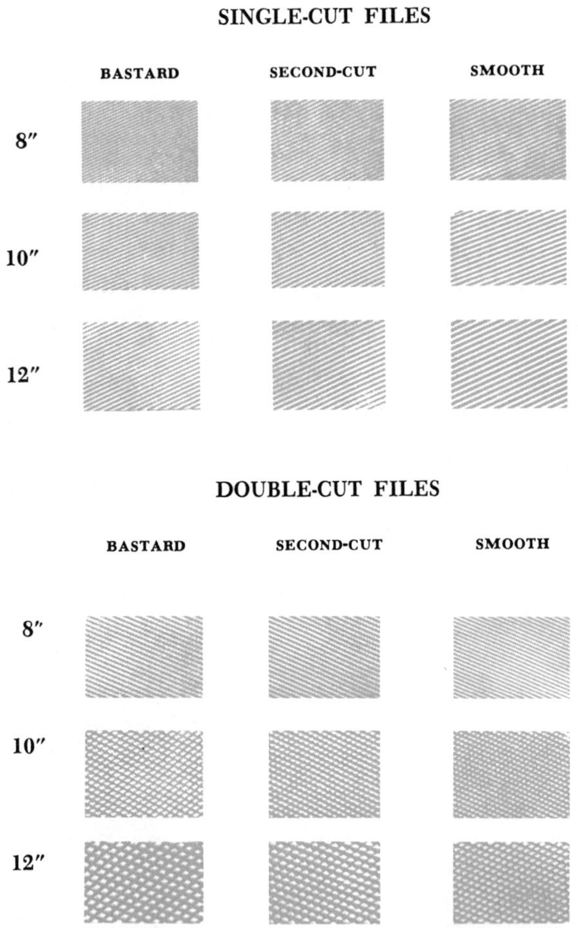

SINGLE-CUT FILES

	BASTARD	SECOND-CUT	SMOOTH
8″			
10″			
12″			

DOUBLE-CUT FILES

	BASTARD	SECOND-CUT	SMOOTH
8″			
10″			
12″			

Fig. 206. Relation Between Teeth Spacings and Lengths of Files (Actual Sizes) (Courtesy, Simonds Saw & Steel Co.)

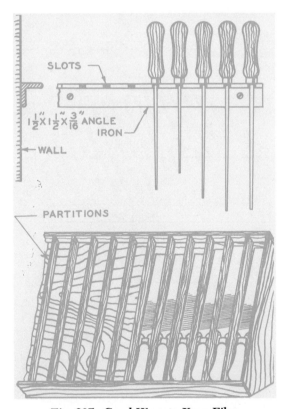

Fig. 207. Good Ways to Keep Files

Table 3
FILES AND THEIR USES

Name and Shape of File	Kind of Cut	Uses
WARDING FILE, parallel in thickness, tapered to the point. Very thin.	Double-cut	Filing notches as in keys. Much used by *locksmiths*. Gets name from *ward*, meaning a notch in a key.
MILL FILE, tapered or blunt.	Single-cut	*Drawfiling* (see § 250), finishing, and lathe work. Also used for finishing brass and bronze.
FLAT FILE, tapered in width and thickness.	Double-cut	One of the most commonly used files for general work.
HAND FILE, equal in width and tapered in thickness, one safe edge.	Double-cut	Finishing flat surfaces. Has one *safe edge* and, therefore, is useful where the flat file cannot be used.
PILLAR FILE, equal in width and tapered in thickness. One safe edge. Narrower and thicker than hand file.	Double-cut	Used for narrow work, such as *keyways* (see § 753), slots, and grooves.
SQUARE FILE, tapered or blunt.	Double-cut	Filing square corners. Enlarging square or *rectangular*[1] openings as *splines*[2] and *keyways* (see § 753).
ROUND FILE (rat-tail), tapered.	Single-cut or Double-cut	Filing curved surfaces and enlarging round holes and forming *fillets*.[3]
HALF-ROUND FILE, tapered. Not a half circle; only about one-third of a circle.	Double-cut	Filing curved surfaces.
THREE-SQUARE FILE, tapered.	Double-cut	Filing corners and angles less than 90°, such as on *taps* (see § 649), *cutters*,[4] etc., before they are hardened.
KNIFE FILE, tapered in width and thickness, shaped like a knife.	Double-cut	Filing narrow slots, notches, and grooves.

[1] *Rectangular* means having four 90° angles.
[2] A *spline* is a long *feather key* (see Section 753) fastened to a shaft so that the pulley or gear may slide along the shaft lengthwise, both turning together.

[3] A *fillet* is a curve that fills the angle made by two connecting surfaces to avoid a sharp angle.
[4] A *cutter* is a sharp tool fixed in a machine for cutting metal.

Review Questions

1. What is the tang of a file?

2. What is the safe edge of a file? Has the hand file always one safe edge?

3. Of what use is the ferrule on a file handle?

4. How should a handle be fitted on a file?

5. How is the length of a file measured?

6. What is the blunt file? A tapered file?

7. What is a mill file? A flat file? A hand file? A half-round file? A square file?

8. For what is a warding file used?

9. What is a single-cut file? A double-cut file?

10. Name the six main kinds of spacings between teeth on files.

11. What is a bastard file? A smooth file?

12. What is a double-cut file? A second-cut file?

13. What information is needed when ordering a file?

14. How should files be kept?

15. Get ten different files and label each, giving the length, shape, cut, and spacing between the teeth.

Coordination

Words to Know

blunt file	shape of file
cut of file	warding
single-cut	mill
double-cut	flat
rasp-cut	hand
cutter	pillar
feather key	square
ferrule	round or rat-tail
file	half-round
edge	three-square
face	knife
heel	spacing between teeth
point	rough
tang	coarse
file handle	bastard
fillet	second-cut
fitting	smooth
partition	dead smooth
rectangular	spline
round edge	tap
safe edge	ward

Drafting

1. Design a rack for your file at home.
2. Design a file handle.

Filing

243. Filing Is an Art

To beginners the file seems very easy to use, but it takes much practice to do good filing. It is one of the most difficult operations in the mechanical field. Few people, except experienced filers, know the different kinds of files and how to use them correctly. A *mechanic* is often judged by the way he files. More files are worn out by abuse than by use.

244. Holding Work for Filing

The work should be a little below the height of the elbows or about 40 to 44 inches from the floor. (See Fig. 156.) It should be held tightly in the vise. The part to be filed should be near the vise jaws to keep the work from *chattering*, Fig. 213 (see § *172*).

Polished surfaces should be protected from the rough, *hardened steel* vise jaws by covering the jaws with *vise jaw caps* (see Figs. 251 and 534). Small or fine work should be held nearer to the worker's eyes than large or rough work.

245. Body Position for Filing

The body position for filing is the same as for sawing with the hand hacksaw (see § *173*). Face the work and stand with one foot ahead of the other. The arch of the right foot should be about 8″ to 12″ from the heel of the left foot. (See Figs. 155 and 156.) The left foot should point toward the bench. The body should make about a 30° angle with the filing stroke. Make long, slow, and steady strokes by swaying forward and backward on the feet, moving the arms very little.

246. Using a File

The file is used for cutting all kinds of metal except hardened steel. Many files are dulled by the teeth touching the hardened jaws of a vise while filing. The file should be

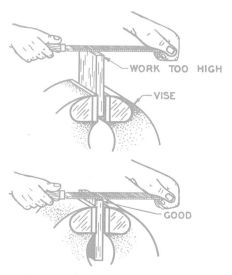

Fig. 213. Chattering Results When the Work Is Held too High in the Vise

Fig. 214. Get Files with Handles

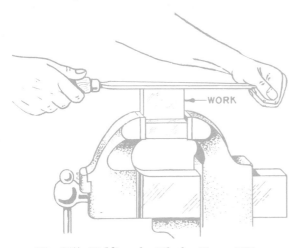

Fig. 215. Holding the File for Heavy Filing

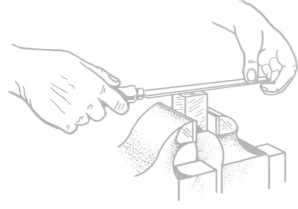

Fig. 216. Holding the File for Light Filing

used only on metal which is not as hard as the file itself. The rule for all cutting is: *The cutting tool must be harder than the material to be cut.* As explained in section *1169,* the file is sometimes used to test the hardness of steel.

Insist on using a file with a handle, Fig. 214. Use only a file with sharp teeth. Grasp the handle of the file with the right hand and hold the palm against the end of the handle with the thumb on top. For heavy filing, place the palm of the left hand on the point of the file with the fingers pressing against the underside, Fig. 215. For light filing, the thumb of the left hand should be placed on the top of the file, Fig. 216.

Place the point of the file on the work; cut by pressing down on the *forward stroke,* known as the *cutting stroke* (Fig. 217), and lifting a little on the *return stroke* to prevent dulling the file. The file cuts only on the cutting stroke. Keep the file level on the work; otherwise the filed surface will be rounded and uneven instead of flat. Use the full length of the file and avoid jerky motions. This is called *cross-filing.*

Remove the correct amount of metal, no more, no less. It would be well for the beginner to look through a magnifying glass to see how close he is to the layout line. (See Fig. 81.)

247. Speed

In filing, the greatest fault with beginners is too much speed; press hard on the file but take slow strokes. The harder the metal to be filed, the slower the stroke should be. (See § *176.*)

248. Pressure

Be sure that the file really cuts on the forward stroke. Rubbing, slipping, or sliding over the metal without cutting makes the cutting edges smooth, bright, and shiny like glass. It also makes the teeth blunt and dulls them. A worn file needs more pressure than a new file. (See § *177.*)

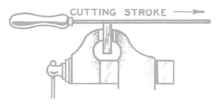

Fig. 217. **Cutting Stroke on a File**

249. Holding File for Small or Fine Work

Only on small or fine work, where the file is too small to hold in both hands, may it be held in one hand. In this case, the forefinger, instead of the thumb, is placed on top (Fig. 218) because the forefinger guides the direction of the file. Note how the left hand also helps to guide the file.

250. Drawfiling

Drawfiling is done to get a finely finished surface, Fig. 219; such a surface is flatter than one made by ordinary filing, which is known as *cross-filing*. A *mill file* is recommended for this purpose. Drawfiling is done by holding the file with one hand on each end of the file, the thumbs about ½″ to ¾″ from the work on each side. Hold the file flat on the work and draw it back and forth, pressing only on the forward stroke.

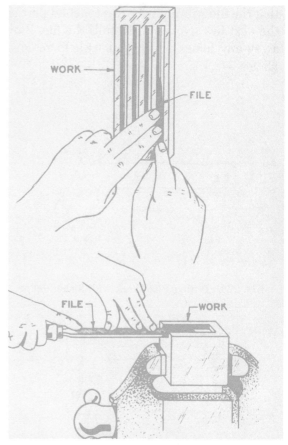

Fig. 218. **Filing Fine or Small Work with the Point of the File**

251. Filing Flat, Square, and Angular Surfaces

Flat work should be tested often with a *straightedge* held in different positions against the light. The straight edge of a steel rule or square may be used for this purpose, Fig. 220. The work is flat if no light can be seen between the straightedge and the surface. It may also be tested for *flatness* on a *surface plate* as explained in section *264*.

Square work should be tested often with a square, Fig. 221. (See Figs. 57 and 62.) The *bevel protractor* should be used to test all angles except *right angles*, Fig. 222.

252. Filing Cast Iron

Before filing cast iron (see § *300*) with a *scaled*[1] *surface*, remove the scale by tapping with a large, *flat cold chisel*. (See Fig. 186.) Wear goggles when removing the scale. The file will be ruined in a few strokes if you

[1] *Scale* is a thin, black, hard skin or crust which forms on metal, especially when heated.

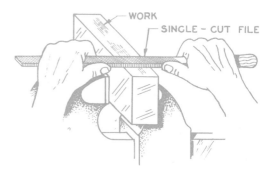

Fig. 219. **Drawfiling**

file the scale. Sometimes it is necessary to chip the scale off with a hammer and cold chisel (see § *218*).

Do not touch the filed part of cast iron with the fingers or hand because no matter how dry the skin may appear there is always enough oil given off and left on the metal so that the file will slip over this touched part on the next few strokes. This dulls the file. Blow away any filings which you wish to remove. (See § *248*.)

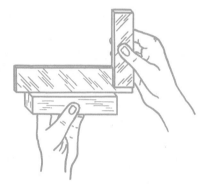

Fig. 220. Testing Flat Work with Straightedge

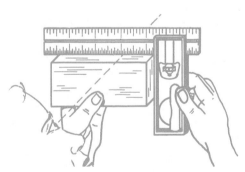

Fig. 221. Testing the Squareness of Work with a Double Square

Fig. 222. Testing an Angle with a Bevel Protractor

253. Filing Soft Metals

Special files are made for cutting soft metals such as *brass, bronze, aluminum, lead, solder,* and *babbitt*. These metals are explained in Unit 21. Filing soft metals with the ordinary file causes the teeth to become quickly clogged with chips which are hard to remove.

254. How Should a File be Cleaned?

File teeth often become clogged with chips and filings called *pins*. These small chips stick in front of the teeth and scratch the work. Keep the file free from chips and filings by brushing it with a wire brush called a *file card*, Fig. 223.

Rub the file card over the file in the direction of the cuts. Sometimes the pins stick so tightly that the file card will not remove

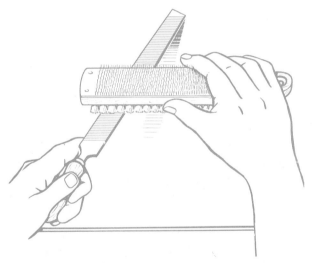

Fig. 223. Cleaning a File with File Card and Brush

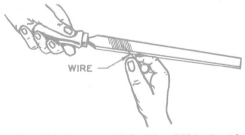

WIRE

Fig. 224. Remove Tight Pins (Chips) with Wire or Sheet Metal

them. In such cases, use a thin piece of sheet metal or a pointed wire to remove them, Fig. 224. Keeping the file clean will save much hard work and will help you to do better work. A file can be cleaned more easily if chalk is rubbed on the teeth before it is used. Never try to clean a file by tapping it on the bench, vise, or work. Files break easily because they are very *hard* and *brittle*. Oil may be removed from a file by rubbing chalk into the teeth and then brushing with a file brush. Clean files give the best results. A new file clogs more than a used file because the teeth on the new file are of uneven height and, therefore, the longer teeth cut off bigger chips which stick in front of the teeth. A file cuts best after it has made about 2500 cutting strokes. This equals about one cubic inch of metal.

Review Questions

1. How should work be held for filing in order to keep it from chattering?

2. How may finished surfaces be protected from the rough jaws of a vise?

3. How should you stand when filing?

4. Should a file be used without a handle? Why?

5. How should a file be held for heavy filing?

6. How should a file be held for fine filing?

7. Does the file cut on the forward or backward stroke? Why?

8. How fast should you file?

9. What happens if the file slips or slides over the metal?

10. What kind of file is used mostly for drawfiling?

11. How should a file be held for drawfiling?

12. Why should you not file the scale on cast iron?

13. How should the scale on cast iron be removed before filing?

14. Why should you not touch the filed part of cast iron with the fingers when filing?

15. What are pins? How can they be removed?

16. What is a file card?

Coordination

Words to Know

aluminum	flat surface
babbitt	lead
brass	pins
bronze	scale
cast iron	scaled surface
cross-filing	solder
drawfiling	square surfaces
file card	straightedge
filing	

Occupational Information

1. Observe your classmates during a class period as they use the file. Note the various misuses you detect.

Grinding a Bearing Surface on a Shaft
with Grinding Attachment on a Lathe
(Courtesy Atlas Press Co.)

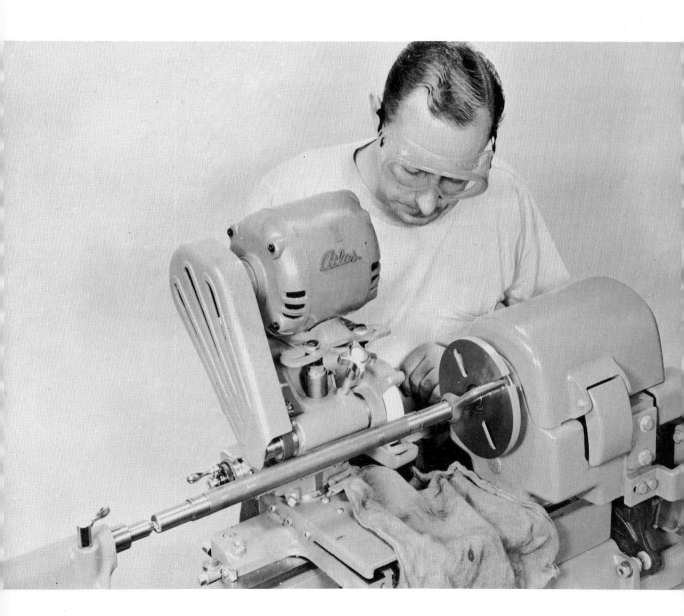

Scrapers and Scraping

260. What Does Scraping Mean?

Scraping means shaving or paring off thin slices or flakes of metal to make a fine, smooth surface.

261. Reasons for Scraping

Scraping is an art. Much practice is needed to make a good true surface. It is slow, expensive work, and is seldom done today. It has been made almost unnecessary by surface grinding and more accurate machining and die casting processes.

Scraping is most often used in fitting soft bearings[1] to a shaft[2], in correcting minor imperfections in machining, or in decorating flat machined surfaces as the ways on a lathe or drill press.

Machined surfaces usually are not perfectly true for a number of reasons: 1) file scratches or tool marks need removing, 2) metal may be of unequal hardness or the metal may have been sprung while being clamped for machining, 3) the cutting tool may wear or have been sprung during the machining. If a very true surface is needed the high spots must be located and removed. This may be

[1] A *bearing* is the part which holds or supports a shaft and inside of which the shaft turns.
[2] A *shaft* is an axle or round bar of metal on which a pulley or gear is fastened or supported.

done by hand scraping or by several types of grinding machines (see Unit 61).

262. Scrapers

Scraping is done with tools called *scrapers*, Fig. 230, which have very hard *cutting edges*. Scrapers are made in many shapes, depending on the work to be done. Those used on flat surfaces are known as *flat scrapers* and *hook scrapers*. Those used on curved surfaces are known as *three-cornered* scrapers and half-round scrapers. The three-cornered scraper may also be used to remove sharp corners or burrs[3]. The half-round scraper, or bearing scraper, has two cutting edges on the concave (hollowed) side.

[3] A *burr* is a thin, rough edge made in cutting.

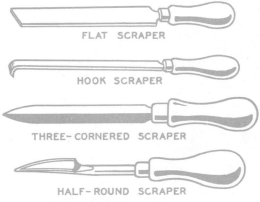

FLAT SCRAPER

HOOK SCRAPER

THREE-CORNERED SCRAPER

HALF-ROUND SCRAPER

Fig. 230. Scrapers

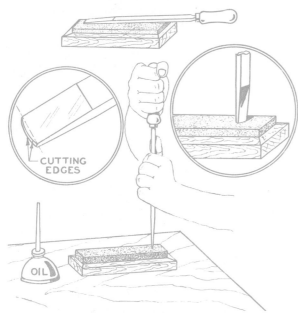

Fig. 231. Oilstoning a Flat Scraper

Fig. 232. Scraping a Flat Surface

Fig. 233. Scraping a Round Bearing

Old files make excellent scrapers. First, grind off the teeth on all sides and then sharpen the cutting edge, Fig. 231. The cutting edge of the flat scraper is at the end. It should be rounded slightly, looking at the broad side, and should be sharpened last.

263. Holding a Scraper

Scrapers are held as shown in Figs. 232 and 233. The handle of the scraper for flat scraping should be held and steadied under the right arm while the blade is guided by both hands; *pressure* is thus put on the cutting edge. As with files, all scrapers except the hook scraper cut on the pushing stroke. Lift the scraper a little on the return stroke. Experience teaches how hard one should press and at what angle the tool cuts the metal easily.

264. Scraping a Flat Surface

A *surface plate* (see § 59) is used to find the high spots on a flat surface. The surface plate should be larger than the surface to be scraped. The top of the surface plate is covered with a very thin film of *Prussian blue.* This blue paint comes in a tube, is about as thick as tooth paste, and may be put on with a small brush. The surface to be scraped is then laid on the surface plate and moved back and forth. Thus the high spots which have to be removed will be marked with Prussian blue from the surface plate. If a thick coat is put on the surface plate, the low spots on the work will be marked as well as the high ones.

Finding the high spots is called *spotting.* Remove the blue marks with a flat scraper. (See Fig. 232.) After scraping off the high spots, test again on the surface plate and again scrape off the high spots. Repeat these operations until the blue marks increase and are evenly spread over the surface of the work. Study where and how much to scrape off.

Red lead may be used instead of Prussian blue (see § *1100*).

265. Scraping a Round Bearing

Round bearings must fit on other sliding or running parts; any *shaft bearing* is an example of this. (See Figs. 233 and 521.) The same way of marking and scraping the high spots of flat surfaces (see § *264*) is also used for round and curved surfaces, Fig. 234. For round surfaces the Prussian blue is put on the shaft or part which is fit into the hollow surface. The half-round scraper and sometimes the three-cornered scraper is used for scraping round and curved surfaces.

266. Frosting or Flowering

This is a finish which is an imitation of frost, patchwork, or checkerboard design, Fig. 235. It is also called *spotting* or *flaking* and is made by scraping off the high spots as was explained in the scraping of flat surfaces (see § *264*). The strokes should be very short, about ¼″ to ½″. Change the direction of the strokes after each marking.

Review Questions

1. What is meant by scraping?
2. Give the reasons for scraping.
3. Describe a flat scraper.
4. Describe a hook scraper.
5. Describe a three-cornered scraper.
6. Describe a half-round scraper.
7. How can an old file be made into a scraper?
8. How should a scraper be held?
9. Why must the surface plate be handled very carefully?
10. How is it used when scraping?
11. What is Prussian blue?
12. Should Prussian blue be put on in a thick layer? Why?
13. What kind of scraper should be used when scraping a flat surface?
14. What is meant by spotting?
15. What kind of scraper is used to scrape round or curved surfaces?
16. What is meant by frosting or flowering?

Coordination

Words to Know

bearing	hook scraper
bearing scraper	Prussian blue
burr	red lead
flaking	scraper
flat scraper	scraping
flowering	shaft
frosting	spotting
half-round scraper	three-cornered scraper

Mathematics

1. How much would it cost to scrape a surface plate if a toolmaker scraped 39 hours at $4.25 per hour?

Occupational Information

1. In what work might a knowledge of scraping be useful?

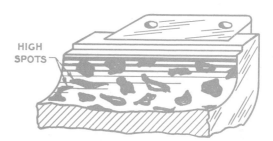

Fig. 234. High Spots to Be Scraped Off a Bearing

Fig. 235. Frosting (Courtesy American Machinist)

Abrasives

276. What Does Polishing Mean?

Polishing means to make smooth, bright, and glossy by rubbing. To polish is to change a rough, uneven, dull surface with irregular scratches to a surface with very fine, uniform, *parallel* (see § 120) cuts or grooves that cannot be seen with the naked eye.

Hand polishing means to rub the surface of the metal by hand, back and forth, with an *abrasive* or with *steel wool*. (*Buffing* is explained in section 1085.)

277. Pride in Work

Things must be beautiful as well as useful. Finely polished, plain surfaces have a beauty all their own. One who takes pride in his personal appearance also takes pride in his work. The surface should be filed carefully until satin smooth and free of machine marks. It is then polished smooth and bright with an abrasive. A *craftsman*[1] must be able to produce a piece of finely polished work. *Metal finishing* is explained in section 1095.

278. What Does Abrasive Mean?

Abrasive comes from the word *abrade* which means to rub off. An abrasive substance is a very hard, tough material which has many sharp cutting edges and points when

[1] A *craftsman* is a man skilled in a manual occupation; a man having a trade; a mechanic.

crushed and ground into grains like sand. (See §§ 1008 and 1009.) Abrasives must be harder than the materials they cut. Several common forms in which abrasives are used in metalworking include the following:

(1) Abrasive cloth (also called coated abrasive)
(2) Loose grain and powder abrasive
(3) Abrasive compounds (in the form of paste, sticks, or cakes)
(4) Grinding wheels
(5) Sharpening stones

This unit is concerned principally with the selection and use of abrasives for hand polishing. Most hand polishing is done with abrasive cloth. Occasionally hand polishing is done with loose grain abrasive powders or abrasive compounds. The use of abrasive polishing compounds for machine buffing and polishing is included in Unit 52. Grinding wheels and their selection are included in Unit 49. Sharpening stones are included in section 1072.

In selecting abrasives one should be familiar with the most common kinds of abrasive material, their properties, grain sizes, and their uses. These factors apply to abrasive cloth, grinding wheels, and to loose grain abrasives. They are included in this unit.

279. Properties of Abrasives

The characteristics of a material are called its properties. Abrasives must possess three common properties: (1) hardness, (2) fracture resistance, (3) wear resistance.

Hardness means the ability of the abrasive to scratch the surface of the material to be polished or ground. The abrasive must be harder than the material to be cut.

Fracture resistance of an abrasive means its toughness, the ability to resist breaking or crumbling when pressed hard against the work during polishing or grinding. The fracture resistance should not be too high nor too low. It should be such that when the abrasive grains become dull they will fracture away, thus exposing new sharp cutting edges. Fracture resistance of grinding wheels is related to the kind of bonding material which binds the grains together (see § 1011).

Wear resistance of an abrasive refers to its ability to resist wear and stay sharp longer. It is related to the hardness of the abrasive material. Thus harder abrasive materials generally are more wear resistant than softer. However, there are some exceptions to this general rule.

280.   Kinds of Abrasives

The common abrasive materials are classified as either natural or artificial abrasives. *Natural* abrasives generally are minerals which come from nature. They occur either in the form of grains like sand, or in the form of large rocklike chunks. The large chunks must be crushed or ground into small abrasive grains. Some common natural abrasives include flint, garnet, emery, corundum, crocus, and diamond. These will be explained in greater detail.

The *artificial* abrasives are man made and are also known as synthetic or manufactured abrasives. With the exception of diamond, artificial abrasives are harder than the natural abrasives. Diamond is the hardest abrasive material. Because of their hardness and wear resistance, the artificial abrasives have largely replaced the natural abrasives in the metalworking industry.

Natural Abrasives

The following are some common natural abrasives.

Flint comes from the mineral quartz — a crystalline, rocklike material. It is used in making the familiar yellowish colored abrasive paper called *sandpaper*. It is one of the oldest kinds of abrasive paper and is used in woodworking.

Garnet is a reddish colored, glasslike mineral which is crushed into fine abrasive grains. It is harder and sharper than flint and is widely used for woodworking.

Emery is one of the oldest kinds of natural abrasive used for metalworking. It is black in color and is composed of a combination of corundum and iron oxide. *Corundum* is aluminum oxide, Al_2O_3. Prized gems such as emerald and ruby are the purest form of corundum. Emery, used for making an emery cloth for polishing metals, is about 60% corundum. Emery grains are not as sharp as artificial abrasives. The cutting action of emery is slight; therefore, it is used largely as a polishing abrasive.

Crocus is a fine, soft, red abrasive of iron oxide, or iron rust. It may be produced artificially or naturally to clean and polish metal surfaces to a high gloss. It is available in the form of *crocus cloth,* or a polishing or buffing compound (see § 1089).

Diamond is the hardest substance known. It is used in the form of abrasive grains which are bonded together to form a thin layer of abrasive. The layer of abrasive is bonded to a wheel, thus forming a grinding wheel. Diamond grinding wheels are used for grinding very hard materials such as cemented-carbide cutting tools (see § 350), ceramic cutting tools, glass, and stone. The diamonds used for this purpose are industrial diamonds in the form of chips or grains. They are much less expensive than the diamonds used for jewelry.

A diamond chip may be brazed on the end of a soft steel bar to make a tool for dressing or truing softer grinding wheels. (See Fig. 874.) (Also see §§ 1056 and 1061.) Diamonds used in industry have been produced artificially during recent years. However, they are still about as expensive as natural diamonds. Fine diamond dust is also used in making lapping compound for lapping hardened steel and other very hard materials.

Artificial Abrasives

The artificial abrasives were developed during the latter part of the 19th century. They are a result of man's effort to produce abrasives which are harder, tougher, and more wear resistant than the natural abrasives.

The artificial abrasives are manufactured at extremely high temperatures in electric furnaces. When first produced, they were very expensive because of the shortage and high cost of electric power at that time. Today, however, electric power is readily available and the artificial abrasives have largely replaced the natural abrasives in the metalworking industry. Three common artificial abrasives include silicon carbide, aluminum oxide, and boron carbide.

Silicon carbide is made by heating a mixture of powdered sand, coke, sawdust, and common salt in an electric furnace. It comes from the furnace in masses of beautiful, bluish crystals like diamonds. The crystals are crushed into fine abrasive grains which are used in making grinding wheels, abrasive stones, and coated abrasives (abrasive cloth).

Silicon carbide is harder and more brittle than aluminum oxide abrasive. It is hard enough to cut aluminum oxide. It is generally used for polishing or grinding materials of low tensile strength, including the following: cast iron, aluminum, bronze, tungsten carbide, copper, rubber, marble, glass, ceramics, pottery, magnesium, plastics, and fiber. Silicon carbide is known by trade names such as Carborundum, Crystolon, Carbolon, and Carbonite.

Aluminum oxide is produced by heating bauxite ore in an electric furnace at extremely high temperatures. With the addition of small amounts of titanium (a lustrous, hard, lightweight, metallic element), greater toughness can be imparted to the aluminum oxide. The center of the solid mass formed in the furnace is aluminum oxide. It is broken up and crushed into fine grains for making grinding wheels, abrasive stones, and coated abrasives.

Aluminum oxide has properties somewhat different than silicon carbide. It is not as hard, but it is tougher and does not fracture as easily. Aluminum oxide abrasives are recommended for grinding and polishing materials of high tensile strength, including the following: carbon steels, alloy steels, hard or soft steels, malleable iron, wrought iron, and tough bronze. Approximately 75% of all grinding wheels in use today are made of aluminum oxide. Aluminum oxide is known by trade names such as Alundum, Aloxite, Borolon, Exolon, and Lionite.

Boron carbide is produced from coke and boric acid in an electric furnace. It is known by the trade name *Norbide*, produced by the Norton Company. It is harder than either aluminum oxide or silicon carbide and can cut either of them. However, it is not as hard as diamond. It is used in stick form to dress or true grinding wheels 10″ or less in diameter (see Fig. 877). It is also used in powder form instead of diamond dust for lapping hardened steel or other very hard materials.

281. Abrasives for Hand Polishing

Abrasives for polishing metal parts by hand are either used in their loose grain form or in the form of abrasive paper or cloth.

282. Grain Size of Abrasives

Grain size refers to the size of the abrasive grains used in the manufacture of abrasive materials. Most abrasive manufacturers produce abrasives for grinding wheels according to the Standard Abrasive Grain Sizes shown in Table 4. Several of the abrasive grain sizes used in the manufacture of coated abrasives are different.

Table 4
ABRASIVE GRAIN SIZES
FOR GRINDING WHEELS
(See Section 282.)

COARSE	MEDIUM	FINE	VERY FINE
10	30	70	220
12	36	80	240
14	46	90	280
16	54	100	320
20	60	120	400
24		150	500
		180	600

The grain sizes given in Table 4 are the number of meshes or holes per inch in the screen, Fig. 245. Thus, a 10-grain abrasive is one which will just pass through a 10-mesh screen, that is, a screen which has meshes 1/10 of an inch square (less the width of a screen strand), 10 meshes per inch, or 100 meshes per square inch.

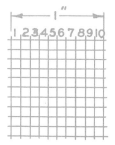

Fig. 245. A 10-Grain Screen (Actual Size)

A. 60-Grain Screen

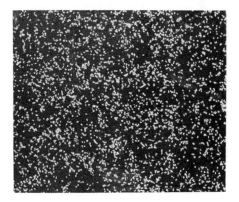

C. 60-Grain Abrasive

B. 60-Grain Screen Enlarged 16 Diameters

D. Abrasive Grains Enlarged 16 Diameters

Fig. 246. A 60-Grain Screen and Grain Which Passes Through It

In Fig. 246:

(A) is a 60-grain screen,

(B) is the 60-grain screen magnified 16 times,

(C) is the actual size of the grain which passes through the 60-grain screen, and

(D) is the grain magnified 16 times.

283. Coated Abrasives

A coated abrasive is composed of a flexible backing material to which abrasive grains are bonded with cement or glue. Hence, *abrasive cloth* and *abrasive paper* are classified as *coated abrasives*. The backing material may be paper, cloth, fiber, or a combination of these materials.

Common abrasive materials include flint, garnet, emery, crocus, silicon carbide, and aluminum oxide. The common coated abrasives used in the metalworking industry include emery, aluminum oxide, silicon carbide, and crocus. Coated abrasives are available in many forms for both hand and machine polishing or grinding. They are available in the form of belts, rolls, sheets, discs, spiral points, and cones, Fig. 252.

Grades of Coated Abrasives

The relative coarseness or fineness rating of coated abrasives is somewhat different than the standard rating given to abrasive grains used for grinding wheels in Table 4. The following are the common abrasive grain sizes used for coated abrasives:

Extra-Coarse — 12, 16, 20, 24, 30, 36

Coarse — 40, 50

Medium — 60, 80, 100

Fine — 120, 150, 180

Extra-Fine — 220, 240, 280, 320, 360, 400, 500, 600

Backing materials on coated abrasives include:

Paper — Used for hand applications for woodworking and fine finishing abrasives.

Cloth — Two weights of cloth are used as backing. The lightweight cloth is called *jeans* and is flexible for hand polishing. The heavyweight cloth is called *drills*. It is more stretch resistant and is used for machine buffing.

Fiber — This type of backing is extra strong, durable, and used for tough machine polishing and grinding applications.

284. How Is Abrasive Sold?

Loose grain abrasive is sold by the pound, usually in cans.

Abrasive cloth is sold by the sheet and in packets of 25, 50, and 100 sheets, Fig. 247. The sheets are usually 9″ x 11″. It is also sold in rolls ½″ to 6″ wide by 25 or 50 yards long, and in endless belts, Fig. 252.

285. Holding Work for Hand Polishing

To keep from scratching a polished surface with the *hardened steel* jaws of the vise, the work should be placed between *vise jaw caps* (see § 681). Jaw caps are usually made from soft brass.

286. Choosing Grade of Abrasive

To hand polish a large, roughly filed surface, first rub it with a medium grade of abrasive, such as No. 80 or 100 abrasive cloth; then

Fig. 247. Abrasive Cloth Storage (Courtesy Minnesota Mining & Mfg. Co.)

continue with finer grades until you get the depth of cuts or grooves you want. For polishing a smooth filed surface, use Nos. 120 or 150 abrasive cloth and finish with No. 180 or a finer grade if desired.

287. How to Polish

It has been explained that the reason for polishing is to change a rough, uneven, dull surface, with irregular scratches to a surface with very fine, uniform, *parallel* (see § 120) cuts or grooves which cannot be seen with the naked eye.

Before polishing is begun but after filing, the surface in Fig. 248 contains many tiny,

Fig. 248. Rough, Uneven Surface (Enlarged)

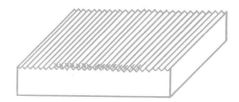

Fig. 249. Surface with Uniform and Parallel Abrasive Cuts or Grooves (Enlarged)

Fig. 250. Polishing Flat Work

Fig. 251. Polishing Round Work

irregular grooves of various depths which run in different directions. It would be well to examine the surface under a magnifying glass. This surface may have been filed, but it still has a dull appearance because the light is reflected in many directions. The cuts and grooves must be changed so that they will be parallel and equal in depth to produce a *bright finish*. When this is done, the light will shine back in the same direction, Fig. 249. The shallower the cuts or grooves, the smoother the finish will become. After changing to a finer grade, change the direction of the strokes to remove the fine cuts or scratches.

A piece of wornout abrasive cloth, moistened with a drop of oil, makes a smoother finish on steel. This surface polished with oil will not rust as quickly as it will if it is polished dry.

288. Polishing Flat and Round Work

When flat work is polished, the abrasive cloth may be rubbed back and forth upon the metal as shown in Fig. 250.

When round work is polished on the bench, the work may be held in a vise, and the abrasive cloth worked back and forth around the work as shown in Fig. 251.

289 What Does Lapping Mean?

Lapping is the fine removal of small amounts of metal from a *hardened steel* surface that is slightly oversize. It is done where and when ordinary grinding would remove too much metal, especially on measuring tools where smooth surfaces and exact sizes are needed. The tool used for this purpose is called a *lap;* it is made of copper, brass, soft cast iron, or lead; it must be of a material softer than the metal to be lapped.

A fine *powder abrasive*, known as *lapping powder*, is used for lapping; the pulverized sizes of the grains of the abrasives are numbered as given in section 282. The lapping powder is made into a paste by mixing it with

Vaseline or *lard oil* (see § 398); it is then called *lapping compound* or *grinding compound*. The lap is coated with the paste and then rubbed against the surface of the part that is to be slightly ground to size. *Lapping* can be a hand or machine operation.

290. Polishing with Steel Wool

Polishing or cleaning of metal by hand may be done with fine steel wool, which is made of *steel shavings*. The fine, sharp edges of the steel shavings scratch the metal and thus polish it. Steel wool is made in seven grades ranging from fine to coarse as follows: 0000, 000, 00, 0, 1, 2, and 3. The fine grades, 0000 and 000, will provide a low-lustre finish on copper, aluminum, and other nonferrous metals.

Review Questions

1. What is meant by hand polishing?

2. What is an abrasive?

3. Name five common forms in which abrasives are used in metalworking.

4. List three properties which abrasives must possess.

5. Explain the principal difference between natural and artificial abrasives.

6. List five kinds of natural abrasive materials.

7. Of what material is emery composed?

8. List three common kinds of artificial abrasives.

9. List several kinds of materials which are ground or polished with silicon carbide abrasives.

10. List several kinds of materials which are ground or polished with aluminum oxide abrasives.

11. List several trade names used for aluminum oxide abrasives.

12. For what purpose is boron carbide used?

13. In what forms are abrasives used for hand polishing?

14. Explain how abrasive grain size is determined.

15. What is the meaning of the term *coated abrasive?*

16. What kinds of backing materials are used on coated abrasives?

17. What kinds of abrasive materials are used for coated abrasives?

18. What kinds of coated abrasive materials are used for metalworking?

19. In what forms are coated abrasives available?

20. List two weights of cloth used as backing for coated abrasives.

21. What information should be specified when ordering abrasive cloth?

22. What grades of abrasive cloth would you select for polishing a large smoothly filed surface by hand?

23. What is lapping?

24. What is steel wool?

Coordination
Words to Know

abrade	grain size
abrasive	grinding compound
abrasive cloth	grinding wheel
abrasive compound	hand polishing
aluminum oxide	jeans
artificial abrasive	lap
backing material	lapping
boron carbide	lapping compound
buffing	lapping machine
coated abrasives	lapping powder
corundum	mesh
crocus	metal finishing
diamond	natural abrasive
drills	Norbide
emery	sharpening stone
emery cloth	silicon carbide
fiber	steel shaving
flint	steel wool
fracture resistance	Vaseline
garnet	wear resistance

Fig. 252. Variety of Commonly Used Coated
Abrasives (Courtesy Norton Co.)

Mathematics

1. How many openings are there in a piece of 36-mesh screen 2″ square?

Social Science

1. What are the dangers of working in a place where there is dust as a result of polishing, especially that done by power?

Occupational Information

1. What is silicosis?

2. Choose a natural abrasive and write a story telling how it is produced.

3. Choose an artificial abrasive and write a story telling how it is manufactured.

Power Shovel Loading
Bauxite in Open-Pit Mine
(Courtesy Aluminum
Company of America)

Part **III**

Getting Acquainted
with Metals

Iron

296. What is Metallurgy?

Metallurgy is the science and technology of metals, including a study of their structure and the various processes of working them. It is the study of metals. A person who does this work is a *metallurgist* (see § 19).

297. Iron

Iron is the most common and most useful metal. We are living in an age of iron and steel. The purest iron comes from the sky in the form of "shooting stars" or *meteors* which we can see at night. Pure iron does not rust in water; however, iron rusts because it contains impurities. Pure iron is seldom used in industry because it is too soft for most work. It is so soft that it can be scratched with the fingernail.

Iron is used in three forms:
(1) *Cast iron.*
(2) *Wrought iron.*
(3) *Steel.*
The first two are explained in sections 300 and 302; steel is explained in Units 19 and 20.

298. Iron Ore

Iron ore is not pure as it comes from iron mines, Fig. 256. Most of the iron ore in the United States is found in the mines of Michigan and Minnesota, known as the *Lake Superior Region* or *Mesabi Range*. Deposits are also mined in Alabama. Iron ore is also imported from foreign countries.

Iron ore is carried from the mines in freight cars that operate on high-loading docks. The ore is dumped into bins holding several carloads each. From these bins the ore is dumped into large boats, Fig. 257. A boat is loaded in a very short time, less than 3 hours. These boats then carry the ore to Chicago, Gary, Detroit, Cleveland, and other steelmaking cities along the Great Lakes. They are called *ore boats,* carrying about 12,000 tons of ore in one load.

Fig. 256. The Rouchelau Open-Pit Mine on the Mesabi Range in Minnesota (Note provision for both rail and truck transportation) (Courtesy U.S. Steel)

131

Fig. 257. Unloading an Ore Boat
(Courtesy U. S. Steel)

Fig. 258. Blast Furnaces Viewed Across Stockpile of Iron Ore (Courtesy U. S. Steel)

Fig. 259. Blast Furnace (Courtesy American Iron & Steel Institute)

Steps in the purifying of iron and making of steel are shown in Fig. 277.

299. Pig Iron

Making pig iron is the first step in the purifying of iron and the making of steel (see § 317 and Fig. 277). Iron ore becomes pig iron when the impurities are burned out in a *blast furnace*. This looks like a tall chimney on the outside, 50′ to 100′ high, Figs. 258 and 259. It is a large, round, iron shell from 10′ to 20′ in diameter covered on the inside with (refractory) bricks or clay which can withstand great heat, Fig. 260. It is called a blast furnace because a blast of hot air is forced into it near the bottom. Each blast furnace has four or five giant stoves which first heat the air.

It takes about 2 tons of iron ore, 1 ton of coke, ½ ton of limestone, and 4 tons of air to make 1 ton of pig iron. The iron ore, coke, and limestone are dumped into the top of the blast furnace which holds about 1000 tons. The burning coke and the blast of very hot air melt the iron ore. The limestone mixes with the ashes of the burnt coke and with the rock and earth of the iron ore, forming waste which is called *slag*. As the iron melts, it drips to the bottom of the furnace.

Steelmakers are constantly seeking improvements in their operations. Some are experimenting with using a mixture of pulverized or powdered coal and oil in the blast furnace to speed up this operation.

When the furnace is emptied, the melted iron flows out into a ladle for transfer to a steel furnace or into a winding trough and then into iron or sand *molds* (see § 961). When it cools *pigs*[1] are formed; hence the name *pig iron*, Fig. 261. The slag which floats on top of the melted iron in the furnace is

[1]The *molds* used in forming pig iron are a number of parallel trenches connected by a channel running at right angles to them. The iron cools in these and forms slabs or bars. These are called *pigs*; they are connected at one end to the long bar called the *sow*, in comparison to a sow with her little pigs.

drained off through a separate hole. The blast furnace works continuously.

Pig iron is very hard and *brittle*. It has three uses:

(1) *Cast iron.*
(2) *Wrought iron.*
(3) *Steel* (see §§ 317-320 and Fig. 277).

Pig iron contains about 93% pure iron and from 3 to 5% *carbon* (see § 320). The remainder is *silicon*[2], *sulfur*[3], *phosphorus*[4], and *manganese* (see § 348).

300. Cast Iron

Cast means to form in a certain shape (see § 990). Pig iron which has been remelted and poured into a certain shape is *cast iron*. It is often called pig iron because some kinds of cast iron contain the same materials. Pig iron is remelted in a *cupola furnace* that is really a small blast furnace (see § 994 and Fig. 259). The melted pig iron is poured into *sand molds* of various shapes which later become parts of machines or other objects (see §§ 965, 966, and 976). The iron is then called *cast iron* and the object is a *casting*.

301. Kinds of Cast Iron

There are several different kinds of cast iron. The properties of the different kinds of cast iron vary to a large degree according to amount, form, and arrangement of the carbon content in the iron. The carbon content[5] actually may range from about 1.7 to 6% in different kinds of cast iron. However, most grades of cast iron have carbon content rang-

[2]*Silicon* is a chemical which is in clays, sand, and rocks. It gives hardness to iron.

[3]*Sulfur* is a yellow, flammable nonmetal. Excess sulfur and phosphorus are injurious in iron and steel. Too much sulfur makes these metals weak and brittle, causing cracks. Modern steel mills attempt to remove all impurities (including carbon) and then carefully add elements as needed for various uses. A little sulfur is added to some steels for better machinability.

[4]*Phosphorus* is a poisonous, active nonmetal. It causes brittleness and coarse grain in iron and steel.

[5]One percent (1.00%) carbon is known as *100-point* carbon, *point 100* carbon, or *100 carbon*.

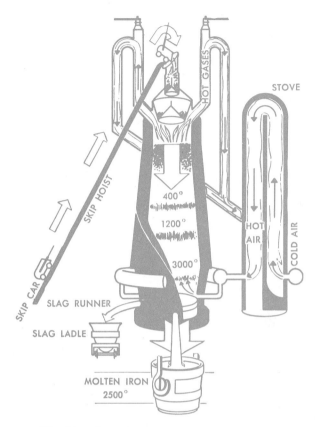

Fig. 260. Cross Section of a Blast Furnace (Courtesy U. S. Steel)

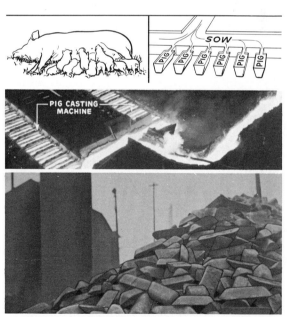

Fig. 261. Pigs (Courtesy American Iron & Steel Institute)

ing from about 2 to 4.5%. When broken, cast iron has a crystallike grain structure at the fracture. The following are several common kinds of cast iron.

Gray Cast Iron

This basic type of cast iron usually contains from 1.7 to 4.5% carbon. It melts at about 2200° F. Most of the carbon is in a *free* state, scattered in the form of *graphite* (carbon) flakes throughout the crystalline grain structure of the metal. This arrangement of carbon makes the cast iron brittle. Thus it fractures easily from sharp blows. It has a gray, crystalline color where fractured. The gray color is due to the tiny flakes of graphite (carbon) mixed in with the grains of iron.

Gray cast iron is the cheapest kind of metal. It is used to make large pipes, stoves, radiators, water hydrants, frames for machines, and other machine parts which must be large and heavy, but in which impact strength is not very important. (Note the difference between *cast iron chips* and *steel shavings* in section 569.) Gray cast iron can be machined easily. Several different grades of gray cast iron are available, each having different properties.

White Cast Iron

This kind of cast iron is so named because of its white, crystalline color at the fracture when broken. The carbon content usually ranges from about 2 to 3.5%. However, most of the carbon in white cast iron is in a chemically *combined* state. Thus it forms a very hard substance called *cementite*, which is *iron carbide* (Fe_3C). White cast iron is so hard that it cannot be machined, except by grinding. Its direct use is limited to castings requiring the surfaces to withstand abrasion and wear. The major use of white cast iron, however, is in making *malleable* cast iron.

Malleable Iron

Metal is malleable if it can be hammered into different shapes without cracking. *Malleable iron* is *cast iron* which has been made soft, tough, strong, and malleable. It generally has about 2 to 2.65% carbon content. It is produced by converting white cast iron to malleable iron by heating at a high temperature for a prolonged period of time (100 to 120 hours) in a heat treatment furnace. This *heat-treatment* process, called *malleablizing*, changes the arrangement of the carbon from its combined state as *cementite* (Fe_3C) to free carbon. The free carbon forms *aggregates* or globules of free carbon at the prolonged high temperature. The surrounding iron then becomes soft and machinable. Malleable castings have many of the tough characteristics of steel. Several different grades of malleable iron are available. They are used for making tough castings for automobiles, tractors, and many kinds of machinery parts.

Ductile Cast Iron

This kind of cast iron is also known as *nodular iron* (a small rounded lump of carbon aggregate in soft iron) or *spheroidal graphite iron*. The carbon in the grain structure of ductile iron is in the free state, in ball-like forms called *nodules*. The iron surrounding the tiny balls of graphite (carbon) is soft, tough, and machineable. Ductile cast iron is produced very much like gray cast iron. Magnesium alloys and certain other elements are added to a ladle of gray iron before it is poured into molds to make castings. These additives, together with proper heat treatment, cause the carbon in the molten iron to form balls or nodules as it cools and becomes solid.

Ductile cast iron has properties similar to malleable iron. It is tough, machineable, and possesses many of the characteristics of steel. It is used for making tough castings for automobiles, farm machinery, and many other kinds of machinery.

Further information concerning the different kinds and grades of cast iron is available in standard handbooks for machinists.

302. Wrought Iron

Wrought iron is purified *pig iron* (Fig. 277). It contains almost no *carbon*, only about 0.04%. Wrought iron is the purest form of iron in commercial use, and is therefore often called just *iron*. Wrought iron as applied to contemporary metal home furnishings is a misnomer, as today these are usually called mild steel. Wrought iron now is not common, but it does have several desirable characteristics not found in steel. These are due to its peculiar grain structure caused by stringy particles of slag running throughout the metal.

An old way of making wrought iron is in a *puddling furnace*, Fig. 262, which looks like a large baker's oven in which the flame is over the metal. Pig iron melts at about 2100° *Fahrenheit* while wrought iron melts at about 2700° F. After the pig iron is melted, it is stirred or *puddled*. This is done so that every part of the melted iron is touched by the flame. Most of the carbon and other impurities is thus burned out. The less carbon that iron contains, the higher is its *melting point* (see Table 12, p. 161). The heat of the furnace is kept high enough to melt pig iron but not high enough to keep wrought iron in liquid form. Thus, as the melted iron becomes purified it becomes pasty. This paste is worked into lumps or balls, called *puddle balls*, which are then taken out of the furnace and squeezed, hammered, and rolled while hot into bars. The bars are piled or fastened into bundles and then reheated, welded together by rolling, and rolled into finished shapes of bars, *sheets,* and *plates* (see § 789) ready to be sold and used.

Wrought iron is very tough, *malleable,* and bends easily cold or hot. It looks stringy when broken. Good wrought iron can be tied into a knot while cold without breaking. It is, therefore, used for work which needs much hammering, bending, twisting, and stretching, such as ornamental iron work, rivets, bolts, wire, nails, horseshoes, chain links, pipes, etc.

You can make many beautiful things for your home out of wrought iron, such as lamps, lanterns, candle holders, flower pot holders, door knockers, smoking stands, etc. Wrought iron rusts very slowly and is easy to weld.

Review Questions

1. What is a metallurgist?
2. What is the most used metal in industry?
3. Is pure iron used in industry? Why?
4. What is iron ore? Where is it found? In what states?
5. What is pig iron?
6. What is the difference between pig iron and iron ore?
7. What is a blast furnace? Describe it.
8. Why is it called a blast furnace?
9. What is a mold?
10. Why is pig iron called by that name?
11. What are the uses of pig iron?
12. What is carbon?
13. What is cast iron?
14. What is a casting?
15. What is a Fahrenheit thermometer?
16. What is the carbon content of cast iron?
17. What percent is 200-point carbon?
18. For what is cast iron used?
19. What does malleable mean? What is malleable iron?
20. For what is malleable iron used?
21. What is wrought iron?

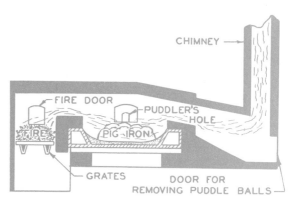

Fig. 262. Puddling Furnace

22. Why is wrought iron often just called iron?

23. What is the carbon content of wrought iron?

24. For what is wrought iron used?

25. What is white cast iron, and what is its principal use?

26. What is ductile cast iron, and what are its uses?

Coordination

Words to Know

Age of Iron and Steel	Mesabi Range
blast furnace	metallurgy
carbon	meteor
cast	ore boat
casting	phosphorus
cast iron chip	pig iron
cupola	puddle ball
ductile cast iron	puddler
Fahrenheit	puddling furnace
gray cast iron	sand mold
iron	silicon
iron mine	slag
iron ore	steel
Lake Superior Region	sulfur
malleable iron	white cast iron
manganese	wrought iron
melting point	

Mathematics

1. If a blast furnace holds 1000 tons of iron ore, coke, and limestone, how many carloads will it take to fill it if each car holds 50 tons?

2. How many carloads will it take to fill a 12,000 ton ore boat if a car holds 50 tons?

3. What is the weight of an iron casting which measures one cubic foot?

4. What is the weight of an iron casting 7″ x 9″ x 15″?

5. How many pounds of carbon are there in one ton of cast iron if it is 500-point carbon?

Drafting

1. Make a list of 5 things that you would specify to be made of cast iron.

2. Make a list of 10 things that you would specify to be made of malleable iron.

3. Make a list of 20 things that you would specify to be made of wrought iron.

Social Science

1. Of what value is iron to civilization? Write a story.

2. Write a story telling what might happen if the United States were suddenly unable to get a supply of iron.

Occupational Information

1. Write a biography of Gabriel Fahrenheit.

Steel

317. Steel

Steel is an alloy obtained by combining manufactured metals. It is a bluish-gray metal which, when broken, looks like crystals or like the break in a lump of sugar. The kinds and uses of steel are many. For certain uses, especially for tools, there is no metal with the abilities of steel. It is brighter and stronger than iron. Steel can be made so hard that it will cut iron. Note the difference between *iron chips* and *steel chips* in section 569.

318. Kinds and Grades of Steel

There are two kinds of steel: *carbon steel* and *alloy steel*. Each kind is divided into several grades.

Carbon Steel

(1) *Low-carbon steel;* also known as *machine steel, machinery steel,* and *mild steel.*
(2) *Medium-carbon steel.*
(3) *High-carbon steel;* also known as *tool steel.*

Alloy Steel

(1) *Special alloy steel,* such as *nickel steel, chromium steel, etc.* (see §§ 344-351).
(2) High-speed steel (see § 352).

319. Iron + Carbon = Steel or Cast Iron

Carbon is found in the form of coal, diamonds and *graphite* (see § 396). Charcoal and coal are mostly carbon. Steel is between *wrought iron* and *cast iron* in carbon content (see §§ 300 and 302). The dividing line between steel and cast iron is usually about 1.7% carbon.

Carbon is easily united with *oxygen.* It makes steel stiff, strong, and hard. Steel is graded by its percentage of carbon. As the carbon in iron and steel is reduced, the *melting point* is increased (see Table 12, p. 161).

Fig. 277 shows the steps in purifying iron ore and making steel. Table 6 gives the carbon content and uses of each kind of *carbon steel.*

Steel can be made from:

(1) Pig iron or cast iron by taking out some of the *carbon.*
(2) Wrought iron by adding *carbon.*
(3) Wrought iron, pig iron, and old scraps of iron and steel by melting them together and then testing and adding or burning out *carbon* until the melted metal contains the amount desired.

320. Five Ways of Making Steel

The five basic ways of making steel are:
(1) Bessemer converter.
(2) Open-hearth furnace.
(3) Crucible furnace.
(4) Electric furnace.
(5) Basic-oxygen process.

HOW STEEL IS MADE

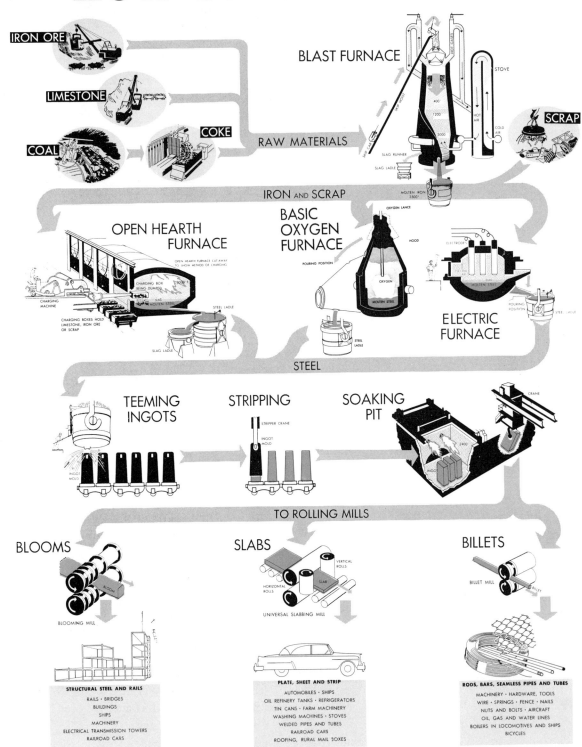

Fig. 277. How Steel is Made (Courtesy U. S. Steel)

321. Bessemer Converter

The Bessemer way of making steel is named after Sir Henry Bessemer who invented it in England in 1856. Steel made this way is called *Bessemer steel*. It was first made in this country in 1864 at Wyandotte, Michigan. The Bessemer method is a quick way to make steel; a ton can be made in about 1 minute.

The main difference between steel and *pig iron* is the amount of *carbon* they contain (see § 299.) Pig iron contains from 3 to 5% carbon, while steel contains less than 2%. Thus, in making steel from pig iron, it is necessary to take out some carbon. The carbon and other impurities are burnt out of melted pig iron by blowing a current of cold air through it. It seems strange that it burns more, in fact it boils, when cold air is blown into it, but that is what happens. This is because the carbon in the pig iron unites with the *oxygen*[1] in the air. When this happens, a more forceful burning takes place. It is the same as when a cold wind makes a bonfire burn more forcefully.

The Bessemer converter is a large tank shaped like a pear with an open top, Fig. 278. It is made of steel and brick which can withstand great heat and is supported on two sides so that it can be tipped to pour out the melted metal. It is 15′ to 22′ high and holds 30 tons of metal. The melted metal is first poured into the converter. The air pressure is great enough to keep the melted metal from flowing backward into the holes. The oxygen of the air burns out nearly all of the carbon. When the carbon burns, a white flame, about 25′ or 30′ high, shoots up from the mouth of the converter with a mighty roar and a great shower of sparks like a volcano. This is a magnificent sight at night. The color of the flame changes as the carbon burns out. When the flame dies

[1]*Oxygen* is a colorless, odorless, tasteless gas. One-fifth of the air is oxygen. Without oxygen there can be no burning; thus if a piece of wood or charcoal that is merely glowing is put into a jar of oxygen, it will burst into flame; likewise the flame of a candle placed into a jar with no oxygen will burn out.

out, it is a sign that most of the carbon has been burnt out, and the air is then shut off. The exact amount of carbon necessary is then thrown in, thus making steel.

This melted steel is poured into large buckets called *ladles*. Through a hole at the bottom of the ladle, the melted steel is then poured into *ingot molds* which are forms for making the steel into blocks, Fig. 277. These blocks of metal are about 20″ square, from 4′ to 6′ long, weigh about a ton, and called *ingots*, Fig. 277. The ingots, still red-hot but cold enough to stand alone, are rolled into shapes ready for use (see Figs. 32 and 283).

Bessemer steel is an inexpensive type of steel used for nails, screws, wire, shafts, rails, and building materials such as beams. Because of its good machinability when .05% to .33% sulfur is added, it is well suited to making machine parts.

In recent years, some steel companies have started to use another kind of Bessemer converter. It is called a basic-oxygen furnace because it uses pure oxygen instead of air. Carbon is removed much faster from the melted pig iron when pure oxygen is blown through the bottom of the converter. Air has only

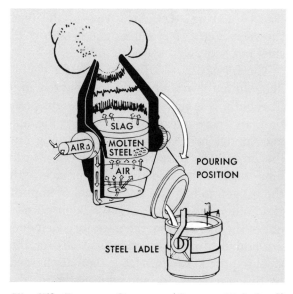

Fig. 278. Bessemer Converter (Courtesy U. S. Steel)

about 20% oxygen. In some cases, the oxygen supply is blown in from the top.

322. Basic-Oxygen Process (BOP)

The *Basic-Oxygen Process,* called the *BOP* process, is somewhat similar to the Bessemer process of making steel. It is rapidly replacing the Bessemer process in the steelmaking industry. A *basic-oxygen furnace,* Fig 277, is used to make steel by this process.

The similarities and differences between the *BOP* and the Bessemer processes can be understood by studying Figs. 277 and 278. With the *BOP* process, pure oxygen is blown into the molten iron through a lance which enters from the top of the furnace. With the Bessemer process air, composed of oxygen and nitrogen, is blown through the molten metal from the bottom. With the BOP process the pure oxygen creates more heat and burns the impurities out of the molten iron much more rapidly than does the atmospheric air.

Steel made by the *BOP* process is of a high quality. Since pure oxygen is used to burn out the impurities in the molten iron, nitrogen which makes steel brittle does not enter the process. Thus, the chemical specifications of the steel can be controlled more accurately with the *BOP* process, and it is a more rapid way of making steel. A furnace of the type shown in Fig. 277 produces about 80 tons of steel per hour.

The furnace is tilted on its side for charging. Molten iron and scrap are charged into its mouth. It is then tilted to an upright position, and pure oxygen is blown into the furnace under high pressure, thus burning out the impurities. Burned lime, converted from limestone, is also added to the furnace with the oxygen to increase the removal of impurities. When the impurities have been burned out of the molten iron, the necessary elements are added to meet the specifications for the steel required. The furnace is then discharged by tilting it on its side and pouring the molten steel into a large ladle.

For many years it was known that oxygen could be used to improve the steelmaking processes, but pure oxygen was too expensive to be used for this purpose. Since 1950 methods of producing pure oxygen at low cost were developed, making its use for steelmaking possible. It has been estimated that during the 1970's approximately 20% of the steel produced in the United States will be made by the basic-oxygen process.

323. Open-Hearth Furnace

Most of the steel in this country is made in the *open-hearth furnace,* Fig. 279. The open-hearth method of making steel can be controlled better than the Bessemer method because the melted metal can be tested for carbon content and more carbon added at any time during the heating.

The open-hearth furnace, which is somewhat like a baker's oven, holds up to 200 tons of metal. It has two pairs of rooms with brickwork built like a checkerboard. Pig iron, wrought iron, and old scraps of iron and steel are placed on a saucer-shaped *hearth.* Hot air and gas are used for heating. The gas passes through the heated brickwork in one of the rooms. Air passes through a different room of heated brickwork. The gas and air then combine and make a very hot flame. One pair of rooms is heated while the other pair is being used. As the one used becomes cool, the air and gas are made to pass through the heated

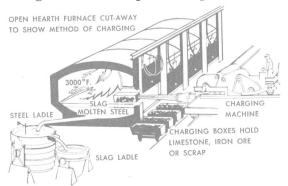

OPEN HEARTH FURNACE CUT-AWAY TO SHOW METHOD OF CHARGING

3000°F.

SLAG
MOLTEN STEEL

STEEL LADLE

CHARGING MACHINE

CHARGING BOXES HOLD LIMESTONE, IRON ORE OR SCRAP

SLAG LADLE

Fig. 279. Open-Hearth Furnace
(Courtesy U. S. Steel)

one. The flames touch the metal from above. Thus a very high temperature keeps the iron in a liquid form. Samples of the white-hot metal are taken, cooled, and tested to find out if they contain the amount of carbon wanted. If too much carbon has been burned out, more can be added. When the melted metal contains the right amount of carbon, it is poured into *ingot molds* (see Fig. 280).

Steelmakers have found that pure oxygen, instead of air, will melt the metal and remove carbon faster. Sometimes a *heat* (batch) *of steel* can be made in only half the time when pure oxygen is used.

Steel made in an open-hearth furnace is called *open-hearth steel* and is used for bridges, rails, bolts, screws, shafts, etc. It is also used for making high-grade tool steel. An advantage of the open-hearth furnace is that old scrap iron and steel, as well as pig iron, can be used.

324. Crucible Furnace

The crucible process is the oldest used for making *high-carbon steel* and *alloy steel* (see §§ 318 and 344). High-carbon steel is made by melting wrought iron and scrap steel in a *crucible* — a melting pot shaped like a barrel, about 20″ high, and 1′ in diameter, made of graphite (see § 396) or clay which can withstand great heat. The amount of *carbon* desired is then placed on top of the wrought iron and steel. A cover is placed tightly over

the top, and a number of these crucibles are put in a hot furnace. The melted iron mixes with the carbon, thus making steel. The melted steel is then poured into *ingot molds.*

Alloy steel is made the same way except that additional materials, such as *chromium* (see § 346), *tungsten* (see § 350), etc., are also put in the crucible. Steel made in a crucible is called *crucible steel*. It is higher grade, stronger, and more expensive steel than either Bessemer steel or open-hearth steel. Crucible steel is used for razors, pens, knives, needles, dies, tools, machine spindles, gears, gear shafts, and other machine parts where stiffness and unusual strength are needed. The crucible furnace has been almost completely replaced by the electric furnace which is a large arc-heated crucible.

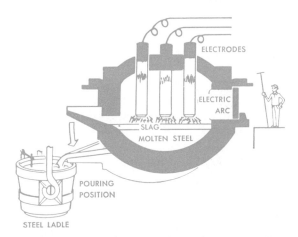

Fig. 281. Electric Furnace (Courtesy U. S. Steel)

Fig. 280. Ingots in Soaking Pit
(Courtesy U. S. Steel)

Fig. 282. Charging Steel Scrap into an Electric Furnace (Courtesy U. S. Steel)

325. Electric Furnace

The electric furnace (see Figs. 281 and 282) is used when close control of temperature and amounts of alloying elements is important. Higher temperatures can be reached with the electric furnace than are possible with other furnaces for making steel. This high-grade steel is called *electric steel*. *High-carbon steel*, special alloy steel (see § 344), and high-speed steel (see § 352) are made this way. They are used for cutting tools, dies, and the like.

Electric *arc furnaces* give very close control of the grain structure of steel. Electric *vacuum-induction* furnaces give close control over the chemistry of steel.

326. Low-Carbon Steel

Low-carbon steel is also known as *machine steel, machinery steel,* and *mild steel*. It contains about .05 to .30% carbon (see Table 6). It is made in the Bessemer converter, the basic-oxygen furnace, and the open-hearth furnace. It is used for forge work, rivets, chains, and machine parts which do not need great strength. It is also used for almost every purpose that wrought iron is used (see § 302 and Table 6). In fact, the production of

Table 6
CARBON STEELS AND THEIR USES

PERCENT OF CARBON IN STEEL	USES
Low-Carbon:	
0.05-0.20	Automobile bodies, buildings, pipes, chains, rivets, screws, nails.
0.20-0.30	Gears, shafts, bolts, forgings, bridges, buildings.
Medium-Carbon:	
0.30-0.40	Connecting rods, crank pins, axles, drop forgings.
0.40-0.50	Car axles, crankshafts, rails, boilers, auger bits, screwdrivers.
0.50-0.60	Hammers, sledges.
High-Carbon:	
0.60-0.70	Stamping and pressing dies, drop-forging dies, drop forgings, screwdrivers, blacksmiths' hammers, table knives, setscrews.
0.70-0.80	Punches, cold chisels, hammers, sledges, shear blades, table knives, drop-forging dies, anvil faces, wrenches, vise jaws, band saws, crowbars, lathe centers, rivet sets.
0.80-0.90	Punches, rivet sets, large taps, threading dies, drop-forging dies, shear blades, table knives, saws, hammers, cold chisels, woodworking chisels, rock drills, axes, springs.
0.90-1.00	Taps, small punches, threading dies, needles, knives, springs, machinists' hammers, screwdrivers, drills, milling cutters, axes, reamers, rock drills, chisels, lathe centers, hacksaw blades.
1.00-1.10	Axes, chisels, small taps, hand reamers, lathe centers, mandrels, threading dies, milling cutters, springs, turning and planing tools, knives, drills.
1.10-1.20	Milling cutters, reamers, woodworking tools, saws, knives, ball bearings, cold cutting dies, threading dies, taps, twist drills, pipe cutters, lathe centers, hatchets, turning and planing tools.
1.20-1.30	Turning and planing tools, twist drills, scythes, files, circular cutters, engravers' tools, surgical cutlery, saws for cutting metals, tools for turning brass and wood, reamers.
1.30-1.40	Small twist drills, razors, small engravers' tools, surgical instruments, knives, boring tools, wire drawing dies, tools for turning hard metals, files, woodworking chisels.
1.40-1.50	Razors, saws for cutting steel, wire drawing dies, fine cutters.

wrought iron has greatly decreased for this reason.

Some of this steel is rolled, while cold, between highly polished rollers under great pressure. This gives it a very smooth finish and exact size. It is then called *cold-rolled steel*.

327. Medium-Carbon Steel

Medium-carbon steel has more carbon and is stronger than low-carbon steel. It is also more difficult to bend, weld, and cut than low-carbon steel. It contains about .30 to .60% carbon. Medium-carbon steel is used for bolts, shafts, car axles, rails, etc. (See Table 6.)

It is frequently hardened and tempered by heat treatment (see §§ 951 and 952). Medium-carbon steels can be hardened to a Rockwell-C hardness of about 40 to 60, depending on the carbon content and the thickness of the material (see §§ 1165 and 1166 and Table 35).

328. High-Carbon Steel

High-carbon steel, known as *tool steel* and *carbon-tool steel*, generally contains about .60 to 1.50% carbon. The best grades of this steel are made in the crucible and the electric furnace. It is called tool steel because it is used to make such tools as drills, taps, dies, reamers, files, cold chisels, crowbars, and hammers (see Table 6). It is hard to bend, weld, and cut. Before cutting, it must be annealed which means that it must be softened (see § 955).

High-carbon steel, when heated to a red heat and suddenly cooled in water or oil, becomes very hard and very brittle. This is called *hardening*. The more carbon the steel contains and the more quickly it is cooled, the harder it becomes (see § 951). High-carbon steel can be hardened to about Rockwell-C 60 to 66, which is hard enough for metal-cutting tools.

High-carbon steel is rolled to the desired shape and is often ground to provide a

smooth finish. Round bars which are ground and polished are called *drill rod* which is used for making drills (see § 489), reamers (see § 582), taps (see § 649), punches (see §§ 701-702), and dowel pins[2].

329. Hot-Rolled Steel

After pig iron or wrought iron has been made into steel (see §§ 299 and 302), some of it is made into large blocks called *ingots* (see Fig. 280). These ingots are rolled while hot between heavy, powerful, steel rollers each about 2′ to 3′ in diameter the same way that clothes are squeezed through a clothes wringer, Fig. 283. The hot steel is rolled between many sets of rollers; each set is a little closer together than the preceding set. When

Fig. 283. Ingot Entering Blooming Mill (Top) and a General View of Rolling Beams (Bottom) in a Steel Mill (Courtesy U. S. Steel)

Notice the blooming mill at lower left and the steel taking finished shape at the far end.

---

[2]A *dowel pin*, in metalwork, is a metal pin used to keep two parts in a certain relation to each other and to keep them from moving or slipping.

finished, this steel is called *hot-rolled steel* because it was rolled while it was hot. Work that must be bent or twisted may be made of hot-rolled steel.

Some ingots are passed through rollers with grooves that press the hot steel into smaller sizes and different shapes (see Fig. 277). Soon the ton of red-hot steel gets longer and thinner; it comes from the rollers like a fiery snake about 200′ long — all in a few minutes. Thus round, flat, and various other shapes shown in Fig. 32 are formed. (See Fig. 283.)

Some ingots are rolled into wide sheets. *Sheet steel* is in gages thinner than .250″.

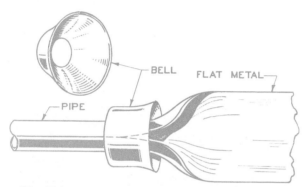

Fig. 284. Drawing a Flat Piece of Metal Through a Bell to Form a Pipe

Fig. 285. Drawing Cold Steel Through a Die, Making Cold-Drawn Steel
(Courtesy Union Drawn Steel Co.)

Plate steel generally is heavier, in fractional thicknesses of ¼″ and up. (See § 789.)

Pipe and tubing are made by *drawing* or pulling a flat piece of steel through a bell-shaped ring called a *bell*, Fig. 284.

After cooling, hot-rolled steel has a thin, black, hard skin or crust which is called *scale*. When a smooth or *bright finish* (see § 740) is desired on the steel, this scale is cut away by a machine in the machine shop.

330. Cold-Rolled Steel

Cold-rolled steel is made from hot-rolled steel, that is, steel that was rolled while hot and rolled again when cold. The hot-rolled steel is a little larger than the final size of the cold-rolled steel; thus it is reduced only a small amount by the cold rolling.

The bars or rods of hot-rolled steel, when cold, are first put in water containing *sulfuric acid* (see § 101). This is known as *pickling* (see §§ 1096-1097). It also removes the black skin or *scale* from the surface of the steel. The sulfuric acid is washed off by dipping the bars in pure water and then in *lime water*.[3] When dry, the bars are rolled while cold between highly finished rollers under great pressure. This gives them a smooth, bright finish and a very exact size. They are then called cold-rolled steel and are often used without any more *finishing* or *machining*.[4]

331. Cold-Drawn Steel

Cold-drawn steel is also made from hot-rolled steel which has been cooled and pickled, and which is a little larger than the final size of the cold-drawn steel. The size is thus reduced only a small amount at a time by *drawing* or by pulling the bar or rod of cold steel through *straightening rolls*.

Cold-drawn steel has a smooth and bright surface and is very exact in size and shape. It

---

[3]*Lime water* is lime mixed with water. It keeps acid, which may still be on the steel, from eating further into it. After the steel is dry, the lime water which remains on the steel keeps it from rusting until it can be rolled.

[4]*To machine* means to cut using a machine.

is often used without any more finishing or machining, Fig. 285.

A *wire-drawing die* (also called a draw-plate) used for drawing wire is shown in Fig. 286. Wire is made by drawing the steel through this die, Fig. 287.

Compare drawing with *drawing out* in section 938.

332. Cast Steel

To *cast* means to form into a certain shape by pouring into a form. When melted steel is poured into molds (see § 961) in the same way as *cast iron* (see § 300) to make a certain shaped object, the resulting metal is called *cast steel*. The object is known as a *steel casting*.

Review Questions

1. From what materials is steel made?
2. What is the difference between cast iron, wrought iron, and steel?
3. Name five kinds of furnaces used for making steel.
4. Describe the Bessemer process of making steel.
5. What is the difference between steel and pig iron?
6. Describe the *BOP* steelmaking process.
7. What is an ingot?
8. For what is Bessemer steel used?
9. Describe the open-hearth process of making steel.
10. For what is open-hearth steel used?
11. What type of furnace makes the greatest quantity of steel?
12. Describe the crucible process of making steel.
13. For what is crucible steel used?
14. How is steel made in the electric furnace?
15. For what is electric steel used?
16. Name the two classes of steel.
17. Name the three grades of carbon steels.
18. What is low-carbon steel? How much carbon is in it?
19. For what is low-carbon steel used?

20. What is medium-carbon steel? How much carbon is in it?
21. For what is medium-carbon steel used?
22. What is high-carbon steel? How much carbon is in it?
23. For what is high-carbon steel used?
24. What does annealing mean?
25. What is drill rod? How is it made?
26. What is hot-rolled steel?
27. What is sheet steel?
28. What is scale on steel?
29. What is cold-rolled steel?
30. What is cold-drawn steel?
31. What is cast steel?
32. What kind of steel would you use to make a cold chisel?

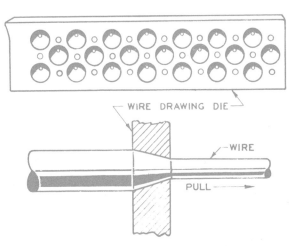

Fig. 286. Die for Drawing Wire

Fig. 287. Drawing Steel Wire (Courtesy U. S. Steel)

Coordination

Words to Know

alloy steel
annealed
arc furnace
basic-oxygen process
Bessemer converter
Bessemer steel
carbon steel
carbon tool steel
cast steel
chromium
cold-drawn steel
cold-rolled steel
crucible furnace
crucible steel
dowel pin
drawplate
drill rod
electric furnace
electric steel
graphite
hardening
hearth
heat of steel
high-carbon steel
high speed steel

hot-rolled steel
induction furnace
ingot
ingot mold
ladle
lime water
low-carbon steel
machine steel
machining
medium-carbon steel
mild steel
open-hearth furnace
open-hearth steel
oxygen
pickling
pipe drawing
plate steel
sheet steel
special alloy steel
steel casting
steel plate
tool steel
tungsten
wire drawing die

Mathematics

1. How many pounds of carbon are there in one ton of 5-point carbon steel?

2. How many pounds of carbon are there in one ton of 30-point carbon steel?

3. If one cubic inch of rolled steel weighs 0.2833 pounds, how much will a bar 4″ x 4″ x 4′ weigh?

Drafting

1. Draw a wire drawing die which can be held and used in a vise in the shop.

Social Science

1. Write a story telling of what value steel is to civilization.

Occupational Information

1. Write a biography of Sir Henry Bessemer.

2. List the steps necessary in making a cold chisel, beginning with iron ore.

Birth of a Beam — Hot Steel Starts at Left and at Right Is Ready for Finishing Touches (Courtesy U.S. Steel)

Steel Alloys

343. What Is an Alloy?

An *alloy* is a mixture of two or more metals melted together to form a new metal which is different from either of the original metals. If a metal is mixed with even a small percentage of another metal, it changes; the color may be changed, it may become harder, the *melting point* may be lowered, etc. (See Table 12, p. 161.) For example, *copper* and *zinc* melted together make *brass;* brass is thus an alloy (see §§ 368, 369, and 371). *Lead* and *tin* melted together make *solder;* solder is an alloy (see §§ 375, 376, and 851). (See also *metallurgist* in § 19.)

344. Special Alloy Steel

Alloy steel contains one or more of the following metals: *nickel, chromium, manganese, molybdenum, tungsten,* and *vanadium.* By adding these metals to steel, special steel can be made that is harder, tougher, or stronger than ordinary carbon steel. These alloy steels are described in the following sections.

345. Nickel Steel

Nickel steel contains *nickel* which adds strength and toughness to steel. (See § 379.)

Nickel steel does not rust easily and is very strong and hard. It is also *elastic,*[1] that is, it can stand vibration, shocks, jolts, and wear. It is used for wire cables, shafts, steel rails, automobile and railroad car axles, and *armor plate.*[2]

346. Chromium Steel

Chromium steel, also known as *chrome,* contains a bluish-white metal called *chromium.* It gives hardness to steel, toughens it, makes the grain finer, and causes it to resist rust, stains, shocks, and scratches. Chromium steel receives some of its color from chromium and is used for safes, rock crushers, and automobile bearings.

Chromium is the basis for *stainless steel,* also known as *high-chromium steel,* which contains from 11 to 26% chromium. It has a lasting, bright, silvery gloss and is used for sinks, table tops, tableware, pots and pans, cutting tools and instruments, candlesticks, plates for false teeth, dental tools, ball bearings, fine measuring tools and instruments, moldings, automobile parts, and valves for airplane engines. It does not rust or *corrode.*[3] It is sometimes brightly polished and used for mirrors.

---

[1]*Elastic* means the ability of a material to return to its original size and shape after bending or twisting.

[2]*Armor plate* is a thick plate or sheet of metal that cannot be punched easily; it is used to cover the sides of battleships.

[3]*Corrode* means to wear away gradually as iron does by rusting. It is a chemical reaction of impurities in the metal to moisture and oxygen.

347. Chrome-Nickel Steel

Chrome-nickel steel, also known as *nickel chromium steel,* contains both *chromium* and *nickel.* It is hard and strong and is used for *armor plate* and automobile parts such as gears, springs, axles, and shafts. Nickel and chromium also are alloyed in large proportions to produce the nickel-chromium type *stainless steels.*

348. Manganese Steel

Manganese steel contains *manganese* which is a hard, brittle, grayish-white metal. It purifies and adds strength and toughness to steel. Manganese steel remains hard even when cooled slowly. It is so very hard that it is difficult to cut. *Wear* makes the surface harder. It is usually *cast* into shape. (See § 990.) Manganese steel can stand hard wear, strain, hammering, and shocks. It is used for the jaws of rock and ore crushers, steam shovels, chains, gears, railway switches and crossings, and safes.

349. Molybdenum Steel

Molybdenum steel contains *molybdenum;* it is called "Molly" for short in steel mills. Molybdenum, a silvery-white metal which is harder than silver, adds strength and hardness to steel and causes it to stand heat and blows. Molybdenum steel is used for automobile parts, high-grade machinery, wire as fine as 0.0004″ in diameter, ball bearings, and roller bearings.

350. Tungsten Steel

Tungsten is a rare, heavy, white metal which has a higher melting point than any other metal. Tungsten adds hardness to steel, makes a fine grain, and causes it to withstand heat. Tungsten is used as an alloying element in tool steels, high-speed steels, and in cemented carbide. It is also used to armor plate.

Cemented-tungsten carbide, also called *tungsten carbide,* is the hardest metal made by man, being nearly as hard as diamond. It is made by molding *powder metals,* including tungsten and carbon. (See §§ 319 and 961.) Tungsten-carbide metal-cutting tools retain their hardness at red-heat temperatures as high as 1700° F. without significant softening. The metal is expensive, so a small piece is *silver soldered* (see § 864) on the tip of a *cutting tool.* (See §§ 556 and 1186.) It is also used for *wire-drawing dies* (see § 331). Such tools, known as *carbide tools,* cut two to four times faster than high-speed steel. They must be sharpened on *diamond grinding wheels* or silicon-carbide grinding wheels.

351. Vanadium Steel

Vanadium steel contains *vanadium* which is a pale, silvery-gray metal. It is brittle and resists *corrosion.* Vanadium gives lightness, toughness, and strength, and makes a fine grain in steel. Vanadium steel can withstand great shocks. It is used for springs, automobile axles and gears, and for other parts that vibrate when in use.

Chromium-vanadium steel, also called *chrome-vanadium steel,* is hard and has great *tensile strength.*[4] It can be bent double while cold and is easy to cut. Chromium-vanadium steel is used for automobile parts such as springs, gears, steering knuckles, frames, axles, connecting rods, and other parts which must be strong and tough but not brittle.

352. High-Speed Steel (HSS)

High-speed steel, also known as *high-speed tool steel* or *self-hardening steel,* is an alloy steel. Its carbon content may range from about 0.70 to 1.50%. Several different grades are available. It generally contains one or more special alloys such as *chromium, vanadium, molybdenum, tungsten,* and *cobalt.* The first four of these elements are carbide formers. They combine with carbon to form carbides such as chromium carbide, vanadium carbide, etc. These carbides are very hard and wear

---

[4]*Tensile strength* means the ability of a metal to withstand stretching without tearing apart. It is indicated by the weight in pounds per square inch (of the cross section area of the metal being tested) which will cause it to pull apart.

resistant; therefore, they make good cutting tools. Cobalt is not a carbide former, but it increases the *red-hardness* of the cutting tool. Thus the tool retains its hardness at higher temperatures. High-speed steel cutting tools retain their hardness without significant softening at temperatures up to about 1100° F., a temperature indicated by a dull, red heat. On the other hand, carbon-tool steel cutting tools start to soften significantly at temperatures above 450° to 500° F. This temperature is indicated by a dark brown or purple heat color.

High-speed steel is made in an electric furnace (see § 325). It is used for cutting tools such as drills, reamers, countersinks, lathe-tool bits, and milling cutters. (See § 489.) It is called high-speed steel because cutting tools made of this material can be operated at speeds twice as fast as those for tools made of carbon-tool steel (see § 328 and Table 17, p. 214). High-speed steels cost about two to four times as much as carbon-tool steels.

353. Cast Alloys

A number of cast alloys has been developed for use in making metal cutting tools. Some trade names[5] include Stellite, Rexalloy, Armaloy, and Tantung. The cast alloys are used as brazed tips on tool shanks, as removable tool bits in lathe toolholders, and as inserts in toolholders and milling cutters. They retain their hardness at high temperatures, up to about 1500° F. Cast alloy cutting tools may be operated at cutting speeds 50 to 75% faster than for high-speed steel cutting tools.

Cast alloys are metals composed of the elements cobalt 35 to 50%, chromium 25 to 35%, tungsten 10 to 20%, nickel .01 to 5%, and carbon 1.5 to 3%. Small amounts of other elements are sometimes added. Since they do not contain iron, they are not steels. They are very hard and cannot be machined, except by grinding.

[5]A *trade name* is a name or term commonly accepted and used in preference to a more technical description.

354. Spark Test of Iron and Steel

The *spark test,* also known as the *emery wheel test,* is one way of discovering what kind of iron or steel was used in an object. Different kinds of iron and steel will give different sparks. The iron or steel is held lightly against the grinding wheel and the sparks carefully watched. Four things should be noticed about the sparks:

(1) The color of the spark.
(2) The shape of the spark as it leaves the grinding wheel and after it explodes.
(3) The quantity of sparks.
(4) The distance the sparks shoot from the grinding wheel.

The color, shape, quantity, and length of the sparks tell how much *carbon* (see § 319) the steel contains, Fig. 301. The sparks are small pieces of metal that have been cut away and heated by rubbing. Instead of the sparks of carbon steel dying out after they leave the grinding wheel, they suddenly broaden, light up, become much brighter, and then disappear. This shows that something is happening after the spark leaves the wheel. The carbon in the particle of metal unites with the *oxygen* in the air. Carbon unites readily with oxygen. This causes more forceful burning. The more carbon in the steel, the brighter and greater in number are the sparks.

The sparks of steel containing much carbon are very numerous and follow around the *circumference* of the wheel (see § 30). Also, the more carbon in the steel the more the sparks look like stars. As the carbon in the steel decreases, the sparks become a darker red and appear more or less like straight lines instead of stars.

A good way to find the amount of carbon in a piece of steel is to compare its sparks with the sparks of a piece of steel of which the carbon content is known. Files contain a high percentage of carbon, usually about 1.30% (See § 328 and Table 6, page 142.) If the

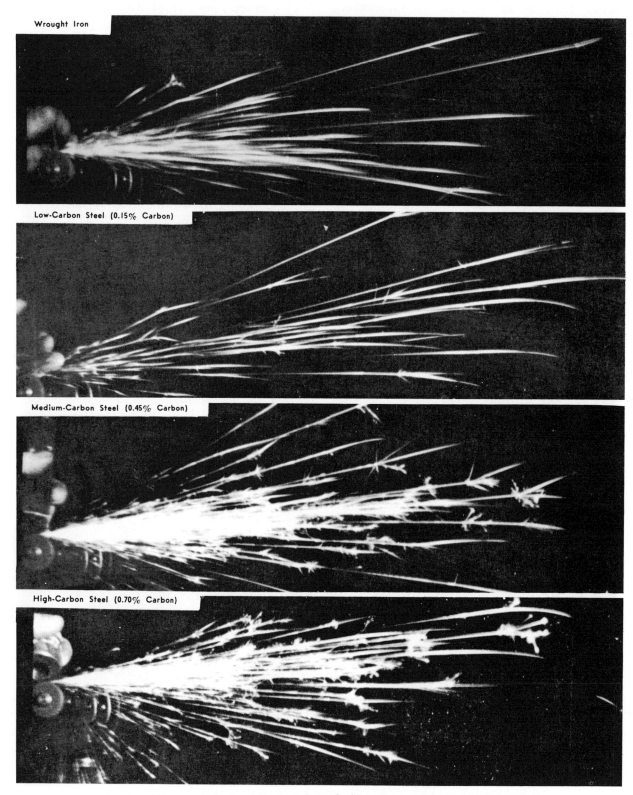

Wrought Iron

Low-Carbon Steel (0.15% Carbon)

Medium-Carbon Steel (0.45% Carbon)

High-Carbon Steel (0.70% Carbon)

Fig. 301. Spark Tests of Iron and Steel. (See Section *354* and Table V.)
(Courtesy National Bureau of Standards)

steel that is being tested gives more starlike sparks than the file, it contains more carbon. If fewer starlike sparks are produced and of a darker red color, the steel contains less carbon than the file. Table 7 describes the different sparks of iron and steel.

355. Description of Iron and Steel Sparks

Wrought iron contains almost no carbon. It gives long, dull red sparks which shoot off in straight streaks, widen in the middle, and then disappear. (See § 302.)

Low-carbon steel contains a small percentage of carbon and gives sparks similar to wrought iron sparks, except that they are brighter and explode or branch out a little. (See §§ 318 and 326.)

Medium-carbon steel contains from 0.30 to 0.60% carbon. (See § 327.) The sparks are brighter with more starlike explosions.

High-carbon steel contains from 0.60 to 1.50% carbon. (See § 328.) It gives off white sparks all of which explode immediately into bright stars and disappear; many of these sparks follow around the circumference of the wheel. This shows that high-carbon steel *burns* easier and quicker than low-carbon steel. This must be remembered when heating high-carbon steel to prevent its *burning*. (See § 1063.)

High-speed steel has a high-alloy content. It gives off sparks which are like the sparks of wrought iron, look like broken lines, and appear dark in color. (See § 302.) They end in dull red, pear-shaped flames a short distance from the wheel. Some of the sparks shoot or branch off at *right angles* (90°) to the main line of sparks. (See § 1065.)

Cast alloys and many *alloy steels* give no light at all.

Table 7
DESCRIPTIONS OF IRON AND STEEL SPARKS
(See Sections 354 and 355)

METAL	DESCRIPTIONS OF SPARKS
WROUGHT IRON	Long, dull red, with dark tips. Shoot off in straight streaks which widen in the middle and then disappear.
STEEL: Low-carbon (also called *Machine Steel* or *Mild Steel*)	Same as wrought iron sparks, except brighter and explode or branch out a little.
Medium-Carbon	Bright with starlike explosions. More and brighter as carbon is increased. The more carbon in the steel the more the sparks look like stars.
High-Carbon (also called *Tool Steel* or *Carbon Tool Steel*	White and explode immediately into bright stars, then disappear. Many sparks follow around wheel. Thus high-carbon steel burns easier and quicker than low-carbon steel; this must be remembered when heating high-carbon steel to keep from burning it.
ALLOY STEEL: High Speed Steel	Sparks of high speed steel are dark, broken lines which end in dull red, pear-shaped sparks a short distance from wheel. Some sparks shoot or branch off at *right angles* to main stream of sparks. Many alloy steels give no sparks at all.

The beginner should first practice with pieces of iron and carbon steel, the carbon contents of which are known; then he may gradually add different alloy steels. He will thus form pictures in his own mind of the different sparks for different metals.

356. SAE and AISI Steel Specifications

The *Society of Automotive Engineers, Inc.,* developed a number system which indicates the chemical composition of the different kinds of steels. This system is known as the *SAE Steel Numbering System* and also as the *SAE Steel Specifications*. Any *steel catalog*

Table 8
SAE STEEL NUMBERING SYSTEM
(See section 356)

KIND OF STEEL	NUMBERS
Carbon Steels	1xxx
Nonsulfurized Carbon Steels .	10xx
Example	1018
Resulfurized Carbon Steels (Free Machining)	11xx
Example	1112
Example	1113
Nickel-Chromium Steels	3xxx
1.25% Nickel, 0.65% Chromium	3140
Molybdenum Steels	4xxx
Molybdenum 0.20 or 0.30% ..	40xx
Example	4024
Chromium Steels	5xxx
Chromium 0.25, 0.40, or 0.50%	50xx
Example (0.25% Chromium, 0.46% Carbon)	5046
Example (1.45% Chromium, 1.00% Carbon)	52100
Chromium-Vanadium Steels ...	6xxx
Nickel-Chromium-Molybdenum Steels (Nickel less than 1.00%)	8xxx
Silicon-Manganese Steel	92xx
Nickel-Chromium-Molybdenum (Nickel 3.25%)	93xx

gives this numbering system. Only examples of it are given in Table 8.

Each kind of steel has a number with four or five digits, usually four digits. The first digit of the number tells what kind of steel it it: 1 is a *carbon steel*, 3 is a *nickel-chromium steel*, etc. For the simple *alloy steels*, the second digit of the number generally (but not always) tells the approximate percentage of the major alloy represented by the first digit. The last two or three digits tell the average percentage of carbon the steel contains in *points* or hundredths of 1% (one percent, 1.00%). Thus, 3140 means that nickel-chromium steel is about 1% nickel and 0.40% carbon. (See nickel steel in § 345.)

Some steels have numbers with five digits; the last three digits indicate the percentage of carbon as, for example, 52100 means that the *chromium steel* contains about 2% chromium (1.45) and about 1.00% carbon. (See *chromium steel* in § 346.)

It may help to know that SAE 1018 or 1020 steel is recommended for parts to be heat treated by *case hardening* or *carburizing* (see § 957). SAE 1113 steel is not recommended for parts to be forged or heat treated, but it machines easily. (See Unit 46.)

A different kind of numbering system is used for the identification of tool steels and stainless steels. The identification system for these steels is included in standard handbooks for machinists.

357. AISI Steel Specifications

The *American Iron and Steel Institute* (AISI) has developed a system which also tells the kind of furnace used to make the steel. Letters are used together with the same numbers used in the SAE systems:

B is acid, Bessemer-carbon steels.

C is basic open-hearth or basic-electric furnace carbon steels.

E is electric furnace alloy steels.

Thus, the letter E in the number means that

the steel was made in the electric furnace (see § 325).

358. Properties of Metals

There are many different types of steel and other metals used in modern industry. Each is selected for its special properties. In fact, engineers sometimes specify the properties required in a particular situation. Then metallurgists and other scientists must develop an alloy or combination of materials having the required properties. This has been especially true for space vehicles.

Common important properties are density (relative weight), tensile strength, hardness, hardenability, ductility, malleability, brittleness, toughness, elasticity, fusibility, weldability, response to heat treatment, heat resistance, corrosion resistance, and machinability. People working with metal should be acquainted with these properties. Manufacturer's catalogs and technical handbooks give specific data for those needing it.

Tensile strength is the strength necessary to pull apart a one-inch square piece of metal. It is usually expressed in pounds per square inch (psi). This is also called *ultimate* tensile strength. *Yield point* is the point (usually much less) at which the metal first begins to stretch with no increase in load.

Hardenability is that property which enables a metal to harden completely through to its center when heat treated. (See §§ 351 and 352.) Some steels rank low in hardenability. This means that they *harden* to a shallow depth at the surface, and the core is softer at the center of the metal. The alloy steels generally rank higher in hardenability than the carbon steels of similar carbon content.

Hardness is the resistance to being dented or penetrated. Some steels are hard enough to cut softer steels. Hardness of some steels can be increased by heat treating. Several kinds of hardness testers are available. (See §§ 1166-1168.)

Ductility means that the metal can be drawn out or stretched without breaking. Aluminum, steel, and copper are very ductile and can be easily formed into wire.

Malleability means that the metal can be hammered, rolled, or bent without cracking or breaking. The more malleable a material, the easier it is formed.

Brittleness means that a material suddenly cracks and breaks easily. Glass is brittle, as is gray cast iron and hardened steels. Usually brittleness is related to hardness.

Toughness in metal refers to its resistance to breaking, bending, stretching, or cracking. It is related to hardness and brittleness. High-carbon steel is very brittle when hardened, but *tempering* reduces hardness and increases toughness (see § 954).

Elasticity is the property which enables metal to be bent or twisted and still return to its original shape without being deformed. Spring steel must be elastic.

Fusibility is the property which enables metal to liquefy easily and join with other metals while liquid.

Weldability is the degree to which a metal may be welded with good fusion and a minimum loss of other properties. Gray cast iron is more difficult to weld without special techniques because the heat required for fusion frequently causes brittleness. The weld may often crack in the process of cooling.

Heat treatment is the heating or cooling of ferrous metals in the solid state to change their mechanical, microstructural, or corrosion-resisting properties. (See Unit 46.) *Hardening temperature* is the point at which the grain structure of steel becomes fine and may be hardened. *Heat-resisting metals* (high-speed steel, cast alloys, and titanium alloys) retain their strength and resist oxidation at relatively high temperatures.

Corrosion resistance is the ability of steel to resist rusting and other chemical action. Chromium, nickel, and titanium in stainless steels increase this resistance. Anodizing and clad-

Table 9
PHYSICAL PROPERTIES OF STEELS

AISI No.	CONDITION OF STEEL	TENSILE STRENGTH (PSI)	BRINELL HARDNESS	MACHINABILITY RATING (B 1112=100)
C 1018	Hot Rolled	69,000	143	52
C 1018	Cold Drawn	82,000	163	65
B 1112	Cold Drawn	82,500	170	100
B 1113	Cold Drawn	83,500	170	130
Ledloy 375	Cold Drawn	79,000	155	220
C 1045	Cold Drawn	103,000	217	60
C 1095	Hot Rolled	142,000	293	..
C 1095	Water Quenched at 1450° F, Tempered at 800° F:	200,000	388	..

ding of aluminum also increase corrosion resistance.

Machinability is the ease with which metal can be machined while maintaining maximum tool life, cutting speed, finished appearance, or any combination of these factors. Traces of finely dispersed lead in steel greatly increase machinability with no great loss of other properties. Sulfur in steel also increases machinability, but is detrimental to welding and other hot forming qualities. Resulfurized and leaded screw steels are widely used for machining parts in lathes and automatic screw machines. Machinability ratings have been computed on the basis of B1112 steel equaling 100. High numbers indicate comparatively better machinability.

Table 9 indicates some properties of several types of steel which are frequently used in industry and in metalworking classes.

Review Questions

1. What is an alloy?
2. Make a list of the alloys mentioned in this unit.
3. Name some of the special alloy steels. For what are they used?
4. What is high-speed steel? For what is it used?
5. Why is it called high-speed steel?
6. What are cast alloys? For what are they used?
7. What is the use of tungsten carbide?
8. Of what use is the spark test?
9. What is meant by SAE 1018 steel?
10. What is the SAE number of carbon steel containing 0.30% carbon?
11. Define machinability.
12. Define the meaning of tensile strength.
13. Define hardenability.
14. Define toughness as applied to steel.

Coordination

Words to Know

AISI Steel Specification	high-speed tool steel
alloy	manganese steel
armor plate	molybdenum
carbide tool	molybdenum steel
cemented-tungsten carbide	nickel
chrome-nickel steel	nickel-chromium steel
chrome steel	nickel steel
chrome-vanadium steel	powder metal
corrode	SAE Steel Number
corrosion	satellite
cutting tool	silver solder
elastic	spark test
emery wheel test	stainless steel
hardenability	tensile strength
high-chromium steel	tungsten carbide
	tungsten steel
	vanadium
	vanadium steel

Social Science

1. Write a story telling what use stainless steel is to civilization.

Occupational Information

1. Write a story telling how wire is made.

Nonferrous Metals

Aluminum, Copper, Brass, Bronze, Zinc, Silver, Gold, Magnesium, Lead, Tin, Babbitt, Pewter, and Nickel

366. Aluminum

Aluminum is a brilliant, silvery white metal. It is one of our most useful metals. Although it costs four or five times as much per pound as iron or steel, it weighs only about one-third as much. It also machines much faster (two to three times deeper cuts at double speeds), costs less to transport, usually needs no finish to prevent rusting, is quite maintenance free, and it has a natural surface beauty. Thus it may be more economical than other metals when all things are considered.

Aluminum is a good conductor of electricity and heat, yet reflects heat when highly polished. It can be drawn into very fine wire, spun or stamped into deep forms, and hammered or rolled into thin foil sheets, some only 0.00025″ thick. (See hammering and spinning §§ 833 and 1215.)

It melts at about 1200° F. and is cast in molds when 100° to 300° hotter. As this is about one-half the temperature required for iron or steel, aluminum is preferred for casting in schools or other situations where initial equipment cost and safety are important. (See Unit 48.)

Anodizing is an electrochemical treatment which imparts a beautifully colored weather-resistant surface on aluminum.

Working with Aluminum

At one time joining aluminum parts was largely limited to using screws, rivets or other mechanical means, but this problem has been solved by improved welding and brazing techniques. (See Units 42 and 43.) Sometimes entire sections are machined from one large plate for greater strength, Fig. 306.

Fig. 306. Skin-Mill Cuts Integral Ribs into Type 7075 Aluminum Plate in making 100-foot Rivetless Wing Structures for Supersonic Aircraft (Courtesy Reynolds Metals)

Fig. 307. Arkansas Bauxite Mine (Courtesy Reynolds Metals)

Fig. 308. Breaking Top Crust of Alumina in Electrolytic Reduction Pot (Courtesy Reynolds Metals)

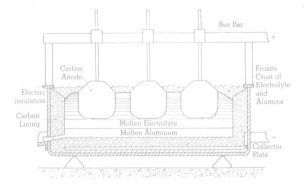

Fig. 309. Electricity in an Aluminum Reduction Pot Passes from Carbon Anodes through the Electrolyte Depositing Molten Aluminum on the Carbon Lining. (Courtesy Aluminum Co. of America)

Working with aluminum is somewhat different than working with steel but not necessarily difficult. Different cutting angles and speeds are recommended as well as different techniques in welding, brazing or soldering. Be sure to check instructions and available references for these specifications before beginning work.

Pure aluminum is too soft for many uses but numerous modern alloys make it ideal for many jobs.

Some of the common uses for aluminum are: aircraft and rocket parts, bodies for railroad cars, trucks, and trailers, pistons, blocks,

Fig. 310. Aluminum Alloy Ingots Clad with High Purity Liners Enter Hot Rolling Mill. Liners Form Thin Corrosion-resistant Coating on Finished Sheet. (Courtesy Reynolds Metals)

Fig. 311. Aluminum Extrusion Emerging from Hydraulic Press (Courtesy Reynolds Metals)

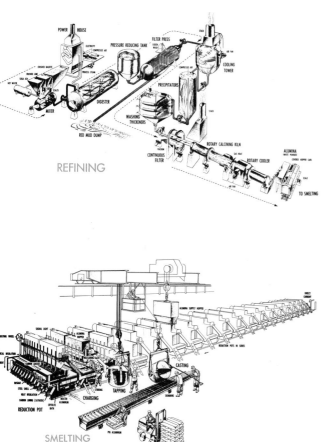

REFINING

SMELTING

and heads for engines, tubing, window frames, structural members, cooking utensils, machine tool housings, foil and collapsible tubes for packaging.

Refining Aluminum

Aluminum is made from an ore called *bauxite*, Fig. 307. Important deposits are in Arkansas, Washington, Oregon, and parts of Canada. It usually is mined in open pits, then refined where cheap electrical power is available in quantity. One-sixth of the earth's crust is aluminum ore, but it is difficult to extract the pure metal.

Crushed bauxite is changed chemically to aluminum oxide — a white powder called *alumina*. This is smelted into aluminum by removing the oxygen in large electrolytic tanks called *reducing pots*, Fig. 308. Electricity passes from carbon anodes through a mixture of the alumina and molten *cryolite* (sodium aluminum flouride). This heats the mixture, and molten aluminum is deposited at the bottom where it can be drained off, Fig. 309. Later the metal is often alloyed, and cast, rolled, or *extruded*[1] into many shapes, Figs. 310, 311, and 312.

FABRICATING ALUMINUM
FROM PIG TO MILL PRODUCT

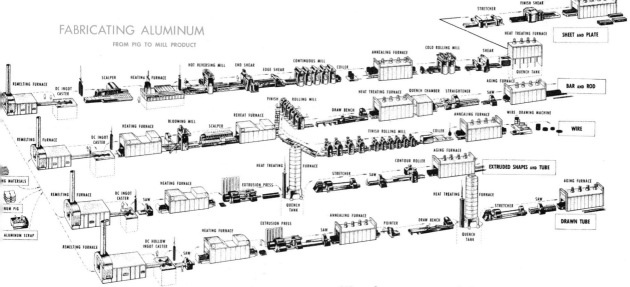

Fig. 312. Refining, Smelting, and Fabricating Aluminum Stock (Courtesy Aluminum Co. of America)

[1]Extrude means to push heated material through a specially shaped opening to form a long strip in that shape. Extruding is much like squeezing toothpaste from a tube.

367. Aluminum Alloys

Other metals are often added to the pure aluminum to improve its physical properties. Industry uses hundreds of varieties of aluminum alloys. These are formed by using various alloying elements and by using various ways of tempering or hardening the metal. The tensile strength for various aluminum alloys may range from 13,000 to 81,000 pounds per square inch. In 1954 the Aluminum Association adopted a standard alloy designation system. In Table 10 four typical alloys are compared with soft and hardened steel.

Aluminum Association Alloy Designations

In the A.A. number, the first digit identifies the major alloying element as follows: 1= 99% pure aluminum or better, 2=copper, 3= manganese, 4=silicon, 5=magnesium, 6= magnesium and silicon, 7=zinc, 8=other elements, 9 is special. These are the main alloying metals. Refer to the footnote showing the composition of each alloy.

The other three digits have technical meanings which will be omitted here. The part of the number following the hyphen (-T36) is the temper designation and a "-0" (1100-0) indicates the alloy to be soft and workable.

Typical Aluminums

Number 1100-0 pure aluminum is naturally soft, ductile, and more resistant to chemical attack than any of the alloys. It is the form most commonly used for hammering and shaping when maximum strength is not needed. However, it gradually becomes hardened as it is worked. When this happens, it must be *annealed*. This is done by heating to 650° F. This temperature is indicated by the heat at which blue carpenters' chalk turns whitish. Then allow the heated aluminum to air cool slowly.

Number 2024 is often used for structural or machining applications. Number 6061 has a number of applications which would require high tensile strength and good welding properties such as railings and protective guards. Number 7075 is used for aircraft and other work where the highest strength is required. These three are strong, heat-treatable alloys.

Metal suppliers furnish data books and charts which list the alloys, meanings of number designations, properties of the alloys and recommended applications. Refer to these for more complete data. Two broad classes of alloys are the wrought alloys for cold working, and the casting alloys.

Table 10
PHYSICAL PROPERTIES[a] OF ALUMINUMS

A.A. No.[b]	Old No.	Hardness (Br)	Tensile Strength (psi)	Cold Work-ability	Machin-ability	Weldability Gas Arc Spot			Corrosion Resistance
1100-0[c]	2S	23	13,000	A+	D	A	A	B	A
2024-T36[d]	24S	130	73,000	E	A	D	B	A	B
6061-T6[e]	61S	95	41,000	C	B	(Good after heat treating)			
7075-T6[f]	75S	150	76,000	D	A	D	D	B	B
C1018 Hot Rolled Steel		143	69,000						
C1095 Tempered Steel		388	200,000						

[a]Code for working properties: A=excellent, B=superior, C=good, D=poor, E=not recommended.

[b]That part of the Aluminum Association Number following the hyphen denotes the amount and kind of temper treatment used in manufacture.

[c]No. 1100-0 is 99% pure soft aluminum.

[d]No 2024 contains 4.5% copper, 1.5% magnesium, and 0.6% manganese.

[e]No. 6061 contains 1.0% magnesium, 0.6% silicon, 0.25% copper, 0.25% chromium.

[f]No. 7075 contains 5.6% zinc, 2.5% magnesium, 1.6% copper, and 0.3% chromium.

368. Copper

Copper is the oldest metal known to man. It is a tough, reddish brown metal. As found in copper mines, located in Arizona, Michigan, Montana, and Utah, it is known as *copper ore*. It is sold in the form of wire, bars, plates, and sheets. Table 34 on page 440 shows the *gages* that are used to measure copper wire, etc.

Copper is the second best carrier of electricity; silver is the best. (See §§ *372* and *442*.) Copper is used for electric, telephone, and telegraph wires and cables. (See § *445*.) It is also used for water heaters, wash boilers, pipes, kettles, window and door screens, roofing, etc. In art metalwork it is used for bowls, vases, ashtrays, etc. Copper is used in *brass*, *bronze, monel metal,* and *German silver* which contains about 50% copper, 30% *zinc*, and 20% *nickel*. German silver is used as a substitute for silver in making inexpensive jewelry. Many beautiful copper articles for the home can be made in the school shop or at home by *hammering* or *spinning* as explained in Units 41 and 58. *Copperplating* is explained in section *1118*. (See also *coppersmith*.)

The surface of copper becomes green in moist air. This may be seen on copper which has not been cleaned for some time. (See § *1109*.) Copper hardens when hammered but can easily be softened or *annealed* (see §§ *836-837*). (See §§ *571* and *1110,* and Tables 11 and 12.)

369. Brass

Brass is a yellow copper-base alloy in which the principal alloying element is zinc. There are many varieties of brass, ranging from about 60% copper and 40% zinc, to as high as 90% copper with only 10% zinc. It can be made harder by adding *tin* or certain other alloying elements. Brass does not discolor nor corrode as fast as copper. It is used for ornamental work, musical instruments, inexpensive jew-

Fig. 313. Copper Wire Will Be Drawn from these Cast "Wire Bars" (Courtesy Anaconda Co.)

elry, screws, door hinges, window locks, small gears, and other parts for watches and clocks.

Many lovely brass articles for the home can be made in the school shop or the home workshop by *hammering* or *spinning* as explained in Units 41 and 58. Like copper, brass hardens when hammered, but by heating and cooling it can be softened (see §§ *836-837*). (See Tables 11 and 12.)

370. Bronze

Bronze is a copper-base alloy in which the principal alloying element is tin. Sometimes it also contains *zinc* or other alloying elements. It is harder and lasts longer than *brass*. It is also more expensive because of the high cost of tin. Bronze is used for bells, statues, medals, propellers, *bushings,*[2] bearings for machines, etc. The one-cent coin, or penny, is bronze. "Bronze" welding rods are more like brass, and today there is no clear defining line between these two alloys of copper. (See Tables 11 and 12.)

371. Zinc

Zinc is a brittle, bluish white metal. It is used as a *coating* for iron and steel for protection against rust. This coating with zinc is called *galvanizing* and is done by dipping the metal into melted zinc. As the zinc cools, it forms into *crystals* which make the spotted

[2]A *bushing* is somewhat like a bearing; it is removable sleeve or collar, as on the handle bar post on a bicycle.

Fig. 314. Galvanized Steel (Courtesy Inland Steel Co.)

color on *galvanized steel*, Fig. 314. *Galvannealed* metal is heated after being galvanized, producing a coating of alloyed zinc and iron or steel. These coated metals are used for wire fences, eave troughs, metal roofing, water tanks, water pipes, buckets, automobile frames, signs, etc.

Zinc is also used in *German silver, brass, bronze* and *dry cell batteries*. Like copper and brass, zinc hardens when hammered. It can be softened by heating and slow cooling. Zinc-based alloys are also widely used in producing die castings for items such as engine blocks for small gas engines, housings for small engines, carburetors, parts of typewriters, car door handles, and parts of portable electric tools.

372. Silver

Silver[3] is a beautiful, shiny, white metal. It is found in the form of *silver ore*. Pure silver is soft. It is used for ornamental work, jewelry, tableware, mirrors, and coins. United States silver coins contain nine parts silver and one part copper. Silver is the best carrier of electricity (see § 442).

Sterling silver is silver with only a little copper added to make it harder. It is used for the best tableware and jewelry.

German silver is made of copper, zinc, and nickel; it does not contain silver. (See Tables 11 and 12.)

373. Gold

Gold is a precious, heavy, beautiful, bright yellow metal. Five bushel baskets of gold would be worth about a million dollars. Grains and *nuggets*[4] of gold are found in river gravels and sands of the seashore. Gold is also found in rocks in the form of *gold ore*. Pure gold is too soft for articles of general use and it is therefore mixed with copper, silver, or other metals.

Gold can be *hammered* into very thin leaves, called *gold leaf*, much thinner than the thinnest tissue paper. The art of covering something with gold leaf or gold powder is called *gilding*. One pound of gold can be made into a wire one mile long.

Gold is used for ornamental work, jewelry, coins, and fillings in teeth. United States gold coins were made of 90% gold and 10% copper.

The purity of gold is measured in karats. Pure gold is 24 karats. Thus, an 18-karat gold ring is made of 18 parts by weight of gold and 6 parts by weight of some other metal. Jewelers abbreviate karat as *k*; for example, 14k gold. They use the spelling *carat* for the weight of precious stones.

White gold, a silvery metal used for jewelry is 15 to 20% nickel added to gold, thus changing the color from gold to white.

Green gold has a greenish cast and is used for jewelry. The 15-karat green gold, for example, is 15 parts gold, 8 parts silver, and 1 part copper. (See Tables 11 and 12.)

---

[3] *Silver* was once called *luna* which in Latin means moon. It was so named because of its likeness to the bright full moon in color.

[4] A *nugget* is a natural lump of precious metal.

Table 11
COMPOSITION[5] AND USES OF ALLOY METALS THAT CONTAIN NO IRON

METAL	PERCENT								USES
	ANTIMONY	COPPER	GOLD	LEAD	NICKEL	SILVER	TIN	ZINC	
Babbitt .... (See § 377)	7	4					89		Bearings and bushings for machines and engines.
Brass (Average) (See § 369)		75						25	Ornamental work, bearings, bushings, musical instruments, inexpensive jewelry, screws, door hinges, window locks, parts for watches and clocks.
Bronze .... (See § 370)		90					10		Bells, statues, medals, coins, propellers, machine bearings, bushings.
German silver .. (See § 368, 372)		50			20			30	Inexpensive jewelry.
Monel metal ... (See § 379)		33			67				Chemical equipment, motor boat propellers, cooking utensils.
Pewter .... (See § 378)	5	3					92		Tableware, ornamental work.
Solder .... (See § 851)				50			50		For fastening metals together.
Sterling silver .. (See § 372)		7.5				92.5			Tableware and jewelry.
White gold .... (See § 373)			80		20				Jewelry.

374. Magnesium

Magnesium is a silver-white, light malleable metal much lighter than aluminum. It is abundant in nature but is always alloyed with another metal because of its high cost. It is usually alloyed with aluminum, contributing to the strength and heat resistance of aluminum. In the pure form it burns easily, giving off an intense white light, so it must be handled with care. It is found in sea water, in minerals, in the chlorophyll of green plants, in seeds, and in animal bones.

Table 12
MELTING POINTS[6] OF METALS

METAL	DEGREES FAHRENHEIT[7]
Solder, 50-50 (See Section 851)	400
Pewter	420
Tin	449
Babbitt	462
Lead	621
Zinc	787
Magnesium	1204
Aluminum	1218
Bronze	1675
Brass	1700
Silver	1761
Gold	1945
Copper	1981
Iron, Cast	2200
Steel	2500
Nickel	2646
Iron, Wrought	2700
Tungsten	6150

[5] *Composition* means the makeup of a material.

[6] The *melting point* of a metal is the temperature at which it melts.

[7] The *Fahrenheit thermometer* was invented by a German named *Gabriel Fahrenheit*. On this thermometer the freezing point of water is 32 degrees and the boiling point is 212 degrees. F is the abbreviation for Fahrenheit.

375. Lead

Lead is a very heavy, bluish gray, poisonous metal. Men working with lead must guard against a disease called *lead poisoning*. Lead is found in the form of *lead ore*. It is the softest metal in general use. Lead is so soft that it can be scratched with the fingernail and can easily be cut with a knife. When freshly cut, it is very bright; this brightness soon disappears when exposed to the air. Water and air, however, have less effect upon lead than upon any other metal and so it is very useful for *lead pipes, storage batteries*, etc.

More lead is used in making *white lead*, which is used in paint, than for any other purpose (see § 397). *Red lead* is explained in section *1100*.

Lead is also used in *pewter, solder*, and other metals (see §§ 378 and 851). It is also used to cover electrical *cables* (see § 445). (See Tables 11 and 12.)

376. Tin

Tin is a shiny, silvery metal. It is found in the form of *tin ore*. After the tin is removed from the ore, it is poured in the form of blocks which are called *blocked tin*. "*Tin cans*" are made of steel and then coated with tin. The tin is less than 1% of the weight of the can. Tin does not rust. Very few articles are made of pure tin. It is used in making *bronze, babbitt metal, pewter, solder*, and other metals, and when used it always increases the hardness and whitens them.

Tin is soft and can be *hammered* or *rolled* into very thin sheets. *Tin foil*, which is tin in sheets, is made as fine as .0002″ thick. It was long used for wrapping tea, tobacco, drugs, cheese, candy, etc., to keep away air and moisture. Because tin is expensive, *aluminum foil* is now used. Tubes, as for toothpaste, were made of tin.

Tin-plate is "*sheet iron*" or *sheet steel*[8] (see §§ 329, 789) coated with tin used for pots, pans, cans, pails, metal roofing, etc. It is often incorrectly called "tin." Copper kettles, used for cooking, are coated with tin to keep the poison from copper out of the cooked food.

Section *791* tells about things that can be made from "tin cans." (See Tables 11 and 12.)

377. Babbitt

Babbitt, also called *babbitt metal*, was invented by Isaac Babbitt. There are two kinds of babbitt. When the base metal or principal metal is lead, it is called lead-base babbitt. When the base metal is tin, it is called tin-base babbitt.

It is an *alloy* (see § 343) made of *lead, tin, copper*, and *antimony*.[9] It does not rust and is used for bearings in machines and engines because it is strong, tough, and lasts long. (See Tables 11 and 12.)

378. Pewter

Pewter is a silvery white metal. It is made of 92 parts *tin*, 5 parts *antimony*, and 3 parts *copper*. Other grades of pewter contain a little more or less tin. The lower grades contain some *lead*. The best pewter contains the least lead because it gives pewter a dull appearance.

Pewter is also called *Britannia metal* because it was first made in Britain. It is used for tableware and ornamental work. Pewter can be made bright and cheerful by polishing as explained in section *1098*. (See §§ *831, 1098*, and Tables 11 and 12.)

379. Nickel

Nickel, a hard, tough, shiny, silvery metal, is found in the form of ore. It does not rust and can be polished to a very bright, silvery finish. It is therefore used for *plating* iron and brass to improve appearance (see § *1117*). Nickel plating may be used under chromium plating on trim for automobiles and appliances. It is also used to toughen steel. Such

---

[8] *Sheet steel* is steel in broad, thin sheets.
[9] *Antimony* is a bright, silvery white, hard, and brittle metal. It is melted into other metals to give them hardness. (See Section 687.)

steel is called *nickel steel* (see § 345). The five-cent coin (a nickel) is made of one part nickel and three parts *copper.*

Monel metal is a white metal containing about two-thirds *nickel* and one third *copper* along with small amounts of other elements. It is strong, tough, does not rust, and shines like silver. Monel metal is used for chemical and cooking equipment, motor boat propellers, and the like.

White gold, a silvery metal used for jewelry, is 15 to 20% *nickel* added to *gold. German silver* contains about 20% *nickel.* (See Tables 11 and 12 on page 161.

Review Questions

1. Describe copper. In what states is copper ore mined?
2. For what is copper used?
3. What parts of an automobile are made of copper? Why are these made of copper?
4. What is brass? For what is it used?
5. What is bronze? For what is it used?
6. Why is the Statue of Liberty, which is molded sheet copper, green in color?
7. Which is more expensive, brass or bronze? Why?
8. Describe zinc. For what is it used?
9. What is meant by galvanizing?
10. For what is silver used?
11. For what is gold used?
12. How is the purity of gold measured?
13. How many karats in pure gold?
14. Describe aluminum. For what is it used?
15. Why is aluminum used for kitchenware?
16. Describe lead. For what is it used?
17. Describe the mining, refining, and fabrication of aluminum stock.
18. Describe tin. For what is it used?
19. What is babbitt metal? For what is it used?
20. What is pewter? For what is it used?
21. Describe nickel. For what is it used?

Coordination

Words to Know

alumina	green gold
anodize	hammering
antimony	karat
babbitt metal	lead ore
bauxite	luna
block tin	magnesium
Britannia metal	monel metal
carat	nickel plating
composition	nugget
cryolite	pewter
extrude	ore
Fahrenheit	reducing pot
thermometer	sheet steel
foil	silver
galvanized steel	spinning
galvannealing	sterling silver
German silver	"tin can"
gilding	tinplate
gold	white gold
gold leaf	white lead
gold ore	

Mathematics

1. How many ounces of copper, zinc, and nickel are there in one pound of German silver if it contains 50% copper, 30% zinc, and 20% nickel?

2. How many ounces of silver and copper are there in 1 pound of United States silver coins *if* they contain 7 parts silver and 3 parts copper?

Social Science

1. Write a story entitled, "The Importance of Copper in Our Daily Lives."
2. Describe the Statue of Liberty.

Occupational Information

1. What is lead poisoning? Write about it and tell in which occupations it must be guarded against.
2. Write a biography of Isaac Babbitt.

Metal Towers and Conductors Help to Insure a Steady Supply of Electric Power for Homes and Industry (Courtesy Aluminum Company of America)

Part **IV**

Care of Equipment

Oils and Cutting Fluids

386. What Is Friction?

When you rub the palms of your hands together, they get warm, even hot. The Indians rubbed sticks together to start fires. A wire bent back and forth quickly gets hot. When a tool is sharpened on the grinding wheel it gets hot. Metal surfaces that rub get hot. This is caused by *friction*.

Friction wears out machines and slows up their speed. Sometimes friction is useful to keep parts such as the brakes on automobiles and airplanes from slipping. Surfaces which should slip must have the friction reduced as much as possible. (See §§ 571, 1053, 1062, and 1065.)

387. What Is a Lubricant?

To *lubricate* means to make smooth and slippery. A *lubricant* is oil, grease, or other material that makes surfaces smooth and slippery and reduces the heat, wear, and vibration caused when they rub together. (See *cutting fluids*, § 571.)

388. Kinds of Oils

There are three main kinds of oils:
(1) *Mineral oils.*
(2) *Animal oils.*
(3) *Vegetable oils.*
Mineral oils are obtained from products which come from the earth. *Petroleum* is by far the leading source.

Animal oils, such as *lard oil, sperm oil*, and *neat's-foot oil*, are oils obtained from the fats of animals. *Fish oils* are oils obtained from fish, such as herring, salmon, sardine, and cod. These oils are thick and have a strong fish odor.

Vegetable oils, such as *linseed oil* and *castor oil*, are oils obtained from plants and vegetables, especially from the seed. All of these oils are described in this unit.

389. Petroleum

Petroleum, or *crude oil*, is a thick *mineral oil*. The United States consumes more petroleum than any other country. From petroleum we get:
(1) *Gasoline.*
(2) *Kerosine.*
(3) *Naphtha.*
(4) *Benzine.*
(5) *Lubricating oil.*
(6) *Cylinder oil.*
(See also *paraffin*, § 443.)

390. Gasoline

Gasoline is produced from *petroleum*. When mixed with air, this engine fuel is very explosive, easily set on fire, and more powerful than dynamite. Gasoline freezes at 50° F. below zero. It is sometimes used in the shop for cleaning, especially for washing dirty and greasy machine parts. However, this is very dangerous because the parts striking together or the *friction* caused by rubbing may spark, catch on fire, and result in bad burns or even death.

391. Kerosine

Kerosine, also known as *coal oil*, is a light oil. It is obtained from *petroleum* and is used in lamps for lighting and as a fuel in jet engines. It is also used for heating, and especially for cleaning greasy and dirty machine parts. Kerosine is sometimes used as a lubricant in cutting hard metals (see Table 15).

392. Naphtha

Naphtha (pronounced *naf-tha*) is obtained from *petroleum*. It is used for cleaning, especially for washing dirty and greasy machine parts. Naphtha is very explosive when mixed with air.

393. Benzine

Benzine is obtained from *petroleum*. It is used for cleaning and is very explosive when mixed with air.

394. Lubricating Oil

Lubricating oil, or *machine oil*, is obtained from *petroleum*. It is used to oil the rubbing surfaces, called *bearing surfaces*, of machinery. Its stiffness or thickness, viscosity, can be measured by the length of time in seconds that a standard amount of oil at determined temperatures can flow through a hole. Stiff or thick oil drips slowly.

A medium-heavy oil is used for general machine oiling. It has a Saybolt universal viscosity rating of 250 to 500 seconds at 100° F., and may be called Type C. A thinner oil (70 to 100 second rating) is used in reservoirs such as at lathe spindles and may be called spindle oil or Type A.

Bed Way Lubricant is a heavy oil (300 to 500 seconds) for sliding surfaces such as cams and lathe beds. Gear Lubricant is used on gears not running in oil to reduce gear noise. (See Table 14 for typical brands.)

395. Cylinder Oil

Cylinder oil, or *motor oil*, is a thick oil obtained from *petroleum*. It is used for oiling hot parts, such as the *pistons* which slide in the *cylinders* of an engine. It is not recommended for machine tool lubrication.

396. Graphite

Graphite is a form of *carbon* (see § 319). It is found in rocks and is used in electric furnaces. Graphite is black, very soft, slippery and used for lubricating some machine parts, especially where there is low speed and much

Table 14
TYPICAL LUBRICATING OILS FOR MACHINES

Company Name	Saybolt Universal Viscosity Rating in Seconds at 100°F.		
	100 Second: Type A LIGHT (SPINDLE OIL)	150-240 Sec.: Type B MEDIUM LIGHT	250-500 Sec.: Type C MEDIUM HEAVY
Mobile	Velocite Oil 10	Gg. Vactra Oil Light	Gg. Vactra Hvy. Med.
Pure	Spindle Oil D	Puropale Medium	Puropale Hvy. Med.
Shell	Vitrea Oil 923	Vitrea Oil 27	Vitrea Oil 33
Sinclair	Cadet Oil A	Warrior Oil	Commander Oil B
South Bend Lathe	CE 2017	CE 2018	CE 2019
Standard (Ind.)	Spindle Oil C	Indoil #15	Indoil # 31

Note: This partial listing of typical brands is given as an aid in procuring comparative grades from the company of your preference. (Courtesy South Bend Lathe, Inc.)

heat. It lasts longer than oil, does not get gummy, and does not attract dust. Much of it is used in making pencils and paints.

397. White Lead

White lead is made from *lead* (see § 375). It is a white powder which is mixed with *linseed oil* to make paint. White lead is poisonous. It may be thinned with *lubricating oil* for lubricating purposes. (See §§ 596, 643, and 656.) *Red lead* is explained in section 1100.

398. Lard Oil

Lard oil is an *animal oil* obtained from lard or hog's fat. It is the best *cutting oil* but is too expensive to be used pure; thus it is often mixed with cheaper oil. It has a different odor than other lubricants. There is a number of different grades of lard oil. (See §§ 388, 643, and Table 15.)

399. Sperm Oil

Sperm oil is oil from the head of the *sperm whale,* one of the largest mammals. It is thinner than lard oil and is used to oil fine, delicate machinery. Sperm oil is sometimes used for cleaning.

400. Neat's-Foot Oil

Neat means cattle, such as bulls, oxen, cows, and sheep. Neat's-foot oil is produced by boiling the feet and shin bones of these animals in water. It is a pale yellow color and is used to soften leather.

401. Grease

Grease is animal fat, such as soft lard or *tallow,* which is the heavy fat from sheep, oxen, cows, and calves. *Cup grease* is a thick, yellowish grease such as is used to lubricate automobile parts. It is made from the fat of animals. The term grease is often used for thick petroleum oils, too.

402. Glycerin

Glycerin is a thick, oily, syrupy, colorless, odorless, liquid obtained from fats or produced synthetically from alcohol. It has a sweet taste and is used as a medicine. Glycerin freezes at a very low temperature and is thus used as a base for anti-freeze solutions for automobile radiators. It is also sometimes used for oiling machines, especially engines.

403. Linseed Oil

Raw linseed oil is a yellow oil crushed and pressed out of the seeds of the *flax plant.* It is used a great deal for paint and varnish.

Boiled linseed oil is made from raw linseed oil by combining certain drying materials with it and then heating it. Boiled oil is a little thicker than raw oil; it dries quicker than raw oil when used in paint.

404. Castor Oil

Castor oil is the oil pressed out of the *castor bean.* While it is a very good lubricant, and is often used in racing cars, it sets after heating so it must be drained immediately after an engine is stopped.

405. Turpentine, Mineral Spirits

Turpentine, called *turps* for short, is an oil obtained from trees. It is explosive when mixed with air. Turpentine is used in paint and for cleaning. (See § *1106.*) It is sometimes used to make the cutting of hard metal easier. As turpentine is toxic (poisonous) to the skin, mineral spirits is often used as a substitute. (See Table 15.)

406. Cutting Fluids

The term *cutting fluid* applies to various types of *cutting oils, cutting coolants, cutting solutions,* and *cutting compounds.* Cutting fluids are applied to metal cutting tools such as drills, taps, dies, reamers, power saws, lathe cutting tools, and milling cutters to make them cut easier. The cutting fluids may be applied with an oil can, or a brush to taps, dies, or drills. The fluid is pumped onto the cutting tools on power saws, lathes, milling machines, and on all types of production machine tools.

Cutting fluids improve the cutting or machining of metals in the following ways:

(1) Carry away heat.

(2) Cool the cutting tool and the work.

(3) Lubricate the face of the cutting tool and the chip.

(4) Prevent the *adhesion* or pressure welding of a *built-up edge* on the cutting tool. A built-up edge is caused by a small metal chip sticking to the cutting edge of a cutting tool.

(5) Aid in flushing away chips.

(6) Improve the quality of the machined surface.

(7) Increase tool life by reducing tool wear.

(8) Permit higher cutting speeds than those used for dry machining.

Most commercially available cutting fluids can be classified under two groups which include *cutting oils* and *emulsifiable oils*. The principal ingredient in cutting oils is *mineral oil*. Other ingredients such as lard oil, sulfur, and chlorine are added to improve their qualities for heavy-duty machining operations.

From the standpoint of composition there are, in general, six types of cutting fluids:

(1) Lard oil.

(2) Mineral oil (straight).

(3) Lard and mineral oil combinations, with or without chlorine or sulfur.

(4) Sulfurized mineral oils.

(5) Sulfurized and chlorinated mineral oils.

(6) Emulsifiable oils (soluble oils).

Emulsifiable oil is often called *soluble oil* or *water-soluble oil*. It is a special type of mineral oil which mixes or disperses evenly in water. Hence, an emulsifiable oil (soluble oil) cutting fluid is made by *adding the oil to the water* (never water to oil), thus forming a milky-white colored solution. The proportion

of water and oil varies according to the severity of the machining operation. For average severity machining operations on ferrous metals, 1 part oil is added to 20 parts water. For average grinding operations 1 part oil is added to 40 parts water. Emulsifiable oil solutions have excellent lubricant and coolant qualities, and they are relatively inexpensive.

Lard oil is one of the best cutting fluids, but it is so expensive that it is seldom used pure. It generally is mixed with less expensive mineral oils. When mixed with mineral oil it is called *mineral-lard oil*.

Soda water is a mixture of water, soft soap, and *sal soda*.[1] It is used as a coolant and keeps work from rusting after it is machined. It is sometimes used instead of emulsifiable oil solutions or other commercial cutting compounds.

Kerosine is sometimes used as a cutting fluid for light-duty machining operations on aluminum alloys and brass. In some cases it is mixed with either mineral oil, lard oil, or both.

407.   Cutting Fluid Selection

For efficient cutting or machining of metals a recommended cutting fluid should be selected. Metals such as cast iron and magnesium, however, are often cut dry. Cast iron contains graphite which lubricates the tool as it cuts. Lard oil or mineral-lard oil should be used for all hand tapping, threading, and reaming of wrought iron and steel. See Table 15 for more complete information. (See also §§ 571, 643, 656, 1031.)

408.   Oil Can

Oil cans are made in a wide variety of shapes and sizes. Small cans are usually used around precision machinery, Fig. 318.

409.   Oil Hole and Oil Groove

An *oil hole* is a small hole through which oil flows to a surface which must be oiled. An *oil groove*, which is usually connected to an oil hole, is a small groove by means of which oil is spread evenly over a surface to be oiled.

---

[1]*Sal soda* is washing soda also called *soda ash*. Its chemical name is *sodium carbonate* and its chemical symbol is Na_2CO_3.

410. Grease Cup

A grease cup is a small, covered cup screwed into a machine near a surface which must be greased. The grease, which is put into the cup, is forced through a hole to the surface to be greased.

411. Oil Cup

An oil cup, Fig. 318, is a small, covered glass or brass cup screwed into a machine near a surface which must be oiled. (See Fig. 521.) The oil, which is put into the cup, flows through a hole to the surface to be oiled.

412. Oil Tube

An oil tube, or *oil pipe,* is a tube or pipe through which oil flows to rubbing parts of machinery (see *tubing* and *tube fittings,* §§

779-781). It is much used on automobiles. A clogged oil tube may be cleaned out by forcing air through it. (See also *oil-tube drills,* § 573.)

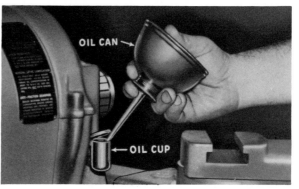

Fig. 318. All Bearings Should Be Oiled Regularly
(Courtesy South Bend Lathe, Inc.)

Table 15
CUTTING FLUIDS FOR CUTTING COMMON METALS

Metals	Power Sawing	Drilling	Reaming	Threading	Turning	Milling	Grinding
Carbon Steels Malleable Iron	EO, MO, ML	EO, Sul, ML	ML, Sul, EO	Sul, ML, EO	EO, Sul, ML	EO, Sul, ML	EO
Wrought Iron Stainless Steels Tool Steels High-Speed Steels	EO, ML, MO	EO, Sul, ML	ML, Sul	Sul, ML, EO	EO, Sul, ML	EO, Sul, ML	EO
Gray Cast Iron	Dry, EO	Dry, EO	Dry, EO	Dry, EO, ML	Dry, EO	Dry, EO	EO, MO
Aluminum Alloys	Dry, EO, MO	EO, MO, ML	ML, MO, EO	ML, MO, EO, K	EO, MO, ML, K	EO, MO, ML	EO, MO
Copper Base Alloys Brass Bronze	Dry, MO, ML, EO	EO, MO, ML	ML, MO, EO	ML, MO, EO	EO, MO, ML	EO, MO, ML	EO
Magnesium Alloys	Dry, MO	Dry, MO	Dry, MO	Dry, MO	Dry, MO	Dry, MO	Dry, MO

Key:

    K — Kerosine
    L — Lard Oil
  MO — Mineral Oils
  ML — Mineral-Lard Oils
  Sul — Sulfurized Oils, with or without chlorine
  EO — Emulsifiable (soluble) Oils and Compounds
  Dry — No cutting fluid

413. Oiling a Machine

All rubbing surfaces, called *bearings*, should be oiled once a day with *lubricating oil*. A machine should be stopped when it is to be oiled. A drop or two of oil in each *oil hole* is enough. If more than this is put in, the oil is wasted because it runs out on the machine; it should then be wiped off with a clean rag. Oil holes and oil cups should be kept clean, Fig. 318. (See §§ 1180-1181.)

414. Pipe System for Cooling Tools and Work

When many machines have to be supplied with a *coolant*, it is pumped from a large tank to the machines through pipes. It then flows back to the tank to be strained and used over and over again. (See §§ 572 and 1031 and Figs. 176 and 451.)

415. Waste Can

Oily rags, if left lying around the shop, may cause a fire. In fact, the oil in the rags can combine with the *oxygen* in the air to cause the temperature to increase so that under unfavorable conditions the result may be *spontaneous combustion,* which means that the fire starts by itself through chemical reaction. Oily rags should be put in a *waste can* made of metal until they can be burned. The waste can should stand on legs and have a cover, Fig. 319. The cover keeps out the air

and the legs keep the bottom of the can off the floor to reduce the chances of the fire spreading if the rags should start to burn in the can.

Review Questions

1. What is friction?
2. What is meant by a lubricant?
3. Name the three kinds of oils.
4. From where do we get mineral oil?
5. What are animal oils?
6. Name some vegetable oils.
7. What oils are obtained from petroleum?
8. Of what use is kerosine in a machine shop?
9. Of what use is lubricating oil?
10. Of what use is cylinder oil?
11. What is graphite?
12. What is white lead? For what is it used?
13. What is lard oil?
14. How can you tell lard oil from other oils?
15. What is sperm oil?
16. What use is made of neat's-foot oil?
17. For what is cup grease used?
18. For what is linseed oil used?
19. For what is castor oil used?
20. For what is turpentine used?
21. List the ways in which cutting fluids improve the machining of metals.
22. What are the principal ingredients used in cutting oils?
23. What are six common types of cutting fluids?
24. How is emulsifiable cutting fluid prepared?
25. What kind of cutting fluid is generally recommended for use in hand reaming, tapping, and threading operations?
26. What is an oil groove?
27. Why should a waste can have legs and a cover?
28. What does spontaneous combustion mean?

COVER KEEPS AIR OUT

FOR OILY RAGS

LEGS KEEP BOTTOM OFF FLOOR SO THAT FIRE WILL NOT SPREAD IF IT STARTS IN CAN

Fig. 319. Safety Container

Coordination

Words to Know

animal oil
castor oil
chlorine
coal oil
coolant
crude oil
cup grease
cutting lubricant
cutting oil
cutting solution
cylinder oil
fish oil
flax plant
friction
gasoline
glycerin
grease cup
kerosine

lard oil
linseed oil
lubricate
machine oil
mineral oil
mineral spirits
motor oil
naphtha
neat's-foot oil
oil can
oil cup
oil groove
oil hole
oil pipe
petroleum
piston
sal soda
soap water

soda ash
soda water
soluble oil
sperm oil
sperm whale
spontaneous
    combustion

sulfur
spout
tallow
turpentine or "turps"
vegetable oil
waste can

Mathematics

1. Seven quarts, 6 pints, and 2½ gallons are taken from a barrel containing 55 gallons of oil. How much is left?

Social Science

1. Write a story telling how petroleum helps civilization.

2. What are the products of petroleum?

Note Lubricant on a Three-High Bar Mill — Upper Bar is Entering the Mill, and the Structural Shape Emerges Below
(Courtesy Aluminum Company of America)

Conveyor carries 1200-pound molds from loading to pouring area. Molds cool as they continue traveling on conveyor overhead. (Courtesy Link-Belt, Division of FMC Corporation)

Belts

421. Why Is a Belt Used?

A belt may be used to:

(1) Carry power from one *pulley* to another (see § 422).

(2) Change the speed of a pulley.

(3) Change the running direction of a a pulley (see § 426).

(4) Carry materials, as a *conveyor*.

422. Relation Between Belt and Pulley

A *pulley* is a wheel on which a belt runs. *Cone pulleys*, also called *step pulleys*, have several steps and are used in pairs, Fig. 325, to get different speeds. The pulley from which power is taken is called the *driving pulley*, or *driver*; the pulley to which power is carried is called the *driven pulley*. Flat pulleys are larger in diameter at the center of the rim than at the edges because the belt always runs to the highest point on the pulley. This highest part or top of the rim is called the *crown* of the pulley.

When the driving pulley is enlarged or the driven pulley is decreased in size, the *speed* of the machine is increased. The increase in speed also means less *power* just as an automobile has more power in low gear than in high. A *variable speed pulley*, Fig. 326, is one where the effective size of a pulley can be varied throughout a continuous range of sizes

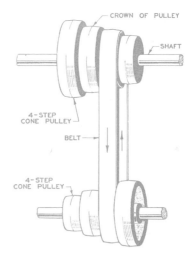

Fig. 325. Cone Pulleys

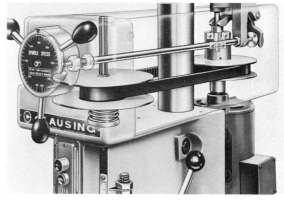

Fig. 326. Variable-Speed Pulley
(Courtesy Clausing Div., Atlas Press Co.)

173

without steps. As more tension is placed on the V-belt (see § *424*), it is pulled closer to the center of the variable pulley, making its effective size smaller. *Always adjust a continuously variable speed pulley while it is running or the belt may be damaged.*

423. Materials Used for Belts

Belts are made of leather, rubber, special composition materials, canvas, rope, and chain. *Leather belts* are made from the hides of bulls, cows, and steers. *Rubber belts* are used in moist or damp places. They are worth-

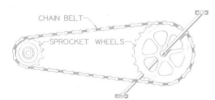

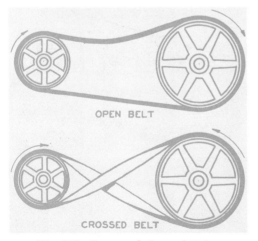

Fig. 327. Chain Belt

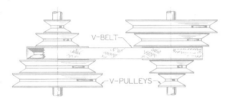

Fig. 328. V-Belt

Fig. 329. Open and Crossed Belts

less in dusty or oily places. *Canvas belts* are used where leather or rubber belts would be ruined. *Rope belts* are used because they are cheap and easy to install. *Chain belts*, Fig. 327, are used for high-speed, heavy loads, and close connections. An example is the chain belt on a bicycle.

424. V-Belts

V-belts run on *V-pulleys*, Fig. 328. Both the belts and the pulleys are V-shaped (see Fig. 411). V-belts are most often made of a combination of rubber, cord, and canvas; they are *endless* (see § *431*). A common use of the V-belt and V-pulley is the *fan belt* on an automobile. V-belts are used where pulleys are close together. For heavy loads, several V-belts are often used side by side.

425. Single-Ply, Two-Ply, and Three-Ply Belts

A *single-ply belt* is one thickness of material, usually leather. A *two-ply belt* is two thicknesses cemented together. (See Fig. 335.) A *three-ply belt* is made of three thicknesses. Single-ply belts are used on pulleys up to 12″ in diameter, two-ply belts on 12″ to 20″ pulleys, and three-ply belts on 20″ to 30″ pulleys.

426. Open and Crossed Belts

An *open belt* connecting two pulleys makes them run in the same direction, Fig. 329. A *crossed belt* changes the direction.

427. Measuring Length of Belt

The length of a new belt may be measured by placing a rope or *measuring tape,* Fig. 330, sometimes called a *tapeline,* over the pulleys on which the belt will run. Another way is to measure the length of the old belt with the rope or measuring tape.

To shorten an old belt, pull the belt tightly around the pulleys, letting the ends lap over each other. The amount of *overlap* is the amount to be cut off.

428. Hair Side vs. Flesh Side of Leather Belt

The smooth side of the leather belt, known as the *grain side* or *hair side,* should run next to the pulley. It is not the roughness of the surface but the close fit between the belt and pulley that reduces slipping and sliding. The smooth, hair side of the belt carries more power than the rough, *flesh side.*

429. Belt Fasteners

There are many ways of fastening the two ends of a flat belt together. They may be fastened with *rawhide*[1] *lacing, steel hooks* or *wire hooks, glue, cement,* or *rivets.* Many patented *metal belt fasteners* are sold and the manufacturers' directions should be followed in using them. *Wire-belt lacing* and *steel-belt lacing* are shown in Fig. 331.

430. Lacing a Leather Belt with Rawhide Lacing

The steps in lacing a leather belt with rawhide lacing are:

Step 1: Cut both ends of the belt square. A sharp knife and a *square* should be used.

Step 2: Choose the *lacing.* Lacing for belts up to 2″ wide should be ¼″ wide; for 2″ to 4″ belts the lacing should be ⁵⁄₁₆″ wide; for belts over 4″ the lacing should be ⅜″ wide.

Step 3: Punch holes in both ends of the belt with a *belt punch,* Figs. 332 and 333(A). Large belts should be punched further from the ends and sides of the belt. Holes should be at least ¾″ apart from center to center. The holes in one end should be directly opposite the holes in the other end to make the ends match. Belts up to 2″ wide should have three holes in each end. Wider belts should have more holes, but

always an odd number of holes, as 3, 5, 7, 9, etc.

Step 4: Put the belt around the shafts or pulleys to be connected and hold the ends together.

Fig. 330. Measuring Tape

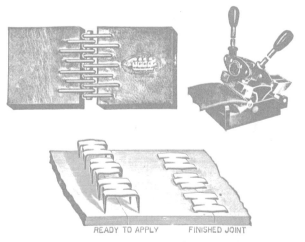

Fig. 331. Wire-Belt Lacings and Steel Belt-Hooks (Courtesy Clipper Belt Lacer Co. and The Bristol Co.)

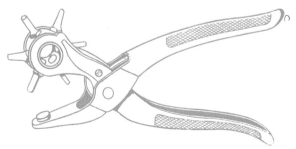

Fig. 332. Leather Punch

---

[1] *Rawhide* is untanned, dressed skin of cattle; it is very hard and tough when twisted into strips and dried.

Step 5: Cross the lacing on the outside of the belt, Fig. 333(D). The pulley side of the belt should have no crossed lacing, Fig. 333(E). Start on the pulley side of the belt; pull the lacing through the center holes 1 and 4 and even up the ends, Fig. 333(B). Pull tight. Continue to pull end X as follows:

Down through hole 2, as in Fig. 333(C) and (D),

Up through 3,

Down through 2,

Up through 3,

Down through 4,

Up through 1,

Down through 4.

Pull the end Y

Down through hole 5, as in Fig. 333(C) and (D),

Up through 6,

Down through 5,

Up through 6,

Down through 1,

Up through 4,

Down through 1.

Step 6: Make two small holes, 7 and 8, about ½″ from holes 1 and 4 with a *belt awl*, Fig. 334, to fasten the ends of the lacing. Push the ends of the lacing through holes 7 and 8. Cut off the unnecessary lacing so that ends about ½″ long are left. Cut short *slits* in these ends of the lacing near the belt and twist the ends around to keep them from slipping out. Wider belts can be laced by the same plan.

431. Cementing Belts

The best way to fasten the ends of a leather belt together is by *cementing*. It is then known as an *endless belt*. It is the safest way because nothing can catch or cut the hands. A *cemented belt* is also stronger than a *laced belt* which is weakened by the punched holes. A cemented belt runs smoother than a laced belt on which the lacing forms a hump which thumps against the pulleys. A joint which begins to separate should be recemented at once.

Good *glue* is a fine cement for leather belts, although special *belt cements* are sold. Meas-

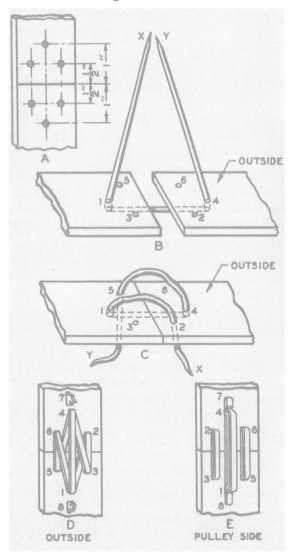

Fig. 333. Lacing Leather Belt

Fig. 334. Belt Awl

ure the length of the belt (see § 427) and add enough for the *lapped joint* shown in Fig. 335. To cement a belt, first shave down the ends of the belt so that when they are lapped on each other the joint will be the same thickness as the rest of the belt; then cement the ends together by clamping between two boards until the cement dries. Put paper between the belt and the boards to keep the boards from sticking to the belt. (See § 432.)

432. The Running Direction of a Cemented Belt

Single-ply belts should run with the smooth side, which is called the *grain side* or *hair side*, next to the pulley (see Fig. 335). The grain side of the belt will carry more power than the *flesh side* which is the rough side. *Two-ply belts* can run only with the grain side next to the pulley because the flesh sides are cemented together. The cemented *laps* will not be as likely to loosen or curl up when run in the direction shown in Fig. 335 as they might if run in the opposite direction.

433. Care of Leather Belts

Lubricating oil should be cleaned off belts with gasoline. After cleaning, a leather belt may be wiped with a cloth moistened with *neat's-foot oil* to keep it from drying and cracking (see §§ 394, 400). *Belt dressing* is a sticky mixture which contains asphalt, *pitch* (see § 841), or *rosin* (see section 852). It is sometimes put on a belt to make it sticky and to keep it from slipping on the pulleys. Such belt dressing is harmful to the belt and should be used only when it is more costly to shut down the machine than to ruin the belt.

434. Shifting Belts

To *shift* a belt means to change it from one pulley to another. Anyone working around machines must know how to shift belts quickly, skillfully, and safely. It is best for the beginner to stop the machine and then pull the belt on the pulley by hand. By doing this he will learn how to *lead* a belt on or off a pulley.

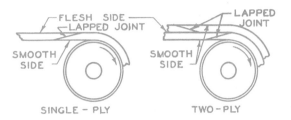

Fig. 335. Cemented Belt Joints for Endless Belts

Later, with a little experience, he can learn how to shift the belt with a stick or the handle of a large wrench while the machine is running. The belt should first be put on the *driven pulley* (see § 422). It is dangerous to shift a running belt with the bare hand.

Review Questions

1. Give three reasons for using belts.
2. What is a pulley? Describe a cone pulley.
3. Describe a V-pulley.
4. What is the difference between a driving pulley and a driven pulley?
5. What is meant by the crown of a pulley? Of what use is it?
6. Describe the variable speed pulley.
7. Name six kinds of belts and give reasons for using each kind.
8. What is a single-ply belt? Two-ply? Three-ply?
9. What is an open belt?
10. What is a crossed belt? Why is it used?
11. What is a measuring tape?
12. How would you take the measurements for a new belt?
13. How would you measure a belt that has to be shortened?
14. What is rawhide?
15. Which side of a leather belt is placed next to the pulley? Why?
16. Name six kinds of belt fasteners.
17. What is the best way to fasten the ends of a leather belt? Why?
18. What is an endless belt?
19. What is neat's-foot oil? For what is it used?

Coordination

Words to Know

belt awl	lapped joint
belt cement	leather belt
belt fastener	measuring tape
belt glue	metal belt fastener
belt punch	metal lacing
belt rivet	open belt
cemented belt	overlap
chain belt	power
cone pulley	pulley
crossed belt	rawhide lacing
crown	rubber belt
driving pulley	single-ply belt
or driver	speed
endless belt	steel-belt lacing
flesh side	step pulley
grain side	tape line
hair side	three-ply belt

variable speed pulley	V-pulley
V-belt	wire-belt lacing

Mathematics

1. How long a belt (open belt) is needed to connect two 14″ pulleys which are 6′ apart from center to center?

2. What is the speed of a 12″ driven pulley if the speed of a 16″ driving pulley is 450 RPM?

3. The speed of a 10″ driving pulley is 650 RPM. What size driven pulley is needed to run 800 RPM?

4. What is the perimeter of a 20″ pulley?

Occupational Information

1. Tell how accidents may occur while persons are working around belts.

2. Write a story telling how leather is made.

Assembly Operation on a Crawler Tractor on a Conveyor-type Assembly Line
(Courtesy International Harvester Co.)

Electrical Equipment

440. Why Is Electricity Important to the Metalworker?

In every shop there are motors, fuses or circuit breakers, cords, switches, plugs, and lights. Many of the tools are also operated by electricity, as the *portable electric drill* (see § 522), *electric soldering copper* (see § 850), *portable electric grinder* (see § 1028), and *electric marker* (see § 1130). These get out of order; parts need to be replaced, fuses must be replaced, and motors must be oiled and cared for.

Every person should know how to keep from getting *shocks* (see § 473). (See *electrician*, § 19.)

441. What Is Electricity?

Electricity is in everything: the table, your body, clothing, etc. The reason we do not notice it or use it is because it is not in motion. Electricity at rest is *static electricity;* electricity in motion is *current electricity*. It is useful only when it is in motion. Electricity is produced by *batteries* or *generators* (§ 459).

In some ways electricity is like water: Water flows through a pipe; electricity flows along a solid wire. The flowing of electricity is called a *current*. (See §§ 464-465.) Electricity gives us power, heat, and light. It gives us entertainment and carries messages. Under control, electricity is our good friend and helper; out of control, it is an enemy. Electricity travels at the same speed as light which is 186,000 miles per second.

442. Conductors

Any material through which electricity flows easily is a *conductor*. Electricity flows better through some materials than through others (see § 444). *Silver* is the best conductor but since it is expensive, *copper* and *aluminum* are often used (see §§ 368, 372, and 374). Water is a conductor; be sure to stand on a dry place when touching electrical things when the current is "on."

443. Insulators

The materials which cover electric wires are *insulators*. Any material which does not allow electricity to pass through it easily may be used as an insulator or *nonconductor*. Insulators are put on conductors to prevent shocks, fires, and short circuits. Thus electric wires are covered with plastic, rubber, cotton, and silk. Other good insulators are air, wood, paper, wax, oil, slate, glass, *porcelain*,[1] *bake-*

[1] *Porcelain* is a fine, beautiful kind of pottery made of fine clay and earth; a fine, white earthenware also called *china* or *chinaware*.

[2] *Bakelite*, made from *carbolic acid* and *formaldehyde*, is a sticky dough which hardens with heat. It is molded into many shapes and by mixing sheets of paper or cloth with the sticky material and baking it under pressure, a

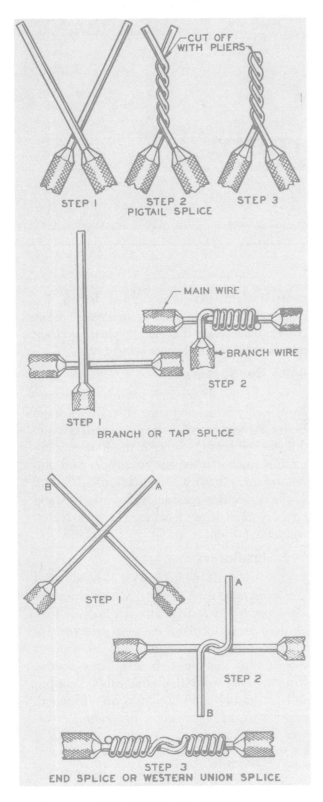

Fig. 343. Electrical Joints

lite,[2] *asbestos,*[3] *mica,*[4] *paraffin,*[5] and *tape* (see § 449). Of course, these must be dry to be completely safe; moisture destroys the insulating qualities of many materials.

444. Resistance

Every material slows up or holds back the flow of electricity to some extent. This holding back is called *resistance.* Compare this with *friction* explained in section 386.

445. Wires

A wire which carries electricity from one place to another is called a *conductor* (see § 442). Such wires are usually made of *copper* (see § 368).

The sizes of these wires are measured by the *American Standard Wire Gage* (see Fig. 635) and are given in Table 34, page 440. Note that the larger the number, the smaller the wire. When larger conductors are needed, the wires are twisted together into *cables.* The wire used in houses is generally No. 12.

Electric wires are covered to protect the wire and act as an *insulator* (see § 443). The insulation must be carefully removed before measuring the wire with the gage.

The *National Electrical Code* tells how wires must be installed (see §§ 446 and 448).

446. National Electrical Code

The National Electrical Code is a book of rules of the *National Board of Fire Underwriters* for electric wiring and electrical things as recommended by the *National Fire Protec-*

very strong sheet is produced. Once heated, bakelite is never again softened by heat. It is used for electrical insulators and as a substitute for celluloid and hard rubber.

[3] *Asbestos* is a stringy kind of rock. Its silky threads can easily be separated and are spun and woven into fireproof clothing, boards, curtains, paper, coverings for stoves and furnace pipes, brake linings, etc.

[4] *Mica* is a mineral, the layers of which easily separate into very thin tough scales or sheets. Most of the mica comes from India.

[5] *Paraffin* comes chiefly from *petroleum* (see Section 389). It is a wax used to make candles and to make paper or wood waterproof.

tion Association. Most electrical work is done according to these rules.

447. Electrical Joints

The place where two or more wires are connected is called a *connection, joint,* or *splice.* The *National Electrical Code* tells how joints may be made (see *electrician, § 19*). Joints must be made in *outlet boxes* and *junction boxes.*

448. Splicing

The three most common joints are the *pigtail splice,* the *branch splice,* and the *end splice,* Fig. 343. The *pigtail splice* is made by twisting together the ends of parallel wires. The *branch splice* or *tap splice* is used to branch off a main line. The *end splice* or *Western Union splice* connects the ends of two wires to extend length.

Before making a splice, the wires at the joints must be exposed by removing the *insulation* (see § 443). Be careful not to nick the wire; a nick weakens the wire and causes it to break. Next scrape the wire clean with the back of the knife. To make sure that the joint is tight and safe it must be *soldered* (see Unit 42). A loose wire at a joint causes heat. Soldering also helps to keep the wires from *corroding. Rosin* or *soldering paste* should be used as a *flux* for soldering electrical joints. (See § 852.) Hold the soldering copper (see § 850) on the underside of the joint, if possible, and spread the solder over the joint, Fig. 344.

449. Tape

After a joint or splice is made, it must be insulated again. Two kinds of tape that are often used to cover wire *joints* (see § 447) are *rubber tape* and *friction tape.* Rubber tape should be stretched as it is wrapped around the joint. Friction tape is made of cotton; it is sticky and is wrapped over the rubber tape. (See § 450).

Plastic electrical tape does the work of both rubber tape and friction tape. It can be put on easily and quickly. Oil, water, and dirt cannot hurt it. This tape is thin and because fewer wraps are needed, it takes up less space; this is important in places like *outlet boxes* and *junction boxes* (see Figs. 349 and 350). Since less tape is needed, there is a saving of cost and time. Neat repairs can be made easily. (See Fig. 346.)

450. Taping a Joint

Every joint must be covered in one of the following ways:

(1) One layer of *rubber tape* and two layers of *friction tape* (see § 449) should be wrapped in opposite directions, Fig. 345. The amount of tape that is used should equal the amount

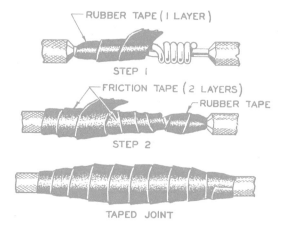

Fig. 344. **Soldering an Electrical Joint**

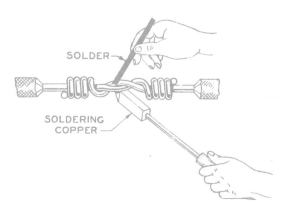

Fig. 345. **Taping a Joint with Rubber Tape and Friction Tape**

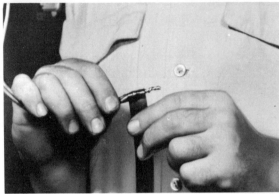

Fig. 346. **Taping Wires with Plastic Electrical Tape**
(Courtesy Norton Co.)

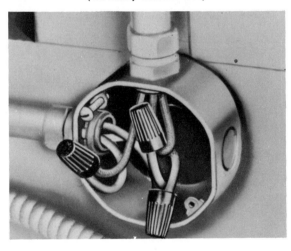

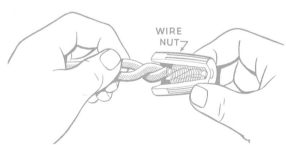

Fig. 347. **Wire Nuts** (Courtesy Ideal
Industries, Inc.)

of *insulation* (see § *443*) that was removed to make the joint.

(2) One layer of *plastic electrical tape* (see § *449*), Fig. 346.

(3) *Wire nuts* (see § *451*).

451. Wire Nuts

Wire nuts are used to connect the ends of electric wires, Fig. 347; they are used without *solder* (see § *448*) and without *tape* (see Figs. 345 and 346.) Wire nuts come in several sizes and are easy to use.

The *insulation* (see § *443*) is first removed from the ends of both wires. A spring or screw thread, inside the shell of the wire nut, screws on the wires in the same way a nut screws on a bolt. As the wire nut is screwed on, the two wires are pressed and twisted together. Wire nuts can be removed and used again.

452. Conduit

Electrical wires are often placed in a metal pipe or tube called *conduit* (pronounced *con-dwit*). One type is called *thin-wall conduit;* it may be bent rather easily. *Rigid conduit* is ordinary steel pipe, smoothed inside with *burrs* removed from the ends (see § *262* and *pipe-burring reamer,* § *772*). The outside is coated with *zinc* or *baked enamel* to keep it from rusting (see §§ *371* and *1101*). The threads on the ends are *pipe threads* (see § *767*).

Flexible conduit, Fig. 348, is used to make connections where some movement is necessary as at a motor.

Fig. 348. **Flexible Conduit**

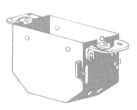

Fig. 349. **Outlet Box**   Fig. 350. **Junction Box**

453. Outlet Box

An outlet box is a metal box placed where electric wires are joined to each other and to switches and outlets for lamps, toasters, fans, heaters, clocks, etc., Fig. 349.

454. Junction Box

A junction box is a metal box in which electric wires are connected to branch off a main line, Figs. 349 and 350.

455. Switches

A switch is used for turning electricity "on" or "off," Fig. 351. One kind of switch is inside a metal box, called a *switch box*, with a handle on the outside; in this way the switch can be put "on" or "off" without getting a shock.

456. How to Tie an Underwriters' Knot

When there is room, a knot is tied on the end of a cord inside a *socket* or *plug* (see Figs. 353 and 354) to take the strain when a person pulls on the cord. This knot is called the *Underwriters' knot*. Fig. 352 shows how to make it. If the knot alone is too small to hold the cord in place, it should be made larger by wrapping it with *tape* (see § 449).

457. Extension Cord

An extension cord is a wire or lamp cord with a *socket* on one end and an attachment *plug* on the other end, Figs. 353 and 354. It enables a person to *extend* a light or other electrical device further away from the wall.

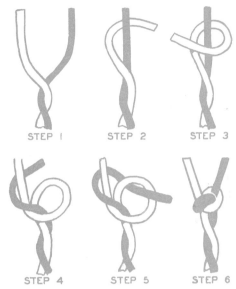

STEP 1   STEP 2   STEP 3

STEP 4   STEP 5   STEP 6

Fig. 352. **Underwriters' Knot**

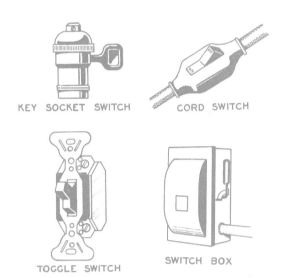

KEY SOCKET SWITCH   CORD SWITCH

TOGGLE SWITCH   SWITCH BOX

Fig. 351. Switches

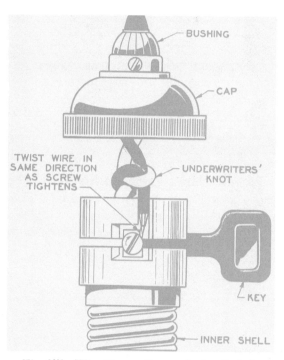

BUSHING

CAP

TWIST WIRE IN SAME DIRECTION AS SCREW TIGHTENS

UNDERWRITERS' KNOT

KEY

INNER SHELL

Fig. 353. **Wire Connection on Socket Switch**

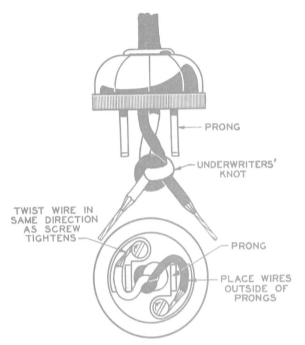

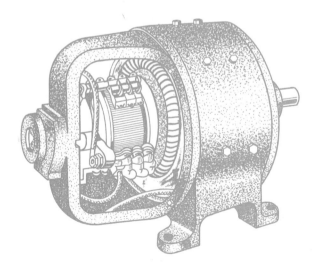

Fig. 354. **Wire Connection on an Attachment Plug**

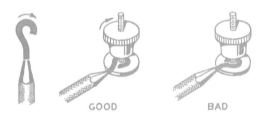

Fig. 355. **Placing Wire Under Nut**

Fig. 356. **Generator**

458. Placing Wire Under a Nut or the Head of a Screw

Fine, loose wires should first be twisted and then *soldered* together (see § *448*). Next, bend the wire around the screw in a *clockwise* direction — the same direction that you turn the screw to tighten it, Fig. 354. Figure 355 shows how to bend the wire under a nut. The wire will in this way wrap itself tighter around the screw as it is tightened.

459. Generator

We get most of our electricity from a machine called a *generator*, Fig. 356. It is in many ways like a motor (explained in section *460*). The generator changes *mechanical power* into electricity. It acts as a pump to keep up the *pressure*, or *voltage* (see § *465*). Generators may be driven by water, steam, electricity, oil, gasoline, or wind energy.

460. Motor

A motor is a machine which changes electricity into *mechanical power*. Motors are made in many sizes and speeds. They run machinery, electric locomotives, and start automobiles; they run fans and air conditioners in factories, offices, and homes; they also run vacuum cleaners, sewing machines, and washing machines. A two *horsepower*[6] motor uses twice as much electricity as a one horsepower motor. (See § *467*.)

All motors, including those that are completely enclosed, should be inspected, cleaned, and oiled regularly. The power should be turned off before starting to work on a motor.

Dirt damages any motor. It may be removed with a vacuum cleaner or air blast. The outside should be wiped with rags. Keep the motor clean at all times.

Moisture also damages a motor because it unites with dirt and softens the covering on the lead-in wires. If oil and grease get inside a motor, costly repairs may be needed.

---

[6]One *horsepower* is the power it takes to lift 33,000 pounds one foot in one minute.

Bearings (see section 261) should be oiled regularly with the right amount of oil. The bearings may be oiled about once or twice a month depending upon how much the motor is used. Put one drop of *lubricating oil* in each *oil hole* and wipe off all wasted oil with a clean rag (see §§ *394, 409*).

Vibration and shaking may damage a motor. Be sure that it is screwed down tightly and that all connections are tight. Some motors, as on refrigerators, are mounted on springs, and should not be clamped down.

If the motor needs any repairs, an *electrician* should do the work.

461. What Is a Circuit?

Electricity produced in one place will flow to another place if a path or *circuit* is made so that it may return to the starting place. The path which electricity follows to furnish the lighting on an automobile, for example, is a circuit. It is like a circle. The current starts at the *battery*, flows through the wires to the lamps, and then back to the battery through the frame.

If the *switch* (see § 455) is "off," a wire or lamp breaks, or anything else happens to break the path of the flowing electricity, then we have a *broken circuit* or *open circuit;* the electricity then stops flowing. There must always be a complete path or circuit for electricity to be useful; it is then called a *closed circuit*. Fig. 357 shows a circuit of a bell.

If there is any way in which electricity can make a "short cut" and return to its starting place without flowing through the entire circuit through which it should pass, it is a *short circuit*. (See § 468.)

462. Series Circuit

When two or more lamps are connected one after the other on the same wire so that the current flowing into the last lamp must first pass through the other lamps, they are in *series*, Fig. 358. Such a *circuit* (see § 461) is a *series circuit*. If one lamp is removed or burns out, all the other lamps stop burning. Some of the small Christmas tree lights are in series; if one light burns out, the other lights likewise go out.

463. Parallel Circuit

When two or more lamps are connected so that the current can flow into each lamp independently, they are connected in *parallel,*

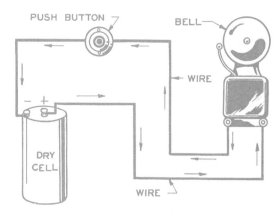

Fig. 357. Circuit of a Bell

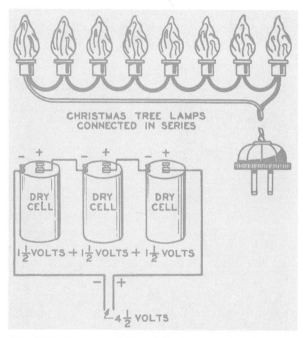

Fig. 358. Lamps and Dry Cells Connected in Series

Fig. 359. Such a circuit is a *parallel circuit*. If one lamp is removed, the other lamps keep on burning. The electric devices in our homes are connected in parallel.

464. Ground

Electricity always tries to escape and flow into the ground. In order to save wire, the earth or *ground* may be used for one of the

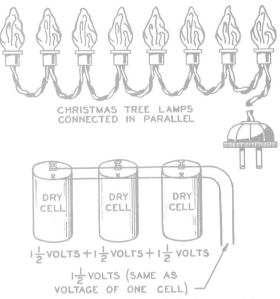

CHRISTMAS TREE LAMPS
CONNECTED IN PARALLEL

DRY CELL   DRY CELL   DRY CELL

$1\frac{1}{2}$ VOLTS + $1\frac{1}{2}$ VOLTS + $1\frac{1}{2}$ VOLTS

$1\frac{1}{2}$ VOLTS (SAME AS VOLTAGE OF ONE CELL)

Fig. 359. Lamps and Dry Cells Connected in Parallel

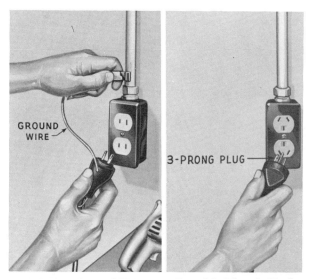

GROUND WIRE

3-PRONG PLUG

Fig. 360. Ground Wire on a Portable Electric Tool

wires for the electricity to flow through. This is the reason why we sometimes see a door-bell wire fastened to a water pipe; the electricity flows through the pipe and then into the ground. The *ground return system* is used in bell, automobile, telephone, and telegraph *circuits* (see § *461*).

Every shop has *portable electric tools* (see § *440*). A *ground wire* is a third wire that connects a portable electric tool or circuit to the ground circuit. If the wiring does not provide a ground, it is the wire on a portable electric tool that must be connected to the ground by fastening it to a pipe as in Fig. 360.

465. What Is a Volt?

Before electricity will flow there must be a force to move it. Water, which flows through a pipe from a high tank, flows with a lot of force or *pressure*. It also flows through a pipe when pressure is produced by a pump. In the same way electricity is caused to flow by pressure which is called *voltage*. *Electromotive force (emf)* is just another name for it. Water flows from a high level to a lower level or from a high pressure to a lower pressure. Electricity also flows from a place of high pressure to a place of lower pressure. Water pressure is measured in pounds per square inch; *electrical pressure* is measured in *volts*.

Dry cells,[7] *batteries,*[8] or *generators* supply this electrical pressure. The pressure of a dry cell is about 1.5 volts. The pressure of each cell in an automobile battery is 2 volts; thus a 6-cell battery has a pressure of 12 volts.

[7] The common *dry cell*, like the one used in a flashlight, is a can made of zinc (see #371) packed with a special kind of paste. In the center of the paste is a stick of *carbon* (see #319). The paste acts on the zinc chemically and produces electricity. A dry cell is really not dry; there must be moisture to make the paste act and there must be chemical action to give off electricity. A dry cell is not a *battery*. A 12 volt automobile battery has six cells. Each cell is a jar containing water, lead, and *sulfuric acid* (see #101). The action of the acid on the lead produces electricity.

[8] A *battery* is a number of *cells* connected so that they work together. A *dry battery* is a number of *dry cells* connected together.

Electrical pressure, or *voltage*, is measured with an instrument called a *voltmeter*. A *lighting circuit*, which supplies electricity for lights, is generally called a 110-volt circuit.[9] (See also § *461*.) The *power circuit*, which supplies electricity for running machines in a shop, is generally called a 220-volt circuit. If a 110-volt lamp were put, let us say, on a 220-volt circuit it would burn out instantly. If a 220-volt lamp were put on a 110-volt circuit, it would burn dimly.

466. What Is an Ampere?

Water may flow through a pipe at the rate of 2 gallons per minute or 4 gallons per minute; the quantity depends upon the size of the pipe and the *pressure*. The quantity of electricity which flows through a wire depends upon the size of the wire and the voltage pressure (see § *465*).

The quantity of electricity which flows, or the strength of the current, is measured in *amperes*. Thus a 10-ampere motor draws twice as much current as a 5-ampere motor (see § *460*). About one ampere flows through the ordinary 100-watt lamp on a 110-volt circuit (see § *467*). This rate of flow of electricity, or *amperage*, is measured by an instrument called an *ammeter*, Fig. 361. (See § *468*.)

467. Watt

The amount of electricity used is measured in *watts*, in honor of *James Watt*, the inventor of the steam engine. A 200-watt lamp uses electricity twice as fast as a 100-watt lamp, gives more light, and costs twice as much to operate. (See § *466*.)

746 watts = 1 horsepower.

Kilowatt means 1000 watts. A *kilowatt hour* is the using of one kilowatt of electricity for one hour. *Watt's law* is:

Watts = Volts x Amperes.

[9] The voltage supplied today is generally about 118 volts, but it has so long been known as 110 that it is usually described in that way.

468. What Is a Fuse?

To *fuse* means to melt. An *electric fuse*, Fig. 362, contains a small lead, zinc, or aluminum wire which has a very low *melting point* (see Table 12, p. 161). When the current becomes too great for the wire to carry, it melts or *blows out*, or *burns out*,

Fig. 361. **Ammeter**

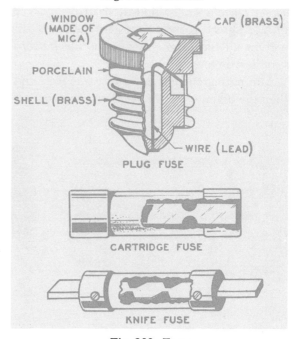

Fig. 362. **Fuses**

which *breaks the circuit* (see § *461*) and shuts off the current; it is then called a *broken circuit*. Thus, a fuse acts like a *safety valve*.

The current carried by a No. 14 house wire should not be more than 15 amperes. (See §§ *445* and *465*.) If the current is greater than this, the wire will get hot and may burn in two or start a fire. This is why 15-ampere fuses are placed in each circuit in most homes. No. 12 wire, which is larger, can carry more current and is used in homes today. If the current gets too strong, the fuse burns out and the current stops flowing.

Plug fuses are used in circuits up to 125 volts; *cartridge fuses* are used for 220 volts and over. Always replace a blown fuse with a new fuse of the same size.

Circuit breakers perform the same function as fuses. When the current is too great, a circuit breaker becomes hot and changes shape. As it makes this change, it breaks the circuit. After it cools it can be reset.

469. Direct Current and Alternating Current

There are two kinds of electric currents: *direct current* (DC) and *alternating current* (AC). Direct current flows in the same direction all the time. An automobile *battery* supplies direct current.

Alternating current flows first one way and then the other. One trip of alternating current

back and forth through a circuit is a *cycle*. There are usually 60 cycles per second, but 50, 40 and even 25 cycles per second are in use. Because almost all power companies furnish alternating current, the current in most homes is, therefore, of this type. In fact, about 90% of all electricity used is alternating current.

470. Transformer

A *transformer*, Fig. 363, is an instrument which changes the voltage of *alternating current* from high to low or low to high (see § *469*). A transformer operates because the direction of current flow changes, so it is used for alternating current. Other devices are used to change the voltage of direct current.

471. What Do Single Phase and Polyphase Mean?

Single-phase means one alternating current circuit. A *single-phase motor* has only two wires. *Polyphase* means two or more alternating circuits working together. Two separate single-phase currents need four wires. If these two currents are used to run a motor or generator, the circuit is *two-phase*. There are very few two-phase circuits.

Three separate single-phase currents need six wires, but a *three-phase circuit* can be arranged to get the same result with only three wires. Thus, if there are two wires, the circuit is single-phase; if there are three wires, it is *three-phase;* if there are four wires, it is *two-phase*.

472. What Is Magnetism?

Every boy knows that a *magnet* can pick up small pieces of iron and steel. This power is called *magnetism*. Nobody knows what it really is. Magnetism is closely related to *electricity*, but they are not the same thing (see § *441*). Magnetism does not travel through wires like electricity. *Hardened steel* holds magnetism well; soft iron does not. The more a magnet is heated, the more it loses its mag-

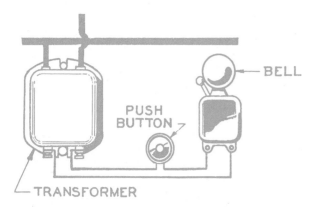

Fig. 363. Bell Circuit, Using a Transformer

netism because heat softens or *anneals* the steel. (See §§ 570, 655, and 955.)

473. How to Avoid Getting a Shock

A person who is careful when using electrical things is quite safe from getting a shock.

Be sure the switch is "off" when repairing wires or changing fuses.

Change fuses only in daylight or use a flashlight; changing fuses in the dark is dangerous.

Stand on a dry place when turning switches "on" or "off." You may get a bad shock if you touch a water pipe or gas pipe at the same time that you touch something that has a bad electrical connection. (See § 464.)

If you see a wire out of place, broken, or hanging down on the street, let it alone and call the police or the electric company at once.

Remember, too, that you cannot see, hear, or smell electricity; when you feel it, it may be too late!

Review Questions

1. Why is it important to know something about the electrical equipment in the home and in the shop?
2. What is electricity?
3. What is static electricity?
4. What is current electricity?
5. Which kind of electricity is useful, static electricity or current electricity?
6. What is a good conductor of electricity?
7. Name some good conductors.
8. What is an insulator?
9. Name some insulators.
10. What is meant by resistance?
11. Of what are most electrical wires made?
12. What gage is used to measure the sizes of these wires?
13. Is a No. 40 wire larger or smaller than a No. 14 wire?
14. What is a cable?
15. What is the National Electrical Code?
16. Name three kinds of tape. How is each used?
17. What is a pigtail splice?
18. What is a branch splice?
19. What is an end splice?
20. For what is conduit used?
21. What is an outlet box?
22. What is a junction box?
23. What is an attachment plug?
24. How should a wire be placed under a screw?
25. What is a dry cell?
26. What is a battery?
27. How should you care for a motor?
28. What is a circuit?
29. What is an open circuit?
30. What is a closed circuit?
31. What is a series circuit?
32. What is a parallel circuit?
33. What is a ground?
34. What is voltage?
35. What is amperage?
36. What is a watt?
37. What are fuses and circuit breakers used for?
38. What is direct current?
39. What is alternating current?
40. What would happen if a 110-volt lamp were put on a 220-volt circuit?
41. What would happen if you put a 220-volt lamp on a 110-volt circuit?
42. How can you avoid getting a shock?
43. Sketch the dials on the electric meter in your home. What is the reading?

Coordination

Words to Know

alternating current	cartridge fuse
American Standard	circuit
Wire Gage	circuit breaker
ammeter	closed circuit
ampere	conductor
battery	conduit
branch splice	current electricity
broken circuit	cycle
burn out	direct current
cable	electrical fuse

electrical pressure
end splice
extension cord
flexible conduit
friction tape
ground return
   system
ground wire
horsepower
insulation
joint
junction box
kilowatt
kilowatt hour
lighting circuit
magnet
mechanical power
National Board of
   Fire Underwriters
National Electrical
   Code
National Fire Pro-
   tection Association
nonconductor
open circuit
outlet box
parallel circuit
pigtail splice
pipe-burring reamer
pipe thread

plastic electrical
   tape
plug fuse
polyphase
power circuit
resistance
rigid conduit
rosin
rubber tape
series circuit
shock
short circuit
single-phase
soldering
splice
static electricity
switch
tape
tap splice
three-phase circuit
transformer
two-phase
Underwriters' knot
volt
voltmeter
watt
Watt's law
Western Union
   splice
wire nuts

Mathematics

1. How much power in watts does a 110-volt lamp use, if it takes ¼ ampere?

2. Make a sketch of the dials on the electric meter in your home What is the reading on your last electric bill?

3. At the price per kilowatt hour that you pay for electricity what would 10,000 kilowatt hours cost?

4. How much will it cost to run your electric toaster for 10 minutes or your radio for one hour?

Drafting

1. Make a sketch of a door bell circuit in your home.

2. Draw a telephone circuit connecting the shops in your school.

Social Science

1. How have the telephone, telegraph, and radio helped the world? Write a story about them.

Occupational Information

1. Write a story about, "How Electricity Helps Us In Our Daily Lives."

2. Explain the electron theory.

3. What is the cause of the northern lights?

4. Discuss the advantages of having licensed electricians.

5. How can persons get shocked?

6. For what inventions is Thomas A. Edison noted?

7. Write a biography of Marconi.

8. Write a biography of Alexander G. Bell.

9. Write a biography of Samuel F. B. Morse, inventor of the telegraph.

10. Write a biography of James Watt.

11. Write a biography of Benjamin Franklin.

Electric Wiring for Electronic Systems
(Courtesy International Harvester Co.)

After final assembly each piece of equipment is thoroughly inspected. All systems must be in proper working condition before it receives the quality control seal of approval. (Courtesy International Harvester Co.)

Steps in Producing an Impact-Extruded Piece — Movement of Metal Takes Place in a Fraction of a Second (Courtesy Aluminum Company of America)

Part **V**

Drill Press Work

Drills, Sleeves, Sockets, and Chucks

484. What Does Drilling Mean?

Drilling means cutting a hole with a tool called a *drill*.

485. Kinds of Drills

The common kinds of drills are *flat drill*, *straight-fluted drill*, and *twist drill*, Fig. 374.

486. Flat Drill

The flat drill is usually a homemade drill (see Fig. 374). It can be made in the shop at a low cost out of a good grade of steel; it is flattened, then hardened and sharpened.

487. Straight-Fluted Drill

The straight-fluted drill or *farmer drill*, named after its inventor, is used for drilling brass, copper and other soft metals (see Fig. 374). It may also be used to drill thin metal. (See § 566.)

488. Twist Drill

The twist drill is the one that is most used in metalwork. Twist drills are made with two, three, or four *cutting lips*, Fig. 375. (See Fig. 376.) The *two-lip drill* is used to drill holes into solid metal while the *three-lip drill* and *four-lip drill* are used to enlarge holes already drilled.

489. Carbon Steel Drills and High Speed Drills

Twist drills are made of *carbon steel* or *high-speed steel* (see §§ 328 and 352). If the drill shank is not stamped *HS*, meaning *high speed*, it is made of carbon steel. Section 354 explains how to tell whether a drill is

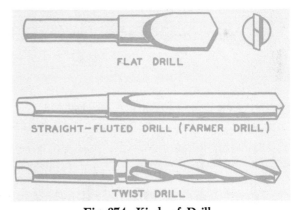

FLAT DRILL

STRAIGHT-FLUTED DRILL (FARMER DRILL)

TWIST DRILL

Fig. 374. Kinds of Drills

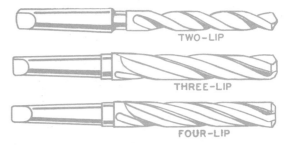

TWO-LIP

THREE-LIP

FOUR-LIP

Fig. 375. Kinds of Twist Drills

carbon steel or high-speed steel by the *spark test*. High-speed steel drills cost two or three times as much as carbon steel drills. Note in Table 17 on page 214 that high-speed drills may be run twice as fast as carbon steel drills.

490. Parts of Twist Drill

The parts of a twist drill are shown in Fig. 376. The *body* is the part in which the

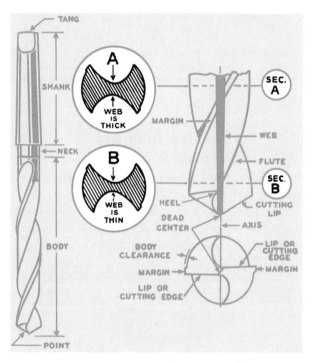

Fig. 376. Parts of a Twist Drill

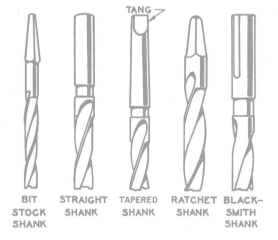

Fig. 377. Kinds of Drill Shanks

grooves are cut. The grooves which run along the sides of the drill are called *flutes*. While drilling, the drill is held by the *shank*. The cone-shaped cutting end is the *point*. The *margin* is the narrow edge alongside the flute. *Body clearance* is the wide part that has been cut away between the margin and the flute; the rubbing between the drill and the walls of the hole is, therefore, reduced and less power is needed to turn the drill. It also keeps from *drawing the temper* out of the drill by overheating (see § 954).

The *web* is the metal in the center running lengthwise between the flutes. It is the backbone of the drill; it gets thicker near the shank and makes the drill stronger. Section A in Fig. 376 was cut from a drill near the shank while section B was cut near the point. Study the difference in the thickness of the web in these two sections.

The *tang* is the flattened end of the shank. It fits into the slot in a *drill sleeve* (see § 497) or the *drill press spindle* (see Fig. 413). It drives the drill and keeps the shank from slipping, especially on large drills. The *lips* are the *cutting edges* of the drill. The *dead center* is the end at the point of the drill; it should always be in the exact center of the point. The *heel* is the part of the point behind the cutting edges.

The flutes are shaped to:

(1) Help to form the cutting edges at the point.

(2) Curl the chips into small spaces.

(3) Form passage for the chips to come out of the hole.

(4) Allow the *cutting fluid* to travel to the cutting edges of the drill (see § 406).

491. Kinds of Drill Shanks

Drill shanks are either *straight* or *tapered*. Five kinds of drill shanks are shown in Fig. 377.

492. Morse and Jarno Tapers

The taper on twist drill shanks is the *Morse taper*. It is about ⅝″ per foot. There is also another taper, known as the *Jarno*[1] *taper*, which is 6/10″ per foot.

493. Numbers of Tapers

The sizes of tapers on shanks are numbered. There are No. 1, No. 2, No. 3 *Morse tapers* and even larger. No. 1 is the smallest size and No. 3 is a larger size. The beginner should look these sizes over carefully so that he will know them at a glance.

494. Sizes of Drills

Small drills are usually purchased in sets, Fig. 378. The size of a drill is known by its diameter, which may be a number gage, a letter, or a fractional size. Table 16 on page 196 shows the sizes from the smallest twist drill, which is No. 80, up to 1″ in diameter.

Gage Numbers

Number drills are made in sizes from No. 80 to No. 1 (0.0135″ to 0.228″ diameters). Note that the larger the number the smaller the drill. (See also Table 34, p. 440.)

Letter Drills

Letter drills are labeled from A to Z (0.234″ to 0.413″ diameters). Note that the letter drills begin where the number drills end.

Fractions

Fraction drills range from 1/64″ to 4″ in diameter or larger. The sizes increase by 64ths of an inch in the smaller sizes and by 32nds and 16ths in the larger sizes. Note that the number and letter drills are between the fractional drills.

If a drill of a certain size is needed but is not in the shop, sometimes the next size smaller or larger drill can be used instead.

[1] *Jarno* is pronounced "Yarno." The *Jarno taper* got its name from Oscar J. Beale who wrote many technical articles and signed them "Jarno."

495. How to Measure a Drill

The diameter of a drill is stamped on the drill near the shank. Very small drills are not stamped and must be measured with *drill gages*, Figs. 379 and 380. Occasionally a drill

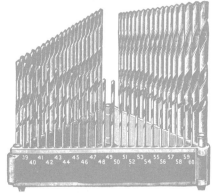

Fig. 378. Set of Number Drills in a Drill Stand (Courtesy Morse Twist Drill and Machine Co.)

FOR NUMBER DRILLS SIZES NO. 1 TO NO. 60

FOR NUMBER DRILLS SIZES NO. 61 TO NO. 80

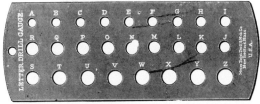

FOR LETTER DRILLS SIZES A TO Z

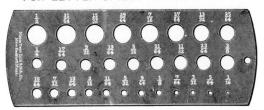

FOR FRACTIONAL DRILLS SIZES 1/16″ TO 1/2″

Fig. 379. Drill Gages (Courtesy Morse Twist Drill and Machine Co.)

Table 16
DRILL SIZES
(See Section 494)

Letter drills begin where *number drills* end.

Number and Letter Drills	Fractional Drills	Decimal Equivalents	Number and Letter Drills	Fractional Drills	Decimal Equivalents	Number and Letter Drills	Fractional Drills	Decimal Equivalents	Number and Letter Drills	Fractional Drills	Decimal Equivalents
80	...	.0135	42	...	.0935		13/64	.2031		13/32	.4062
79	...	.0145		3/32	.0937	6	...	.2040	Z	...	.4130
	1/64	.0156	41	...	.0960	5	...	.2055		27/64	.4219
78	...	.0160	40	...	.0980	4	...	.2090		7/16	.4375
77	...	.0180	39	...	.0995	3	...	.2130		29/64	.4531
76	...	.0200	38	...	.1015		7/32	.2187		15/32	.4687
75	...	.0210	37	...	.1040	2	...	.2210		31/64	.4844
74	...	.0225	36	...	.1065	1	...	.2280		1/2	.5000
73	...	.0240		7/64	.1094	A	...	.2340			
72	...	.0250	35	...	.1100		15/64	.2344		33/64	.5156
71	...	.0260	34	...	.1110	B	...	.2380		17/32	.5312
70	...	.0280	33	...	.1130	C	...	.2420		35/64	.5469
69	...	.0292	32	...	.1160	D	...	.2460		9/16	.5625
68	...	.0310	31	...	.1200	E	1/4	.2500		37/64	.5781
	1/32	.0312		1/8	.1250	F	...	.2570		19/32	.5937
67	...	.0320	30	...	.1285	G	...	.2610		39/64	.6094
66	...	.0330	29	...	.1360		17/64	.2656		5/8	.6250
65	...	.0350	28	...	.1405	H	...	.2660			
64	...	.0360		9/64	.1406	I	...	.2720		41/64	.6406
63	...	.0370	27	...	.1440	J	...	.2770		21/32	.6562
62	...	.0380	26	...	.1470	K	...	.2810		43/64	.6719
61	...	.0390	25	...	.1495		9/32	.2812		11/16	.6875
60	...	.0400	24	...	.1520	L	...	.2900		45/64	.7031
59	...	.0410	23	...	.1540	M	...	.2950		23/32	.7187
58	...	.0420		5/32	.1562		19/64	.2969		47/64	.7344
57	...	.0430	22	...	.1570	N	...	.3020		3/4	.7500
56	...	.0465	21	...	.1590		5/16	.3125			
	3/64	.0469	20	...	.1610	O	...	.3160		49/64	.7656
55	...	.0520	19	...	.1660	P	...	.3230		25/32	.7812
54	...	.0550	18	...	.1695		21/64	.3281		51/64	.7969
53	...	.0595		11/64	.1719	Q	...	.3320		13/16	.8125
	1/16	.0625	17	...	.1720	R	...	.3390		53/64	.8281
52	...	.0635	16	...	.1770		11/32	.3437		27/32	.8437
51	...	.0670	15	...	.1800	S	...	.3480		55/64	.8594
50	...	.0700	14	...	.1820	T	...	.3580		7/8	.8750
49	...	.0730	13	...	.1850		23/64	.3594		57/64	.8906
48	...	.0760		3/16	.1875	U	...	.3680		29/32	.9062
	5/64	.0781	12	...	.1890		3/8	.3750		59/64	.9219
47	...	.0785	11	...	.1910	V	...	.3770		15/16	.9375
46	...	.0810	10	...	.1935	W	...	.3860		61/64	.9531
45	...	.0820	9	...	.1960		25/64	.3906		31/32	.9687
44	...	.0860	8	...	.1990	X	...	.3970		63/64	.9844
43	...	.0890	7	...	.2010	Y	...	.4040		1	1.0000

may be incorrectly stamped; so it is always best to measure it with a drill gage or with a *micrometer*, Fig. 381. A new drill may be measured across the *margins* at the point; a worn drill must be measured at the ends of the flutes near the *neck*. (See § *1144* and Table 34, p. 440.)

496. Ordering Twist Drills

When ordering a twist drill give the:
(1) Diameter of drill.
(2) Shape of shank.
(3) Kind of steel, that is, whether *carbon steel* or *high-speed steel* (see § 489).
For example:
(1) ¾″ diameter.
(2) Taper shank.
(3) High-speed steel.

497. Drill Sleeves

Taper shanks on drills come in several sizes, such as No. 1, No. 2, and No. 3 *Morse tapers* (see § *493*). The *drill press spindle* (see Fig. 413) has a hole with a No. 2 or a No. 3 Morse taper.

A drill with a No. 1 taper will not fit into a spindle with a No. 2 or a No. 3 taper. There-fore, to make the drill fit, a *sleeve* like the one shown in Fig. 382 with a No. 1 *tapered hole* is placed on the drill shank. The outside of this sleeve has a No. 2 taper. If this taper is still too small to fit into the drill press spindle, the sleeve with a No. 2 tapered hole and a No. 3 outside taper is also used, thus enlarging the drill shank until it fits snugly into the drill press spindle. The first sleeve is known as a *No. 1 to No. 2 Morse-taper sleeve* while the second is a *No. 2 to No. 3 Morse-taper sleeve.*

The drill sleeve has a flattened end called a *tang* which fits a slot in the drill press spindle and keeps the drill and drill sleeve from slipping.

498. Drill Sockets

Sometimes it is necessary to use a drill with a No. 3 taper shank in a drill press spindle with a No. 2 tapered hole. The drill socket, Fig. 383, makes this possible. It has a large hole and a small Morse-taper shank.

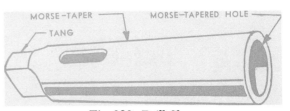

Fig. 381. Measuring a Drill with a Micrometer

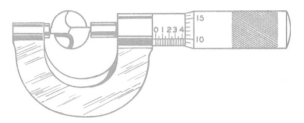

Fig. 382. Drill Sleeve

Fig. 383. Drill Socket

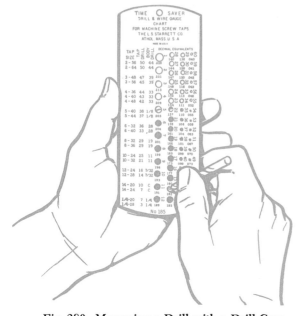

Fig. 380. Measuring a Drill with a Drill Gage

499. Drill Chuck

Straight shank drills must be held in a drill chuck, Fig. 384. This is fitted with a *Morse taper shank,* called an *arbor,* which fits into the *drill press spindle.* The drill chuck shown here has three *jaws.* It grips the drill between the jaws and is adjusted by turning the outside with a *chuck key.* (See § 561).

Review Questions

1. Name two kinds of steel from which drills are made.

2. How can you tell whether a drill is made of carbon steel or high-speed steel?

3. Of what use is the tang on a drill?

4. What are the uses of the flutes on a drill?

5. What is the name of the taper on twist-drill shanks?

6. What are the sizes of tapers on drill shanks?

7. Name the parts of a twist drill.

8. What part of the drill should be measured with a micrometer to find its size?

9. What is a drill gage? Why is it used?

10. What information must be given to order a twist drill?

11. For what is a drill sleeve used?

12. What is a drill chuck? Why is it used?

Coordination

Mathematics

1. Is a $1\frac{7}{64}''$ drill larger than a $1\frac{1}{32}''$ drill?

2. What is the difference between a No. 35 drill and a size D drill?

3. What is the difference between a No. 18 drill and a $\frac{3}{64}''$ drill?

4. If the small end of a 12″ tapered bar is 0.525″, how large is the other end if the taper is $\frac{5}{8}''$ per foot?

5. What is the difference in the cost of a $\frac{3}{4}''$ taper shank drill made of carbon steel and one made of high-speed steel?

Drafting

1. Draw a No. 2 to No. 3 Morse-taper drill sleeve.

Words to Know

arbor	letter drill
carbon steel drill	Morse-taper shank
chuck jaw	Morse-taper sleeve
chuck key	straight-fluted drill
drawing the temper	straight shank drill
drill chuck	tapered shank
drill gage	three-lip drill
drill press spindle	twist drill
drill shank	body clearance
drill sleeve	flute
drill socket	heel
drill stand	lips
drilling	margin
farmer drill	neck
flat drill	point
four-lip drill	shank
gage number	tang
high speed steel drill	web
Jarno taper	two-lip drill

Occupational Information

1. In which trades is a knowledge of drills and drilling important?

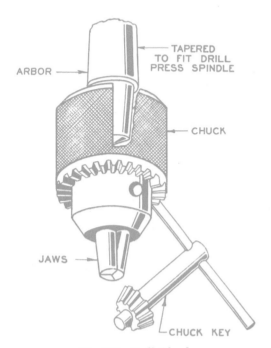

ARBOR —

TAPERED TO FIT DRILL PRESS SPINDLE

— CHUCK

JAWS —

CHUCK KEY

Fig. 384. Drill Chuck

Drill Sharpening

505. Importance of Drill Sharpening

Nearly all drilling troubles are caused by wrong sharpening. The results of a badly sharpened drill may be:

(1) A broken drill.

(2) A hole which is the wrong diameter.

(3) A hole which is not perfectly round.

(4) A rough finish, Fig. 390.

506. Drill Sharpening

Four things must be watched when sharpening a drill:

(1) Lip clearance (see Figs. 391-393 and §§ 507-508).

(2) Length of lips (Fig. 394 and § 509).

(3) Angle of lips (see Fig. 394 and § 509).

(4) Location of dead center (see Fig. 395 and § 509).

If the first three are correct, the fourth will also be correct.

507. Lip Clearance

Lip clearance is made by grinding away the metal behind the cutting edges, Fig. 391, so the cutting edges can cut into the metal.

If there were no lip clearance as on *A* in Fig. 391, it would be impossible for the drill to cut into the metal; the bottom of the drill would rub, but not cut. The metal behind the cutting edges must be ground away as on *B*

Fig. 390. Rough Hole Made by a Dull Drill (Courtesy Cleveland Twist Drill Co.)

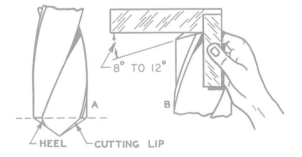

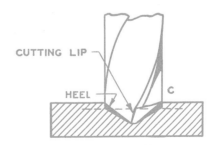

Fig. 391. Lip Clearance

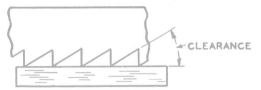

Fig. 392. Clearance on Saw Tooth

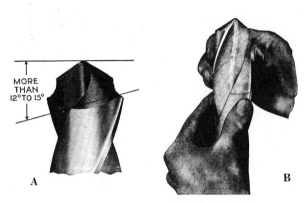

A   B

Fig. 393. Results of Wrong Lip Clearance
(Courtesy Cleveland Twist Drill Co.)

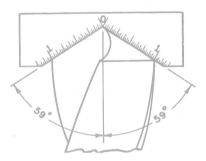

Fig. 394. Lips Are Same Length with Equal
and Correct Angles

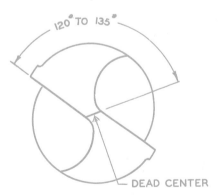

Fig. 395. Angle of Dead Center with Cutting Edge

and *C*. Note in *B* and *C* how much lower the *cutting lip* is than the *heel*; also note that in *C* the cutting lip has already removed metal ahead of the heel as shown by the dark part of the hole on each side of the drill.

Lip clearance may be likened to *clearance* of a saw tooth, Fig. 392.

508. Angle of Lip Clearance

The correct *lip clearance* for a regular point in general-purpose drilling of most steels should be from 8° to 12° (see *B*, Fig. 391). For drilling soft materials under heavy *feeds* the angle of lip clearance may be increased to 12° or 15°. If it is more than 15°, the corners of the cutting edges are too thin and may break off as shown in *A*, Fig. 393.

If the angle of lip clearance is much less than 8°, it acts the same as when there is no clearance and the drill cannot cut into the metal. It may then break in the center along the web as *B* in Fig. 393.

509. Length and Angle of Lips

The two lips must be the same length and their angles must be equal, Fig. 394. For ordinary work 59° is recommended. If the two lips are the same length and at equal angles as shown in Fig. 394, the *dead center* will also be centrally located, Fig. 395. The line across the dead center should be between 120° and 135° with the cutting edge.

If the angles of the cutting edges are more than 59°, the drill will not cut easily into the metal and, therefore, will not hold its position centrally because of being too flat. If the angles of the cutting edges are less than 59°, more power will be needed to turn the drill, or the drill will cut slower because of the longer cutting edges.

Only one lip will cut if the dead center is in the center but the angles are different as in Fig. 396. One cutting edge will wear quickly and the hole will be oversize.

If the angles on the cutting edges are equal but the lips are of different lengths, as in Fig. 397, the dead center will not be in the center.

The hole will then be larger than the drill. It may be compared with putting the hub of a wheel anywhere except the exact center. The strain on the drill press is thus very great, wobbling of the spindle results, the drill wears down rapidly, and breakdowns often follow.

The worst conditions occur when the lips are of unequal lengths and the angles on the cutting edges are also unequal, Fig. 398. The hole is then larger than the drill and the drill and drill press are strained. Note that the short lip cuts a smaller hole than the long lip.

510. Rake Angle

The rake angle of the drill is the angle between the *flute* and the work, Fig. 399. If the rake angle were 90 degrees or more, there would be no edge to do the cutting. If the rake angle is too small, the cutting edge is too thin and it breaks under the strain of the work. The rake angle also helps to curl the chips; a large rake angle rolls the chips tightly while a small rake angle rolls them loosely. The rake angle, as made by manufacturers, should not be changed for ordinary drilling. (See § *1188*.)

511. Drill-Grinding Gage

A drill-grinding gage should be used when grinding drills, Fig. 400. Such a gage measures the lengths and angles of the *cutting lips* (see § *509*). Compare the drill-grinding gage in Fig. 400 with the *drill gages* in Figs. 379 and 380.

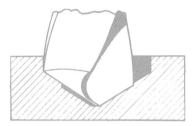

Fig. 397. Lips of Unequal Lengths

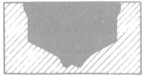

Fig. 398. Lips of Unequal Lengths and Unequal Angles on Cutting Edges

Fig. 399. Rake Angle

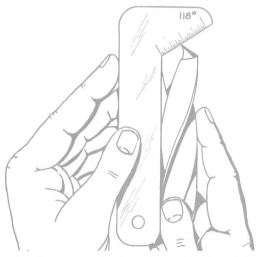

Fig. 400. Measuring Lengths and Angles of the Cutting Lips with a Drill-Grinding Gage

Fig. 396. Angles of Cutting Edges Are Unequal

512. Grinding Drills by Hand

In small shops, drills must be sharpened on the grinder by hand. It is best to ask the instructor to show you how to hold and grind a drill by hand. Also study Fig. 401 and read Section *1062*. You will have to do much practicing. (See § *513*).

513. Grinding Drills by Machine

While it is necessary to grind drills by hand in small shops (see § *512*), better and faster work can be done when they are ground by

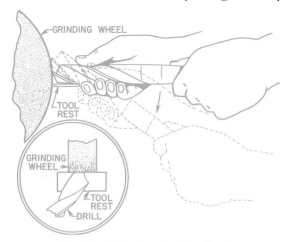

Fig. 401. Grinding Drill by Hand

Fig. 402. Grinding a Drill with a Drill-Grinding Attachment (Courtesy Atlas Press Co.)

machine as shown in Fig. 402. This is especially true if many drills are used. The part connected to the grinder in this picture is called a *drill-grinding attachment*. Read also section *1062*.

Review Questions

1. What three things should be watched when sharpening a twist drill?
2. What is lip clearance?
3. What is the result of too much lip clearance?
4. What is the result of too little lip clearance?
5. What happens when the angles of the cutting edges are unequal?
6. What happens when the lips of a drill are of unequal lengths?
7. How can a drill be made to cut oversize?
8. What is the rake angle?
9. Of what use is a drill-grinding gage?
10. What is the difference between a drill gage and a drill-grinding gage?
11. Is it better to grind a drill by machine than by hand? Why?

Coordination

Words to Know

cutting lip	drill-grinding gage
drill-grinding attachment	lip clearance
	rake angle

Mathematics

1. What is the complement of a 59° angle?
2. What is the supplement of a 59° angle?

Drafting

1. Design a drill-grinding gage which you can make in the shop.
2. Design a drill-grinding attachment which can be made in the shop.

Occupational Information

1. List the tradesmen who must know how to sharpen drills.
2. Write a story on the "Evolution of Drilling."

Drilling Machines

519. What Is a Drilling Machine?

A drilling machine is a machine which holds and turns a drill to cut holes in metal. It is also called a *drill press*, or just *drill*.

520. Kinds of Drilling Machines

Among the kinds of drilling machines are:
(1) *Hand drill* (see § 521).
(2) *Portable electric drill* (see § 522).
(3) *Handfeed drill press* (see § 523).
(4) *Back-geared upright drill* (see § 524).
(5) *Gang drill* (see § 525).
(6) *Multiple-spindle drill* (see § 526.)
(7) *Radial drill press* (see § 527).

521. Hand Drill

A common drilling tool which is used for very light work is known as the *hand drill*, Fig. 408. It is held with the left hand while the right hand turns the crank which causes the drill to turn. The left hand must press hard enough to make the drill cut.

522. Portable Electric Drill

A small drilling machine which can be carried from job to job is the *portable electric drill*, Fig. 409. It can be run from any electric light socket. Fig. 410 shows how it is used. It is important that portable electric tools be grounded (see § 464).

Fig. 408. Hand Drill

Fig. 409. Portable Electric Drill

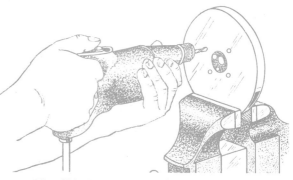

Fig. 410. Using a Portable Electric Drill

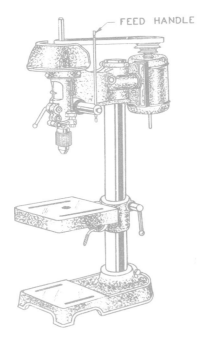

Fig. 411. Handfeed Bench Drill Press

523.   Handfeed Drill Press

Small, light work may be drilled on the *handfeed drill press*. This is a small press in which only the smaller drills are used. It may be one which sets on the bench, called a *bench drill*, Fig. 411, or it may be a floor model, Fig. 412. It is the simplest drill press and may be called *sensitive* because you can *feel* all the strains on the drill in the *feed handle*. There are no *gears;* it is driven by the most simple and most direct way possible.

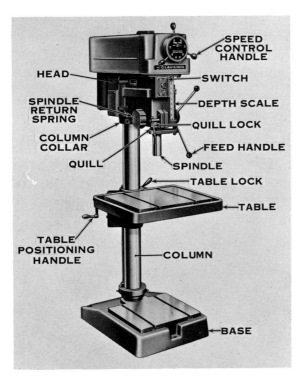

Fig. 412. Handfeed Floor Drill Press
(Courtesy Atlas Press Co.)

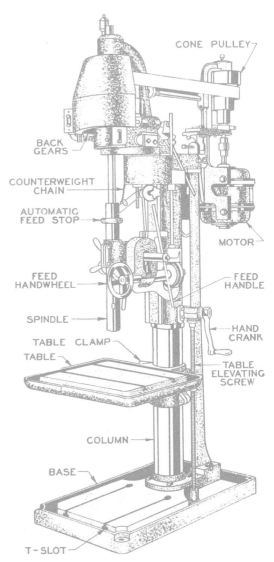

Fig. 413. Back-Geared Upright Drill Press
with Power Feed

524. Back-Geared Upright Drill Press

This machine is like the sensitive drill press except that it is larger and more powerful, Fig. 413. It has *gears* for changing the speeds; these are called *back gears*. Also, besides *feeding* (see section 188) by hand as on the sensitive drill press, this machine has an *automatic feed*, that is, it uses power to lower the drill (see § 568). Larger drills can be used than in the sensitive drill.

525. Gang Drill

The gang drill, Fig. 414, is a drilling machine in which two or more drill presses are *ganged* or made into one machine. Each *spindle* may be run alone. This machine is used mainly in *mass production* where different drill press operations are done, one after another. Some work may be done by one spindle and then passed to the next spindle for the next operation, and so on. One spindle may hold a small drill, a second may hold a large drill, a third may hold a *countersink* (see Fig. 462), and so on; the work is thus passed along the table from one spindle to the next. (See Fig. 451.)

526. Multiple Spindle Drill Press

This drilling machine has a number of spindles fastened to the main spindle with *universal joints*, Fig. 415. Each of these spindles holds a drill and all the drills run at once, thus drilling at one time as many holes as there are drills, Fig. 416 (see also Fig. 434).

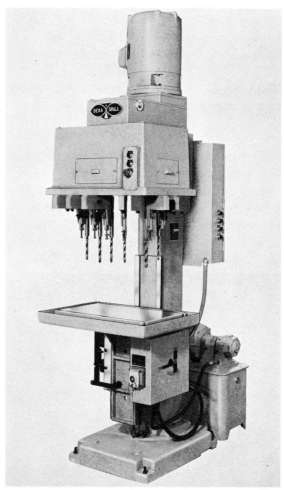

Fig. 415. Multiple-Spindle Drill Press
(Courtesy Precision Tool & Mfg. Co.)

Fig. 414 Gang Drilling on Automobile Parts
(Courtesy Clausing Div., Atlas Press Co.)

Fig. 416. Multiple-Spindle Drill Presses
(Courtesy American Machinist)

This machine is also used in *mass production*. It is a great timesaver where many pieces, each having a number of holes, have to be drilled. It does away with setting up the job many times. One machine does the work of many machines and the space that these machines would otherwise occupy is saved.

527. Radial Drill Press

This machine has a movable *arm* on which the spindle is mounted. The spindle may be moved and set at different distances from the post or *column*. The arm may also be swung around to the left or right, Fig. 417. The arm may be raised or lowered so that work of different heights may be drilled. The radial drill press is used for large, heavy work, such as machine frames, which cannot be moved easily to drill several holes. It is, therefore, necessary to shift the position of the drill. The radial drill makes this possible.

528. Parts of the Drill Press

The names of drill press parts are the same for all drill presses (Figs. 411-413). The *base* of the drill press is the support for the machine; it is bolted to the floor and has *T-slots* so that large work may be bolted to it for drilling. The *column* is the post to which the *table* is fastened; the table holds the work in

Fig. 417. Drilling Hole in Large Casting with Radial Drill Press
(Courtesy National Machine Tool Builders Assn.)

place while it is being drilled. It also has *T-slots*. By turning the *hand crank* which causes the *table elevating screw* to turn, the table may be raised or lowered and then clamped in place by tightening the *table clamp*. Every drilling machine has a *spindle* which holds and turns the drill. It is upright on most machines and is held by an arm which is fastened to the column. To keep the spindle from dropping, it is balanced by a *spindle return spring* which supports the *quill* —a housing around the rotating spindle moved up and down by the *feed handle*. Some spindles may be counterbalanced by a weight which moves up and down inside the column. This weight is fastened to the spindle with a chain called the *counterweight chain*.

One *cone pulley* is fastened to the spindle and another is connected to the *motor*. The steps of the cone pulley give as many speeds as there are steps. The *back gears*, located inside the front pulley, give additional speeds. Stop before shifting gears. A variable speed drive gives a continuous range of speeds shown on a dial (Figs. 326 and 412). It is adjusted only while the drill is running.

The feed stop may be set so the drill will stop cutting when the desired depth is reached. This is useful for repetitive drilling.

529. How Are the Sizes of Drilling Machines Measured?

Drilling machines range widely in sizes. The size of an *upright drill press* is measured by the distance from the drill to the column multiplied by two. Thus, a 20-inch drill press can drill the center of a 20-inch circle.

The size of a *radial drill press* is measured from the drill to the column. Thus, a 6-foot radial drill press can drill the center of a 12-foot circle.

Review Questions

1. What is a portable electric drill? A sensitive drill? A bench drill? A back-geared up-

right drill press? A gang drill? A radial drill press?

2. Name the main parts of a drill press.
3. What is meant by automatic feed?
4. Of what use are the back gears?
5. Should the back gears be shifted while the drill press is running? Why?
6. How is the size of a drill press measured? A radial drill press?

Coordination

Words to Know

automatic feed	table elevating
back-geared upright	screw
drill press	T-slot
bench drill	feed handle
drilling machine	feeding
drill press	gang drill
automatic feed stop	gear
back gears	hand drill
base	handfeed drill press
column	mass production
cone pulley	multiple-spindle drill
counterweight	press
chain	portable electric drill
hand crank	quantity production
motor	radial drill press
spindle	sensitive drill
table	universal joint
table clamp	

Mathematics

1. What is the total cost of all the drilling machines in your school?

Occupational Information

1. Get pictures and costs of the following drilling machines:
    (1) Portable electric drill.
    (2) Bench drill.
    (3) Back-geared upright drill press.
    (4) Radial drill press.
2. What is the difference between a drilling machine operator and a machine setup man?

Holding Work for Drilling and Other Machining Operations

534. Setting Up Work

Setting and clamping a workpiece in a machine vise, holding fixture, or directly to a machine tool table is known as *setting up*. The setup tools and the procedures used are similar for setting up workpieces on such common machine tools as drill presses, milling machines, shapers, and planers. (See Figs. 424-430.) For safe and accurate machining operations such as drilling, shaping, and milling, the workpiece must be set up and held securely. A variety of machine tool vises and setup tools is used for this purpose.

535. Fastening Work on the Drill Press Table

To keep the work from turning with the drill, always clamp it tightly on the *drill press*

Fig. 423. Drill Broken as a Result of Work Springing

table and clamp the table to the *column* (see Fig. 413). If the work springs or moves while it is being drilled the drill may bend and break, the work may be thrown from the table, and great injury may result to the operator and to the machine. Fig. 423 shows the results of the work springing.

Drill press tables, as well as the tables on other kinds of machine tools, have *slots* through which bolts may be slipped for clamping. Even when work seems well clamped, it often pulls loose. When this happens, step away from the machine and shut off the power.

A small nick on the drill press table will keep the work from lying perfectly flat. Some devices and methods of supporting and holding work on the drill press table are shown in Figs. 424-432. Similar work-holding devices and setups are used on other machines such as shapers and milling machines.

536. Strap Clamps

Six kinds of strap clamps are shown in Fig. 424. They are *plain clamp* or *strap, U-clamp, gooseneck clamp, screw-heel clamp, finger clamp,* and *double-finger clamp.* They are used to hold down the work. (See Figs. 426-427, 431-432.) These clamps are often made in the shop but may be bought just like any other tool. The *U-clamp* can be removed without removing the nut from the bolt. The *gooseneck clamp* can be used with a shorter bolt than the other clamps.

Sometimes the work is too high to be clamped in the ordinary way. In such cases, one or more holes are sometimes drilled in the sides of the work and *finger clamps* are placed in these holes to clamp the work to the table.

537.   T-Slot Bolts

T-slot bolts are usually used with the strap clamps. They may also be used to *bolt* the *drill vise* to the drill press table. The head of the bolt is made to fit the *T-slot* in the table. (See Figs. 424, 426-428, and 430.)

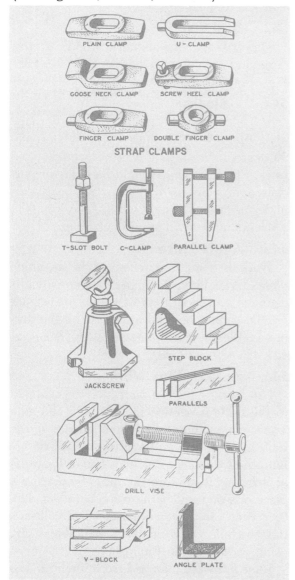

Fig. 424. **Tools for Holding Work on Drill Press**

538.   C-Clamp

A C-clamp, shaped like the letter C, is measured by the greatest distance it can be opened between the jaw and the end of the screw (see Fig. 535). It is made in many sizes and is very useful when clamping work to the table of the drill press. (See Figs. 424-425, and 428.)

539.   Parallel Clamp

A parallel clamp, also called a *toolmaker's clamp* or *machinists' clamp*, may be used to clamp work in place for drilling. (See Figs. 424 and 429 and §§ 91 and 683.)

540.   Jackscrew

The jackscrew, also known as a *planer jack*, ranges in height from two inches upward. It may be used for leveling or supporting odd-shaped work. (See Figs. 424, 428, and 926.)

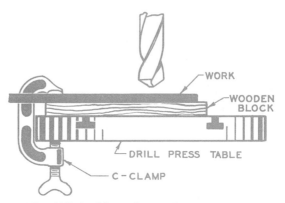

Fig. 425. **Holding Flat Work with a C-Clamp**

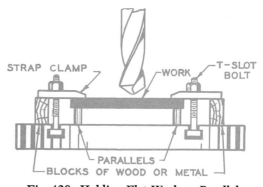

Fig. 426. **Holding Flat Work on Parallels**

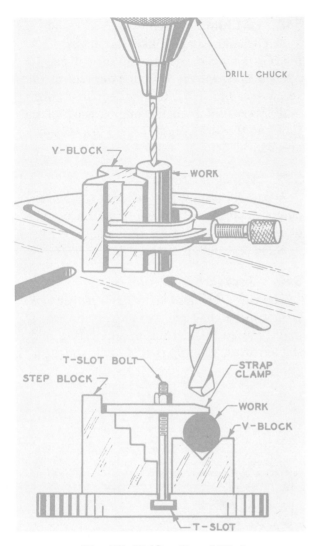

Fig. 427. Holding Round Work

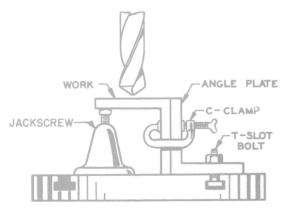

Fig. 428. Using Angle Plate and Jackscrew to Hold Work

541. Step Block

The step block is used to support and *block up* one end of a *strap clamp*. This levels the clamp so that both ends are the same height from the table. (See Figs. 424 and 427.)

542. Parallels

Parallels are strips of cast iron or steel with opposite sides *parallel*. They come in pairs exactly alike in size. Parallels are used in leveling or *blocking up* the work. A parallel is placed under each end of the work. (See Figs. 424, 426, and 429-431.)

543. Drill Vise

The drill vise is clamped to the drill press table and the work is held in the vise. (See Figs. 424 and 430.)

544. V-Blocks

A V-block gets its name from its *V* shape (see Fig. 424). The angle of the *V* is usually 90 degrees. V-blocks are used to hold round work, Fig. 427. They should be made or purchased in pairs so that one can be placed under each end of long work. (See Fig. 69.) They are made with or without *clamps*.

545. Angle Plate

Work is sometimes clamped to an *angle plate*, also called a *toolmaker's knee* which is clamped to the drill press table. Such work usually cannot be held otherwise on the drill press table while it is being drilled. (See Figs. 424, 428-429 and § 90.)

546. Holding Flat Work

Flat work, such as a *plate*, may be clamped to the table as shown in Figs. 425 and 426. The C-clamp should be on the left side of the table and the body of the clamp should be behind the work as in Fig. 425. The drill can be kept from cutting into the table by placing a piece of wood under the work as in Fig. 425, by setting the work so that the drill will pass into the hole in the center of the table, or by using *parallels* as in Fig. 426.

Some flat work may be held in the *drill vise* as explained in section 543 and Fig. 430.

547. Holding Round Work

Round work such as rods may be held in *V-blocks* as shown in Fig. 427.

548. Holding Odd-Shaped Work

Special holding tools may be needed to hold odd-shaped work. Some work may be fastened to an *angle plate* as shown in Figs. 428 and 429. Odd-shaped work held with *U-clamps* and *adjustable bolts* is shown in Figs. 431 and 432.

549. What Is a Drill Jig?

If many pieces of the same kind have to be drilled, time and money can be saved by designing and making a *drill jig*, Fig. 434, which is a tool for holding the work while it is being drilled. (See also Fig. 451.) There are many forms of drill jigs. The time which would be necessary to lay out the holes to be drilled in every piece is saved by using a drill jig. Of course, it takes time and costs from a dollar to hundreds and even thousands of dollars to make a jig. Costs must, therefore, be studied carefully before starting a job to see whether a jig would save time and money. A jig also helps to drill the holes more exactly than any other way (See *toolmaker* in Unit 2.)

550. What Are Drill Bushings?

Drill jigs are fitted with hardened steel bushings, called *drill bushings*. Fig. 433 shows three kinds of drill bushings, namely, *flush bushing*, *flanged bushing*, and *slip bushing*. They fit both the jigs and the drill. The drill bushing guides the drill.

Review Questions

1. What is a setup on a drill press?
2. Why should the work be clamped to the drill press table?
3. What is a strap clamp?
4. Describe a U-clamp.
5. For what are T-slot bolts used?
6. Describe a C-clamp. How is its size measured?
7. What is a step block?

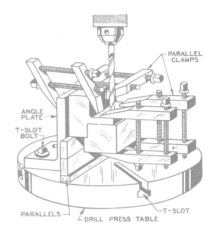

Fig. 429. Using Angle Plate, Parallels, and Parallel Clamps to Hold Work

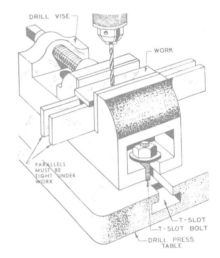

Fig. 430. Using Drill Vise and Parallels to Hold Work

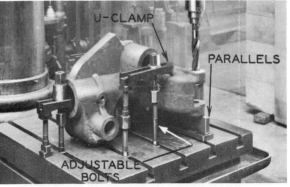

Fig. 431. Holding Odd-Shaped Work with U-Clamps and Adjustable Bolts
(Courtesy McGraw-Hill Book Co.)

8. What shape of metal is held with V-blocks?

9. What is a drill jig?

10. What is a drill bushing?

Coordination

Words to Know

adjustable bolt	plain clamp or strap
drill bushing	screw-heel clamp
drill jig	setting up
drill vise	slip bushing
double-finger clamp	slot
finger clamp	spherical
flanged bushing	step block
flush bushing	strap clamp
gooseneck clamp	T-slot clamp
jackscrew	U-clamp
parallels	

Drafting

1. Design a 4″ C-clamp.

2. Design a parallel clamp.

Fig. 432. **Holding Spherical Work with U-Clamps and Adjustable Bolts**
(Courtesy McGraw-Hill Book Co.)

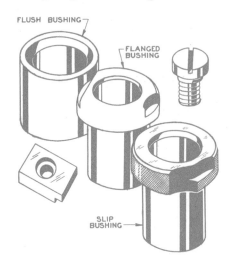

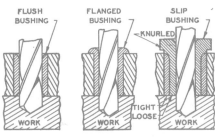

Fig. 433. **Drill Bushings**

Fig. 434. **Drill Jigs** (Courtesy Pratt & Whitney Co.)

Drilling

556. Rule for Cutting

The *cutting tool* must be harder than the material to be cut. (See also § 935.)

557. Drilling Speed

Drill speed is the distance a drill would travel in 1 minute if it were laid on its side and rolled. Thus a 1″ drill, turning 100 *revolutions*[1] per minute, would roll $1 \times 3.1416 \times 100 \div 12 = 26.18'$ per minute (*circumference* of a circle = diameter $\times$ 3.1416). Dividing by 12 changes the inches to feet.

The speed at which a drill may be turned depends upon:

(1) Its diameter.
(2) Whether it is made of *carbon steel* or *high-speed steel* (see §§ 328, 352, and 489).
(3) The hardness of the metal that is being drilled.

The smaller the diameter of the drill, the greater should be the speed; the larger the diameter, the slower should be the speed. Too slow a speed in drilling small holes is inefficient and can cause the drill to break. Table 17 shows that high-speed drills can be run twice as fast as carbon-steel drills. It also shows the speeds at which different metals should be drilled. Use a slow speed to drill hard metal and a fast speed to drill soft metal. If the corners of the cutting edges wear away quickly, Fig. 440, the speed should be reduced. The speed of a drill may be increased until it begins to show signs of wear; it should then be reduced a little and run regularly at this reduced speed.

Rules concerning speeds cannot be strictly followed because of the many different conditions. The operator's experience and judgment must help him decide at what speed a drill should be run to obtain the best results.

558. Feed

The *feed* of a drill is the distance it cuts into the metal in one turn. It is different for each size of drill and the various materials to

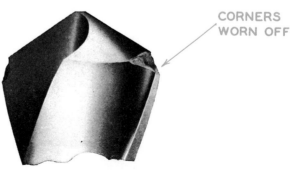

CORNERS
WORN OFF

Fig. 440. Result of Too Much Speed in Drilling
(Courtesy Cleveland Twist Drill Co.)

[1] *Revolution* means one turn completely around.

Table 17. DRILLING SPEEDS AND FEEDS
For Use with High-Speed Steel Drills
(See sections 557 and 558)

	SPEED IN REVOLUTIONS PER MINUTE (RPM) FOR HIGH-SPEED STEEL DRILLS (REDUCE RPM ONE-HALF FOR CARBON-STEEL DRILLS)				
DIAMETER OF DRILL	LOW-CARBON STEEL CAST IRON (SOFT) MALLEABLE IRON	MEDIUM-CARBON STEEL CAST IRON (HARD)	HIGH-CARBON STEEL HIGH-SPEED ALLOY STEEL	ALUMINUM AND ITS ALLOYS ORDINARY BRASS ORDINARY BRONZE	FEED PER REVOLUTION INCHES
	80-100 FT. PER. MIN.	70-80 FT. PER. MIN.	50-60 FT. PER. MIN.	200-300 FT. PER. MIN.	
⅛″	2445-3056	2139-2445	1528-1833	6112-9168	0.002
¼″	1222-1528	1070-1222	764-917	3056-4584	0.004
⅜″	815-1019	713-815	509-611	2038-3057	0.006
½″	611-764	534-611	382-458	1528-2292	0.007
¾″	407-509	357-407	255-306	1018-1527	0.010
1″	306-382	267-306	191-229	764-846	0.015

be drilled. The drill should be fed into the metal just as fast as it can cut.

As with speed, rules about feed cannot be strictly followed. Experience and judgment must again help to decide how fast the drill should be fed into the metal. The sizes of drills and the general feeds are given in Table 17 above. The feed should be the same for high-speed steel drills as for carbon-steel drills (see § 489).

Soft metals, such as brass and aluminum, can be drilled with a faster feed than hard metals.

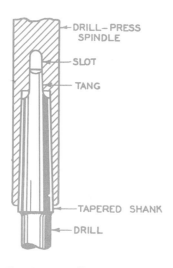

Fig. 441. Putting a Drill in a Drill-Press Spindle

559. Drill Press Lubrication

Oil the drill press daily. Be sure to use *lubricating oil* (see § 394). Put only a drop or two of oil in each *oil hole*. (See §§ 409 and 413.)

560. Putting Drill in Drill Press Spindle

A *tapered-shank drill* (see Fig. 377) must be well cleaned before putting it in the *drill press spindle*, Fig. 441 (see also Fig. 453). Examine the *shank* of the drill to make sure that it is not scratched or nicked. A scratched or nicked shank will not fit perfectly in the spindle and will cause the drill to wobble.

The *tang* of the drill should be in the same position as the *slot* in the spindle; a quick upward push fastens the drill in the spindle. The slot holds the tang and turns the drill with the spindle so that the drill cannot slip.

If the taper shank of the drill is too small to fit the spindle, place a *drill sleeve* (see Fig. 382) over the shank of the drill. Be sure that the drill sleeve is not scratched or nicked.

Section 574 tells how to remove a drill or drill chuck from the drill press spindle.

561. Putting Drill in Drill Chuck

A *straight-shank drill* (see Fig. 377) may be held in a *drill chuck* (see Fig. 384) which is held in the drill-press spindle. Tighten the chuck as much as you can with the *chuck key* so that the drill will not slip.

The drill chuck has three holes into which the chuck key may be inserted to tighten the jaws; by tightening up the jaws from three places, instead of just one, you get a better and more even grip on the drill. Many drill shanks get chewed up and ruined because they slip in the chuck.

Be sure to remove the chuck key from the drill chuck.

562. Laying Out Hole for Drilling

A layout should be made to show where the hole should be before it is drilled. The first step in laying out a hole to be drilled is to find the *center* (see §§ *115-118*). Next, put a small punch mark exactly at this center by tapping the *prick punch* very lightly with the hammer (see Fig. 98).

If the punch mark is to one side, as *A* in Fig. 442, it is necessary to slant the prick punch to move the mark exactly to the center, Fig. 443. Finish up with a light blow on the prick punch held in an upright position. When completed, the punch mark should be exactly in the center. (See *B* in Fig. 442.)

If the hole does not have to be drilled exactly, the punch mark should be made larger with a *center punch* to lead the point of the drill; then the work is ready for drilling. If the hole must be drilled exactly, read section 563.

563. Laying Out Hole for Exact Drilling

If a hole must be drilled exactly, a better layout than described in section *562* is needed. This is done as follows: Find the center of the hole (see §§ *115-118*) and put a small prick-punch mark at this center. Then, with the divider, scribe a circle the same size as the hole to be drilled (see Fig. 83), placing one leg of the divider in the prick-punch mark to keep it from slipping. Scribe a smaller circle inside the first one. This is called a

proof circle, Fig. 444; it helps to check that the drill is cutting in the center as will be seen when the hole is drilled (see § *564*). Next, put small prick-punch marks on both circles. Finally, enlarge the prick-punch mark in the center of the circles with a *center punch*. The layout is now ready for drilling.

564. Drilling Hole to Layout

After the hole is laid out as shown in Fig. 444, it is ready for drilling. To drill the hole, place the point of the drill, while it is turning,

Fig. 442. Punch Mark Before and After Correction

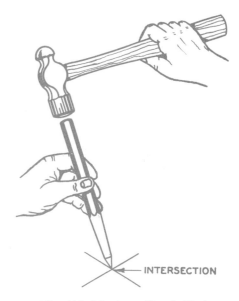

Fig. 443. Moving a Punch Mark

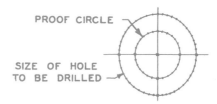

Fig. 444. Layout of a Hole for Exact Drilling

exactly over the center-punch mark and enlarge it a little with the drill, Fig. 445. Then raise the drill from the work and see if the circle made by the drill is *concentric*[2] with the *proof circle*. (See § 563.) If it is concentric, then the drilling may be continued until the hole is finished.

If the circle made by the drill is not concentric, but *eccentric*[2] as in Fig. 446, the drilled circle must be drawn back so that it will be concentric to the proof circle. This is known as *drawing the drill* and is explained

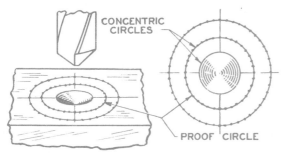

Fig. 445. Checking the Accuracy of the Hole

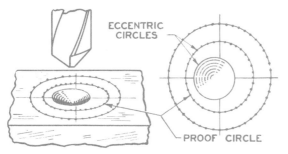

Fig. 446. Circle Made by the Drill is Eccentric to the Layout

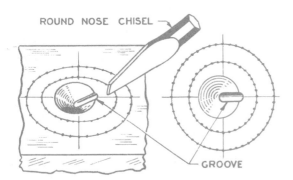

Fig. 447. Groove Is Cut to Draw the Drill to Proper Position

in section *565*. *Eccentricity* is caused by:

(1) Drill sharpened incorrectly (see § 506).
(2) Punch mark made with center punch not in exact center (see Fig. 442).
(3) Drill wobbling (see § 509).
(4) Hard spots in metal.

565. How to Draw the Drill

The way to draw the drill back to the center of the circle is to cut a groove down the side of the hole made by the *point* of the drill with a *round nose chisel* (see Fig. 186) or a *center punch;* this must be done on the side farthest from the *proof circle*, Fig. 447. This groove is then drilled out; the drill bites into the edge of the groove, makes an egg-shaped hole, and thus shifts the center of the drill to the center of the proof circle.

The drill can only be shifted as long as the two lip corners *A* and *B* shown in Fig. 448 do not touch the metal. After the groove has been drilled out, see if the new circle made by the drill is *concentric* (see Fig. 445) with the proof circle. If not, another groove must be cut and the steps repeated until the circle made by the drill is concentric with the proof circle, after which the hole may be drilled until finished.

566. Cautions when Drilling a Through Hole

A twist drill that is just breaking through the other side of the hole acts just like a corkscrew. This is when drilling a hole with a twist drill is the most dangerous. The drill

[2]*Concentric* means having the same center. *Eccentric* means having different centers.

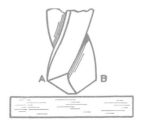

Fig. 448. Drill can Shift Only Until Corners *A* and *B* Start Cutting

may grab and break off or the work may be torn loose from its holdings. To prevent this, hold back on the feed as the drill point begins to break through the underside of the work. *Straight-fluted drills* do not act this way. (See 487.)

567. Drilling Large Holes

The larger the drill the thicker is the *web* between the *flutes* and the wider is the *dead center* (see Fig. 395). This dead center does not cut; it interferes with the drill cutting into the metal. To overcome this when drilling a large hole, a small hole (a little larger than the thickness of the web of the large drill) is first drilled through the metal. This small hole is called a *pilot hole*, Fig. 449. The large drill may then be used to enlarge the hole. The pilot hole must be drilled exactly to the layout because the large drill will follow the pilot hole exactly. Thus the pilot hole leads or steers the large drill.

568. Drilling Holes to Depth

Most drilling machine spindles or quills are marked in inches and have a *feed stop* (see Figs 412 and 413). To drill a hole to a certain depth, this stop may be set, making use of the depth scale, so that cutting will stop when the desired depth is reached. This is especially useful when many holes of the same depth have to be drilled. If there are no marks on the spindle, a mark may be made with a pencil to show the depth of the hole. (See § 570.)

569. Chips

Note the difference between cast iron and steel *chips* or *shavings*, Fig. 450. When the drill is correctly sharpened, *cast iron chips* are small, broken pieces of metal while *steel shavings* are long curls. (See Fig. 971.)

Chips and shavings have sharp edges and points and may cause bad cuts if picked up with the fingers. They should be removed from the work with a blunt tool or a brush.

570. Keep Flutes Clean of Chips

During the drilling be sure that the flutes of the drill are kept open. Clogging of the flutes may cause the drill to break. To prevent this, the drill may have to be pulled out of the hole a number of times and the chips cleared away.

The flutes are more likely to clog when drilling cast iron than when drilling steel. This is also more likely to happen when drilling deep holes than when drilling shallow ones. When drilling deep holes it may be necessary to take the chips out of the hole with a long *magnet* (see § 472) or to blow them out through a long tube. When a tube is used, it should be bent so that the chips will not fly into the operator's face. Oil-tube drills may be used to drill deep holes (see § 573).

571. Drilling with Cutting Fluids

When drilling, the metal chips rub over the lips of the drill and cause heat. The curling of the chips over the cutting edges of the drill also causes heat, much the same as when a piece of wire is bent back and forth quickly.

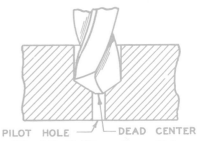

Fig. 449. Drilling a Large Hole

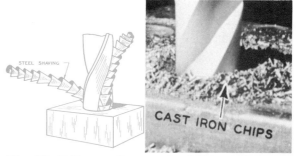

Fig. 450. Difference Between Steel Chips and Cast Iron Chips (Courtesy United Chromium, Inc.)

This heat may *draw the temper* (see § 954) and soften the drill. A *cutting fluid* should, therefore, be used to take the heat away from the lips of the drill and to wash away the chips (see §§ 386 and 387). The drill will thus last longer, and the hole will be smoother. The cutting fluid should be used to cool and lubricate the work. The fluid should be dropped into the hole alongside the drill, thus allowing the oil to run down the flutes of the drill.

Copper is a soft, ductile, and a good heat conductor metal. For this reason, a drill may be fed into the material with a high rate of feed. However, the lip clearance angle of the drill must be greater when drilling soft material. This is true because the high feed rate will cause the lip clearance angle surface to rub as it advances into the metal. Excessive rubbing will result in a *glazed*, hard, shiny, surface in the hole. The proper cutting action must take place or the drill will be ruined.

Cast iron and copper do not require a cutting fluid. However, an emulsifiable oil solution is sometimes used for cooling purposes when drilling these materials. The cutting fluid also tends to keep down dust from the chip when drilling many holes in cast iron. When a few holes are drilled, ordinary lubricating oil may be used. When several holes are drilled, cutting fluids should be used, Table 15, page 169. If the drill squeaks or chatters, it is usually a sign that the drill is dull or the setup is incorrect. (See § 406.)

572. Cooling Systems

In shops where quantities of lubricant are needed, large systems of tanks and pumps are set up and the *cutting fluid* is forced through pipes to the work on the machines, Fig. 451. Machines on which much cutting fluid is used have troughs around the tables to keep the fluid from running to the floor, Fig. 451. (See §§ 414 and 571.)

Fig. 452. **Oil-Tube Drills**

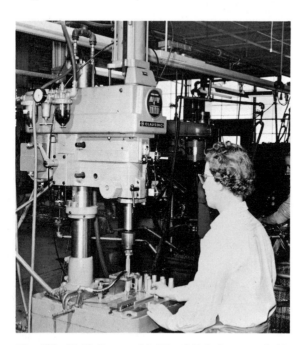

Fig. 451. **Drill Press with Piped Lubricant and Air Feed Increases Production 100% in Appliance Manufacturing Concern**
(Courtesy Clausing Division, Atlas Press Co.)

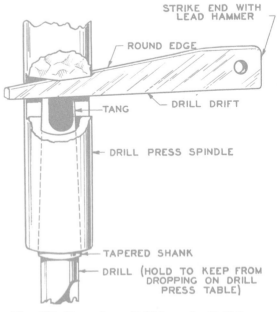

Fig. 453. **Removing a Drill from the Drill-Press Spindle with a Drill Drift**

573. Oil-Tube Drills

Since heat is produced at the *point* of the drill, it is best, especially when drilling deep holes, that the oil be applied at the point of the drill. Thus, oil-tube drills, Fig. 452, are sometimes used. The oil is pumped through the drill to the *drill point*. As it is carried up the flutes, it takes away the heat and washes away the chips.

574. Removing Drill from Drill Press Spindle

The drill or drill chuck should be removed from the drill press spindle with a *drill drift*, Fig. 453. Note that one edge of the drill drift is rounded while the other edge is flat.

To remove the drill or drill chuck, put the end of a drill drift into the slot of the spindle with the rounded edge of the drill drift against the upper, rounded part of the slot (see Fig. 441). Hold the drill with one hand so that it will not drop and nick the drill press table. Strike the wide end of the drill drift lightly with a *lead hammer*. (See Fig. 538.)

A drill drift should also be used to remove a drill from a *drill sleeve* or a *drill socket* (see Figs. 382 and 383).

Review Questions

1. What does RPM stand for?
2. Should a small drill run slower or faster than a large drill, drilling the same material?
3. How can you tell when a drill is running too fast?
4. Why must the hole in the spindle be clean before putting a drill, sleeve, or chuck in it?
5. Should a tapered shank drill be placed in a drill chuck? Why?
6. What kind of drill should be placed in the drill chuck?
7. Why does a drill chuck have three holes?
8. What is a layout for drilling?
9. Name the drill-press layout tools.
10. What is a proof circle?
11. What is the meaning of concentric?
12. What is the meaning of eccentric?
13. How may the chips be removed from a deep hole?
14. Should a lubricant be used when drilling cast iron? Why?
15. What is wrong when a drill squeaks while drilling?
16. How should a drill chuck be removed from the spindle?
17. How should a drill sleeve be removed from a drill?

Coordination

Words to Know

concentric	lead hammer
drill drift	pilot hole
drilling speed	proof circle
eccentric	revolution
eccentricity	taper-shank drill
glazing	

Mathematics

1. What is the difference between RPM and peripheral speed?
2. How many RPM should a ⅞″ carbon-steel drill make to cut steel?
3. How many RPM should a ⅝″ high-speed steel drill make to cut cast iron?

Drafting

1. Design a drill drift.

Occupational Information

1. How may one be injured while drilling?

Other Drill Press Operations

Countersinking, Counterboring, Reaming, Spot Facing, and Tapping

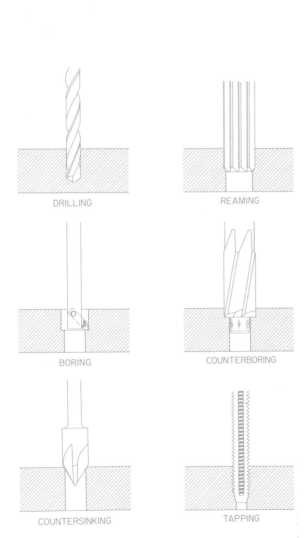

DRILLING

REAMING

BORING

COUNTERBORING

COUNTERSINKING

TAPPING

Fig. 457. Six Common Operations that Can Be Performed on a Drill Press

580. Other Drill Press Work

Other work than drilling may be done on the drill press. Six basic kinds of *hole machining operations*, Fig. 457, are commonly performed on a drill press:

(1) *Drilling.*
(2) *Reaming.*
(3) *Countersinking.*
(4) *Counterboring* and *Spot Facing.*
(5) *Tapping.*
(6) *Boring.*

Another kind of operation, *spot-finishing*, can also be done on a drill press. This is explained in section 1115.

The basic hole machining operations listed above can also be performed on many other kinds of machine tools. They can be performed on such basic machine tools as the metal-turning lathe (see Unit 57) and on vertical and horizontal milling machines (see Unit 60). These operations can also be performed on special mass-production machine tools such as turret lathes, screw machines, tapping machines, boring machines, and multipurpose machine tools. The same principles involved in doing the six hole-machining operations on a drill press also apply when performing these operations on other kinds of machine tools.

581. Reasons for Reaming

A drilled hole is always larger than the diameter of the drill. Several reasons are given in section 564. When a perfectly round hole of a certain diameter with straight and smooth walls is desired, the hole should first be drilled $\frac{1}{64}''$ or $\frac{1}{32}''$ smaller than the final diameter of the hole and then *reamed*.[1] Section 584 explains the sizes of drills and reamers needed.

582. Kinds of Reamers

Reaming is done with a multiple-tooth cutting tool called a *reamer*, Fig. 459. The reamer is a *finishing tool* which machines holes straight and true to the exact size desired.

Reamers are available in a wide variety of types and sizes. They generally are made of carbon-tool steel (see § 328) or high-speed steel (see § 352). They are also available with cemented carbide-tipped (see § 350) cutting edges. Carbon-tool steel reamers generally are satisfactory for hand reaming applications. High-speed steel reamers and reamers with carbide-tipped cutting edges wear longer and stay sharp longer for machine reaming applications.

Principal Kinds

The many types of reamers can be classified in two ways: those which are turned by hand, called *hand reamers,* and those used on machines, called *chucking* or *machine reamers,* Fig. 458. *Hand reamers* have a straight shank with a square end. They are turned with a tap wrench which fits over the square end, Fig. 460. *Chucking reamers* may have either tapered shanks with a standard morse taper, or they may have plain, straight shanks which fit into collets or adapters on special production machines. Taper-shank reamers generally are used on drill presses and metalworking lathes. The tapered shank fits into the tapered spindle of the drill press. A taper-shank reamer, like a taper-shank drill, can also be installed in the tailstock of a metalworking lathe, Fig. 1050.

[1]*Ream* comes from the German word *raümer* which means a person, tool, or instrument that cleans and makes room. Hence, the tool for cleaning out and enlarging a drilled hole is called a *reamer.*

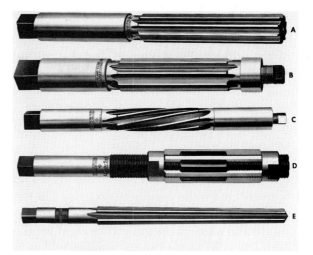

Fig. 458. Types of Hand Reamers
(Courtesy Cleveland Twist Drill Co.)
  A. **Straight-fluted**
  B. **Expansion, straight flute**
  C. **Expansion, LH helical flute**
  D. **Adjustable**
  E. **Taper pin**

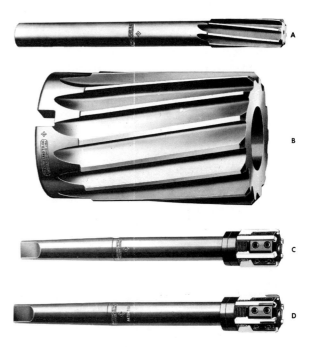

Fig. 459. Types of Machine Reamers
(Courtesy Cleveland Twist Drill Co.)
  A. **Straight-shank**
  B. **Helical-fluted shell**
  C. **Adjustable**
  D. **Carbide-tipped adjustable**

Cutting Action

A drill cuts with its cutting edges on the end of the drill. Machine reamers are *end-cutting* reamers which have their cutting edges on the end, and they cut in much the same manner as a drill. The cutting edges are beveled at a 40° to 50° angle, usually 45°, at the end of the reamer.

Hand reamers, however, cut in a manner quite different than machine reamers. Hand reamers cut on the periphery (outside) at the tapered portion of the reamer. The flutes on solid-hand reamers are ground straight for the entire length, except for a portion which is ground with a *starting taper* at the end. The tapered portion does the cutting with a *scraping* action, very much like a hand-scraping tool. (See § 260.) The length of the tapered portion of the reamer is generally about equal to the diameter of the reamer.

Flutes

The flutes on reamers may be *straight* or *helical*. Straight-fluted reamers work well for reaming average materials. Helical-fluted reamers are designed for reaming materials which are considered difficult to ream. The

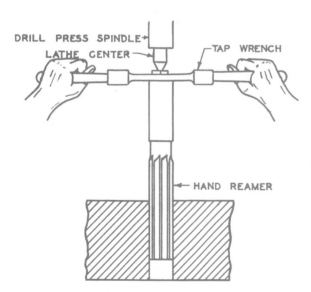

Fig. 460. Steadying a Hand Reamer with a Lathe Center in the Drill-Press Spindle (Hand Reaming)

helical flutes aid in producing smoother and more accurate holes.

Solid Type

The solid type reamers of both the hand and chucking types, Figs. 458 (*A*) and 459 (*A*), are made from one solid piece of steel. They are designed to produce a hole of one specific size. They cannot be adjusted to cut oversize or undersize.

Expansion reamers, Fig. 458 (*B*) and 458 (*C*), are designed so that the diameter can be expanded slightly to produce a hole slightly oversize for a desirable fit. This kind of operation is often necessary in assembly and maintenance work. The maximum amount of expansion varies according to the diameter of the reamer. It may range from 0.006″ for a ¼″ reamer to 0.012″ for a 1½″ reamer. The reamer is provided with an adjustment screw which is used for expanding the diameter of the reamer. It cannot be adjusted to produce undersize holes. An undersize pilot is provided on the end of some expansion reamers, Figs. 458 (*B*) and 458 (*C*), to aid in aligning the reamer for straight cutting. Expansion reamers may be either the hand or chucking type.

Adjustable reamers, Figs. 458 (*D*), 459 (*C*), and 459 (*D*), can be adjusted to produce holes of any size within the size adjustment range of the reamer. These reamers are available in either the hand or chucking type, in size ranges from ¼″ to about 3¹¹⁄₃₂″ diameter. Hand reamers from ¼″ to ¹⁵⁄₁₆″ diameter are available in size ranges in steps of ¹⁄₃₂″. A ¼″ reamer may be adjusted for holes from ¼″ to ⁹⁄₃₂″, a ⁹⁄₃₂″ reamer for holes from ⁹⁄₃₂″ to ⁵⁄₁₆″, and so on. Reamers larger than ¹⁵⁄₁₆″ have adjustment size ranges in steps of ¹⁄₁₆″ or larger. The adjustable hand reamer in Fig. 458 (*D*) is provided with cutting blades which slide in precise, tapered slots. The diameter of the reamer is adjusted by loosening the nut on one end of the blades and tightening the nut on the other end, thus sliding the blades in the slots. When the blades become worn out they may be replaced with new blades without grinding.

Shell reamers are primarily machine reamers. They are available with straight flutes or with helical flutes as shown in Fig. 459 (*B*). They have a tapered hole which fits tightly on an arbor. Shell reamers of several sizes may fit the same arbor.

Other Reamers

See *taper-pin reamer* in section 752, *pipe-burring reamer* in section 772, and *pipe reamer* in section 775.

583. Care of Reamers

The *reamer* is a very fine tool and must, therefore, be handled with the greatest of care. Particular pains must be taken to protect the *cutting edges*, for a small nick or *burr* (see § 262) will cause the reamer to cut oversize and also to scratch the inside wall instead of making a smooth finish. It is best to store each reamer in a separate wooden box or space in the tool cabinet.

584. Hole Size for Machine Reaming

The reamer should be used to make only a light, *finishing cut*. If a drawing calls for a ⅞″ reamed hole, then a drill ¹⁄₆₄″ smaller, or ⁵⁵⁄₆₄″, must first be used and the hole then reamed with a ⅞″ reamer. Thus, a 1″ reamed hole would need a ⁶³⁄₆₄″ drill. The difference between the sizes of the reamer and the drill, which is ¹⁄₆₄″, is called the *allowance*.

For reamed holes larger than 1″, the allowance may be ¹⁄₃₂″. Therefore, a 2″ reamed hole would need a 1³¹⁄₃₂″ drill. The usual allowances for reamed holes are ¹⁄₆₄″ for up to 1″ holes and ¹⁄₃₂″ for holes from 1″ to 2″.

Fig. 131 shows how a reamer should be measured with a micrometer.

585. Hand Reaming

Hand reaming is performed when extreme accuracy is required. It is done with *hand*

reamers which are specially designed for hand reaming. A cut of 0.002″ is usually recommended. *Never take cuts greater than 0.005″ with a hand reamer.* Hence, never allow more than 0.005″ material allowance. Holes which are to be hand reamed are generally drilled about ¹⁄₆₄″ to ¹⁄₃₂″ undersize first. They are then bored about 0.002″ to 0.005″ under the desired size of the reamed hole. Another method involves drilling and rough reaming to about 0.002″ undersize, followed by hand reaming. Rough reaming is done with a reamer intentionally ground about 0.002″ undersize, thus leaving an allowance of 0.002″ for hand reaming.

It helps, when hand reaming, to put a lathe center (see § 1193) into the drill press spindle and to hold it tightly against the small hole in the end of the reamer while turning the reamer with a tap wrench. It steadies the reamer and keeps it straight with the hole until it is started. A slow, steady, screwlike motion by the reamer with fast *feed* (see § 558) gives the best results. The reamer should never be forced or strained and should always be turned *clockwise*[2] even when removing it from the hole.

586. Machine Reaming

The *machine reamer* is used in the *drill press spindle* just like a drill, Fig. 461. It must always be in a straight line with the hole. For

[2]*Clockwise* means the direction in which the hands of a clock turn.

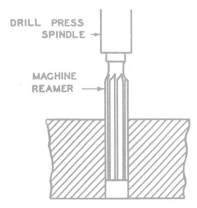

DRILL PRESS SPINDLE →

MACHINE REAMER →

Fig. 461. Reaming on the Drill Press (Machine Reaming)

this reason, it is best to remove the drill and insert the reamer without disturbing the setup of the work.

The *speed* for reaming should be much slower than for drilling, while the feed is usually faster than for drilling (see §§ 557

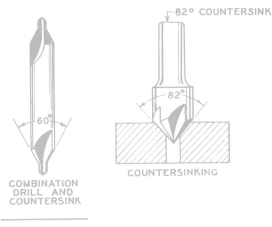

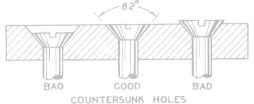

Fig. 462. Countersinking

Fig. 463. Counterboring for a Fillister Head Screw
(Courtesy The Foote-Burt Co.)

and 558). Cutting fluid should always be used when reaming steel. (See Fig. 598 and Table 15, page 169.)

587. Reasons for Countersinking

Sometimes the top of a drilled hole must be made larger for the *head* of a *flat-head screw* so that its top will be even with the top of the work, Fig. 462. This is known as *countersinking*.

Centerdrilling is explained in section 1191. A centerdrill is sometimes used as a starting drill to locate a hole that is to be drilled by a larger drill. (See also § 564.)

588. Countersinks

Countersinking is done with a *countersink*. There are several forms of countersinks. (See Fig. 462.) The difference in countersinks is the *angle* of the cutting edges (see § 84). One kind has an angle of 82° for *flat-head screws;* the other kind, known as a *combination drill and countersink*, or *centerdrill*, has an angle of 60°. The centerdrill has a small drill point and is used mainly to countersink the ends of the work to be held between *centers* on the *lathe* (see § 1193 and Fig. 1032).

589. Countersinking

Countersinking on the drill press is shown in Fig. 462. The 82° *countersink* should run at a slow speed to avoid *chattering* (see § 172) while the *centerdrill* should run at a high speed. Use cutting oil when countersinking steel. (See centerdrilling on lathe in Fig. 1032.)

590. Reason for Counterboring

The heads of *fillister-head screws* are usually set down into the work, Fig. 463. Making the top of a hole larger to receive the head of a fillister-head screw is called *counterboring*.

591. Counterbore

Counterboring is done with a cutting tool known as a *counterbore* (see Fig. 463). It has a small end which leads or steers the tool into the hole and keeps it central; this small end is called a *pilot*.

592. Counterboring

Counterboring is done after the hole is drilled. (See Fig. 463.) The *speed* for counterboring should be slower than for drilling (see § 557). The *pilot* should be oiled before entering the hole to keep it from getting rough. Use cutting oil when counterboring steel.

593. Spot Facing

Spot facing is somewhat like counterboring except that in spot facing only a little metal is removed around the top of the hole. Only the surface is made smooth and square to form a flat *bearing surface* for the head of a *cap screw* or for a nut, Fig. 464. Spot facing is done with a *spot-facing tool* after the hole is drilled, Fig. 465.

594. What Does Tapping Mean?

The forming of *screw threads* on the inside of a hole, as the threads in a *nut*, is called *tapping*. Since "Taps and Tapping" are explained in Unit 33, only tapping in the drill press is explained here.

595. Taps

Tapping is done with a tool called a *tap*. (See Fig. 507.) It is a screwlike tool with two, three, or four *flutes*. (See § 649.) The size of the tap and the *number of threads per inch* (see §§ 610-611) are always stamped on the *shank* of the tap. The edges of the threads formed by the flutes do the cutting.

596. Tapping on the Drill Press

A hole must be drilled before it can be *tapped*. Note that the drilled hole must be smaller than the size of the tap in order to leave enough metal to form the threads. (See Fig. 509.) The drilled hole should be a little larger than the diameter at the bottom or *root of the thread*. (See § 652.) If the drilled hole is too small, the tap will break. Refer to Table 20 on tap drill sizes for this information.

Hand Operated

The tap may be held in a drill chuck. It must be in a straight line with the hole and may then be screwed into the hole by running the drill press by hand, forming the threads as it goes, Fig. 466. Ask the teacher to show you how to do this. A thin mixture of *white* lead and cutting fluid (see §§ 394 and 397) is good for tapping steel. (See Table 15, page 169.)

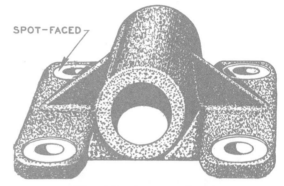

Fig. 464. Spot-Faced Holes

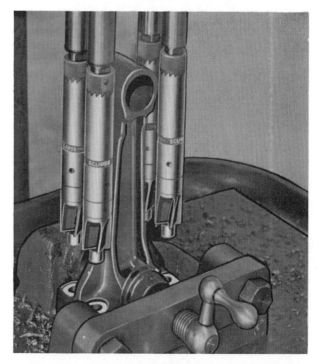

Fig. 465. Spot-Facing to Form a Bearing Surface
for a Cap Screw
(Courtesy Eclipse Counterbore Co.)

After the hole is tapped, the tap may be taken out by running the drill press backwards by hand.

Tapping with Power

A *tapping attachment*, as shown in Fig. 467, may be mounted on a drill press for tapping. The tap is mounted in a collet chuck which is provided in the tapping attachment. The workpiece to be tapped must be mounted securely in a vise. The vise should also be clamped or bolted down to the drill press table. The tap should be carefully aligned with the hole so that the thread will be tapped straight.

Several kinds of tapping attachments are available for use on drill presses. The tapping attachment in Fig. 467 is the nonreversing-type which *does not require that the drill press spindle be reversed to extract the tap* after tapping the hole. With this type of attachment, the tap enters the hole with right-hand rotation as pressure is applied downward on the drill-press feed handle. When the hole is tapped to depth, pressure on the feed handle is released and the tap stops rotating, even though the drill press spindle continues to rotate. The tap is extracted from the hole by applying upward pressure on the spindle with the drill-press feed handle. The upward pressure causes the tap to rotate in a reverse direction, opposite to the spindle rotation.

Some tapping attachments used on drill presses are the reversing-type. With this type, the drill press spindle must be reversed in order to extract the tap after tapping to the desired depth.

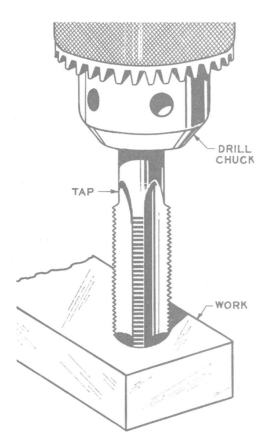

Fig. 466. **Tapping on the Drill Press**
This is an accurate method to use for alignment.

Fig. 467. **Tapping Attachment Mounted on Drill Press (Courtesy Supreme Products — Rigid Tool Co.)**

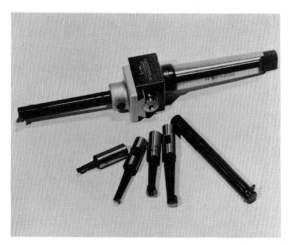

Fig. 468. Adjustable Boring Head and Boring Tools
(Courtesy I.S.U. Photographic Service)

597. Boring

Boring, Fig. 457, is performed to produce a very straight hole to accurate size. When a drill or reamer of the proper size is not available, a hole may be bored to accurate size instead. For ordinary boring, the hole is drilled from ¹⁄₁₆″ to ⅛″ undersize and is then bored to the desired size.

Boring is performed with a single-point cutting tool as in Figs. 457 and 468. In Fig. 468 a *boring bar* is inserted in a *boring head* which may be inserted in the tapered spindle of a drill press or milling machine. The boring head can be adjusted to bore holes accurately to 0.001″ (one thousandth of an inch), or closer. The *cutting-tool bit* mounted in the boring bar in Figs. 457 and 468 is held in place by a setscrew. The tool bit can be resharpened or replaced when worn out. Holes may also be bored with similar boring tools on a metalworking lathe, as shown in Figs. 1051 and 1052.

Review Questions

1. Name some of the work which can be done on the drill press, besides drilling.

2. Does a drill cut a hole exactly its own size? Why?

3. Does a reamer cut a hole exactly its own size?

4. What is the difference between a machine reamer and a hand reamer? List several kinds of reamers.

5. How much metal should be left for the hand reamer to cut away?

6. How much metal should be left for a machine reamer to cut away?

7. Explain how a machine reamer cuts. Also, how does a hand reamer cut?

8. What should you do if the tapered shank of the reamer is too small to fit into the drill press spindle?

9. In what way is an expansion reamer different from an adjustable reamer?

10. What is meant by countersinking?

11. For what is a combination drill and countersink used?

12. What are the included angles of countersinks?

13. What is the difference between countersinking and counterboring?

14. What is the difference between counterboring and spot facing?

15. What is meant by tapping?

16. What is the name of the tool used for tapping?

17. Explain how tapping may be done on a drill press.

18. Is the tap drill the same size as the tap? Why?

19. How can you find out what size tap drill to use?

20. What size tap drill is needed for a ¼″ UNC tap? ⅜″ UNC tap? ⁷⁄₁₆″ UNC tap? ¼″ UNF tap? ⁵⁄₁₆″ UNF tap? ½″ UNF tap?

21. What is a good cutting fluid for tapping?

22. Explain what boring is and how it is done on a drill press.

Coordination
Words to Know

allowance
cap screw
centerdrill
chucking reamer
combination drill
  and countersink
counterbore
countersink
expansion reamer
fillister-head screw
finishing cut
hand reamer

lathe center
machine reamer
pilot
reaming
root of thread
set-up
shank
spot facing
spot-facing tool
tap drill
tapping
tap wrench

Mathematics

1. What size drill should you use for a ⅞″ reamed hole?

2. What size drill should you use for a 1⅜″ reamed hole?

3. What is the tap drill size for a ¾″ UNC tap?

4. What is the tap drill size for a ¾″ UNF tap?

Occupational Information

1. What are the duties of a drilling machine operator?

This Punch Press has Dual Controls on the Stroke Which are
Controlled by Two Workmen to Insure Safety
(Courtesy International Harvester Co.)

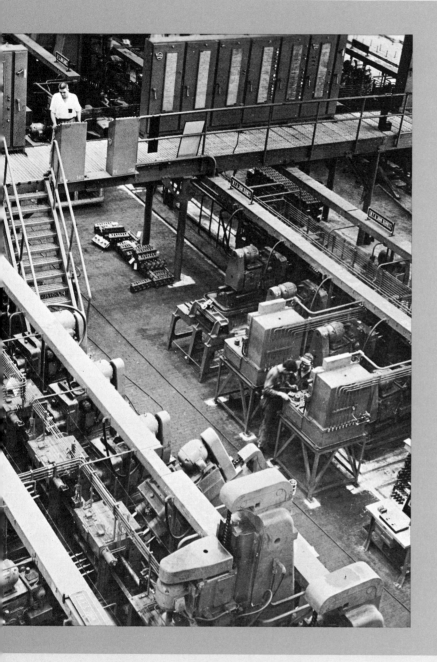

Automobile Engine Block
Heads Are
Automatically Drilled
and Tapped on This
Transfer Machine
(Courtesy Chrysler Corp.)

Threads, Dies,
and Taps

Part *VI*

Screw Threads

602. What Is a Screw Thread?

The winding groove around a bolt, screw, or in the hole of a nut forms a thread, also called a *screw thread,* Fig. 471. (See § 37.) The thread on a rod or screw is an *external thread,* Fig. 471. The thread on the inside of a hole or nut is an *internal thread,* Fig. 471. A thread is an *inclined plane* that spirals around the circumference of the internal and external surface of a bolt or nut. It is also one of the six basic machines.

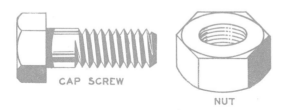

Fig. 471. **Threads on Screw and Nut**

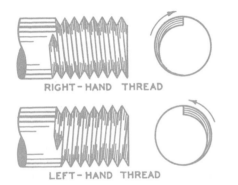

Fig. 472. **Right-Hand and Left-Hand Threads**

603. Right-Hand and Left-Hand Threads

A bolt which is turned *clockwise* to screw it into a nut has right-hand threads (RH), Fig. 472. Most threads are right hand. A bolt which is turned *counterclockwise*[1] to screw it into a nut has *left-hand threads* (LH). For example, the *shaft* on a grinder, which has two grinding wheels (see Fig. 858), has left-hand threads on one end and right-hand threads on the other end. The threads in the nut in each case are also left-hand or right-hand just as the threads on the shaft. (See § 1037.)

604. Single, Double, Triple, and Quadruple Threads

A *single thread* is formed by cutting one groove, Fig. 473. Most screws and bolts are single threaded. A *double thread* has two grooves, a *triple thread* has three grooves, and a *quadruple thread* has four grooves alongside each other. Double, triple, and quadruple threads are also known as *multiple threads* which means more than one thread.

In one turn on a single thread, the nut moves forward the distance of one thread, on a double thread it moves twice as far, on a triple thread it moves three times as far, and on a quadruple thread four times as far.

---

[1]*Counterclockwise* (CCW) means opposite to the direction in which the hands of a clock turn.

Whether a piece is single threaded or multiple threaded may be determined by looking at the end of the bolt or screw and counting the grooves that have been started. The thread on a fountain pen is a good example of a multiple thread.

605. Major Diameter of a Thread

The *major diameter* was formerly known as the *outside diameter*, abbreviated *OD*. It is the largest diameter of a straight external or internal thread, Fig. 474. On an external thread, the major diameter is the actual diameter measured across the outside diameter of the thread, Fig. 474. On an internal thread,

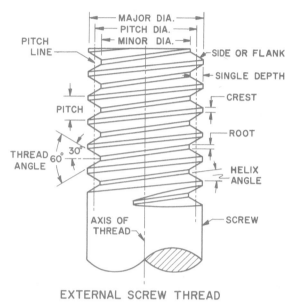

EXTERNAL SCREW THREAD

Fig. 474. Principal Parts of a Screw Thread

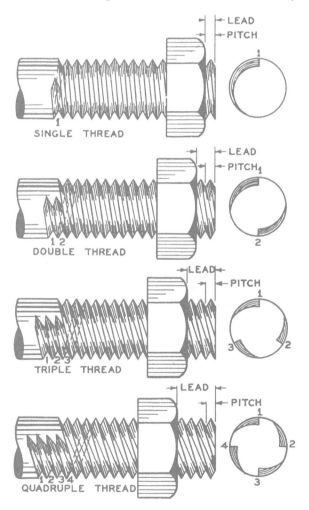

Fig. 473. Single, Double, Triple, and Quadruple Threads

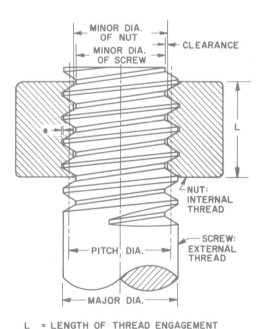

L = LENGTH OF THREAD ENGAGEMENT
e = EXTENDED MAJOR DIAMETER OF TAP FOR CLEARANCE

Fig. 475. Comparison Between the Minor Diameters of a Screw and a Nut, Showing Clearance

External threads and internal threads have the same basic pitch diameters.

the major diameter is the diameter at the bottom or root of the thread, Fig. 475.

The major diameter is similar to the nominal (basic) size. The *nominal size* is used for general identification, such as identifying the thread size as ¼″ or ½″ diameter. The *basic size* is the size from which size limits (see § 1141) are derived by applying *tolerances* (see § 1142) and *allowances* (see § 1143). Thus the basic size of the thread on a ½″ diameter rod or bolt is ½″, and this is also the nominal size.

In modern production, tolerances and allowances are applied to the major diameter and other parts of screw threads. Therefore, the actual major diameter is usually a few thousandths of an inch smaller or larger than the basic size. The major diameter of an external thread is usually smaller. However, on an internal thread, the major diameter is usually larger than the basic size. Tolerances and allowances also apply to the minor diameter (§ 606) and the pitch diameter (§ 609) of screw threads. The tolerances and allowances for screw threads of various sizes are available in standard handbooks for machinists.

606. Minor Diameter of a Thread

The *minor diameter* was formerly known as the *root diameter* (RD). It is the smallest diameter of a straight external or internal thread, Figs. 474 and 475.

The bottom surface which joins the two sides of the thread groove is called the *root*, Fig. 474. The root of an external thread is at its minor diameter, Fig. 474. The root of an internal thread is at its major diameter, Fig. 475.

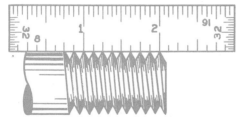

Fig. 476. Finding Number of Threads per Inch with a Steel Rule

The top surface which joins the sides of a thread is called the *crest*, Fig. 474. The crest of an internal thread is at its minor diameter.

The minor diameter (*RD*) of a screw thread is equal to the *major diameter* (*OD*) minus the *double depth* (*DD*).

Thus: RD = OD − DD

607. Thread Depth

The *depth of thread* (*D*), which is also called *height,* is the vertical distance between the top (crest) and the bottom (root) of the thread groove. This is the *single depth* of *thread.*

608. Double Depth of Thread

The *depth of thread* multiplied by two equals the *double depth of thread* (*DD*).

Thus: D × 2 = DD

The double depth of thread must be known to find the *minor diameter* of the thread.

609. Pitch Diameter (PD)

On a perfect thread the *pitch diameter* (*PD*) is an imaginary line which passes through the thread at a point where the width of the thread and the width of the groove are equal, Figs. 474 and 475. Through careful control of the pitch diameter, when cutting threads, the proper fit (see § 618) or class (see § 620) of thread can be produced. The pitch diameter may be measured with a screw thread micrometer, Fig. 126. (Also see § 644.)

The pitch diameter (*PD*) equals the *outside diameter* (*OD*) minus the *single depth* (*D*) of an external thread. (See Fig. 474.)

Thus: PD = OD − D

Thread *clearance* (also called *crest clearance*) is provided between internal and external mating threads, as shown in Fig. 475.

610. Finding Number of Threads Per Inch with a Steel Rule

The *number of threads per inch* on a bolt may be found by placing the edge of a steel rule on the threads as shown in Fig. 476. The

1″ mark should be directly above one of the threads. Then count the number of grooves or spaces in 1″; this number will be the *number of threads per inch.*

611. Finding Number of Threads Per Inch with Screw-Pitch Gage

The quickest and most exact way to find the number of threads per inch on a bolt or a nut is with a *screw-pitch gage,* Fig. 477. Try different *blades* of the gage on the threads until you find one that fits, Fig. 478. The number stamped on the blade is the *number of threads per inch.*

612. Pitch of Thread

The pitch (P) of the thread is the distance from a point on one thread to a corresponding point on the next thread. (See Figs. 474 and 480.) The *pitch* equals 1″ divided by the number of threads per inch. For example, a screw having 8 threads per inch has a pitch of ⅛″, that is, 1″ ÷ 8 = ⅛″. This means that a screw has threads that are ⅛″ apart from center to center. (See *micrometer screw* § 153.)

613. Lead of Thread

The *lead* of a thread (pronounced to rhyme with bead) is the distance the screw moves into the nut in one complete turn (see Fig. 473). Thus, on a *single thread* the lead is the same as the *pitch;* on a *double thread* the lead equals twice the pitch, and on a *triple thread* the lead equals three times the pitch, etc.

614. Sharp V-Thread

The simplest form of thread is the sharp V-thread. (See Fig. 479.) It is necessary to know about this thread because other threads are formed from it. Its form is like an *equilateral triangle,*[2] that is, a triangle with three equal sides and three equal angles. The sides of the V-thread are V-shaped and form a 60° angle.

[2]The sum of the three angles of *any* triangle equals 180°.

Fig. 477. Screw Pitch Gage

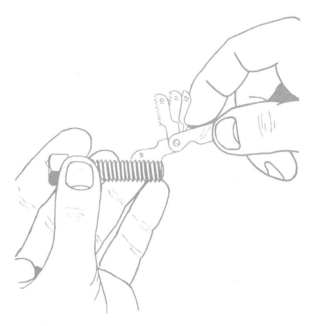

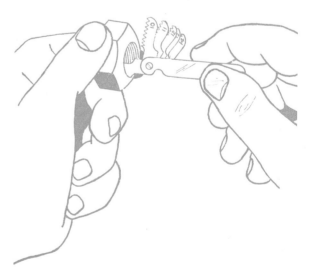
Fig. 478. Using a Screw Pitch Gage to Find the Number of Threads per Inch

The sharp edges of this thread are easily nicked and wear off quickly; for this reason it is not commonly used. It is, however, used where tight fits are necessary, such as the threads on a *pipe* (see Fig. 610).

615. United States Form Thread (USF)

The cross sectional shape of a screw thread is called its profile or *form*. To overcome the objections of the sharp V-thread form, Fig. 479, the *United States Standard Form* thread was developed, Fig. 480. It was developed during the 1860's and became widely adopted by American industries. Since the 1920's this

thread form became known as the *American (National) Form*. In 1948 this thread form, with minor modifications, was adopted as the *Unified (National) Form* thread, Fig. 481. It is the thread generally used on bolts, screws, and nuts in this country.

This thread form is like the sharp V-thread, except that ⅛ of the thread appears to have been taken off the top to fill in the bottom of the thread, thus making flat tops and bottoms called *flats*. This makes the depth of the USF thread ¾ as deep as the sharp V-thread. Hence, a bolt or screw with this form of thread is stronger than one with the sharp V-thread.

Calculations for the American (National) Form Thread

The following formulas may be used when making the calculations for cutting an external American (National) Form thread on a lathe: (See Fig. 480).

$$\text{Pitch} = P = \frac{1}{\text{number of threads per inch}}$$
$$\text{Depth} = D = 0.6495 \times P$$
$$D = \frac{0.6495}{\text{number of threads per inch}}$$

$$\text{Flat} = F = P \div 8$$

The depth of an internal screw thread is generally less than the depth of the external threads. The depth of the internal American (National) Form thread is equal to 0.54127 × P or 0.54127 divided by the number of threads per inch.

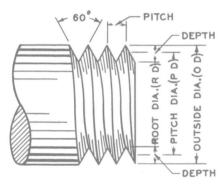

Fig. 479. Parts of a Thread

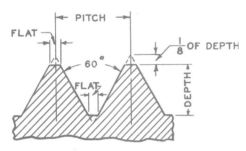

Fig. 480. External American (National) Form Thread (Formerly United States Standard Form Thread)

$$\text{Pitch} = P = \frac{1}{\text{No. of Thds. per Inch}}$$
$$\text{Depth} = D = 0.6495 \times P$$
$$(\text{or})$$
$$D = \frac{0.6495}{\text{No. of Thds. per Inch}}$$
$$\text{Flat} = f = P \div 8$$

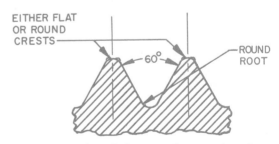

Fig. 481. Unified National Form Thread

Clearance

The difference between the depth (or height) of the internal and external threads provides for a clearance between the threads, as shown in Fig. 475.

Calculations for the Unified (National) Form Thread

The calculations for an external *Unified* (*National*) *Form* thread may be made with the following formulas: (See Figs. 480 and 481).

$$\text{Pitch} = P = \frac{1}{\text{number of threads per inch}}$$

$$\text{Depth} = D = 0.61343 \times P$$

$$D = \frac{0.61343}{\text{number of threads per inch}}$$

$$\text{Flat at crest} = F = \frac{P}{8}$$

The depth of the external Unified (National) Form thread is slightly less than the depth for the American (National) Form thread. However, these two kinds of threads are essentially the same, and permissible production tolerances permit them to be used interchangeably in most instances.

The depth of the internal Unified (National) Form thread is equal to $0.51427 \times P$, or 0.51427 divided by the number of threads per inch.

616. Various Regulatory Thread Standards

At one time each manufacturer made as many threads per inch on bolts, screws, and nuts as suited his own needs. For example, one made 10 threads per inch on ½″ bolts, another made 12 threads, still another put on 13 or 15 threads per inch. Bolts of one manufacturer would not fit nuts made by another. Each bolt, screw, and nut had to be specially made. To overcome this trouble, several thread *standards*,[3] were agreed upon.

United States Standard Thread (USS)

The USS thread was one of the first thread standards adopted by industry in the United States. It was first adopted by the U.S. Navy in 1868. The form of this thread is the same as the United States Standard Form thread in Fig. 480. The USS thread was available in a *coarse* thread *series* only.

Later, about 1924, additional specifications concerning tolerances, allowances, and fits were added, and the USS thread became known as the *National Coarse* (*NC*) thread (see § 617). In 1948, with further additions and modifications concerning tolerances, allowances, and fits, the NC thread became known as the *Unified National Coarse* (*UNC*) thread. Although the NC thread is still used to a limited extent, it has been largely replaced by the UNC thread.

Table 19 gives the *number of threads per inch* for all USS, NC, and UNC sizes up to one inch. Note that for each diameter there is a certain number of threads per inch, that is, a standard *pitch*.

Society of Automotive Engineers (SAE) Thread

Another early thread standard, the *SAE* thread, was adopted about 1911. These threads also have a thread form which is the same as the United States Form thread, Fig. 480. The SAE thread standard, however, includes a *fine thread series*. The fine threads were designed to serve the needs of the automobile industry. Tests on automobiles have shown that fine threads can be tightened more easily. It also takes more vibration to loosen a nut or bolt with fine threads.

About 1924, additional specifications concerning tolerances, allowances, and fits were added, and the *SAE* thread became known as the *National Fine* (*NF*) thread. In 1948, with

---

[3]*Standard* is a rule, example, model, or measure for comparison; something set up as a model for measuring, such as standard time, standard of living, or standard weights and measures.

further additions and modifications concerning tolerances, allowances, and fits, the *NF* thread became known as the *Unified National Fine* (*UNF*) thread. Although the NF thread still has limited use in American industry, it has been largely replaced with the UNF thread.

Table 19 gives the number of threads per inch for all SAE, NF, and UNF sizes up to one inch. Note in every case that threads in the fine thread series have a finer thread than for a thread of the same diameter in the coarse thread series. For example a ¼″ UNC screw has 20 threads per inch, while a ¼″ UNF screw has 28 threads per inch.

Extra-Fine Thread (EF)

The Society of Automotive Engineers also developed the Extra-Fine Thread series. These threads also had a thread form which was the same as the United States Standard Form thread. The EF series of threads has finer pitch threads than the standard SAE fine thread series (see Table 19). Threads in this series are recommended where finer pitches of threads are desirable for short lengths of thread engagement. They are recommended for thin nuts, for thin-walled tubes, and for similar uses.

The EF thread series, with certain additions and modifications, was adopted as the National Extra-Fine (*NEF*) thread standard in 1933. In 1948, with further additions and modifications, the NEF thread was adopted as a Unified Extra-fine (*UNEF*) thread standard. Table 19 gives the number of threads per inch for NEF and UNEF threads through one inch diameter.

617. American (National) Standard Screw Threads

During World War I the need arose for more *standardizing*[4] of screw threads. Congress, in 1918, set up the National Screw

[4]*Standardize* means to *make* a rule, example, or model for measure or comparison.

Table 19
SCREW THREADS

DIAMETER			THREADS PER INCH		
No.	Inch	Decimal Equivalent	UNC (NC) (USS)	UNF (NF) (SAE)	UNEF (NEF) (EF)
0		.0600		80	
1		.0730	64	72	
2		.0860	56	64	
3		.0990	48	56	
4		.1120	40	48	
5	⅛	.1250	40	44	
6		.1380	32	40	
8		.1640	32	36	
10		.1900	24	32	
12		.2160	24	28	32
	¼	.2500	20	28	32
	5⁄16	.3125	18	24	32
	⅜	.3750	16	24	32
	7⁄16	.4375	14	20	28
	½	.5000	13	20	28
	9⁄16	.5625	12	18	24
	⅝	.6250	11	18	24
	11⁄16				24
	¾	.7500	10	16	20
	13⁄16				20
	⅞	.8750	9	14	20
	15⁄16				20
	1	1.0000	8	14	20

Thread Commission to study the problem and adopt new screw thread standards for American industries and government services. Its aim was to eliminate unnecessary thread sizes and to use existing sizes as much as possible.

As a result of the efforts of the committee and other cooperating agencies, the original *American (National) Screw Thread Standard* was approved in 1924. The thread profile was designated the *American (National) Form* of thread. This thread form is basically the same as the *United States Standard Form* thread, Fig. 480. However, additions concerning tolerances, allowances, and fits were included under the new thread standard. Further additions were included in the *American (Nation-*

al) *Screw Thread Standard* and were approved in 1933.

The following common screw thread series were included in the *American (National) Screw Thread Standard*:

(1) National Coarse Thread (*NC*): Adopted from the USS thread. (See Table 19.)

(2) National Fine Thread (*NF*): Adopted from the SAE fine thread. (See Table 19.)

(3) National Extra-Fine Thread (*NEF*): Adopted from the EF thread. (See Table 19.)

(4) Other less common thread series, such as the 8-thread series (*8N*), the 12-thread series (*12N*), and the 16-thread series (*16N*) were also included.

(5) National Special (*NS*): Included special pitch-diameter combinations not included in the above thread series.

618. Fits of Threads

The *National Screw Thread Commission* also established four classes of *fits* for use with American (National) Standard Screw Threads (see also § *665*).

Class 1 (Loose Fit)

The loose fit is for threaded parts that can be put together quickly and easily even when the threads are slightly damaged or dirty. A considerable amount of shake or looseness is not objectionable. This class of fit is now obsolete.

Class 2 (Free Fit)

The free fit is for threaded parts that are to be put together or adjusted with the fingers. A little shake or looseness between threaded parts is not objectionable. This class includes most of the screw thread work. (See § *37* for explanation of note in Fig. 17.)

---

[5]*Unified and American Screw Threads* (ASA B1.1-1949) and later edition, *Unified Screw Threads* (ASA B1.1-1960), published by the American Society of Mechanical Engineers, New York.

Class 3 (Medium Fit)

The medium fit is for the higher grade of threaded parts which are to be put together or adjusted with the fingers and must have the least amount of shake or looseness between the threaded parts. It is the same as class 2, Free Fit, except that the fit is somewhat closer.

Class 4 (Close Fit)

The close fit is for the finest threaded work where very little shake or looseness is desirable and where a screwdriver or wrench may be necessary to put the parts together. This class of fit is now obsolete.

The class 2 and class 3 fits are still used with American (National) Standard Form threads when these threads are used. A different system of thread classes is used with the Unified (National) Form threads.

619. Unified (National) Form Thread

In 1948 the United States, Canada, and Great Britain agreed to adopt the *Unified (National) Form* thread to provide interchangeability of threaded parts in these countries. It is essentially the same as the *American (National) Form* thread, except that it generally has *rounded roots* and may have either *rounded* or *flat* crests as in Fig. 481. American industries use flat crests, while the English prefer rounded crests. The rounded root is optional on both the external and the internal threads for most applications; however, for some applications the root must be rounded.

The Unified Screw Thread system includes several series of threads. The following common screw thread series are included in the American Standard, *Unified Screw Threads*:[5]

(1) Unified National Coarse Thread (UNC): adopted from the NC thread. (See Table 19.)

(2) Unified National Fine Thread (UNF): Adopted from the NF thread. (See Table 19.)

(3) Unified National Extra-Fine Thread

(UNEF): Adopted from the NEF thread. (See Table19.)

(4) Other less common series, such as the 8-thread series (8UN), the 12-thread series (12UN), and the 16-thread series (16UN) are also included.

The *UNC, UNF,* and *UNEF* thread series are interchangeable with the *NC, NF,* and *NEF* series on most of the common sizes, except on the "Class 4," close fits (see § *618*). However, the "Class 4," close fit, has been obsolete since 1948. The Unified thread system has largely replaced the American (National) thread system in American production. Specifications for these threads are available in standard handbooks for machinists.

The American Standards Association (*ASA*) has been formed into a new group called the United States of America Standards Institute (*USAS*). Now the abbreviation *ASA* refers to the same group called *USAS*. The *ASA* will be deleted from all new publication of standards and will be identified by *USAS*.

620. Unified Thread Classes (Fits)

Six *classes of threads,* formerly called *fits,* are used with standard Unified screw threads. The term *fits* has been dropped. The six classes include three external classes and three internal classes. The external thread classes are designated 1A, 2A, and 3A. The internal classes are designated 1B, 2B, and 3B. Thread fit means the degree of tightness between mating threads. Normally, class 2A and class 2B threads are mated. However, any unified class of external thread may be mated with any internal class, so long as the product meets the specified fit requirements. The following classes of mated threads have tolerances which permit the indicated type of fit:

Classes 1A and 1B: loose fit
Classes 2A and 2B: free fit
Classes 3A and 3B: close fit

When classes 2A and 3B are mated, the tolerances permit an intermediate fit ranking between the free and close fits.

621. Square Thread

A square thread is formed like a square, Fig. 482. The depth and width of the groove are equal. The height and width of each ridge between the grooves are also equal. Thus, the groove and ridge form two squares. The screw on a *machinist's vise* sometimes has square threads. There is a trend, at present, to use the acme thread instead of the square thread. (See § *622*.) (See Fig. 530.)

622. Acme Thread

Acme threads are usually used on the *lead screw* of a *lathe.* (See Fig. 990.) They are also used on many other kinds of machine tools. The angle of the thread is 29°, Fig. 483. Information concerning pitches, fits, tolerances, and allowances for acme threads is available in handbooks for machinists.

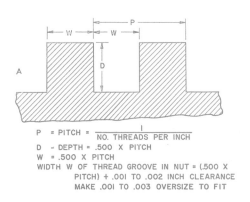

P = PITCH = $\frac{1}{\text{NO. THREADS PER INCH}}$
D - DEPTH = .500 X PITCH
W = .500 X PITCH
WIDTH W OF THREAD GROOVE IN NUT = (.500 X PITCH) + .001 TO .002 INCH CLEARANCE MAKE .001 TO .003 OVERSIZE TO FIT

Fig. 482. Square Thread

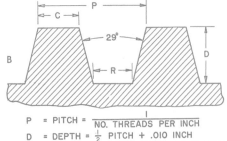

P = PITCH = $\frac{1}{\text{NO. THREADS PER INCH}}$
D = DEPTH = $\frac{1}{2}$ PITCH + .010 INCH
C = FLAT ON TOP OF THREAD = P X .3707
R = FLAT ON BOTTOM = (P X .3707) − .0052

Fig. 483. Acme Thread (Old Standard Acme General-Purpose Thread)

Review Questions

1. What is a double thread? Triple thread? Quadruple thread? Multiple thread?

2. How can you tell whether the thread on a bolt is right hand or left hand?

3. What is meant by major diameter?

4. What is meant by the depth of a thread?

5. What is meant by DD?

6. What is meant by minor diameter?

7. To what is the pitch diameter equal?

8. What is the pitch of a thread?

9. What is the lead of a thread? What is the difference between lead and pitch?

10. Describe two ways to measure the number of threads per inch.

11. Describe a V-thread.

12. Describe the USF thread.

13. Describe the USS thread.

14. Describe the SAE thread.

15. Describe the American (National) Standard screw threads.

16. Describe the UNF threads.

17. For what are Extra-Fine threads used?

18. Describe the classes of fits used with the American (National) Form threads.

19. Describe six classes of threads used with the Unified screw thread system.

20. Describe a square thread.

21. Describe an Acme thread.

Coordination

Words to Know

Acme thread
aeronautics
allowance
American (National)
    Form thread
American (National)
    Screw Thread
    Standard
basic size
counterclockwise
depth of thread
double depth of
    thread
double thread
equilateral triangle
Extra-Fine thread
flats
lead of thread
left-hand thread
machine screw
major diameter
minor diameter
multiple thread
National Coarse
    Thread Series
National Fine
    Thread Series
National Screw
    Thread
    Commission
nominal size
number of threads
    per inch
outside diameter
pitch diameter
pitch of thread
quadruple thread
right-hand thread
root diameter
rounded or flat crest
rounded root
screw pitch gage
sharp V-thread
single depth of thread
single thread
Society of Automotive
    Engineers thread
square thread
standardize
standard pitch
tolerance
triple thread
Unified (National)
    Form thread
United States Form
    thread
United States
    Standard thread

Mathematics

1. What is the minor diameter of a 1-8 UNC thread?

2. What is the minor diameter of a 1-14 UNF thread?

3. What is the pitch diameter of a ¾-10 UNC thread?

Drafting

1. Draw a 1″ diameter, 8 pitch, UNC thread.

2. Draw a 1″ diameter, 4 pitch, square thread.

3. Draw a 2″ diameter, 4 pitch, Acme thread.

Threading Dies and Threading

Fig. 492. Round-Adjustable Split-Threading Die

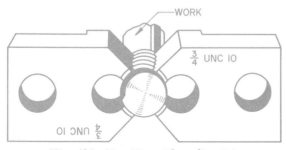

Fig. 493. Two-Piece Threading Die

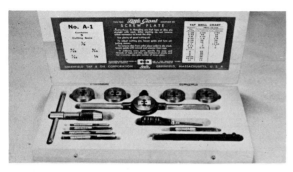

Fig. 494. Screw Plate (Set of Taps and Dies)
(Courtesy Greenfield Tap & Die Corp.)

636. What Is a Threading Die?

A threading die is a round or square block of *hardened steel* with a hole containing *threads* and *flutes* which form *cutting edges*. It is used to cut threads on a round bar of metal, such as the threads on a bolt.

One kind of threading die is shown in Fig. 492. It is called a *round, adjustable, split die. Adjustable* means that it can be set to cut larger or smaller. Another kind is the *two-piece die*, Fig. 493. It is made in two halves which match each other. *Dies* and *taps* (see § 649) may be bought in a set, called a *screw plate*, Fig. 494.

637. Left-Hand and Right-Hand Dies

A left-hand die cuts *left-hand threads*. (See § 603.) It has the letter L stamped on it. If the L is not on the die it is a *right-hand die*.

638. Sizes of Threading Dies

The size of the threading die and the number of threads per inch are stamped on the die, as ¼-20 which means that the die will cut a thread with a *major diameter* of ¼″ and having 20 threads per inch (see §§ 605, 610, and 611). The sizes of screw threads as given in Table 19, page 236, are also the sizes of threading dies.

639. Collets and Guides

The threading dies fit into a holder called a *collet*, Fig. 495. The *guide* is a ring which is held in place under the die and fits around the bar or bolt to be threaded. It guides the die so that it will go on the work squarely.

640. Diestock

The tool for holding and turning the threading die and collet is called a *diestock*. It is often just called a *stock,* Fig. 496.

641. Setting the Threading Die

Most dies can be set to cut the thread a little oversize or undersize. This is done by

turning the *setscrew* (see Fig. 492) with a screwdriver, Fig. 497; the setscrew is sometimes on the top instead of at the side of the die.

642. Threading with Stock and Die

Cutting threads on a round rod or bolt with a die and stock is called *threading. Hardened steel* should not be threaded with a threading die (see § 952). Note again that the cutting tool must be harder than the metal to be cut.

The end of the work should be *beveled*[1] to make starting easier; this may be done with a file, Fig. 498. Hold the work upright in the vise. Fasten the die in the diestock. The threads are beveled a little on one side

[1]*Beveled* means tapered, sloped, slanted, inclined.

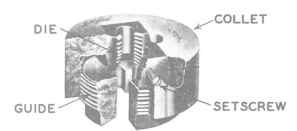

Fig. 495. Die, Collet, and Guide (Courtesy Greenfield Tap & Die Corp.)

Fig. 496. Diestock

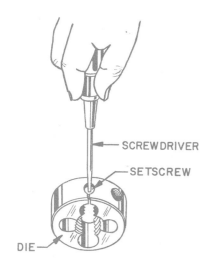

Fig. 497. Setting a Die

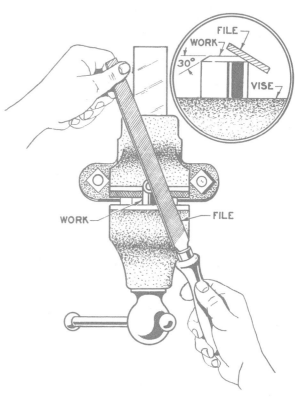

Fig. 498. Beveling the End of Work Before Threading

of the die, Fig. 499, to make starting easier and to form the thread gradually. Always start cutting a thread with this beveled side.

Place the die over the end of the work. Grasp the diestock with both hands near the die, Fig. 500, press down firmly upon the work, and at the same time, slowly screw it on the work *clockwise* (see § 585). The die cuts the thread as it goes. Be sure that the die goes on squarely; a lot of skill is needed to do this. After the thread is started, grasp the two diestock handles and with a steady movement continue screwing the die on the work, Fig. 501. It is then no longer necessary to press down because the die will draw itself on the work when turned.

Back up the die now and then to break and clean away the chips and to make the

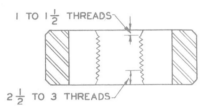

Fig. 499. **Bevel on Threading Die**

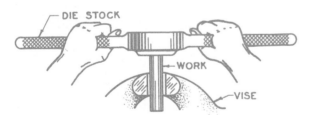

Fig. 500. **Starting to Cut a Thread with a Stock and Die**

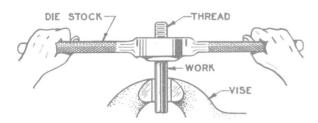

Fig. 501. **Cutting the Thread with the Stock and Die**

threads smooth. "Back up one step and go ahead two." Continue in this way until you have the length of thread you want. Clean the thread, die, and other parts when the threading is done.

643. Cutting Fluids for Threading

Use *lard oil* or *mineral-lard oil* when threading steel and only enough to keep the work moist. (See § 398.) Oil which runs all over the work, the bench, and the floor is wasted. A cutting fluid is not necessary when threading cast iron. (See Table 15, p. 169.)

644. External Thread Measurement

External threads must be cut to the correct depth to produce the proper *fit* or *class of thread*. (See § 620.) If the pitch diameter, Figs. 474, 475, is too large, the thread fits too tightly. If it is too small it fits too loosely. The exact pitch diameter may be measured with a thread micrometer to determine whether it is within specified size limits for the fit or class of thread desired. Tables which show the maximum and minimum pitch diameter dimensions for various fits and classes of screw threads are included in standard handbooks for machinists.

The correct fit (see § 618) or class (see § 620) of screw threads can also be determined in the following ways:

(1) With a thread roll snap gage, Fig. 940. (See § 1151.)

(2) With a thread ring gage, Figs. 938 and 939. (See § 1151.)

(3) It may be estimated by testing how it fits in a standard mating nut or threaded hole.

Review Questions

1. What is a threading die?
2. Describe a round, adjustable, split die.
3. What is a two-piece die?
4. What is a screw plate?
5. What does ¼-20 on a die mean?
6. What is a diestock?

7. How may a die be set to cut oversize or undersize?

8. Why should the end of the work be beveled before threading?

9. Why is it necessary to back up the die while threading?

10. What kind of lubricant should be used for threading steel?

11. List several ways in which the fit or class of threads can be determined.

Coordination

Words to Know

adjustable	screw plate
beveled	threading
collet	threading die
diestock	threading lubricant
left-hand die	thread micrometer
right-hand die	thread roll snap gage
round adjustable	thread ring gage
split die	two-piece die

Sharpening a Threading Die with a Small Grinding Wheel
(Courtesy Norton Co.)

Taps and Tapping

649. Taps

A tap is a screwlike tool which has threads like a bolt and three or four *flutes* cut across the threads, Fig. 507. It is used to cut threads on the inside of a hole, as in a nut. The edges of the thread formed by the flutes are the *cutting edges*, Fig. 508. One end of the tap is square so that it can be turned with a wrench.

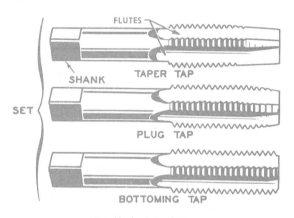

Fig. 507. Set of Taps

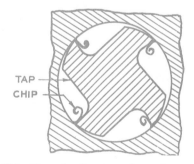

Fig. 508. How the Cutting Edges of a Tap Cut

Taps, also called *hand taps,* are made from *carbon-steel* or *high-speed steel* and are *hardened* and *tempered* (see §§ 328, 352, 951 and 954). They come three in a set and are known as *taper tap, plug tap,* and *bottoming tap.*

The end of the *taper tap* has about six threads *tapered* so that it will start easily and so that the threads will be cut gradually as the tap is turned into the hole.

The *plug tap* has three or four threads tapered at the end and is used after the taper tap.

The *bottoming tap* has a full thread to the end and is used to cut a full thread to the bottom of a hole.

650. Left-Hand and Right-Hand Taps

A left-hand tap cuts *left-hand threads.* (See § 603.) It has the letter L stamped on the shank. If there is no L, it is a *right-hand tap.*

651. Sizes of Taps

Taps are made the same sizes as bolts and screws. The size (*outside diameter*) of the tap and the *number of threads per inch* are stamped on the *shank* of the tap. (See §§ 605, 610-611.) For example, ¼-20 means that the outside diameter of the tap is ¼″ and that there are 20 threads per inch. Table 20 on page 246 gives the sizes of taps.

652. Tap Drills

A hole of a certain diameter must be drilled before it can be tapped. If the hole is too large, a *full thread* will not be formed; if too small, it will be hard to turn the tap. The drill which is used to make a hole before tapping is called the *tap drill*. Note that this hole must be smaller than the *major diameter* (see § 605) of the tap so as to leave enough metal from which to form the threads, Fig. 509.

The right size tap drill must be used. Its size should be a little larger than the diameter at the bottom or *root* of the thread, known as the *minor diameter* (see § 606). To save the time of figuring, *tap drill sizes* are put in the form of a table such as Table 20. The tap drill, recommended for average work, produces threads which are about 75% of the depth of external threads. Tables can be found in books, catalogs, on wall charts, and on drill gages as in Fig. 380.

653. Tapping

Cutting *inside threads* as in a *nut* is called *tapping*. After the hole has been drilled with the *tap drill* it is ready for tapping, that is, the forming of the threads by the tap.

Clamp the work in the vise with the hole in an upright position. First use a *taper tap*. (See Fig. 507.) Clamp its square end in the *tap wrench*, Fig. 510. The *T-handle tap wrench* is used for holding small taps. Grasp the tap wrench with the right hand directly over the tap and place the tap in the hole. Press down and start to screw the tap *clockwise* into the hole, Fig. 511. A steady, downward pressure on the wrench is needed to get the thread started. Skill is needed to keep the tap square with the work. Place a square or a wide steel rule several places against the tap as in Fig. 512 to make sure that the tap is square with the work. If it is not square, back it out of the hole a little, straighten it, and with some side pressure screw it into the hole again. This must be repeated until the tap is well started in the hole and cannot get out of

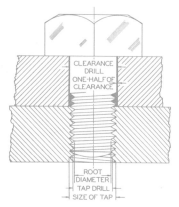

Fig. 509. Comparing Sizes of Tap, Tap Drill, and Root (Minor) Diameter of Thread

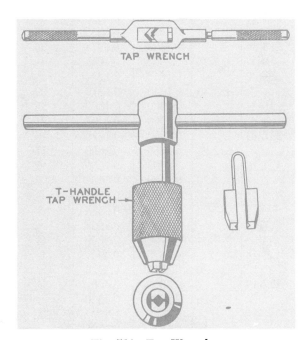

Fig. 510. Tap Wrenches

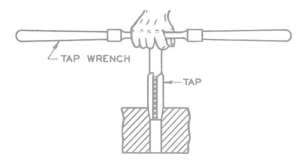

Fig. 511. Start the Threads with a Taper Tap

Table 20
SIZES OF TAPS, TAP DRILLS[1], AND CLEARANCE DRILLS[2]
(See section 652 and Table 16)

SIZE OF TAP		OUTSIDE DIAMETER (INCHES)	ROOT DIAMETER (INCHES)	SIZE OF TAP DRILL (IN INCHES) FOR 75% THREAD DEPTH			CLEARANCE DRILL (INCHES)		CLEARANCE (INCHES)
UNC NC (USS)	UNF NF (SAE)			NUMBER AND LETTER DRILLS	FRACTIONAL DRILLS	DECIMAL EQUIVALENT	SIZE	DECIMAL EQUIVALENT	
	#0-80	0.0600	0.0438	...	$\frac{3}{64}$	0.0469	#51	0.0670	0.0070
#1-64	...	0.0730	0.0527	53	...	0.0595	#47	0.0785	0.0055
	#1-72	0.0730	0.0550	53	...	0.0595	#47	0.0785	0.0055
#2-56	...	0.0860	0.0628	50	...	0.0700	#42	0.0935	0.0075
	#2-64	0.0860	0.0657	50	...	0.0700	#42	0.0935	0.0075
#3-48	...	0.0990	0.0719	47	...	0.0785	#36	0.1065	0.0075
	#3-56	0.0990	0.0758	45	...	0.0820	#36	0.1065	0.0075
#4-40	...	0.1120	0.0795	43	...	0.0890	#31	0.1200	0.0080
	#4-48	0.1120	0.0849	42	...	0.0935	#31	0.1200	0.0080
#5-40	...	0.1250	0.0925	38	...	0.1015	#29	0.1360	0.0110
	#5-44	0.1250	0.0955	37	...	0.1040	#29	0.1360	0.0110
#6-32	...	0.1380	0.0974	36	...	0.1065	#25	0.1495	0.0115
	#6-40	0.1380	0.1055	33	...	0.1130	#25	0.1495	0.0115
#8-32	...	0.1640	0.1234	29	...	0.1360	#16	0.1770	0.0130
	#8-36	0.1640	0.1279	29	...	0.1360	#16	0.1770	0.0130
#10-24	...	0.1900	0.1359	25	...	0.1495	$1\frac{3}{64}$	0.2031	0.0131
	#10-32	0.1900	0.1494	21	...	0.1590	$1\frac{3}{64}$	0.2031	0.0131
#12-24	...	0.2160	0.1619	16	...	0.1770	$\frac{7}{32}$	0.2187	0.0027
	#12-28	0.2160	0.1696	14	...	0.1820	$\frac{7}{32}$	0.2187	0.0027
$\frac{1}{4}''$-20	...	0.2500	0.1850	7	...	0.2010	$1\frac{7}{64}$	0.2656	0.0156
	$\frac{1}{4}''$-28	0.2500	0.2036	3	...	0.2130	$1\frac{7}{64}$	0.2656	0.0156
$\frac{5}{16}''$-18	...	0.3125	0.2403	F	...	0.2570	$2\frac{1}{64}$	0.3281	0.0156
	$\frac{5}{16}''$-24	0.3125	0.2584	I	...	0.2720	$2\frac{1}{64}$	0.3281	0.0156
$\frac{3}{8}''$-16	...	0.3750	0.2938	...	$\frac{5}{16}$	0.3125	$2\frac{5}{64}$	0.3906	0.0156
	$\frac{3}{8}''$-24	0.3750	0.3209	Q	...	0.3320	$2\frac{5}{64}$	0.3906	0.0156
$\frac{7}{16}''$-14	...	0.4375	0.3447	U	...	0.3680	$2\frac{9}{64}$	0.4531	0.0156
	$\frac{7}{16}''$-20	0.4375	0.3725	...	$2\frac{5}{64}$	0.3906	$2\frac{9}{64}$	0.4531	0.0156
$\frac{1}{2}''$-13	...	0.5000	0.4001	...	$2\frac{7}{64}$	0.4219	$3\frac{3}{64}$	0.5156	0.0156
	$\frac{1}{2}''$-20	0.5000	0.4350	...	$2\frac{9}{64}$	0.4531	$3\frac{3}{64}$	0.5156	0.0156
$\frac{9}{16}''$-12	...	0.5625	0.4542	...	$3\frac{1}{64}$	0.4844	$3\frac{7}{64}$	0.5781	0.0156
	$\frac{9}{16}''$-18	0.5625	0.4903	...	$3\frac{3}{64}$	0.5156	$3\frac{7}{64}$	0.5781	0.0156
$\frac{5}{8}''$-11	...	0.6250	0.5069	...	$1\frac{7}{32}$	0.5312	$4\frac{1}{64}$	0.6406	0.0156
	$\frac{5}{8}''$-18	0.6250	0.5528	...	$3\frac{7}{64}$	0.5781	$4\frac{1}{64}$	0.6406	0.0156
$\frac{3}{4}''$-10	...	0.7500	0.6201	...	$2\frac{1}{32}$	0.6562	$4\frac{9}{64}$	0.7656	0.0156
	$\frac{3}{4}''$-16	0.7500	0.6688	...	$1\frac{1}{16}$	0.6875	$4\frac{9}{64}$	0.7656	0.0156
$\frac{7}{8}''$- 9	...	0.8750	0.7307	...	$4\frac{9}{64}$	0.7656	$5\frac{7}{64}$	0.8906	0.0156
	$\frac{7}{8}''$-14	0.8750	0.7822	...	$1\frac{3}{16}$	0.8125	$5\frac{7}{64}$	0.8906	0.0156
$1''$- 8	...	1.0000	0.8376	...	$\frac{7}{8}$	0.8750	$1\frac{1}{64}$	1.0156	0.0156
	$1''$-14	1.0000	0.9072	...	$1\frac{5}{16}$	0.9375	$1\frac{1}{64}$	1.0156	0.0156

[1]If you cannot get the size of tap drill given here, see Table 16, "Drill Sizes," on page 196 to find the size of drill nearest to it; be sure to get a drill a little larger than the *root diameter* of the thread. (See Section 608.)

[2]The drill that makes a hole so that a bolt or screw may pass through it is called a *clearance drill*. This drill makes a hole with a *clearance* for the *nominal diameter of thread* (see Section 605). The *clearance* equals the difference between the clearance drill size and the nominal diameter of the bolt or screw:

Clearance drill = Diameter of bolt or screw + Clearance

Example: The clearance for a ¼″ bolt or screw is ¹⁄₆₄″; the size of the clearance drill should, therefore, be ¼″ + ¹⁄₆₄″ or ¹⁷⁄₆₄″.

square. Put cutting oil on the tap to tap steel. (See § 643.)

Continue to turn the tap with one hand until the thread has a good start. It is then no longer necessary to press down because the tap will draw itself into the work when turned. Grasp the tap wrench by the two handles and with a slow, firm, steady movement continue screwing the tap into the hole, Fig. 513. Back up the tap now and then to break and clear away the *chips* and to make the threads smooth. "Back up one step and go ahead two."

Tapping may also be done on the drill press as explained in section 596. Taps should be cleaned after being used.

654. Changing Taps to Prevent Breakage

Taps, especially small ones, are easily broken while tapping. This breakage may be reduced by changing from one tap to another. For example: Use a *taper tap* (see Fig. 507) until it is hard to turn; then back it out and use the *plug tap* until it also is hard to turn; back it out and use the *bottoming tap* until it is hard to turn. Repeat, using the *taper tap* again as in the beginning. Continue changing taps until the hole is completely tapped. Each tap thus cuts only a little at a time. Changing from one tap to another takes less time than tapping a hole with a taper tap alone because great care is needed to prevent breakage and this care slows up the tapping.

655. Tapping Blind Holes

A *blind hole* is one which goes only part way through the work. If the hole does not go through the work, the *taper tap* (see Fig. 507) should be followed by a *plug tap*. If full threads to the bottom of the hole are wanted, a *bottoming tap* must also be used. Clean out the hole now and then so that the *chips* collecting in the bottom of the hole will not keep the tap from going to the bottom. A *magnet*

or a long tube (see § 570) may be needed to clean out the chips. The tap should not be turned after reaching the bottom because it may break.

656. Cutting Fluids for Tapping

Cutting fluids for tapping are the same as for *threading* explained in section 643.

657. Causes of Broken Taps

Taps break for the following reasons:

(1) A hole that has been drilled too small needs more pressure and strain than the tap can stand and, therefore, it breaks.

(2) A tap that is lopsided in the hole will stick tight and then break. (See Fig. 512.)

(3) The tap wrench acts like a *lever*[3] and with it a great twisting force can be put upon the tap; it is with this force that many taps are broken.

(4) Lack of oil will cause a tap to stick tight and break.

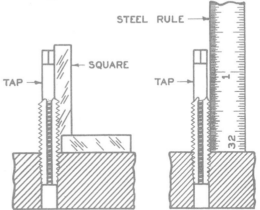

Fig. 512. The Tap must be Square with the Work

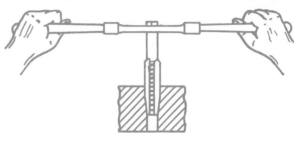

Fig. 513. Hold the Tap Wrench in this Manner After Thread has been Started

---

[3]A *lever* is a strong bar, such as a crowbar, used to lift or move something.

(5) Failure to back up the tap will cause the *chips* to crowd in front of the *cutting edges*. More force is then needed to push these larger chips and this extra force is often more than the tap can stand.

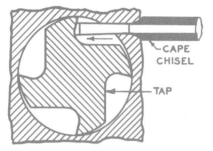

Fig. 514. Removing a Broken Tap with a Cape Chisel and Hammer

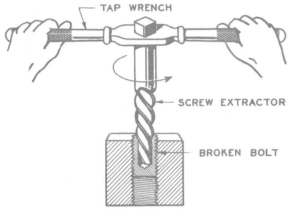

Fig. 515. Removing a Broken Bolt with a Screw Extractor

Fig. 516. Tap Extractor is Used to Remove Broken Taps (Courtesy The Walton Co.)

(6) Turning a tap after the bottom of the hole is reached will cause it to break.

658. Removing a Broken Tap from a Hole

A broken tap stuck in a hole may cause much trouble because it is difficult to remove. It is often necessary to make repeated efforts to remove a broken tap; much of the workman's time is lost and the job is slowed up. Thus, it is expensive. A broken tap may be removed from a hole with a *tap extractor*, as shown in Fig. 516.

A tap, broken near the top of the hole, may sometimes be removed by placing a dull *cape chisel* (see Fig. 186) in the *flute* of the tap and striking light blows with the hammer as shown in Fig. 514. Another way is to drop a little *nitric acid*[4] in the hole. The acid will eat the steel and loosen the tap so it can be removed with the cape chisel as just explained. Be sure to wash the acid out of the hole afterward to keep the acid from further eating the threads.

659. Removing a Broken Bolt from a Hole

A broken bolt or screw that is not hardened (see § 952) may be removed from a hole with a *screw extractor*, Fig. 515. First drill a hole in the broken bolt. Then put the correct size screw extractor in the hole and with a *tap wrench* turn it *counterclockwise*. (See § 603.) The screw extractor acts like a corkscrew. It grips into the sides of the hole, and when the right force is used the bolt begins to turn and come out.

If a screw extractor is not handy, drive a *diamond point chisel*, shown in Fig. 186, into the drilled hole and remove as shown in Fig. 515.

660. Tap Size Limits

Taps are available with either *cut* threads or *ground* threads. The ground threads have a precision, ground finish, and they produce

[4]*Nitric acid* is a powerful acid made up of nitrogen, hydrogen, and oxygen. It is poisonous and eats most metals.

tapped threads to a very accurate size. They are also more expensive than taps with cut threads. Both carbon tool steel taps and high-speed steel taps are available with cut threads. However, high-speed steel taps are also available with ground threads.

The size of the pitch diameter (see § 609) of a tap determines the depth and the fit of a tapped thread. Internal threads may be tapped for various classes of threads, such as classes 1B, 2B, and 3B. (See § 620.) The thread may be either a loose or tight fit, depending on the pitch diameter of the tap.

Taps with ground threads are available with standard, oversize, or undersize pitch diameters. The size limits of the pitch diameter are indicated by a *pitch diameter limit number,* such as L1, H1, H2, or H6, on the shank of ground thread taps. When purchasing taps of this type, the *limits code number* and the fit or class of thread to be tapped should be specified. If they are not specified, the supplier generally sends taps with pitch diameter size limits which produce tapped threads for a Class 2 fit for National Form threads or Class 2B for Unified Form threads. These fits are generally used on most commercially available bolts, screws, and nuts.

The recommended taps, including their limits code numbers, for various thread fits and classes of threads, are included in standard handbooks for machinists. For example, a ⅜-16 UNC ground thread tap for a Class 2B thread would be identified with the letter G and with the additional number H5; for a Class 3B thread the code number would be GH3.

661. Internal Thread Measurement

Internal threads must be cut to the correct depth in order to produce the proper fit or class of thread (see §§ 618 and 620). If the pitch diameter (see § 609) of the internal thread is too large, the bolt or screw will fit too loosely. If too small, it will fit too tightly. Internal threads may be checked for the cor-rect fit or class of thread with thread plug gages, as shown in Fig. 937. The procedure is explained in section 1151.

Review Questions

1. What is a tap and for what is it used?
2. Describe a taper tap. Plug tap. Bottoming tap. For what is each used?
3. What does ¼-20 stamped on the shank of a tap mean?
4. What is a tap drill?
5. Why is the tap drill smaller than the tap?
6. What size tap drill does a ½-13 UNC tap need?
7. What is a tap wrench?
8. How can you keep the tap square with the work?
9. What kind of lubricant should you use for tapping steel?
10. Why is it necessary to back up the tap while tapping?
11. Name six causes of broken taps.
12. How can a broken tap be removed from a hole?
13. How can a broken bolt be removed from a hole?

Coordination
Words to Know

blind hole	plug tap
bottoming tap	screw extractor
hand tap	taper tap
inside thread	tapping lubricant
left-hand tap	T-handle tap wrench
lever	

Mathematics

1. What is the tap drill size for a ⁷⁄₁₆-14 UNC tap? A ⁷⁄₁₆-20 UNF tap?
2. If 30 pounds of force are being exerted at the ends of an 8″ tap wrench handle, what is the force applied to a ¼″ tap?

Drafting

1. What is the tap drill size for a ⁹⁄₁₆-12 UNC tap? a ⁹⁄₁₆-18 UNF tap?
2. Design a parallel clamp.

Assembling Drive Shafts
for Cotton Picker
Spindles
(Courtesy **Today,**
International Harvester Co.)

Part **VII**   **Fitting and Assembling**

Fits and Fitting

665. Meaning and Importance of Fitting

In metalwork, *fitting* means preparing mating parts to touch or join each other in such a way that one will turn inside another, one will slide upon another, or the parts will hold tightly together so that they cannot move upon each other.

Sawing, chipping, filing, scraping, grinding, or cutting by machine may be necessary to make the parts fit. Judgment and great skill are needed in fitting; these qualities are especially necessary to perform the *operations* just mentioned.

666. Who Does Fitting?

The *aircraft-and-engine mechanic* and *auto mechanic* fit wheels, pistons, valves, crankshafts, camshafts, etc. The *diemaker* and *diesinker* fit parts of dies to each other. The *erector* fits the different parts of a machine together. The *gage maker* must do much fitting when making gages. The *gas fitter, pipe fitter, plumber,* and *steam fitter* fit pipes and *pipe fittings* (see § 768). An *inspector* must know various kinds of fits in order to inspect work. A *lathe hand* must make parts on the lathe to fit other parts. The *machinist* must fit

parts such as wheels, pulleys, bearings, and shafts when he is repairing machines. The *metal patternmaker* must fit the different parts of a pattern. A *sheet metalworker* makes joints that must fit. A *toolmaker* must fit the different parts of the tools that he makes.

667. Kinds of Standard Fits

The term *fit* is used to signify the range of tightness which exists between two mating parts. The kind of fit which exists is a result of the application of tolerances (explained in § 1142) and allowances (explained in § 1143). When parts are produced within the maximum and minimum size *limits* (see § 1141) specified on a drawing, they may be assembled with the desired kind of fit. Some parts have to fit together tightly while others have to fit loosely.

A system of *standard fits* has been established for the design and assembly of mating parts. The American Standard, now USAS, *Preferred Limits and Fits for Cylindrical Parts* (ASA B4.1-1955)[1] includes three general groups of classifications for fits between plain (nonthreaded) cylindrical parts. The general classifications are designated with symbols for educational purposes only. The symbols are not to be shown on drawings. Instead, the dimensional size limits for each part are specified on the drawing for the specific kind of fit de-

---

[1]Extracted and adapted from American Standard, *Preferred Limits and Fits for Cylindrical Parts* (ASA B4.1-1955), with the permission of the publisher, The American Society of Mechanical Engineers, New York.

sired. Three general groups of classifications of fits, including their symbols, are as follows:

Running and Sliding Fits (*RC*)

Locational Fits (*LC, LT,* and *LN*)

    locational clearance fit (*LC*)

    locational transition fit (*LT*)

    locational interference fit (*LN*)

Force Fits (*FN*)

These letter symbols are used with additional numbers to designate specific classes of fits within each general group classification. Examples of running or sliding fits include *RC* 1 for close-sliding fits, *RC* 4 for close-running fits, *RC* 7 for free-running fits, and so on. The many specific classes of fits (indicated by two letters and a number) are included in tables in handbooks for machinists. Each symbol represents a complete fit, including minimum and maximum clearance or interference. The minimum and maximum size limits for mating parts up to 20″ diameter also are given in the tables.

Fits of threads and *classes of threads* are explained in sections 618 and 620.

668. Running and Sliding Fits (RC)

The *sliding fit* is a snug or close fit with some clearance between two parts so that one will move upon or against the other. There

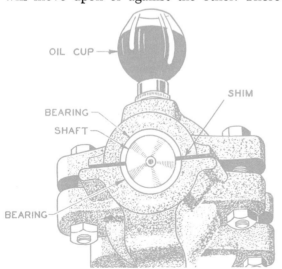

Fig. 521. Shaft Running in a Bearing

should be no wobbling. Examples of sliding fits are a *piston* sliding up and down in a *cylinder* of an automobile or the parts sliding on the *bed* of a *lathe* (see Fig. 990).

The *running fit* is used where one part runs or turns inside another; for example, the *shaft* running in a *bearing,* Fig. 521. (See § 261 and Fig. 597.) The fit must not be so tight that it keeps the shaft from turning.

Section 265 tells how a *round bearing* is scraped to make a running fit. The *shim* and its uses are explained in section 750.

669. Locational Fits

The *locational fits* are intended for the purpose of accurately locating the position of mating parts. Some mating parts must be located rigidly and accurately, while others may be located with some looseness for ease in assembling them. Hence, three general groups of locational fits were established in the American Standard, now USAS, (ASA B4.1-1955)[2].

Locational clearance fits (*LC*) are intended for use in the assembly of stationary parts where some clearance is permissible between the mating parts. Fits within this group may range from snug fits to fits with a medium amount of clearance.

Locational interference fits (*LN*) are used where accuracy of location and rigidity of mating parts are most important. These fits are used to transmit a frictional load from one part to another because of their tight fit. To meet these conditions, mating parts must be assembled with force fits (see § 670).

Locational transitional fits (*LT*) are ranked between clearance fits and interference fits. They are used where accuracy of location is important, and where a small amount of either clearance or interference is permissible between the mating parts.

670. Force Fits (FN)

Force fits or *shrink fits* include several classes of fits which involve interference be-

[2]See footnote 1, page 251.

tween mating parts. Generally the hole size is a standard or basic size, while the shaft is slightly larger, thus causing definite interference. Parts assembled with a force fit may be assembled in three ways: (1) they may be driven together with a hammer, thus forming a *drive fit;* (2) they may be pressed together with an arbor press, Fig. 561, or other kind of large press, thus forming a regular *force fit;* (3) they may be assembled with a *shrink fit,* which will be explained shortly.

Force fits are used where parts must be held together very tightly. With these fits parts can be fastened together almost as tightly as though they were made from one piece. Force fits are used to assemble gears, pulleys, bearings, collars, and similar parts on shafts. Railroad car wheels are put on their axles in this way under pressures of 100 to 150 tons with large presses. The hole diameter of the wheel is a little smaller than the hole diameter of the axle.

Shrink Fits

These fits are classified under force fits, since they involve interference between mating parts. However, where heavy driving or pressing forces are not practical or possible, the parts are sometimes installed by *shrinking* one part on the other. A pulley, gear, or collar may be fastened to a shaft by shrinking it on

the shaft. The hole diameter is slightly smaller than the shaft. The pulley or part with the hole is made larger by heating it (to cause the hole to expand) and slipping it over the shaft. The pulley is then allowed to cool and shrink on the shaft. Thus the pulley is held on the shaft with much greater pressure than if it were pressed or driven on. The pulley and shaft are nearly as tight as though they were one piece.

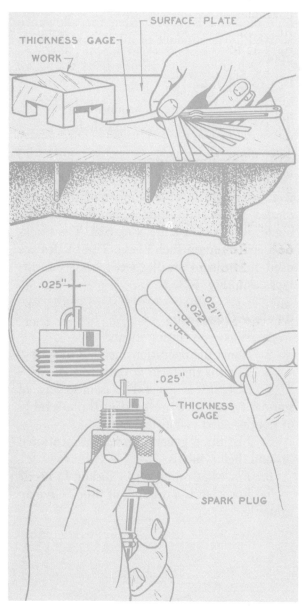

Fig. 523. Using a Thickness Gage

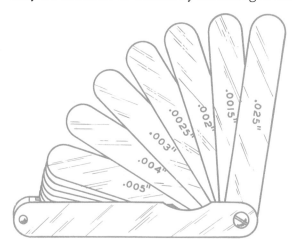

Fig. 522. Thickness Gage (Feeler Gage)

671.   Allowances for Different Fits

When a *shaft* is fitted to a *bearing* (see Fig. 521), the diameter of the shaft should be a little smaller than the diameter of the bearing to allow space for a *film of oil* between the surfaces and to allow the shaft to get larger from the heat caused by rubbing (see § 720). The difference in the diameters is called the *allowance* for the fit (see § 1143). For example, if the shaft diameter is 0.500″ and the hole diameter is 0.501″, then the allowance is 0.001″. The amount of allowance depends upon:

(1)   Size of work.
(2)   Kind of metal.
(3)   Amount of metal around hole.
(4)   Smoothness of hole and shaft.

672.   Thickness Gage

The thickness gage, also known as *feeler gage,* is made up of a number of thin, steel *blades* which fold into a handle like the blades of a pocket knife, Fig. 522. The thickness is marked on each blade. The blades are used to measure small spaces between surfaces as in Fig. 523.

Review Questions

1.   What does fitting mean?
2.   Name the operations needed in fitting.
3.   What is the term *fit* used to signify?
4.   List three general classifications of standard fits which are used in the assembly of nonthreaded cylindrical parts.
5.   List three general groups of locational fits and their symbols.
6.   For what purpose is a sliding fit used?
7.   For what is a running fit used? Give an example.

8.   For what purpose is a locational fit used?
9.   List three general kinds of force fits.
10.   For what purpose is a force fit used? Give several examples.
11.   Explain how parts are assembled with a shrink fit.
12.   For what purpose is an arbor press used?
13.   What is meant by allowance?
14.   What is meant by tolerance?
15.   What is meant by size limits?
16.   In what type of book can you find more complete information concerning the many classes of fits?
17.   What is a thickness gage? For what purpose is it used?
18.   How thin is the thinnest leaf in Fig. 522?
19.   How thick is the thickest leaf in Fig. 522?

Coordination

Words to Know

allowance	press fit
arbor press	round bearing
drive fit	running fit
expansion	shrink fit
feeler gage	shrinking
fit	size limits
force fit	sliding fit
locational fit	thickness gage
operation	tolerance

Mathematics

1.   If steel expands $\frac{3}{16}$″ per foot when heated, how much would an 8½″ bar expand?
2.   If the shaft diameter is 2″ and the hole diameter is 2.002″, what is the allowance for the fit?

Assembly Tools

679. What Does Assembling Mean?

Assembling means putting the parts of something together. For example, automobile parts are put together into complete automobiles, Fig. 529. Tools for holding, setting, and fastening are needed.

This unit describes tools used in assembling which may also be used in other work. The opposite to *assemble* is *disassemble* which means to take apart. (See *fitting* in § 665 and *assembler* in § 19.)

680. Machinist's Vise

The machinist's vise, also called *bench vise*, Fig. 530, is fastened near the edge of the bench with bolts. It is often used to clamp

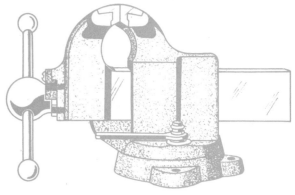

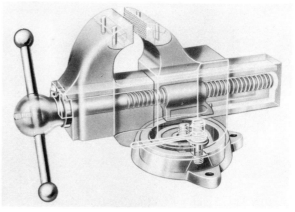

Fig. 530. Machinist's Vise (Courtesy Charles Parker Co.)

Fig. 529. Assembling Transmission and Engine (Courtesy Chevrolet Division, General Motors)

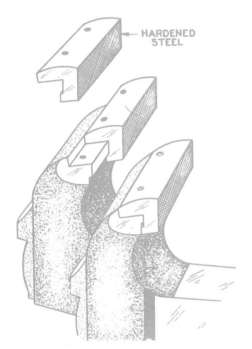

Fig. 531. Vise Jaws

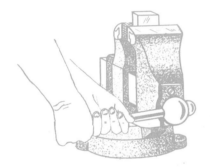

Fig. 532. Tightening Vise by Pulling One End
of the Handle

Fig. 533. Tightening Vise with One Hand on
Each End of the Handle

parts together while they are being assembled. The top of the vise should be about the height of the worker's elbow which is about 40 to 44 inches from the floor (see Fig. 156). Vises are measured by the width of the *jaws*, which are made of *hardened steel*, Fig. 531.

The *handle* of the vise acts as a lever; thus the *screw* and lever help to make a powerful clamp. The way to tighten the vise is shown in Fig. 532. Here, all the force is on one end of the handle. Another way to tighten the vise is shown in Fig. 533. Here the force is divided between the two ends of the handle. If more force than this is used, the vise will be damaged. (See *square thread* in § 622 and pipe vise in § 769.)

681. Vise Jaw Caps

Vise jaw caps, Fig. 534, are made of copper, brass, wood, leather, or other soft material. They are slipped over the steel jaws of the vise so as not to scratch or *nick* the *finished surfaces* on the work. (See Figs. 239 and 251.)

682. C-Clamp

The C-clamp is shaped like the letter C, Fig. 535. It is made in many sizes and is very useful to clamp parts together while they are being assembled, Fig. 536. (See § 538.)

683. Parallel Clamp

The parallel clamp has two steel jaws which are opened or closed by turning two screws. (See Fig. 67.) It is used to hold small work. The jaws should always be *parallel*; this is why the clamp is called a *parallel clamp*.

Fig. 534. Vise Jaw Caps

684. Pliers

There are many kinds of pliers, some of which are shown in Fig. 537. They are handy tools and are used for cutting small wire and for holding, gripping, twisting, turning, pulling, and pushing.

The *slip-joint plier*, also known as *combination plier*, is used for gripping; it can also cut small size wire. The *slip joint* makes it possible to grip large parts.

The *side-cutting plier* is especially useful for cutting wire and nails. It is used by *electricians* for cutting electric wires. The flat, square *jaws* are useful for bending corners on thin metal.

The *flat-nose plier* is shown in Fig. 643.

The *round-nose plier* is used to bend small wire and thin metal and to hold small parts.

Some pliers have long jaws and are called *long-nose pliers*.

685. Machinist's Hammer

The machinist's hammer, also called *ball peen hammer*, has been described in sections *60* and *216*. In assembly work it is used for striking and driving. Figs. 570-572 show how it is used for *riveting*. Use a light hammer for light work and a heavy hammer for heavy work.

686. Soft Hammers and Mallets

Striking two *hardened steel* parts against each other is dangerous because hardened steel is *brittle*; it breaks easily when struck by

another piece of hardened steel. In section *254* it was mentioned how easily a file, which is made of hardened steel, can be broken. Thus, it is also dangerous to strike two hardened steel hammers together or to strike any other hardened steel object with the hardened steel *face* (see Fig. 39) of a *machinist's ham-*

Fig. 536. Using C-Clamps (Courtesy Adjustable Clamp Co.)

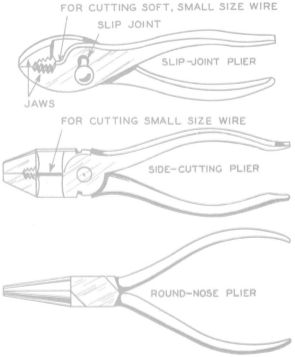

Fig. 537. Pliers

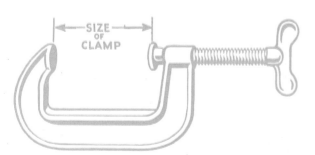

Fig. 535. C-Clamps

mer. (See § 685.) A *chip* of hardened steel (which may break off under these conditions) has very sharp edges, flies as fast as a bullet, and can cause great injury if it strikes someone.

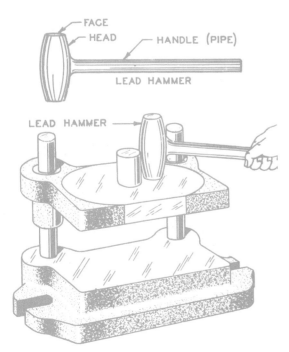

Fig. 538. **Hammering with a Lead Hammer**

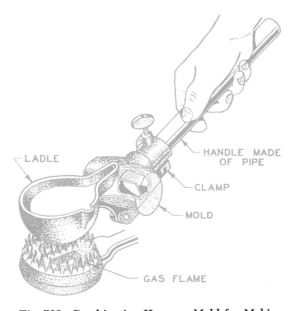

Fig. 539. **Combination Hammer Mold for Making a Lead Hammer**

Soft hammers, with *heads* (see Fig. 538) made of lead, copper, leather, rubber, or other soft materials are used to strike hardened steel surfaces. They are also used to strike thin or soft metals or *finished surfaces* so that nicks will not be made. (See § § 687 and 688.)

687. Lead Hammer

A lead hammer, Figs. 538 and 539, is used for striking *finished surfaces* where the steel hammer would dent or nick the surface. The *head* of a lead hammer is made of *lead*. The *handle* is usually a piece of pipe around which the melted lead is poured.

Lead hammers can be made in the shop with a *combination hammer mold*, Fig. 539. One end of the pipe handle is clamped in the *mold* (see also § 961). Put pieces of lead in the *ladle*, which is a dipper fastened to the mold, and then heat until the lead is melted. Then tip the ladle and the melted lead will flow through a hole into the mold and around the end of the pipe.

A lead hammer made of pure lead may be too soft and *mushroom* too easily (see Fig. 188). It will last longer if a little *antimony* (see § 377) is melted into the lead when making the lead hammer. Lead hammers with battered or *mushroomed faces* should be re-melted and made over into new ones. (See *lead casting* in section 993.)

688. Mallet

A mallet is usually made of wood, Fig. 540; it is used for the same reasons mentioned in section 686. (See Fig. 640.)

Fig. 540. **Using a Mallet**

689. Screwdrivers

Screwdrivers are used to turn or *drive* screws with *slotted* heads. They are made in many sizes and several shapes, Fig. 541. The size is measured by the length of the *blade* which is made of *tool steel, hardened* and *tempered* at the *point.* (See §§ *328, 952,* and *954.*)

The screwdriver point should be correctly shaped; it must fit the slot in the screw, Fig. 542. The *hollow-ground* sides (see § *1066*) of the point must press against the sides of the slot.

To avoid injuring the hand if the screwdriver slips, lay small work on the bench when using a screwdriver, Fig. 543, instead of holding it in the hand. *Burrs* (see Fig. 546 and § *262*) made by a screwdriver slipping out of a screw slot should be filed off to prevent cutting the hands.

The blades on some of the larger screwdrivers are square; a wrench may be used to turn such a screwdriver, Fig. 544.

An *offset screwdriver* has a bent handle. It is used where a straight screwdriver will not reach, Fig. 545. (See *offsets* in Fig. 770-771.)

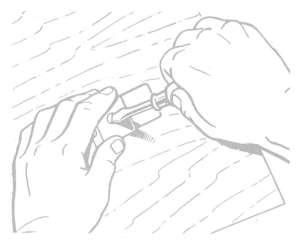

Fig. 542. Shape of a Screwdriver Point

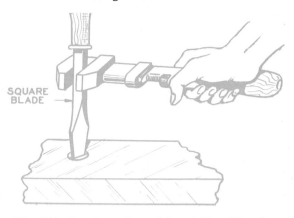

Fig. 543. Hold Small Work on the Bench when Using a Screwdriver

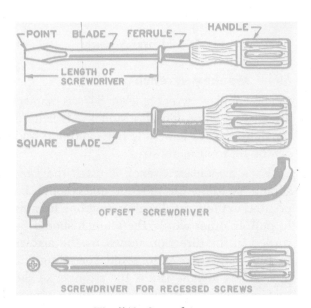

Fig. 541. Screwdrivers

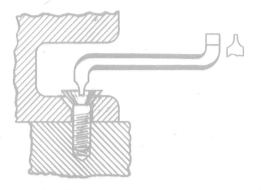

Fig. 544. Turning a Screwdriver with a Wrench

Fig. 545. Using an Offset Screwdriver

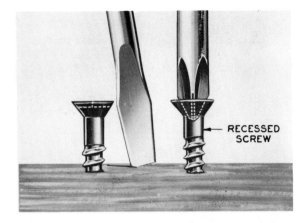

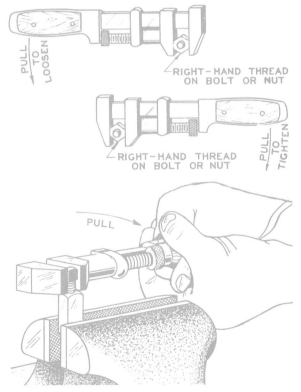

Fig. 546. **Using a Screwdriver for Recessed Screw;
Regular Screwdriver may Slip and Damage Work
or Screw** (Courtesy American Screw Co.)

Fig. 548. **Point Jaws in Direction of Pull**

The use of a screwdriver for *recessed
screws* is shown in Fig. 546.

690. Wrenches

There are many kinds of wrenches. Some
are *adjustable* which means that they can be
made larger or smaller to fit different sizes of
bolts and nuts; others are *nonadjustable;* that
is, they fit only one size bolt or nut. The basic
types of wrenches fit these classifications.

Adjustable Wrenches

> *Monkey wrench* (see § 691).
> *Adjustable-end wrench* (see § 692).
> *Adjustable S-wrench* (see § 692).
> *Vise-grip wrench* (see § 693).
> *Pipe wrench* (see § 694).

Nonadjustable Wrenches

> *Open-end wrench* (see § 695).
> *Box wrench* (see § 697).
> *Socket wrench* (see § 698).
> *Spanner wrench* (see § 699).

Fig. 547. **Monkey Wrench**

691. Monkey Wrench

The monkey wrench, Fig. 547, is named
after its inventor, Charles Moncky. It is used
for tightening or loosening bolts and nuts and
can be set to fit many sizes.

When a monkey wrench is used, the *jaws*
should be tight on the nut and should be
pointed in the same direction that one intends
to pull. In other words, the wrench should be
turned in the direction shown by the arrows
in Fig. 548 in order to avoid spreading the
jaws. The *movable jaw* is the stronger of the
two and can, therefore, stand more strain.
(See § 700.)

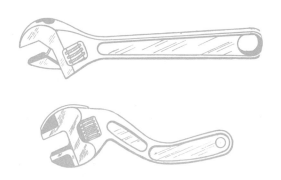

Fig. 549. Adjustable Wrenches

Fig. 550. Vise-Grip Wrench

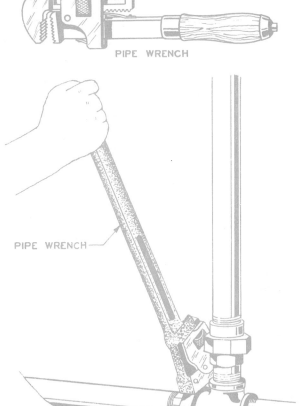

Fig. 551. Using Pipe Wrenches

692. Adjustable Wrenches

The *adjustable end wrench*, Fig. 549, is a strong tool which is used for general work in the shop. Its jaws are pointed at such an angle that it can be used in close corners and unhandy places where a *monkey wrench* is useless.

The *adjustable S-wrench*, Fig. 549, is for general use in the shop. Its S-shape makes it useful in many places where a *monkey wrench* cannot be used.

693. Vise-Grip Wrench

The *vise-grip wrench*, Fig. 550, also called vise-grip plier, is a handy tool and is used by many mechanics. It does many things faster and easier than any other tool; it acts like a vise, clamp, plier, pipe wrench, open-end wrench, or locking tool. The vise-grip wrench holds round, square, or other shapes. It works in close places and the strong, steel jaws lock to the work and will not slip.

694. Pipe Wrench

The pipe wrench is used to hold or turn pipes or other round pieces of metal, Fig. 551. The *teeth* should be kept clean to keep the wrench from slipping. When using the pipe wrench, point the *jaws* in the direction you intend to pull as in Fig. 548. (See *pipe tong* in § 770.)

695. Open-End Wrenches

A number of open-end wrenches are shown in Fig. 552. Some have a *single end*, others have a *double end*, some are *straight*, some are *S-shaped*, while on others the *head* makes a 15° or 22½° angle with the center line of the handle.

The S-shaped, the 15°, and the 22½° wrenches are used in narrow spaces where a straight wrench cannot make a quarter of a turn (90°) for a *square nut*, or a sixth of a

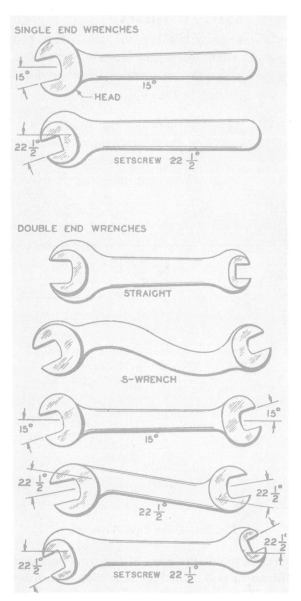

Fig. 552. Open-End Wrenches

turn (60°) for a *hexagon nut* (which has six sides). The use of the 15° wrench is shown in Fig. 553, the uses of the S-shaped and 22½° wrenches are about the same.

696. Sizes of Open-End Wrenches

Table 22 on page 263 tells the size of the open-end wrench needed for a certain sized *bolt, nut,* or *cap screw.* (See Figs. 585 and 591.) The size of an open-end wrench is measured by the size of the opening. Each wrench is stamped with its size.

The size of a *bolt* is measured by the diameter of the body, including the threads. A *nut* is measured by the diameter of the bolt which it fits. Thus, a wrench with a ⅜″ opening will fit a ¼″ bolt, a No. 10 machine screw nut, or a No. 10 stove bolt nut.

For an explanation of the meaning of *American Standard* (now United States American Standards) in Table 22, see section *619.*

697. Box Wrenches

Box wrenches have closed ends, Fig. 554, that is, the *head* of the wrench goes completely around the nut or bolt head.

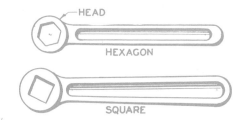

Fig. 554. Box Wrenches

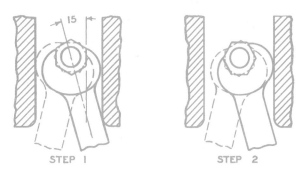

Fig. 553. Use of 15° Wrench

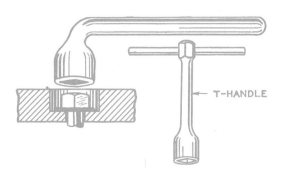

Fig. 555. Socket Wrenches

Table 22
OPEN-END WRENCH SIZES FOR AMERICAN STANDARD BOLTS, NUTS, AND CAP SCREWS
(See Section 696)

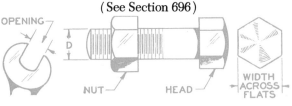

All dimensions given in inches.

WRENCH OPENING ——— WIDTH ACROSS FLATS[1] OF BOLT HEADS AND NUTS	UN- FINISHED AND SEMI- FINISHED BOLTS (D)	FINISHED BOLTS ——— NUTS AND JAM NUTS (D)	CAP- SCREWS (D)	MACHINE SCREW NUTS AND STOVE BOLT NUTS (D)
5/32	...	...	...	#0, #1
3/16	...	...	...	#2, #3
1/4	...	...	...	#4
5/16	...	...	...	#5, #6
11/32	...	...	...	#8
3/8	1/4	...	...	#10
7/16	...	1/4	1/4	#12, 1/4
1/2	5/16	...	5/16	...
9/16	3/8	5/16	3/8	5/16
5/8	7/16	3/8	7/16	3/8
3/4	1/2	7/16	1/2	...
13/16	...	1/2	9/16	...
7/8	9/16	9/16	5/8	...
15/16	5/8	...	...	...
1	...	5/8	3/4	...
1 1/8	3/4	3/4	7/8	...
1 5/16	7/8	7/8	1	...
1 1/2	1	1	1 1/8	...
1 11/16	1 1/8	1 1/8	1 1/4	...
1 7/8	1 1/4	1 1/4	...	...

698. Socket Wrenches

Socket wrenches, Fig. 555, are used to turn nuts and bolt heads which are in deep places or below the surface of the work. (See *socket head setscrew* in Fig. 589.)

699. Spanner Wrenches

Spanner wrenches have one or two *pins*, Fig. 556. These pins fit into holes or slots in round nuts or threaded collars to loosen or tighten them.

700. Using Wrenches

Always use a wrench that fits the bolt or nut snugly. When using an *adjustable wrench* (see § 690), set the *movable jaw* until it fits tightly on the bolt or nut. Use small wrenches for small bolts and nuts and large wrenches on large bolts and nuts.

A wrench is a *lever* (see section 657); the longer the handle the greater is the force of the lever. It is very important that you study how much a bolt or nut should be tightened with a wrench. You can tell by the *feel* or sense of touch whether a bolt or nut is about to twist off or whether the threads are beginning to *strip*[2] (See also § 691.)

701. Drift Punch

A drift punch, sometimes called a *tapered punch* or *aligning punch*, Fig. 557, is smooth and *tapered*. It may be used to arrange holes in a straight line, to drive out *pins* as shown in Fig. 558 (see also Fig. 598), or to drive out *rivets*. (See § 722.)

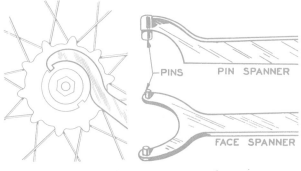

Fig. 556. Spanner Wrenches

Fig. 557. Drift Punch

[1] *Across flats* means the distance from one flat side of a square or hexagonal bolt head or nut to the opposite flat side; *across corners* means the distance from one corner to the opposite corner.

[2] *Strip* means to pull or tear off.

702. Pin Punch

A pin punch, Fig. 559, has a straight end and is used to drive out *cotter pins* and *tapered pins*. (See Figs. 597 and 598.) The pins should first be loosened with a *drift punch* (see Fig. 557) and then driven out with the pin punch, Fig. 560.

703. Arbor Press

An arbor press is a machine for pressing parts of machinery together or forcing them apart, such as pressing a shaft in or out of a pulley or gear, Fig. 561.

Fig. 559. Pin Punch

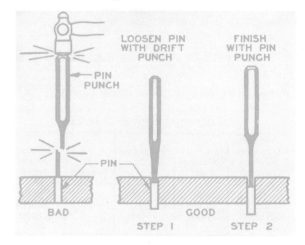

Fig. 560. Use of the Pin Punch

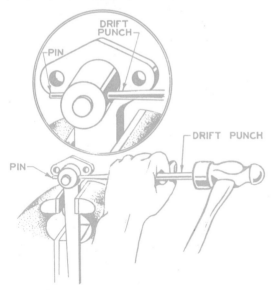

Fig. 558. Aligning Holes and Loosening a Pin with a Drift Punch
(Courtesy The Cincinnati Tool Co.)

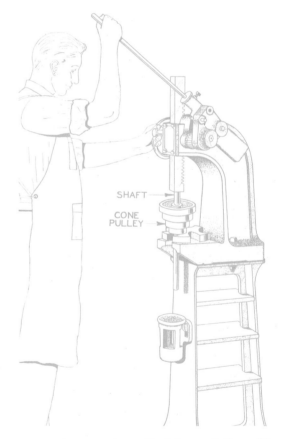

Fig. 561. Pressing a Shaft into a Pulley with an Arbor Press

Review Questions

1. What does assembling mean?
2. What are vise-jaw caps?
3. What does a C-clamp look like?
4. Why is a parallel clamp called by that name?
5. Name three kinds of pliers. For what is each used?
6. Of what are soft hammers made?
7. Describe the lead hammer. How is it made?
8. What is a mallet?
9. How is a screwdriver measured?
10. Of what kind of steel is the blade of the screwdriver made?
11. What happens to the slot in the screw if the screwdriver slips?
12. What is the purpose of the square blade on some screwdrivers?
13. Describe an offset screwdriver. For what is it used?
14. Name some adjustable wrenches.
15. Name some nonadjustable wrenches.
16. In which direction should the jaws point when using a monkey wrench or pipe wrench?
17. For what is the pipe wrench used?
18. What is an open-end wrench?
19. What is a single-headed wrench? A double-headed wrench?
20. For what are the S-shaped, 15°, and 22½° wrenches used?
21. What is a box wrench?
22. For what is a socket wrench used?
23. For what is a spanner wrench used?
24. For what is a drift punch used?
25. For what is a pin punch used?
26. For what is an arbor press used?

Coordination

Words to Know

across corners	pin spanner
adjustable end wrench	pipe wrench
	plier
adjustable S-wrench	recessed screw
assemble	round-nose plier
bench vise	screwdriver
box wrench	blade
combination	ferrule
hammer mold	handle
combination plier	point
cotter pin	setscrew wrench
disassemble	side-cutting plier
double end wrench	single-end wrench
drift punch	slip-joint plier
face spanner	slotted
15° wrench	socket wrench
finished surface	soft hammer
hexagon nut	spanner wrench
long nose plier	square nut
machinist's vise	S-wrench
mallet	straight wrench
monkey wrench	strip
mushroomed face	tapered pin
nonadjustable	tapered punch
offset screwdriver	22½° wrench
open-end wrench	vise-grip wrench
pin punch	

Mathematics

1. A 6-foot lever measures 5′ from the fulcrum on the long end and 1′ on the short end. How many pounds can be lifted if 100 pounds are applied on the long end?

Occupational Information

1. Describe the assembly line in an automobile plant.

Rivets and Riveting

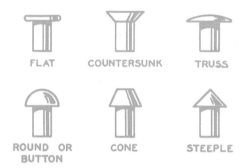

FLAT COUNTERSUNK TRUSS

ROUND OR BUTTON   CONE   STEEPLE

Fig. 566. Rivets

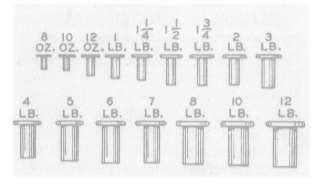

Fig. 567. Tinners' Rivets (Actual Size)

Fig. 568. Amount of Rivet Needed to Form Head

714. Meaning and Reasons for Riveting

Riveting is the fastening of pieces of metal or other material together with *rivets,* Figs. 566 and 567. Rivets are used to hold pieces together permanently. The rivet is put through holes in the pieces to be fastened together, Fig. 568. The rivets may be solid or they may be hollow with a tubular form, Fig. 574. The small end of solid rivets is hammered into the form of a head, as in Figs. 570 and 571. Hollow rivets are *clinched* at the small end with a special riveting tool. (See Figs. 575 and 576.)

Many kinds of rivets are used for fastening pieces of metal together. Nonmetallic materials such as leather, plastic, fiber, and canvas also are fastened with rivets. Special kinds of rivets are used for fastening these materials. In this unit, we are principally concerned with the kinds of rivets and riveting procedures used for riveting metals.

Many metal fastening jobs which were formerly riveted are now welded. This is true of structural-steel products such as bridges and steel frames of large buildings. However, riveting is still widely used for fastening metals and other nonmetallic materials.

Rivets are used for fastening metals which are not easily welded, or where welding is not practical. Rivets are used instead of welding in cases where the heat required for welding would reduce the strength of the metal or cause it to warp severely. They are often used to fasten aluminum sheetmetal in the construction of aircraft, small boats, and other aluminum products. In modern manufacturing plants riveting is done rapidly and economically with special riveting tools and machines.

The heads of rivets are sometimes used to decorate and add beauty to an object, especially in the field of *art metalwork* which is explained in Unit 41.

715.   Who Does Riveting

A person who rivets is a *riveter*. Riveting is done by *sheet metalworkers;* by *ornamental ironworkers* on fences, gates, railings, etc.; by *structural ironworkers* on steel frames of large buildings and bridges and on the *steel plates* (see § 329) on the sides of a ship. The *boilermaker* rivets the plates which make up the boiler. The *tinsmith* rivets cans, pans, pots, pails, etc. The *coppersmith* rivets tanks, kettles, pipes, funnels, etc.

716.   Rivets

Rivets are metal pins that look like bolts without threads. They are made of different metals, such as soft iron or steel, aluminum, copper, and brass. They are available in many different sizes and shapes of heads. The most common kinds of heads are shown in Fig. 566. Rivets of many other special shapes are made. They may be either *solid,* as shown in Figs. 566 and 567, or they may be of *tubular* or special form as shown in Fig. 574.

Size

The size of a rivet is measured by the diameter and length of the body. The head is not included in the length except on those designed to be countersunk. They generally are available in diameters ranging from ⅛″ to ⅜″, and in lengths from ¼″ to 3″. The kinds most commonly used for hand riveting in school shops and maintenance shops are solid rivets ⅛″, ⁵⁄₃₂″, and ³⁄₁₆″ diameter, with flat or round heads. Rivets ⅛″ in diameter with round heads are commonly used in making art metal projects.

Solid rivets generally are sold by the pound and in boxes of 100 or 1000. When purchasing rivets, specify the following: diameter, length, kind of head, and kind of material.

Tinner's rivets, Fig. 567, are used for riveting sheet metal. They are made of soft steel, either plain or coated with tin. The tin coating makes them easier to solder and makes them resist rust. The sizes of tinner's rivets are given in ounces or pounds per 1000; a 6 oz. rivet means that 1000 rivets weigh 6 ounces; a 2 lb. rivet means that 1000 of these rivets weigh 2 pounds. As the weight increases, so does the diameter and length. (See Fig. 567.)

717.   Choosing a Rivet

Choose a rivet that is .003″ to ¹⁄₆₄″ smaller in diameter than the holes in the pieces to be riveted. It should be long enough to extend through the pieces to be riveted, plus enough metal from which to form a *head,* which is about 1½ times the diameter of the rivet, Fig. 568.

If the rivet is part of the design of the project, select a round-head rivet. If the rivet is not to be noticed, use a flat-head rivet. If the back of the work must be flush when using round-head rivets, countersink the hole (see § 588) and rivet as shown in Fig. 573. Allow the rivet to extend a small amount above the surface, just enough to fill the countersunk hole when headed. The rivet selected generally should be made of the same material as the metal being riveted.

718.   Rivet Spacing

As a general rule, rivets should not be spaced closer together than three times the diameter of the rivet. Generally, for adequate strength, they should not be spaced farther apart than 24 times the diameter. Thus the minimum space between two ⅛″ diameter rivets is 3 × ⅛″, or ⅜″ apart. The maximum distance recommended between two ⅛″ diameter rivets is 24 × ⅛″, or 3″. (See Fig. 578.)

719.   Rivet Set

A rivet set is a *hardened steel* tool with a hollow in one end, Fig. 569. It is used to shape the end of a rivet into a round, smooth head. Rivet sets are made in various sizes, designated by the following numbers: 00, 0, 1, 2,

through 8. A No. 8 rivet set generally is used for 10 or 12 ounce tinner's rivets. The No. 8 is the smallest size; and the No. 00 is the largest.

720.   Riveting

Holes are first punched or drilled through the metal pieces. On thin gage sheet metals, the holes are punched in one of three ways: (1) with a pin punch, Fig. 560; (2) with a solid punch, Fig. 641; (3) with a hand punch, Fig. 641. The procedure for punching holes is explained in section 797. On thick gage sheet metals or on metal bars, the holes generally are drilled.

The holes in the two pieces should be carefully laid out. Put the rivet through the holes, press the pieces together, and place the head of the rivet on something solid, such as a steel block. The head of the rivet can be kept from flattening by resting it on a *riveting block,* which is made of steel and has a hollow like

Fig. 569. Rivet Set

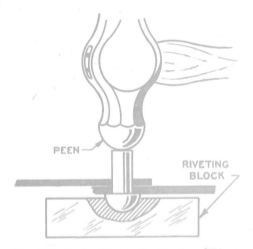

Fig. 570. Strike First in the Center of Rivet

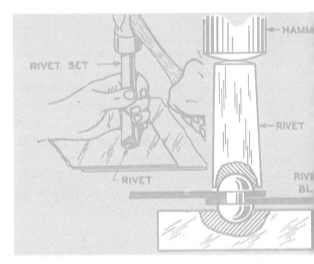

Fig. 572. Forming the Rivet Head with the Rivet Set

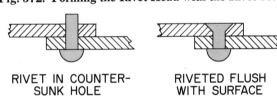

RIVET IN COUNTER-
SUNK HOLE

RIVETED FLUSH
WITH SURFACE

Fig. 573. Form Rivet Head Flush with Surface
in Countersunk Hole

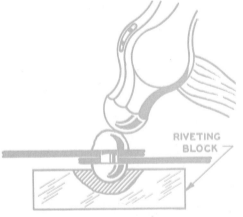

Fig. 571. Rounding the End of the Rivet by Peening

the shape of the rivet head, Fig. 570. Strike blows in the center of the end of the rivet with either the *face* or the *peen* of a *ball peen hammer* until the end of the rivet is spread out a little. Then strike it with the peen until it is quite round on top like a mushroom, Fig. 571. Too much hammering will bend the metal out of shape. A *riveting hammer*, Fig. 638, may be used instead of a ball peen hammer for riveting if desired. The flat face of the hammer may be used to flatten the rivet slightly and fill in the hole. The head is then rounded off with lighter blows. Next, place the *rivet set* on the hammered end of the rivet and strike the rivet set, Fig. 572. A round, smooth head is thus formed. (See *boilermaker* and *structural ironworker*, § 19.)

721. Hot and Cold Rivets

Iron and steel get larger when heated; that is, the metal *expands*. Iron and steel expand $\frac{1}{8}''$ to $\frac{3}{16}''$ per foot when red hot. A piece of steel, 1' long when cold, will measure $12\frac{1}{8}''$ to $12\frac{3}{16}''$ when red hot. Thus an iron rivet gives more strength when heated before riveting because it *shrinks* as it cools, holding the pieces more tightly together. Large rivets, such as those used to rivet structural steel beams together, are hammered when hot. Small rivets are hammered when cold. (See § 964.)

722. Removing Rivets

Rivets are used to fasten pieces together permanently, but it is sometimes necessary to remove rivets. Fig. 194 shows how the head of a rivet is cut off with a *cold chisel* and hammer. After the head is cut off, the rest of the rivet may be driven out with a *drift punch* and *hammer*. (See § 701.) Blind rivets may be removed by drilling as described in § 724.

723. Tubular and Special Rivets

A wide variety of tubular rivets of standard and special design are used in producing many appliances and hardware items. Several common types are shown in Fig. 574. In modern

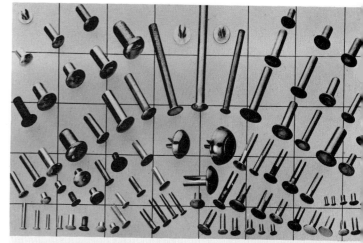

A. Typical Standard Rivets

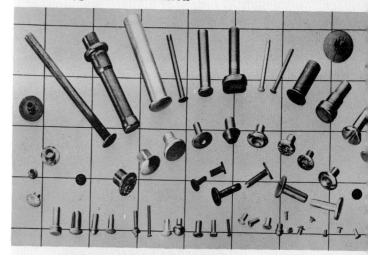

B. Typical Special Rivets

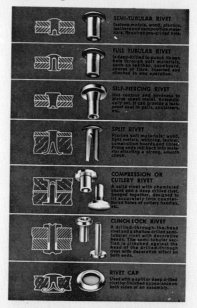

C. Section View of Typical Applications

Fig. 574. Standard and Special Tubular Rivets
(Courtesy Chicago Rivet and Machine Co.)

production procedures, these rivets generally are inserted in the stock and clinched with special riveting machines or tools.

724. Blind Rivets

Blind rivets are so named because they can be inserted and set from the same side of the workpiece. Solid rivets and other kinds of rivets generally require access to both sides of the work being riveted. Blind rivets, often called *Pop*[1] rivets, clinch inside with a pull from the tool from the outside, as shown in Fig. 575. The stem or mandrel fractures and breaks off when the head is clinched. In school shops, maintenance shops, and home workshops, a plierlike tool, Fig. 576, is used for clinching blind rivets. Power-operated setting tools are often used in industrial plants where many rivets are used.

Blind rivets may be used for fastening sheet metal, thin flat metal bars, and nonmetallic materials such as fiber or plastic. They may be used for fastening metal to metal, plastic to metal, and fiberglass to metal. Their principal advantage is that they may be inserted and set from the same side. This makes them handy for riveting both small and large containers, cabinets, and similar items. They are used on items such as automobiles, aircraft, appliances, furniture, sheet metal duct work, toys, and for numerous other purposes.

Types

Blind rivets are available in a wide variety of different designs, types, sizes, and kinds of materials. Three common *pull-stem* types, shown in Fig. 577, include the following:

(1) Open-end type with domed head. (Also available with countersunk head.)

(2) Closed-end type with hollow core and domed head. (Also available with countersunk head.)

(3) Closed-end type with countersunk head and filled core. (Also available with domed head.)

An example of the use of open-end type rivets with domed heads is shown in Fig. 578. The closed-end type[2] seal is liquid and pressure-tight when set. It may be used for con-

[1]*Pop Rivet* is the trademark for blind rivets manufactured by the USM Fastener Company, Division of the United Shoe Machinery Corporation.

[2]Patent held by the USM Fastener Company, Division of United Shoe Machinery Corporation.

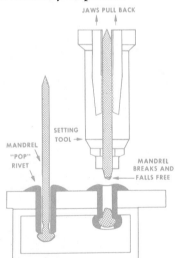

Fig. 575. Blind Rivets Clinch Inside with a Pull from the Tool Outside (Courtesy U.S.M. Fastener Co.)

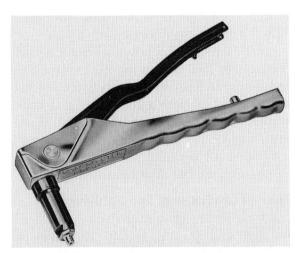

Fig. 576. Riveting Tool for Clinching Blind Rivets (Courtesy U.S.M. Fastener Co.)

tainers and items which must be pressure tight.

Other types of blind rivets include the *drive-pin* type and the *explosive*-type, Fig. 579. The former is clinched with a drive pin, while the latter is clinched by chemical expansion with an explosive charge. The charge is activated by a hot iron or similar tool.

Blind rivets are available with domed heads or countersink heads (120°), as shown in Fig. 577, or with larger flanged heads. They are made of the following materials: aluminum, steel, copper, monel, and stainless steel. They generally are made in diameters ranging from $\frac{3}{32}''$ to $\frac{1}{4}''$ and in various lengths up to $\frac{3}{4}''$.

Rivet Selection

For best results, the length of the rivet selected should be such that it will clinch with a short head as shown in Figs. 577 and 578. However, with careful riveting procedures, rivets of the same length may be used for materials of various thickness, as shown in Fig. 580. The rivet generally should be made of metal which is similar to the metal being

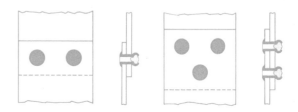

Fig. 578. Lap Joints Riveted with Blind Rivets
(Open-End Type Rivets)
(Courtesy U.S.M. Fastener Co.)

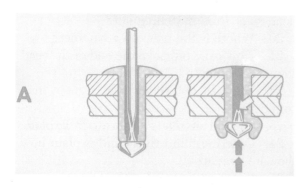

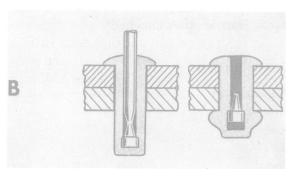

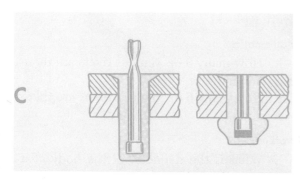

Fig. 577. Common Pull-Stem Types of Blind Rivets
(Courtesy U.S.M. Fastener Co.)
A. Open-End Type with Domed Heads
B. Closed-End Type with Hollow Core
C. Closed-End Type with Countersunk Head
and Filled Core

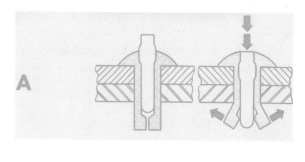

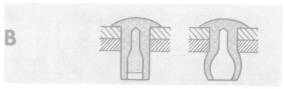

Fig. 579. Blind Rivets
(Courtesy U.S.M. Fastener Co.)
A. Drive-Pin Type
B. Explosive-Type

riveted. For added strength the rivets may be located closer together, or in double rows, as shown in Fig. 578.

Removing Rivets

When necessary, blind rivets may be removed by drilling the rivet out. The drill diameter should be equal to the diameter of the hole before the rivet was set.

Review Questions

1. Why are metal pieces riveted together?
2. List several kinds of nonmetallic materials which may be fastened with rivets.
3. List several kinds of products which are constructed by fastening with rivets.
4. Of what are rivets made?
5. Describe the four shapes of rivet heads that are used most.
6. How is the size of a rivet measured?
7. Is the head of the rivet generally included in the length?
8. How are rivets sold?
9. How much larger in diameter should the hole be than the rivet?
10. What happens if the diameter of the rivet is too small?
11. How long should a rivet be?
12. For what purposes are tinner's rivets used?
13. What factors should be considered in selecting the kind of rivet to use for a particular job?

14. Describe the procedure used to produce a rivet head flush with the surface of the stock being riveted.
15. List a general rule which may be used regarding the minimum and maximum spacing between rivets.
16. What is a rivet set?
17. How are rivet holes made?
18. What is a riveting block?
19. How can you keep the head of a round-head rivet from flattening out?
20. Where is the peen on a hammer?
21. How can you make the end of the rivet round and smooth?
22. Why do hot rivets hold tighter than cold rivets?
23. Should all rivets be heated? Explain.
24. Describe blind rivets and explain how they are headed.
25. List several uses for blind rivets.
26. List several kinds of tubular or special rivets. How are they clinched?

Coordination

Words to Know

blind rivet	rivet set
cold rivet	shrink
hot rivet	solid rivet
Pop rivet	tinner's rivet
riveting	tubular rivet
riveting block	

Mathematics

1. How many 8 oz. tinner's rivets are there in 1 pound?
2. How many 6 oz. tinner's rivets are there in 1 pound?

Drafting

1. What is the diameter of the body of a 10 oz. tinner's rivet?

Occupational Information

1. What are the dangers of structural iron work?
2. What are the dangers of boilermaking?

Fig. 580. Blind Rivets in this Assembly are the Same Length (Courtesy U.S.M. Fastener Co.)

Fasteners

Bolts, Screws, Nuts, Washers, Shims, Pins, and Keys

727. Metal Fasteners

Metal parts can be held together with different *metal fasteners,* such as rivets, bolts, screws, pins, and numerous special fastening devices. *Rivets* and *riveting* are explained in Unit 36. Others are explained in this unit. The workman must use good judgment in deciding upon the best kind of fastener.

728. Bolts and Screws

Bolts and screws are made in many shapes and sizes. The kinds most used are shown in Fig. 585.

Rough and *semifinished* bolts and screws are rolled, pressed, hammered, or punched out of cold or hot metal. *Finished* bolts and screws are cut out of a bar of steel by a screw machine, which is a special automatic lathe. See Unit 57.

729. Use of Bolts and Screws

Bolts and screws are usually used to fasten together parts which have to be taken apart later. A *bolt* is used where one can get at both sides of the work with wrenches. A *screw* is used where only one side can be reached with a wrench or screwdriver.

730. Sizes of Bolts and Screws

The sizes of bolts and screws are measured by the diameter and length of the *body;* the *head* is not included in the length except on flat-head bolts and screws, Fig. 584. It is best to refer to dealers' catalogs to find out what sizes are made.

A list of the fasteners required, including bolts, screws, pins, washers, etc., should be listed in the bill of materials with the plan for a project or product to be produced. An example of a form which may be used for making a bill of materials is shown on the plan sheets in Figs. 33 and 35.

An explanation of the information listed in the bill of materials follows:

  (1) Name of part:
      A) Name of bolt, screw, or nut.
  (2) How many needed.
  (3) Kind:
      A) Kind of thread (if it is made with more than one kind of thread).
      B) Kind of finish (if made in more than one finish).
  (4) Size:
      A) Diameter (in inches or gage number) $\times$ length.

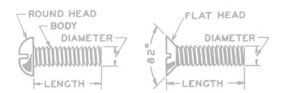

Fig. 584. **Measurements of Bolts and Screws**

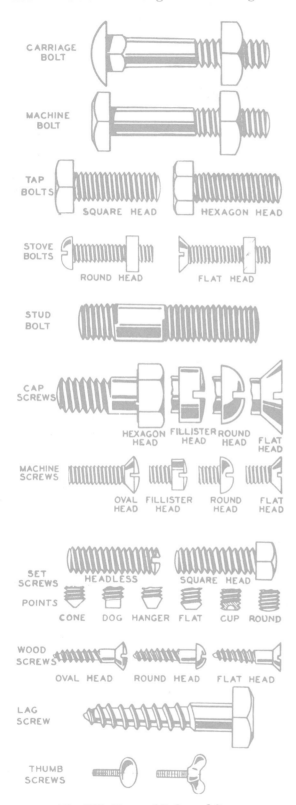

Fig. 585. Types of Bolts and Screws

(5) Shape:
  A) Shape of head (if it is made with more than one shape of head).
  B) Shape of point (setscrews only).

731. Carriage Bolts

A carriage bolt has a *round head* (see Fig. 585). The part of the body under the head is square. It has a black, *rough finish* (see § 728) and has the *Unified (National) Coarse thread* (see § 619).

A carriage bolt is usually used to fasten a wooden part to metal. The square part under the head sinks into the wood, and thus the bolt cannot turn while the nut is being *screwed* on.

732. Machine Bolts

A machine bolt (see Fig. 585) has either a square or *hexagonal* head. It is made with a black, *rough finish* or *finished* all over (see § 728). A machine bolt has a *Unified (National) Coarse thread (UNC)* or a *Unified (National) Fine thread (UNF)* (see § 619).

733. Tap Bolts

A tap bolt is like a *machine bolt* except that the whole body is threaded. It may be used with or without a nut. (See Fig. 585.)

734. Stove Bolts

A stove bolt has either a round or flat head which is slotted so that it can be turned with a screwdriver. (See Fig. 585.) It is made with the *UNC thread.* (See § 617.) The head of the *flat-head stove bolt* is included in the length while the head of the *round-head stove bolt* is not. Stove bolts are sold 100 in a box.

735. Stud Bolts

A stud bolt has no head and is threaded on both ends. (See Fig. 585.) One end of the stud bolt has more threads than the other. Its use is shown in Fig. 586. The *cylinder head* of an automobile engine is fastened to the *cylinder block* by screwing the nuts on the *stud bolts*. By removing the nuts, the cylinder head can be lifted off while the stud bolts remain in the cylinder block.

736. Cap Screws

Cap screws are made with heads of several different shapes. (See Fig. 585.) They are usually *finished* all over (see § 728) and are made with *UNC* or *UNF threads*. (See § 619.) Cap screws are used when it is not handy to get at both sides of the work with wrenches. The head of the cap screw presses against the top piece and holds the parts together as shown in Fig. 587. The use of the *flat-head screw* is explained in section 587, and the use of the *fillister head cap screw* is shown in Fig. 463.

737. Machine Screws

Machine screws are made with heads of several different shapes (see Fig. 585) and are made with either the *UNC* or *UNF thread*. (See § 619.) They are made of steel, aluminum, or *brass*. The smaller diameters are measured by *gage numbers*. The sizes range from number 0 (.060") to ⅜" in diameter. Note in Table 34, page 440, that the gage numbers are the same for both machine screws and wood screws.

Machine screws are sold by the *gross* which equals twelve dozen. (See Table 19, page 236.)

738. Setscrews

Setscrews are made with *square heads* and *headless*. (See Fig. 585.) Both kinds are made with different *points*. Setscrews are *case-hardened* (see § 957) and are used to fasten pulleys and collars on shafts as shown in Fig. 588. *Headless setscrews* are described in the next section.

739. Headless Setscrews

The headless setscrew is made for safety. (See Fig. 588.) Screws with heads are dangerous on moving parts; the workman may be caught and injured. (See Fig. 492.)

There are two kinds of headless setscrews. One kind has a slot for a screwdriver. The other kind, known as a *socket-head setscrew*, has an *hexagonal* hole (see § 50). A special wrench is needed, Fig. 589.

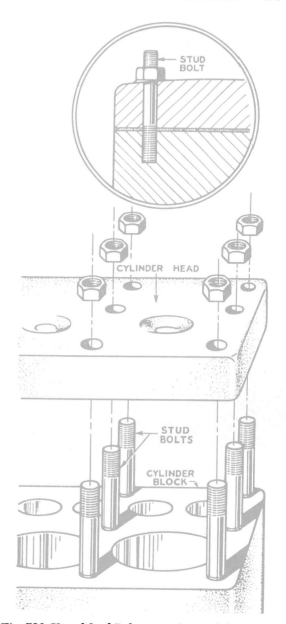

Fig. 586. Use of Stud Bolts on an Automobile Engine

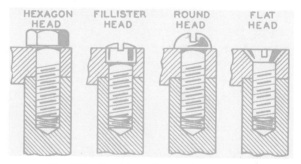

Fig. 587. Position of Cap-Screw Heads

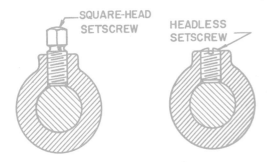

Fig. 588. Setscrews

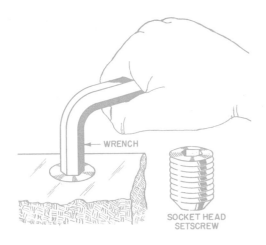

Fig. 589. Socket-Head Setscrew and Wrench

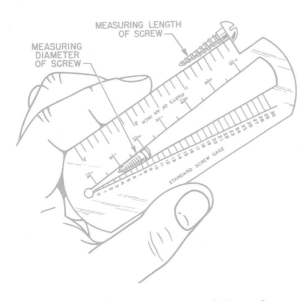

Fig. 590. Gaging Wood Screw with Screw Gage

740. Wood Screws

Wood screws are made with flat, round, or oval heads. (See Fig. 585.) The heads are slotted so that they can be turned with a screwdriver. The angle of the flat head is 82°. Wood screws are made of iron or brass and come in *bright*[1], *blued,* or *nickeled finishes* (see §§ 1112 and 1117). The body and threads come to a point known as a *gimlet point.*

The diameter of a wood screw is measured on the body under the head by the *American Standard Screw Gage.* Note in Table 34, page 440 that the gage numbers are the same for both wood screws and machine screws. Fig. 590 shows how a wood screw is measured by placing it in the opening of the *screw gage* until it touches on both sides; the number where it touches is the *gage number.*

Wood screws are often used to fasten metal parts to wood. They are sold by the *gross* which equals twelve dozen.

741. Lag Screws

A lag screw has a *square head* like a bolt and is threaded like a *wood screw.* (See Fig. 585.) It is used for heavy work such as fastening a machine to a wooden floor.

742. Thumbscrews

A thumbscrew is a screw with one or two *wings* or with a *knurled head.* It is used where a screw must be turned by the thumb and finger. (See Figs. 535, 539, 585, and § 1200.)

743. Nuts

There are many different shapes and sizes of nuts; samples of these are shown in Fig. 591. The size of a nut is measured by the diameter of the bolt it fits. In other words, a ½″ nut fits a ½″ bolt.

Rough and *semifinished* nuts are pressed, hammered, or punched out of cold or hot metal. *Finished* nuts are cut out of a bar of steel by machine.

---

[1]*Bright finish* is the natural color of steel made shiny by the finishing cut on a machine or by polishing.

744. Machine-Screw Nuts

A machine-screw nut (see Fig. 591) is cut out of an *hexagonal* bar of steel. It is a flat on the *bearing surface*. The thread is either *UNC* or *UNF*. (See § 619.) Machine-screw nuts are sold by the *gross*.

745. Jam Nuts and Lock Nuts

A jam nut (see Fig. 591) is sometimes called a *lock nut* or *check nut*. It is thinner than an ordinary nut and is used as a lock to keep another nut from loosening by vibration, Fig. 592. Although the jam nut is usually put on last, the thick nut may be put on last to make use of the greater strength. Another type of lock nut, a preassembled washer and nut, is also available.

746. Castle Nuts

A castle nut (see Fig. 591) has slots across the top. The parts which extend upward make it look like a castle, hence the name. A *cotter pin* (see Fig. 599) is slipped in a slot and through a hole in the bolt to lock the nut to the bolt and thus keep the nut from jarring off. Castle nuts are usually used to hold wheel bearings and wheels in place.

747. Wing Nuts

A wing nut (see Fig. 591) has two, thin, flat *wings* and is used where a nut has to be turned with the thumb and finger. (See Fig. 154.)

748. Washers

Washers serve several purposes in fastener assemblies. They are used primarily as a bearing surface for bolts, nuts, and screws. They are sometimes used with rivets when fastening leather, fiber, canvas, and similar soft materials. They also serve to distribute the load over a greater area, protect the surface, and prevent movement of parts.

The common *flat washer* is a thin, round, metal disk with a hole in the middle, Fig. 593. It is used as a *bearing surface* under a nut or under the head of a bolt or screw.

The size of a washer is measured by the diameter of the bolt that it fits; thus a ½″ washer is for a ½″ bolt. Flat washers are sold by the pound.

749. Lock Washers

Lock washers serve as a spring takeup between bolts or screws and the workpiece. They also serve to lock the nut or screw in place, thus preventing movement or loosening due to vibration. The *helical spring*-type lock washer, Fig. 593, looks like a coil from a spring. Lock washers of this type are available in light, medium (regular), heavy, and extra-heavy types for screws and bolts from size No. 2 to 3″ diameter. They are hardened and

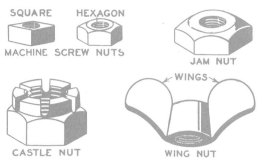

Fig. 591. Types of Nuts

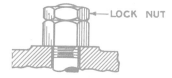

Fig. 592. Lock Nut

Fig. 593. Washers

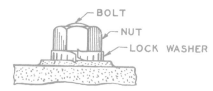

Fig. 594. Use of Lock Washer

tempered and are used under a screw or nut to lock it in place so it will not jar loose, see Fig. 594.

Tooth-type lock washers, Fig. 595, of hardened steel will wedge into the bearing surfaces to prevent bolts, nuts, or screws from turning or loosening due to vibration. Several standard types are shown in Fig. 595.

The *external type* has teeth on the largest radius and therefore provides the best locking ability. Hence, it should be used whenever possible. It is recommended for use with fasteners which have heads large enough to contact the teeth.

Internal type lock washers, Fig. 595, are recommended for use with fillister head screws or other screws with small heads, where it is desirable to hide the teeth.

Heavy-duty internal-type lock washers, Fig. 595, are recommended for use on large bolts and nuts on heavy machinery.

Countersink type lock washers, Fig. 595, are used with countersink flat-head screws, with either 82° or 100° countersink angles.

External-internal-type lock washers, Fig. 595, are used in assemblies where a larger bearing surface is desired. They are used with oversized screw holes or between adjustable parts to prevent rotational movement.

Preassembled *screw and washer assemblies,* called *sems,* Fig. 596, have a lock-washer fitting loosely below the screw head. The ex-

EXTERNAL TYPE   INTERNAL TYPE   EXTERNAL-INTERNAL   HEAVY DUTY   COUNTERSUNK TYPE

Fig. 595. Common Tooth-Type Lock Washers
(Courtesy Great Lakes Screw Corp.)

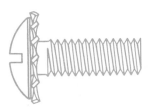 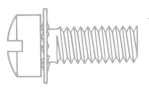 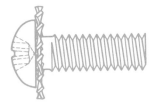

Truss Head Screw and
External Tooth
Lock Washer

Fillister Head Screw
and Internal Tooth
Lock Washer

Round Head Screw and
Internal-External Tooth
Lock Washer

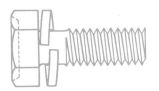 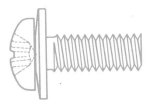 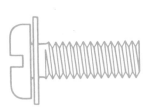

Hexagon Head Screw and
Spring Lock Washer

Pan Head Screw and
Conical Spring Washer

Pan Head Screw and
Plain Flat Washer

Fig. 596. Preassembled Screw and Washer
Assemblies (ASA. B18.12 — 1962)

panded rolled thread diameter prevents the washer from falling off. They are used for more rapid assembly on modern assembly lines. Preassembled *lock washer and nut units* are also available. These also speed up assembly work.

750. Shims

A shim is a thin sheet of metal, wood, or paper placed between two surfaces to keep them a certain distance apart or so that the shim is a support. The two halves of a *bearing* around a *shaft* may be separated a little by placing shims between them as shown in Fig. 597. (See also Fig. 521.) This lessens the tightness on the shaft. As the bearing wears down and gets loose, a shim may be removed to get a closer fit. (See *running fit*, § 668.)

A shim is used as a support when, for example, it is placed under a leg of a machine so that it will be level, Fig. 598.

751. Cotter Pins

A cotter pin, also called a *cotter key,* is made of wire. It is slipped through a hole in a bolt behind a nut to keep the nut from turning. Note the right way to lock the nut, Fig. 599. The head of the cotter pin should fit into the slot of the nut; one leg should be bent over the end of the bolt and the other leg should be bent over the side of the nut.

752. Tapered Pins

A tapered pin is often used on a job such as fastening a pulley or collar to a shaft, Fig. 600. The *taper* equals ¼″ per foot. Tapered

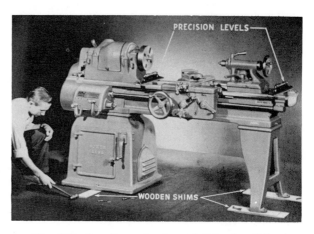

Fig. 598. Leveling a Lathe with Wooden Shims
(Courtesy South Bend Lathe, Inc.)

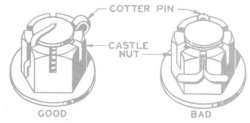

Fig. 599. Use of Castle Nut and Cotter Pin

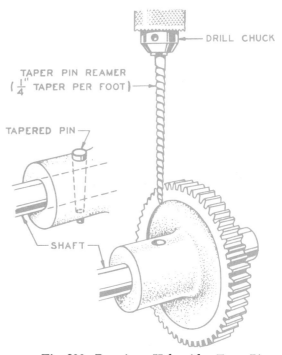

Fig. 600. Reaming a Hole with a Taper Pin
Reamer for a Tapered Pin

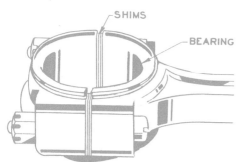

Fig. 597. Use of Shims Between the
Halves of a Bearing

pins are made in lengths from ⅜″ to 6″. The hole into which the pin fits is first drilled and then *reamed* with a *taper-pin reamer* which has the same taper as the pin. (See Fig. 600.) Taper pins are made in 17 standard sizes which are designated by numbers. The sizes are included in handbooks for machinists.

753. Keys

Keys are made in several shapes. They are used to keep pulleys and gears from moving on *shafts*, Fig. 601. Half of the key fits in a

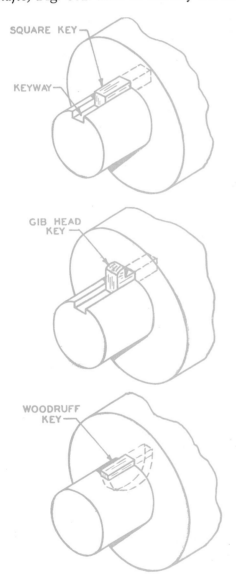

SQUARE KEY

KEYWAY

GIB HEAD KEY

WOODRUFF KEY

Fig. 601. Types of Keys

keyway, which is a slot in the shaft, and the other half fits into a slot in the pulley or gear; the pulley or gear is thus fastened to the shaft.

The *square key,* also known as a *feather key,* is the one that is most used.

The *gib-head key* is useful where it is necessary to remove the key from one side of the pulley or gear. A *wedge* (see § 61) may be used to back the key out of the hole.

The form of a *Woodruff key* is a half circle.

754. Retaining Rings

Retaining rings, Fig. 602, are a relatively new type of fastener used in assembling parts of modern metal products. They generally are inserted and seated in either internal or external grooves with a special plier-like tool, Fig. 603. Self-locking types do not require a seating groove. The principal function of retaining rings is to provide a shoulder for holding, locking, or positioning parts of assemblies. Internal-type retaining rings are used in bored holes. External types are used on shafts or studs.

755. Self-Tapping (Sheet Metal) Screws

Self-tapping screws, Figs. 604, 607, 608, and 609, cut their own threads in soft steel, aluminum, and other soft metals. They are driven into punched or drilled holes which are slightly larger than the minor diameter (see § 606) of the screw thread. As they are driven into the hole, they produce threads in either one or both parts being fastened, thus forming mating threads.

Self-tapping screws eliminate the need for a tapping operation, or for fastening with nuts, soldering, or riveting on many kinds of metal products. They are used for economical assembly of sheet metal and other sheet materials such as plastic, plywood, asbestos, and fiber materials. They are used by sheet metalworkers for installing heating, ventilation, and air conditioning ducts and equipment. They are used for assembling many parts on automobile bodies, radio and television chassis, stoves, refrigerators, and other appliances used in the home.

There are many kinds of self-tapping screws available. They are available with a wide variety of head styles, Fig. 605, and with a variety of driving recesses, including clutch heads, slotted heads, phillips recessed heads, and hexagonal heads (see Fig. 606). Some of the common head styles used on self-tapping screws are shown in Figs. 607 and 608. Self-tapping screws are made in diameters according to screw gage numbers, which are the same as those used for wood screws and machine screws. (See Table 34, p. 440.) Most of the many types of self-tapping screws may be classified under the following three headings:

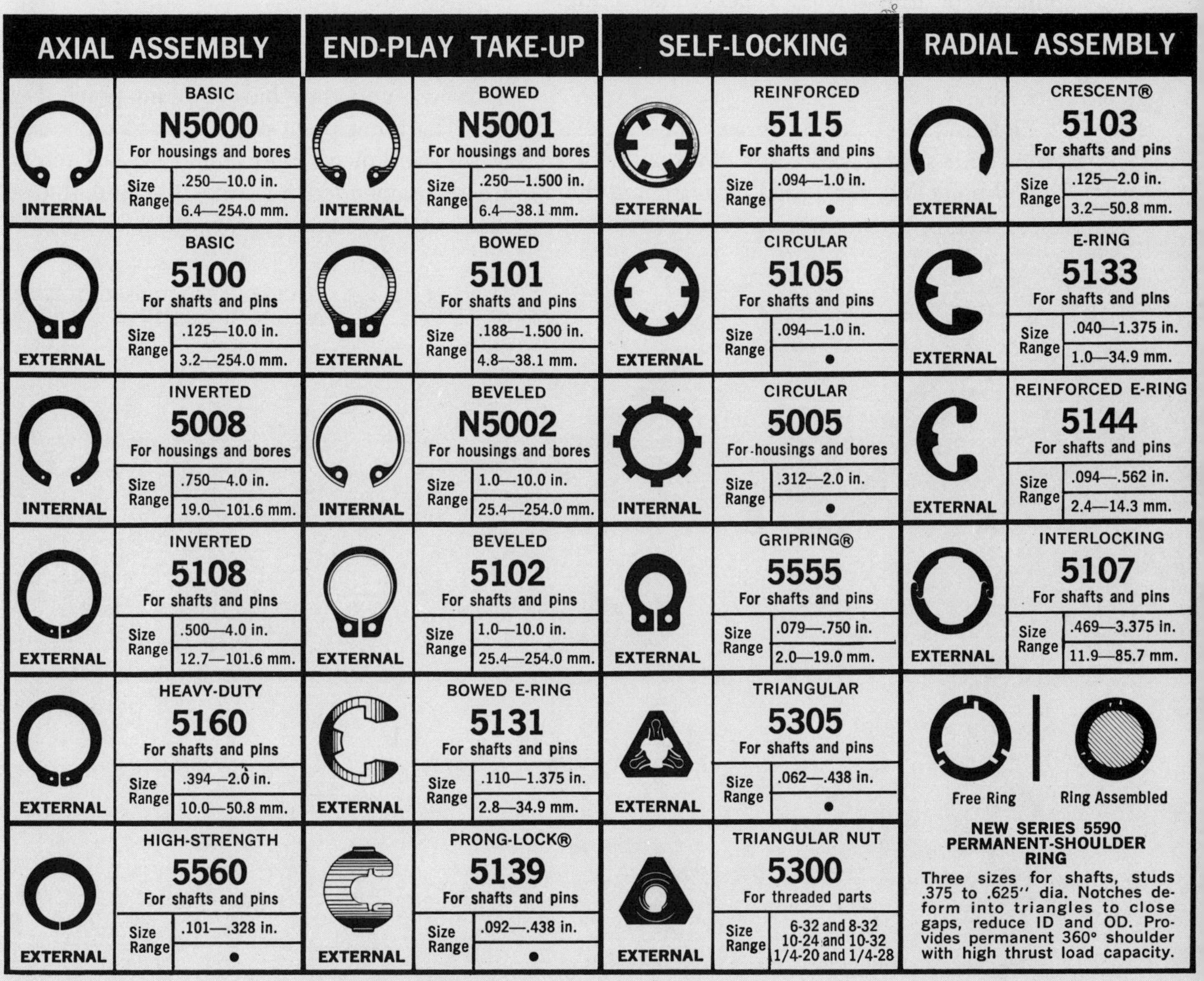

AXIAL ASSEMBLY		END-PLAY TAKE-UP		SELF-LOCKING		RADIAL ASSEMBLY	
INTERNAL	BASIC **N5000** For housings and bores — Size Range .250—10.0 in. / 6.4—254.0 mm.	INTERNAL	BOWED **N5001** For housings and bores — Size Range .250—1.500 in. / 6.4—38.1 mm.	EXTERNAL	REINFORCED **5115** For shafts and pins — Size Range .094—1.0 in. / ●	EXTERNAL	CRESCENT® **5103** For shafts and pins — Size Range .125—2.0 in. / 3.2—50.8 mm.
EXTERNAL	BASIC **5100** For shafts and pins — Size Range .125—10.0 in. / 3.2—254.0 mm.	EXTERNAL	BOWED **5101** For shafts and pins — Size Range .188—1.500 in. / 4.8—38.1 mm.	EXTERNAL	CIRCULAR **5105** For shafts and pins — Size Range .094—1.0 in. / ●	EXTERNAL	E-RING **5133** For shafts and pins — Size Range .040—1.375 in. / 1.0—34.9 mm.
INTERNAL	INVERTED **5008** For housings and bores — Size Range .750—4.0 in. / 19.0—101.6 mm.	INTERNAL	BEVELED **N5002** For housings and bores — Size Range 1.0—10.0 in. / 25.4—254.0 mm.	INTERNAL	CIRCULAR **5005** For housings and bores — Size Range .312—2.0 in. / ●	EXTERNAL	REINFORCED E-RING **5144** For shafts and pins — Size Range .094—.562 in. / 2.4—14.3 mm.
EXTERNAL	INVERTED **5108** For shafts and pins — Size Range .500—4.0 in. / 12.7—101.6 mm.	EXTERNAL	BEVELED **5102** For shafts and pins — Size Range 1.0—10.0 in. / 25.4—254.0 mm.	EXTERNAL	GRIPRING® **5555** For shafts and pins — Size Range .079—.750 in. / 2.0—19.0 mm.	EXTERNAL	INTERLOCKING **5107** For shafts and pins — Size Range .469—3.375 in. / 11.9—85.7 mm.
EXTERNAL	HEAVY-DUTY **5160** For shafts and pins — Size Range .394—2.0 in. / 10.0—50.8 mm.	EXTERNAL	BOWED E-RING **5131** For shafts and pins — Size Range .110—1.375 in. / 2.8—34.9 mm.	EXTERNAL	TRIANGULAR **5305** For shafts and pins — Size Range .062—.438 in. / ●		Free Ring	Ring Assembled
EXTERNAL	HIGH-STRENGTH **5560** For shafts and pins — Size Range .101—.328 in. / ●	EXTERNAL	PRONG-LOCK® **5139** For shafts and pins — Size Range .092—.438 in. / ●	EXTERNAL	TRIANGULAR NUT **5300** For threaded parts — Size Range 6-32 and 8-32 10-24 and 10-32 1/4-20 and 1/4-28		**NEW SERIES 5590 PERMANENT-SHOULDER RING** Three sizes for shafts, studs .375 to .625" dia. Notches deform into triangles to close gaps, reduce ID and OD. Provides permanent 360° shoulder with high thrust load capacity.	

Fig. 602. Truarc (Trade-Mark) Retaining Rings
(Courtesy Waldes Kohinoor, Inc.)

1. Thread-Forming (sheet metal) Screws, Fig. 607.
2. Thread-Cutting Screws, Fig. 608.
3. Metallic Drive Screws, Fig. 609.

Thread-Forming Screws

Self-tapping screws within this classification include types A, B, C, AB, and BP, Figs. 604 and 607. These thread-forming screws form *chip-free* mating threads by squeezing and displacing metal as they are driven into punched or drilled holes. Types A and B, Fig. 604, are also known as *sheet metal* screws. They are available with a variety of heads, Fig. 605.

Type-A (sheet metal) screws have a relatively wide-spaced, coarse-pitch thread with a *gimlet* point. They are used for fastening thin sheet metals, thicknesses up to and including

20 gage or $\frac{1}{32}$ inch. They are also used for fastening resin impregnated plywood and asbestos compositions. Because of the gimlet point, exact alignment of the workpieces is not always necessary. This type of thread point starts into the workpiece rapidly. It also exerts very high pressures on the material as it forms the thread. Hence, screws of this type are not recommended for use with brittle plastics or other brittle materials. The more recently designed type-AB screw is rapidly replacing the type-A screws.

Type-B (sheet metal) screws have a narrower spaced, finer pitch thread than the type-A screws, and they have a blunt point, Fig. 604. The blunt point requires good alignment of the workpieces and holes. Type-B screws are recommended for both thin and thicker sheet metals, ranging from 0.015" to 0.200"

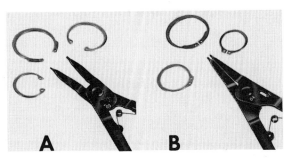

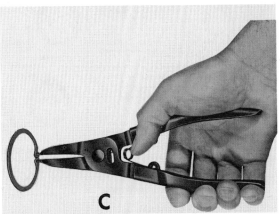

Fig. 603. Retaining Ring Pliers Used to Install Retaining Rings (Copyright 1964, 1965 Waldes Kohinoor, Inc. Reprinted with permission.)
A. Internal Ring
B. External Ring Pliers
C. Insert Pliers into the Ring

	Type	USA Standard	Manufacturer
THREAD FORMING TAPPING SCREWS		AB	AB
	NOT RECOMMENDED – USE TYPE AB	A	A
		B	B
		BP	BP
		C	C
THREAD CUTTING TAPPING SCREWS		D	1
		F	F
		G	G
		T	23
		BF	BF
		BT	25
		U	U

Fig. 604. Type Designation of Tapping Screws and Metallic Drive Screws
(Extracted from USAS B18.6.4—1966 and reprinted with the permission of the American Society of Mechanical Engineers)

thickness. They are also recommended for use on aluminum and other nonferrous metal castings, asbestos compositions, and fiber materials.

Type-BP (sheet metal) screws, Fig. 604, have essentially the same threads as the type-B screws, except that the type-BP has a sharp point to aid in correcting for misalignment of the holes.

Type-AB (sheet metal) screws, Fig. 604, have the same thread as the type-B screws, but they also have a gimlet point as on the type-A screws. The type-AB screws are rapidly replacing type-A screws and also type-BP screws. They are recommended and preferred for most applications for which both type-A and type-BP screws are used. They are used for thin sheet metals, resin inpregnated plywood, wood, and asbestos compositions, where a sharp point is preferred. Use No. 6 screws for thin sheet metals up to 20 gage. Use larger screws for thicknesses up to 18 gage.

Type-C self-tapping screws have finer threads which are essentially the same as the threads on standard machine screws. They also have a blunt point which requires good hole alignment. Type-C screws are recommended for thicker sheet metals, ranging from 0.030 to 0.100″ thickness. They are recommended where the chips from *thread-cutting* screws are objectionable.

Sizes

Thread-forming screws range from No. 0 to ½″ diameter and from ³⁄₁₆″ to 2″ length. Com-

mon gages used for sheet metal projects in the school shop include No. 6 diameter by ⅜″ length, No. 6 diameter by ½″ length, and No. 8 diameter by ½″ length.

Procedure for Installing Self-tapping Screws

1. Locate and prick punch the location for the hole.

2. Punch or drill the holes. The drill or punch should be slightly larger (several thousandths of an inch) than the minor (root) diameter of the screw. For example, a ⁷⁄₆₄″ drill is used for a No. 6 type-A screw. A ⅛″ drill is used for No. 8 type-A screw. The hole size can be estimated by holding the drill behind a screw. The minor diameters or hole sizes for the various kinds and sizes of self-tapping screws are included in standard handbooks for machinists.

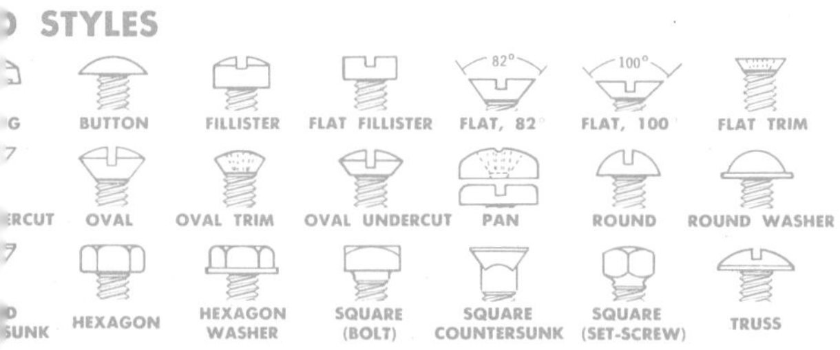

DRIVING RECESSES

Slotted   Phillips Recess   Frearson Recess   Clutch Recess   One-Way

Fig. 606. Kinds of Driving Recesses Used on Screws (Courtesy Great Lakes Screw Corp.)

TAPPING SCREWS

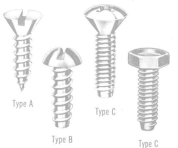

Type A   Type B   Type C   Type C

Thread-forming tapping screws form their own threads by metal replacement when driven into an untapped hole.

Diameter Range: No. 4 to ⅜″
Length Range: 3/16″ to 3″

Fig. 607. Thread-Forming Tapping Screws (Courtesy Great Lakes Screw Corp.)

STYLES

BUTTON   FILLISTER   FLAT FILLISTER   FLAT, 82°   FLAT, 100°   FLAT TRIM

OVAL   OVAL TRIM   OVAL UNDERCUT   PAN   ROUND   ROUND WASHER

HEXAGON   HEXAGON WASHER   SQUARE (BOLT)   SQUARE COUNTERSUNK   SQUARE (SET-SCREW)   TRUSS

Fig. 605. Kinds of Head Styles Used on Threaded Fasteners (Courtesy Great Lakes Machinery Corp.)

3.   Align the holes with a punch. Clamp the two pieces together firmly and insert the screw with a screwdriver.

Thread-Cutting Screws

Screws in this classification include several types of self-tapping screws, Figs. 604 and 608, which form threads by actual removal of metal chips with a cutting action. The screw is hardened steel, and it cuts the mating thread in a manner similar to a tap cutting a standard machine screw thread.

Several types of self-tapping, thread-cutting screws are shown in Fig. 604. Type-BF and BT screws have blunt points and spaced-threads as on type-B threads. They are used with thin materials, plastics, soft nonferrous metals, and die castings.

Type-D, F, G, and T thread-cutting screws, Fig. 606, have fine threads which are similar to standard machine screw threads. These screws are hardened and have blunt ends. The ends have tapered entering threads

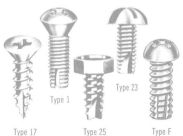

Thread cutting screws cut their own threads when driven into an untapped hole.

Diameter Range:
No. 4 to ⅜"
Length Range:
3/16" to 3"

Type 17   Type 25   Type F

Fig. 608. Thread-Cutting Tapping Screws
(Courtesy Great Lakes Screw Corp.)

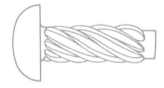

Fig. 609. Metallic Drive Screw (Type U)
(Extracted from ASA B18.12 — 1962 and reprinted with permission from the American Society of Mechanical Engineers)

with one or more chip cavities for cutting mating threads.

Thread-cutting screws are used for fastening sheet metal, structural steel, cast iron, nonferrous forgings, plastics, aluminum, and zinc. They are available in sizes ranging from No. 0 to ½" diameter and in lengths from ⅛" to 2½". They are also available with a wide variety of head shapes.

756. Metallic Drive Screws

Metallic drive screws, type-U, Figs. 604 and 609, are made of hardened steel and have multiple threads and a pilot-type nose. They are a thread-forming type screw, which form chip-free threads by displacing metal. The screw is driven or forced into drilled or punched holes in workpieces to be held together, thus forming threads. The holes should be slightly larger in diameter than the pilot end of the screw. They are intended for permanent assembly. Metallic drive screws are used on ferrous and nonferrous castings, plastics, and sheet metals from 0.060" to ½" thickness. They should not be driven into materials of thickness less than the diameter of the screw.

Review Questions

1.   How are bolts and screws measured?
2.   For what are bolts used?
3.   For what are screws used?
4.   For what are carriage bolts used?
5.   What is a tap bolt?
6.   What is a stove bolt?
7.   What is a stud bolt? For what is it used?
8.   For what is a cap screw used?
9.   How is a machine screw measured?
10.   For what is a setscrew used?
11.   Name six kinds of points on setscrews.
12.   For what is a headless setscrew used?
13.   Name three kinds of heads on wood screws.
14.   How is the diameter of a wood screw measured? How is the length measured?
15.   What is a gimlet point?

16. Describe a lag screw. For what is it used?

17. Describe a thumbscrew.

18. How is the size of a nut measured?

19. For what is a jam nut used?

20. For what is a castle nut used?

21. Describe a wing nut.

22. How is the size of a washer measured?

23. What purpose does a lock washer serve?

24. Describe a helical spring-type lock washer.

25. List five kinds of tooth-type lock washers.

26. What kind of fastener is a *sem?*

27. For what purpose is a shim used?

28. For what purpose is a cotter pin used?

29. Describe a taper pin and explain its use.

30. What is the difference between a square key, a gib-head key, and a Woodruff key?

31. For what purpose are retaining rings used?

32. What are self-tapping screws?

33. List several advantages in fastening sheet metal with self-tapping screws.

34. List several uses for self-tapping screws.

35. What kinds of heads are available on self-tapping screws?

36. List three principal classifications of self-tapping screws.

37. How are the diameters of self-tapping screws designated?

38. Explain the difference between thread-forming and thread-cutting types of self-tapping screws.

39. Explain briefly, the procedure for installing self-tapping screws.

40. List several types of thread-forming, self-tapping screws.

41. Explain metallic drive screws and how they are used.

Coordination

Words to Know

American Standard Screw Gage	machine-screw nut
	metal fastener
blued finish	nickeled finish
bolt	oval head
bright finish	retaining rings
carriage bolt	round head
castle nut	self-tapping screws
check nut	semifinished
cotter key	sems
cylinder block	setscrew
cylinder head	setscrew point
drive screw	shim
fillister head	socket-head setscrew
finished	socket-head setscrew wrench
flat head	
flat washer	spring washer
gage number	square key
gib-head key	stove bolt
gimlet point	stud bolt
gross	tap bolt
headless setscrew	taper-pin reamer
hexagonal head	thread-cutting screws
jam nut	thread-forming screws
keyway	thumb nut
lag screw	thumbscrew
lock nut	washer
lock washer	Woodruff key
machine bolt	wood screw

Mathematics

1. A tapered pin, 3″ long, is $\frac{3}{16}$″ in diameter on the small end. What is the diameter of the large end?

Drafting

1. Get 25 different bolts and screws. List them on a bill of materials.

Pipe, Pipe-Fitting Tools, and Tubing

764. Uses of Pipe and Tubing

Pipes and tubes carry electric wires, water, gas, air, steam, and many other liquids and gases from one place to another. In the home they carry water, gas, steam, and electric wires. On an automobile they carry gasoline, oil, and water. In the shop they are also used for stair railings and for guards or railings around machines.

Common pipe is made of *wrought iron* or *steel* (see § 302 and Fig. 284). *Galvanized iron pipe* has been coated with *zinc* (see § 371). *Lead pipe* is made of *lead* (see § 375). Pipe used to carry electric wires is called *conduit* (see § 452). *Seamless pipe* is made from a solid block of steel; it has no joint or *seam*.

765. Who Uses Pipe-Fitting Tools?

Pipe-fitting means measuring, cutting, fitting, and putting pipes and *pipe fittings* together. A person who fits pipe is called a *pipe fitter*. A *plumber* installs and repairs water pipes, sinks, bathtubs, etc. A *steam fitter* installs pipes and fittings for steam heating, etc. A *gas fitter* installs gas stoves, gas heaters, gas meters, etc. The *electrician* installs pipes, called *conduit* (see § 452), inside of which electric wires are placed. The *auto mechanic* repairs gasoline and oil tubing on automobiles, buses, trucks, and tractors. The *airplane mechanic* repairs gasoline and oil tubing on airplanes.

Pipe-fitting tools can also be very useful in making repairs on the automobile and around the home or farm. Every *mechanic* must at times do pipe-fitting, either in the home, on the car, in the shop, or at his regular work.

766. Pipe Sizes

Many years ago Robert Briggs *standardized* (see § 617) the sizes of pipe. Thus we have the *Briggs Pipe Standard*, also called the *American Standard*, which is used in the United States.

Pipe comes in lengths of 12′ to 20′. It is always measured by the diameter of the hole. Thus a ½″ pipe has a ½″ hole. Hence, ½″ is called the *nominal size* or *nominal diameter* of the pipe. The size of the hole, however, is usually a little larger or smaller than the nominal size, depending upon the wall thickness of the pipe. The actual size of the hole is called the *actual diameter*. The *outside diameter* must be kept a certain size so that the *threads* will be a *standard size*.

Table 23 gives the dimensions of pipes up to 2½″. When the diameter of the pipe is doubled the *area* increases four times.

767. Pipe Threads

American Standard and *American National* pipe threads are used for assembling pipes and pipe fittings. Three types of American Standard pipe threads are used:

American Standard Taper pipe threads (NPT)

American Standard Straight pipe threads (NPS)

American Standard Dry-seal pipe threads (NPTF)

The NPT thread is commonly used for general-purpose pipe-fitting jobs requiring a seal against liquid or gas leakage. Further information concerning the different types of pipe threads is available in handbooks for machinists.

Both ends of a pipe have *threads*. The threads on pipes are *V-shaped* (see § 614). NPT threads are *tapered* ¾″ per foot on the diameter which equals ¹⁄₁₆″ per inch, Fig. 610. This makes a very tight joint. The *angle* between the sides of the thread is 60°. Several threads on the end are perfect; the next two threads have perfect bottoms but flat tops; the last four threads have flat tops and bottoms. Table 23 gives the *number of threads per inch* for different sizes of pipe. (See §§ 610 and 611.)

768. Pipe Fittings

Pipe fittings, called *fittings* for short, are shown in Fig. 611. They are usually made of *cast iron* or *malleable iron* (see §§ 300-301) and are used to make turns and to change from one size of pipe to another. They are screwed on the threads on the ends of pipes.

A short piece of pipe with threads on both ends on the outside is called a *nipple*. A piece of pipe that is so short that the threads cover it entirely is called a *close nipple*.

A *coupling* has threads on the inside and is used to connect two pieces of pipe. A *reducing coupling* is screwed on the outside of a pipe to change to a smaller or larger size.

When the threaded ends of two pipes meet, the best way to connect them or draw them together is with a *union;* it can be taken apart easily to make repairs, without taking all of the pipes apart.

A *cap* is screwed over the end of a pipe to close the hole. A *plug* is screwed into a pipe fitting to close the hole.

Table 23
PIPE DIMENSIONS
(See Sections 766 and 775)

PIPE DIAMETERS			THREADS PER INCH	TAP DRILL SIZE
NOMINAL SIZE	ACTUAL INSIDE	ACTUAL OUTSIDE		
⅛	0.270	0.405	27	¹¹⁄₃₂
¼	0.364	0.540	18	⁷⁄₁₆
⅜	0.494	0.675	18	¹⁹⁄₃₂
½	0.623	0.840	14	²³⁄₃₂
¾	0.824	1.050	14	¹⁵⁄₁₆
1	1.048	1.315	11½	1⁵⁄₃₂
1¼	1.380	1.660	11½	1½
1½	1.610	1.900	11½	1²³⁄₃₂
2	2.067	2.375	11½	2³⁄₁₆
2½	2.468	2.875	8	2⅝

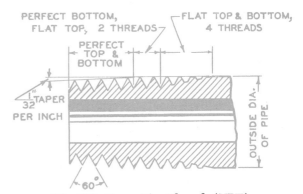

Fig. 610. Taper Pipe Threads (NPT)

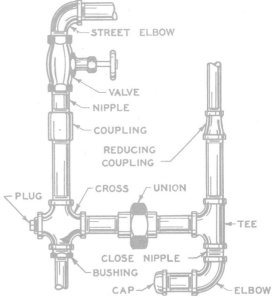

Fig. 611. Pipe Fittings

A *bushing* is used to connect two pipes or pipe fittings of different sizes.

An *elbow*, or *ell*, is used to make a turn. A *street ell* has threads on the outside on one end; the other end has threads on the inside.

A *tee* is shaped like a *T* and is used to connect a pipe from the side of another. A *cross* is shaped like a cross and is used where four pipes come together.

A *valve* is used to turn the flow on or off.

The size of a fitting is measured by the diameter of the hole in the pipe on which it is to be screwed. Thus, a ½″ elbow fits on a ½″ pipe, although the hole in the elbow is large enough to fit the threads on the outside of the pipe.

769. Pipe Vise

A vise which is specially made to hold pipe is called a *pipe vise*, Fig. 612. The *jaws*

of a *machinist's vise* (see Fig. 530) can grip a piece of pipe only in two places while the pipe vise grips it in four places. In order to hold pipe in the machinist's vise so that it would not turn between the jaws, it would be necessary to tighten the jaws so much that they would crush or flatten the pipe. A pipe vise should be fastened to the end of a bench so that long pipe can be cut and *threaded*.

770. Pipe Wrench and Pipe Tong

The *pipe wrench* has been described in section 694. Large pipe and *pipe fittings* may be screwed together by using a *pipe tong*, also called *chain tong*, Fig. 613.

771. Pipe Cutter

A pipe cutter is a tool for cutting pipe, Fig. 614. It has three, small, round cutters made of *hardened steel*.

Fig. 613. Pipe Tong

Fig. 614. Pipe Cutter

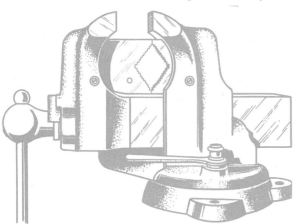

COMBINATION MACHINIST'S AND PIPE VISE

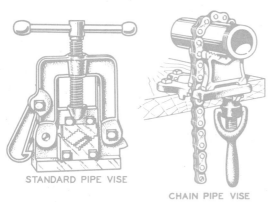

STANDARD PIPE VISE

CHAIN PIPE VISE

Fig. 612. Pipe Vises

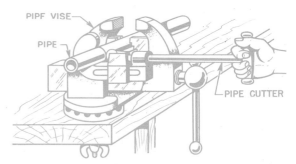

Fig. 615. Cutting Pipe with Pipe Cutter

The pipe cutter is slipped over the pipe so that the three cutters touch the pipe where the cut is to be made. By turning the handle, the cutters are pressed against the pipe, Fig. 615. At the same time, the whole tool should be swung around the pipe which causes the cutters to cut a groove around the pipe. The handle is then turned again to press the cutters further into the pipe, and the groove is cut deeper. This is repeated until the pipe is cut off.

A *hacksaw* may be used instead of a pipe cutter (see Figs. 150 and 170).

772. Pipe-Burring Reamer

The pipe-burring reamer, Fig. 616, is used to cut away the rough edges or *burrs* inside the end of the pipe after it has been cut with a *pipe cutter*, Fig. 617. These rough edges make the hole in the pipe smaller and slow up the flow of water or for whatever the pipe may be used.

773. Pipe Dies and Diestock

Threads on pipes are cut with *pipe dies*, Fig. 618. These look something like the dies described in Unit 32. The dies are held in a *diestock*. The threads inside NPT pipe dies, however, are tapered ¾″ per foot just the same as the NPT pipe threads.

Pipe dies are used as shown in Fig. 619. (See §§ 642-643.) They are marked with the size of pipe on which they are to cut threads. Thus, ½″ pipe dies will cut threads on a ½″ pipe. (See Table 23.)

Some pipe dies are made in two parts so that they can be made to cut smaller or larger by setting them closer or farther apart. Such dies are called *adjustable pipe dies*.

Most pipe dies and diestocks have an S and short lines stamped on them which mean that when the S on the die and the S on the diestock come together the dies will cut a *standard* size thread (see § 616).

774. Tap Drill Sizes for Pipe

A *tap drill* is the drill used to drill a hole before it can be tapped. Thus, a tap drill for

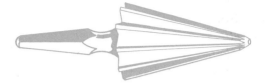

Fig. 616. Pipe-Burring Reamer

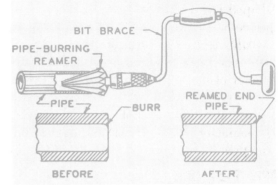

Fig. 617. Using Pipe-Burring Reamer

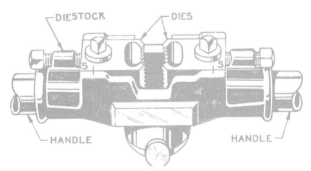

Fig. 618. Pipe Dies and Diestock

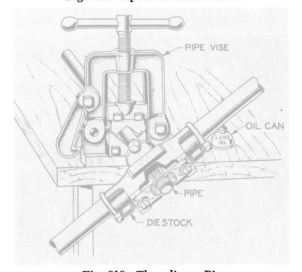

Fig. 619. Threading a Pipe

Fig. 620. Pipe Reamer

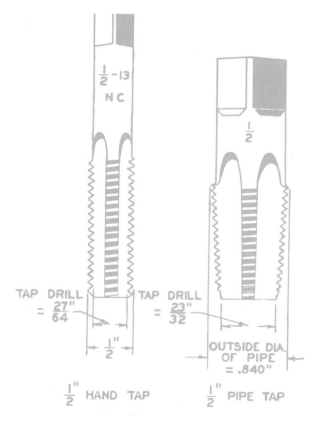

Fig. 622. Difference in Sizes Between NPT Pipe Tap and Tap for Tapping Nuts with Unified National Form Threads (Actual Size)

Fig. 623. Welding Pipe (Courtesy National Cylinder Gas Co.)

a ½″ pipe tap is much larger than the beginner would suspect; the tap drill for a ½″ pipe tap is $2\frac{3}{32}$″. (See Table 23.)

775. Pipe Reamer

A drilled hole that is to be tapped should be tapered with a *pipe reamer*, Fig. 620. This makes the hole more like the shape of the *pipe tap*, Fig. 622; therefore, the tapping is easier and the wear on the tap is reduced.

A pipe reamer is used when good work is desired and especially when large holes are to be tapped. Oftentimes the hole is tapped right after drilling without the use of the pipe reamer.

776. Pipe Tap

An NPT pipe tap, Fig. 622, which looks something like the taps described in section 649, is used to cut threads on the inside of a pipe or pipe fitting. Such threads are *tapered* and, therefore, the tap is also tapered. Thus, when the pipe and its fittings are screwed together, they make a tight joint and the water, steam, or gas will not leak out. The pipe tap is used as described in section 653.

A pipe tap measures larger than the size marked on it. Note how much larger in diameter a ½″ pipe tap is than a ½″ tap for tapping nuts, Fig. 622. This is because a ½″ pipe tap, for example, is made to cut threads in the hole of a fitting which will fit over ½″ pipe. (See Table 23 and *cutting fluids*, § 643.)

777. Put Pipe Compound on Joints

Before screwing pipe and pipe fittings together, a little *red lead* or pipe compound (see § 1100) should be smeared on the threads. This makes a tight joint so that the water, steam, or gas will not leak out. It also keeps the metal from rusting.

778. Pipe Welding

Joints on pipes are often made by *welding* the pipes together, using the *oxyacetylene flame*, Fig. 623, or the *electric arc*. (See §§ 783 and 874.)

779. Tubing

Pipes made of thin metal are called *tubing*. They are made chiefly of brass, copper, or aluminum. *Seamless tubing* is tubing which has no joint or *seam* along the side. Tubing is used for such purposes as carrying oil and gasoline from one part of an automobile to another.

780. Sizes of Tubing

Tubing is usually measured and ordered by the outside diameter and the thickness of the metal. It is made in sizes from ⅛″ to 10″. Some time ago the thickness of the metal was measured by what is known as the *Stubs' or Birmingham gage.* (See Table 34, p. 440.) This gage was used for *seamless tubing* of copper, brass, steel, and aluminum. The wall thickness of tubing is now specified by decimal parts of an inch.

781. Tube Fittings

Tube fittings are used to connect tubing in the same way as *pipe fittings* are used to connect pipes. They also have the same names as pipe fittings. (See Fig. 611.)

782. Flaring Tool

The end of a tube must be spread out or *flared* before a *tube fitting* (see § 781) can be connected to it. This is done with a *flaring tool,* Fig. 624.

783. Bending Pipe or Tubing

When a pipe or tube is bent, the outer part of the bend is stretched, while the inner part is squeezed together. Because of this, the pipe or tube flattens and often breaks when bent. To prevent this, pack the pipe or tube tightly with fine, dry sand and plug the ends so that the sand will not drop out. The sand must be dry or an explosion will result from heating the pipe to bend it. Keep the *seam* of the pipe on the side of the bend. Next, heat the place where the bend is to be made and then bend it. (See § 937.) Fig. 625 shows a pipe being heated with an *oxyacetylene flame* and bent. (See §§ 778 and 874.)

A long, curved bend may be made by slipping the pipe into a hole in a post, Fig. 626, and by bending a little at a time. Or, a *hickey* may be used to make the bend, Fig. 627. A hickey may be made by screwing a large *tee* (see Fig. 611) on a pipe three or four feet long. Again, the bending must be done a little at a time.

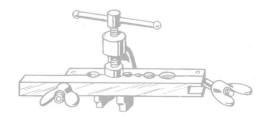

Fig. 624. Flaring Tool

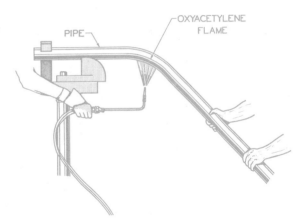

Fig. 625. Heating and Bending a Pipe

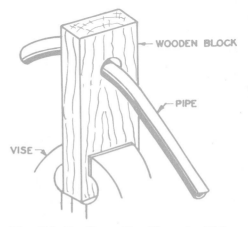

Fig. 626. Bending a Pipe Through a Hole in a Wood Block

Fig. 627. Bending Pipe with a Hickey

**Fig. 628. Drilling a Hole in a Brick Wall
with a Star Drill**

784.   Drilling with a
Star Drill or Masonry Drill

It is sometimes necessary to drill a hole into a brick, stone, or concrete wall to let a pipe pass through or to fasten something to the wall. This kind of drilling is done with a *star drill* or a masonry drill, Fig. 628. The point of a star drill is shaped like a cross or star. The drill is struck lightly with a hammer and turned a little between blows.

A masonry drill is a twist drill with a *carbide tip* (see § 350). It is used like any other twist drill.

Review Questions

1. Name some uses of pipe.
2. How is pipe measured?
3. What is meant by the nominal diameter? Actual diameter? Outside diameter?
4. How many times does the area of a pipe increase when the diameter is doubled?
5. What is the shape of a pipe thread?
6. Why is the pipe thread tapered?
7. Measure a pipe fitting.
8. Describe a pipe vise.
9. Why is a pipe vise better for holding pipe than a machinist's vise?
10. For what are chain tongs used?
11. For what is a pipe cutter used?
12. For what is a burring reamer used?
13. Why should the burrs be removed from the inside on the ends of the pipe?
14. For what are pipe dies used?
15. What is the tap drill size for a ⅜″ pipe? For a ¾″ pipe?
16. For what is a pipe reamer used?
17. For what is a pipe tap used?
18. To what diameter of the pipe does the size of the tap refer?
19. How is tubing measured? What gage is used?
20. How can a pipe or tube be bent without flattening or breaking it?
21. How can a hole be drilled in a stone wall?

22. List three kinds of American Standard pipe threads.

Coordination

Words to Know

actual diameter	nipple
adjustable pipe die	pipe bushing
American Pipe Standard	pipe cutter
	pipe die
American Standard Dry-seal pipe thread (NPTF)	pipe diestock
	pipe fittings
	pipe-fitting tool
American Standard straight pipe thread (NPS)	pipe reamer
	pipe tap
	pipe tee
American Standard taper pipe thread (NPT)	pipe tong
	pipe vise
	pipe welding
Briggs Pipe Standard	plug
	reducing coupling
chain tong	seam
close nipple	seamless tubing
coupling	star drill
cross	street ell
elbow or ell	Stub's or Birmingham gage
flaring tool	
galvanized iron pipe	tube fitting
hickey	union
masonry drill	valve

Mathematics

1. What is the outside diameter of a ½″ pipe?

2. What is the tap drill size for a ½″ pipe tap?

3. How much more water will a 2″ pipe carry than a 1″ pipe?

4. If the diameter of a pipe is doubled, how much larger is the area?

Drafting

1. What is the tap drill size for a ¼″ pipe tap?

2. Get 20 pipe and tube fittings. List them on a bill of materials.

Social Science

Discuss the advantages of having properly installed, sanitary plumbing.

Occupational Information

1. List the advantages and disadvantages of being a plumber.

Stamping Bread Pans
from Sheet Metal on
Double-Action Draw Press
(Courtesy Aluminum
Company of America)

Part **VIII** **Work with Sheet Metal**

Sheet Metalwork, Hand Tools, and Cutting Tools

789. Meaning of Sheet Metal and Importance of Sheet Metalwork

Sheet steel generally is in thicknesses less than .250″, and it is designated by decimal equivalents of an inch or by gage numbers. Plate steel is in fractional thicknesses, generally ¼″ and up. (See §§ 329 and 793.)

Sheet metalwork is the making of stove and furnace pipes, furnaces and ventilators, metal roofs, metal ceilings, metal signs, automobile and airplane bodies, boats, metal furniture, refrigerators, kitchenware, etc.

Much sheet metal is now used instead of wood. Things made of sheet metal are used on the farm, in the home, in offices, and in shops. In sheet metalwork, the sheet metal used is usually *steel, galvanized steel, copper, brass, zinc, aluminum,* and *tinplate.*

790. Who Does Sheet Metalwork?

A knowledge of sheet metalwork is useful in many trades. A person who works with sheet metal is a *sheet metalworker.* The *tinsmith* or *tinner* makes cans, pans, pots, pails, etc. The *coppersmith* makes kettles, tanks, boilers, etc., out of copper. The *machinist* may need to make guards for machines, belts, etc.; he also makes *shims* (see § 750). The *toolmaker, diemaker,* and *diesinker* make *gages* and *templates* (see § 126) from sheet metal. The *auto mechanic* bumps dents out of bodies and fenders of automobiles (see

Fig. 540); he also makes shims. Knowing how to do sheet metalwork will also help you to make repairs around the home, such as repairs on the furnace, roof, eave troughs, automobile, and kitchenware.

791. Making Things from Sheet Metal

Many toys and useful articles can be made from sheet metal. The beginner can learn a great deal by making ash trays, tool trays, cans for measuring liquids, dust pans, and small planters.

Larger articles, such as tool boxes, work stands, mailboxes, bird feeding trays, larger planters, minnow buckets, wastebaskets, funnels, and magazine holders, are often made in schools. Careful attention to the quality of layout and workmanship will be necessary if your construction is to look like a first class job.

792. What Is a Pattern?

When your mother makes a dress she needs a pattern. When the tailor makes a suit he needs a pattern. If you want to make a box, funnel, stove pipe, or any other sheet-metal job, you must first make a pattern. The pattern of a box, for example, is a flat piece of paper or sheet metal cut to the outline or stretched-out shape or form of the box, Fig. 634. It is sometimes called a *stretchout.* Note how *bending lines* are shown; a small, freehand circle is drawn at each end of the line.

The marking of lines on sheet metal is called *laying-out*. (See Units 5-8.) To lay out the patterns for the different sheet-metal jobs, you need to know something about *geometry* (see § 19); the more geometry you know, the more different types of patterns you can lay out. There are three ways to lay out a pattern:

(1) By drawing the lines on paper and then transferring them to the sheet metal by using *carbon paper*.[1]

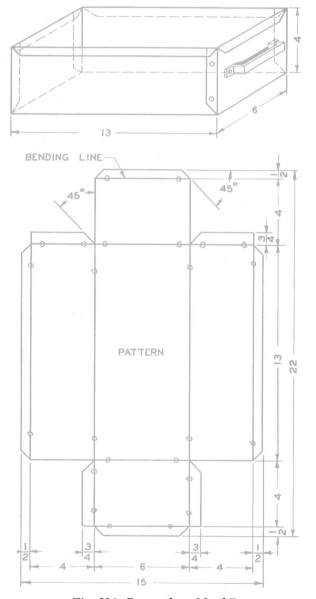

Fig. 634. Pattern for a Metal Box

(2) By drawing the lines on paper as before, then holding the paper on the sheet metal with weights to keep it from slipping while making small prick-punch marks through the paper. Make punchmarks at all corners, *intersections* of lines (see Fig. 98), ends of lines, and centers of circles and *arcs* (see § 30). Curves are made by putting the punch marks close together. After punching, the paper is removed and the punch marks used as guides for scribing the lines, circles, arcs, and curves. Use a steel rule or square and a *scriber* or *scratch awl* (see Figs. 40 and 636) to scribe the straight lines and a *divider* or *trammel* to make circles and arcs (see Figs. 42, 43, and 637).

(3) By measuring and scribing the lines, circles, arcs, and curves directly on the metal.

If two or more metal pieces are to be cut alike, use a piece of metal that has been cut out for a pattern or *template*. (See § 126.)

793. Sheet Metal and Wire Gages

Sheet metal and wire gages have slots with which the thickness of sheet metal or the diameters of wires are measured, Fig. 635. Each slot is numbered. The sheet metal or wire is the same number as the slot which it fits. The *decimal equivalent* of the number is

---

[1]*Carbon paper* is paper with one side coated with carbon or lampblack. It is used between two sheets of paper to make copies of whatever is printed on the top sheet.

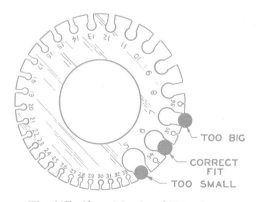

Fig. 635. Sheet Metal and Wire Gage

on the other side of the gage. (See § 132.) The numbers are called *gage numbers* (see § 1144).

Check with Table 34, page 440, for the names of the different gages, what they measure, and the decimal equivalent of each gage number. Note that the *Manufacturer's Standard Gage for Steel Sheets* is used to measure the thickness of iron and steel sheets,

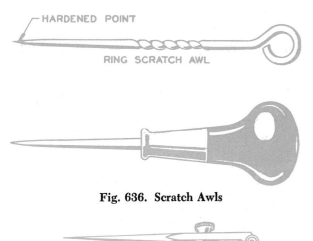

Fig. 636. Scratch Awls

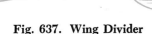

Fig. 637. Wing Divider

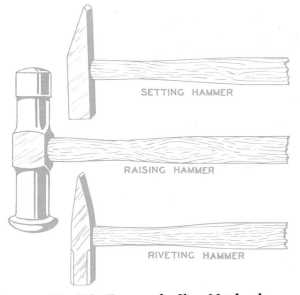

Fig. 638. Hammers for Sheet Metalwork

while the *American or Brown & Sharpe Gage,* also called *American Standard Wire Gage,* is used to measure the thickness of all other metals. Be sure that the gage which you use is stamped according to the material you wish to measure, as "U.S. Standard Gage," "American Steel & Wire Gage," "American Steel & Music Wire Gage," etc.

Since several different kinds of gages are used for measuring different kinds of sheet metal and wire, confusion sometimes results. Hence, when ordering sheet metals or wire, one should always specify the decimal thickness of the material in inches, the name of the gage, and the gage number.

794. Scratch Awl

A scratch awl is a steel tool with a point on one end, Fig. 636. It is used to scratch layout lines on sheet metal. Some scratch awls have wooden handles. A *scriber* (see Fig. 40) may be used instead.

795. Wing Divider

The divider used most often by sheet metalworkers is often called a *wing divider.* It is shown in Fig. 637. It is used to *scribe* circles and parts of circles. (See § 65.)

796. Hammers

Several kinds of hammers are used in sheet metalwork, Fig. 638. The *riveting hammer* is used for riveting (see Unit 36). The *setting*

Fig. 639. Setting Down with a Setting Hammer

hammer is used for hammering or tucking in the edges of sheet metal; it is especially useful for *setting down* the edges when making a *double seam*, Fig. 639. (See §§ 811, 823, and 824.)

There are many shapes of *raising hammers;* some of their uses are explained in section 836. (See also Fig. 678.) The polished surfaces on raising hammers should be carefully protected against nicks because they show on the work and spoil its appearance.

To keep from stretching and nicking sheet metal, it should be struck with a *mallet*, Fig.

Fig. 640. Forming a Corner with a Mallet
(Courtesy Niagara Machine & Tool Works)

640 (see Fig. 540). Section 61 tells about the *hammer handle*.

797.   Punches

The punches in Fig. 641 may be used to punch holes in sheet metal. A pin punch, Fig. 559, also may be used for punching holes in sheet metal. The *hollow punch* makes large holes; the other punches make small holes. Measure the size of the hollow punch by the diameter of the hole that it punches.

To use the *solid punch (tinner's punch)* or hollow punch, lay the sheet metal on a block of lead or wood, place the punch on the sheet metal, and strike a heavy blow with a hammer, Fig. 642.

The *hand punch* may be used as you use a punch for cardboard. It punches holes near the edge of the metal.

798.   Pliers

The square jaws of the *flat nose plier*, Fig. 643, are used to bend square corners in sheet metalwork. The *side-cutting plier* and the *round-nose plier* are described in section 684.

799.   Ways to Cut Sheet Metal

Sheet metal that is soft (see § 197) may be cut with a *hand hacksaw*, a *coping saw, jew-*

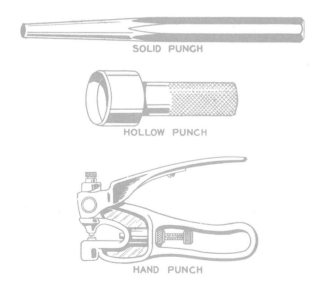

Fig. 641. Types of Punches

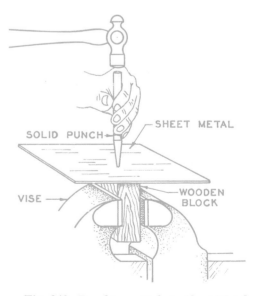

**Fig. 642. Punching a Hole in Sheet Metal
with a Solid Punch**

eler's saw, or a *cold chisel* (see §§ 179, 181, and 220). Other tools used to cut sheet metal are the *snip, double-cutting shear, bench shear, squaring shear, ring and circle shear,* and *lever shear.*

800. Snips

A snip, also called a *tinner's snip, tinsnip,* or *hand shear,* Fig. 644, is used like a scissors to cut thin, *soft metal.* It should be used only to cut 20-gage or thinner metal.

To cut to a corner, the snip should be set so that the *point* will finish in the corner. Keep the *bolt* tight; the *blades* must fit closely against each other.

A *left-hand snip* should be used by a left-handed person.

The *scroll hawk's bill snip* cuts curves, Fig. 645.

801. Double-Cutting Shear

The double-cutting shear has three *blades* and is used to cut around cans, stove and furnace pipes, etc., Fig. 646. The pointed lower blade is pushed through the metal to start the cut.

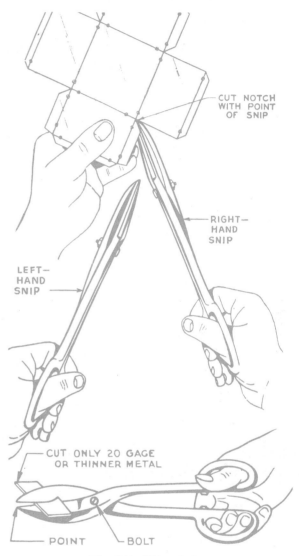

Fig. 644. Using Snips

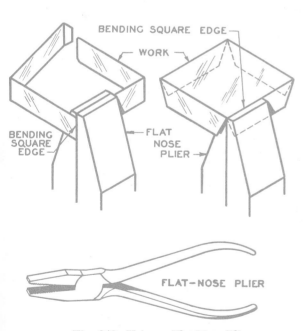

Fig. 643. Using a Flat-Nose Plier

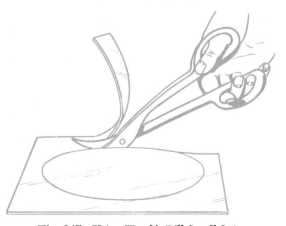

Fig. 645. Using Hawk's Bill Scroll Snips

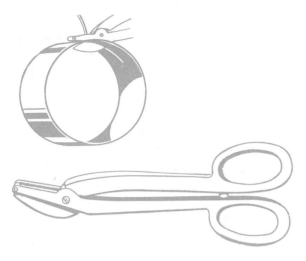

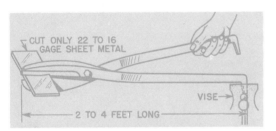

Fig. 646. Using Double-Cutting Shear to Cut a Cylinder

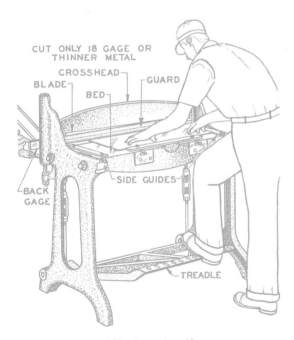

Fig. 647. Bench Shear

Fig. 648. Squaring Shear

802. Bench Shear

The bench shear, Fig. 647, is a large pair of scissors from 2′ to 4′ long. One handle may be held in a vise or *bench plate* (see Fig. 659) while the other handle is moved up and down to do the cutting. The bench shear should be used to cut only 22- to 16-gage *soft* sheet metal.

803. Squaring Shear

The squaring shear, Fig. 648, is operated with the foot and is used to cut thin, *soft metal* (see § 197). It should be used only to cut 18-gage or thinner metal; it is especially useful for cutting strips of sheet metal and for trimming and cutting the edges square to each other, hence the name.

The *side guides* on the table help to keep the metal square with the *cutting edges*. The squaring shear is also useful for cutting many pieces of the same size because the *gage* can be locked at the desired setting. The fingers should be kept away from the *blade* which should have a *guard*.

804. Ring and Circle Shear

The ring and circle shear, Fig. 649, is used to cut circular pieces of sheet metal as, for example, those used for the bottoms or covers of buckets.

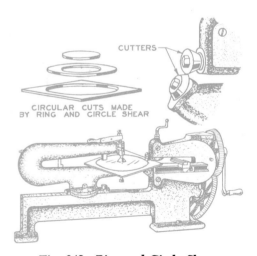

Fig. 649. Ring and Circle Shear

805. Lever Shear

A lever shear is used for punching holes and cutting notches, corners, and small rods, Fig. 650.

Review Questions

1. What is sheet metal?
2. What is plate steel?
3. What is sheet metalwork?
4. For what is sheet metal used?
5. Who does sheet metalwork?
6. What is a pattern?
7. What is a scratch awl?
8. What is a riveting hammer?
9. What is a setting hammer?
10. What is a raising hammer?
11. For what are solid and hollow punches used?
12. What thickness of metal should be cut with a snip?
13. What is a bench shear?
14. What thickness of metal should be cut with a bench shear?
15. What is a squaring shear? What thickness of metal should be cut with it?
16. For what is the ring and circle shear used?
17. For what is the lever shear used?

Coordination

Words to Know

American or Brown & Sharpe Gage	scroll snip
	setting hammer
bench shear	sheet-metal gage
carbon paper	sheet metalwork
circular cut	snip
double-cutting shear	solid punch
flat-nose plier	squaring shear
guard	blade
hand punch	cutting edges
hand shear	gage
hollow punch	guide
left-hand snip	stretchout
lever shear	tinner's snip
raising hammer	tinsnip
ring and circle shear	wing divider
riveting hammer	wire gage
scratch awl	

Mathematics

1. Why is it necessary to know something about geometry to lay out sheet-metal patterns?

Drafting

1. Draw a funnel, any size, so that it can be made in the shop.

Occupational Information

1. In what trades is a knowledge of sheet metalwork important?

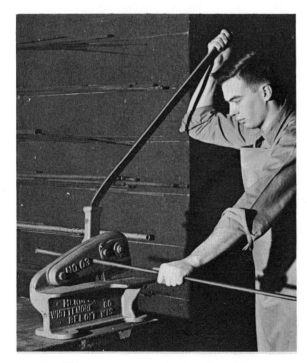

Fig. 650. **Using Lever Shear and Rod Parter**

Stamping Automobile Hoods
— Sheets Are Fed and Stampings Removed Automatically
(Courtesy Buick Div., General Motors Corp.)

Bending Sheet Metal

811. Hems and Seams

Several kinds of hems and seams are shown in Fig. 656. A *hem* is an edge or border made by folding. It stiffens the sheet of metal and does away with the sharp edge. A *seam* is a joint made by fastening two edges together.

The *single hem* is made by folding the edge of the sheet metal over to make it smooth and stiff. It may be made by bending over the *hatchet stake* (see Fig. 660) and then finishing with a *mallet*. Small pieces may be pinched and bent in a vise and then finished with a mallet (see § *812*). It may also be made in the *bar folder* (see Fig. 663).

The *double hem* is made by folding the edge over twice to make it stiff and smooth.

The *wired edge* is smooth and very strong. It is made by first making an *open fold*. An *open fold* is a rounded bend. It is made on the bar folder or on the *turning machine* (see Fig. 667). To make an open fold, set the *gage* of the bar folder at 1½ times the diameter of the wire and set the wing equal to the diameter of the wire.

The wire is placed in the fold, and the fold is finished with a *setting hammer*, Fig. 657. Or, after placing the wire in the fold, the metal may be bent over a little with a mallet and finished on the *wiring machine* (see Fig.

668). The making of a wired edge on a circular object, as on the top edge of a waste basket is explained in sections *820* and *821*.

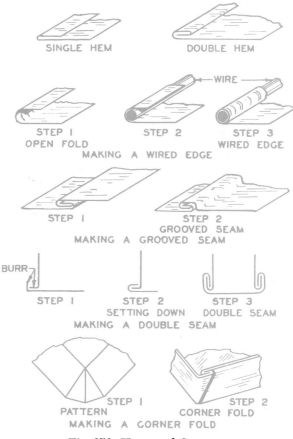

Fig. 656. Hems and Seams

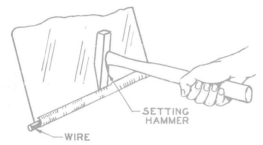

Fig. 657. Finishing a Wired Edge with Setting Hammer

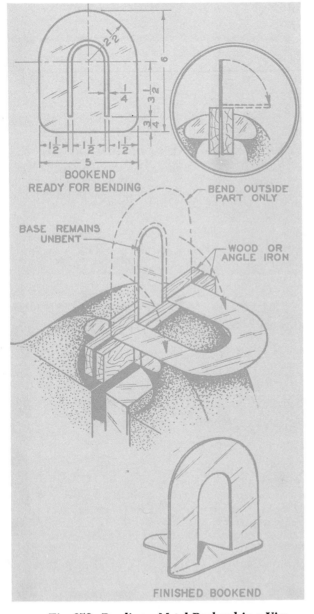

BOOKEND
READY FOR BENDING

BEND OUTSIDE PART ONLY

BASE REMAINS UNBENT

WOOD OR ANGLE IRON

FINISHED BOOKEND

Fig. 658. Bending a Metal Bookend in a Vise

The *grooved seam* is made by hooking two single hems together and then locking them with a *hand groover* (see Fig. 661) or with a *grooving machine* (see Fig. 662).

The *double seam* fastens the bottom to a pail or can (see §§ 796, 814, and 822-824).

The *corner fold* is useful on corners of pans which are made to hold liquids.

Three kinds of *joints* that are often used in sheet metalwork are explained in section 855.

812. Bending Sheet Metal in a Vise

It is sometimes necessary to bend sheet metal in a vise. The *bookend* in Fig. 658 must be bent in a vise. Note that only the outside is bent; the inside must remain unbent because it is the base upon which the bookend stands.

813. Bench Plate

The bench plate, Fig. 659, is fastened to the bench with bolts as shown in Fig. 640; the holes are used to hold the *bench shear, stakes,* etc. (See Figs. 647 and 660.)

814. Stakes

Many bends and forms in sheet metalwork must be made on *stakes,* Fig. 660. They are the sheet metalworker's *anvils* (see § 916).

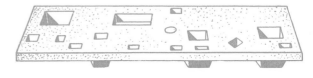

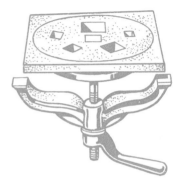

Fig. 659. Bench Plates

The square end of the stake is set in a hole in the *bench plate* (see Figs. 659 and 640).

The *double-seaming stake* is used to make the *double seam*.

The *beakhorn stake* is used for riveting, forming round and square surfaces, bending straight edges, and making corners.

The *bevel-edged square stake* is used to form corners and edges.

The *hatchet stake* is used to make straight, sharp bends and for folding and bending edges.

Small tubes and pipes may be formed on the *needle-case stake*.

Cone-shaped articles may be formed on the *blowhorn stake*. The use of the *hollow mandrel stake* is shown in Fig. 661.

Sheet metal should be hammered with a *mallet* to keep from stretching and nicking it. (See Figs. 540 and 640.)

815. Hand Groover

The hand groover is used to *groove* and flatten a seam as shown in Fig. 661. Groove the ends first, then finish the rest of the seam. (See *grooved seam* in Fig. 656.)

816. Grooving Machine

The grooving machine, Fig. 662, is a machine which makes *grooved seams* and *countersunk seams*. It *grooves* and flattens the seams which have been started on the *bar folder* (see Figs. 656 and 663).

817. Bar Folder

The bar folder, Fig. 663, is a machine for folding or bending sheet metal edges (see § *811*).

818. Brake

A brake, Fig. 664, is a machine for bending and folding sheet metal. The *bar folder* in Fig. 663, only bends or folds the metal near the edge, but the brake can bend or fold the

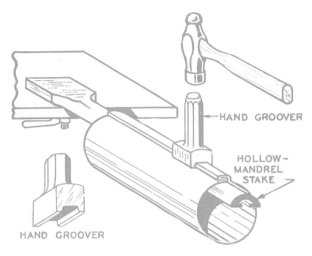

Fig. 661. Grooving a Seam with Hand Groover

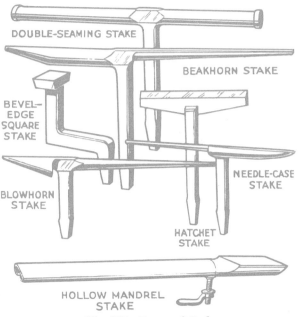

Fig. 660. Types of Stakes

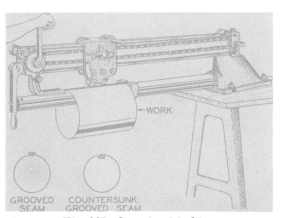

Fig. 662. Grooving Machine

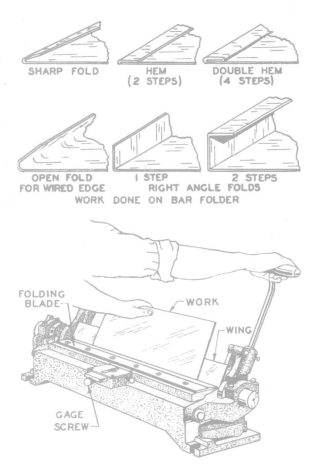

SHARP FOLD   HEM (2 STEPS)   DOUBLE HEM (4 STEPS)

OPEN FOLD FOR WIRED EDGE   I STEP   2 STEPS   RIGHT ANGLE FOLDS

WORK DONE ON BAR FOLDER

FOLDING BLADE   WORK   WING   GAGE SCREW

Fig. 663. Bar Folder

metal any distance from the edge. *Moldings* can be made on the brake by using a *mold*, Fig. 665.

819. Forming Machine

Stove pipes, cans, etc., are formed out of flat sheet metal on the *slip-roll forming machine*, Fig. 666. It has three *rolls* which can be set different distances apart; the curves are formed between the rolls.

If the metal to be formed has a *wired edge*, the wired edge may be slipped into one of the *grooves* at one end of the rolls.

820. Turning Machine

Sometimes a *wired edge* (see Fig. 656) is made as, for instance, on the top edge of a waste basket. A *turning machine*, Fig. 667, is used to make the rounded edge into which the wire is placed.

To make this rounded edge, set the *gage* about 2½ times the diameter of the wire away from the center of the groove in the *roll*. Be sure the rolls are set to fit each other. Then place the work on the lower roll and against the gage. Screw down the top roll so that it grooves the work a little when turning the crank. Next, screw the upper roll down a little more, raise the work a little with the left hand, and turn the crank again. The groove is thus made deeper.

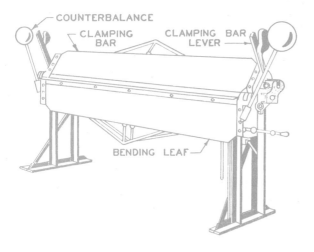

COUNTERBALANCE   CLAMPING BAR   CLAMPING BAR LEVER   BENDING LEAF

Fig. 664. Brake

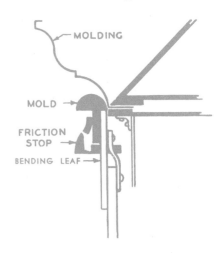

MOLDING   MOLD   FRICTION STOP   BENDING LEAF

Fig. 665. Making Molding with a Mold on a Brake

Repeat these steps several times, each time screwing the top roll down a little more and raising the work with the left hand until the work held with the left hand is straight up and down and touches the side of the top roll. The groove or rounded edge is now ready for the wire and may be taken out of the machine.

821. Wiring Machine

After the edge of the work has been made round in the *turning machine* (see § 820), the wire is placed into the rounded edge which is then hammered over a little with a mallet. The edge of the metal may then be completely pressed over the wire with a *wiring machine,* Fig. 668. The *wired edge* may be used on flat work as well as round work. (See *wired edge* in section *811.*)

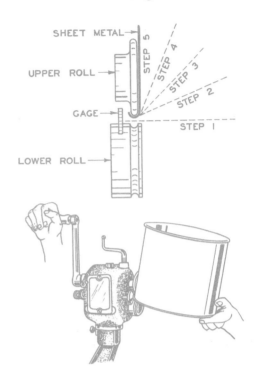

Fig. 667. Turning Machine

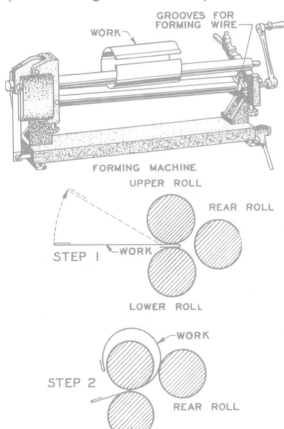

Fig. 666. Forming with Rolls on the Slip-Roll Forming Machine

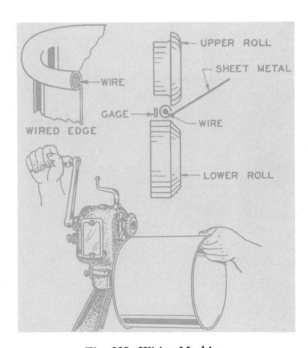

Fig. 668. Wiring Machine

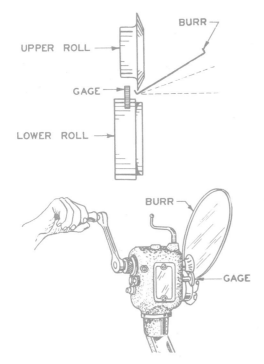

Fig. 669. Burring Machine

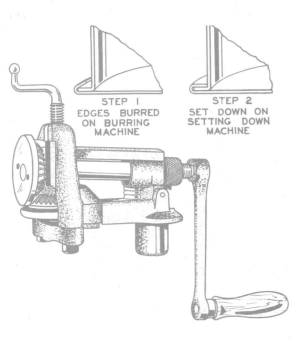

Fig. 670. Setting Down Machine

822. Burring Machine

The burring machine, Fig. 669, is used to make a *burr* on the edge of the bottom for a can and on the end of a *cylinder* (see § 33). The making of such burrs is the first step in making a *double seam* with the *double-seaming machine* .(See *double seam* in Figs. 656 and 671.) The handling of the metal with the left hand is the same as when turning the edge on the *turning machine*. The beginner should practice on scraps of metal.

823. Setting-Down Machine

After the *burrs* on the end of a cylinder and on the edge of the bottom for a can have been made with the *burring machine*, the *seams* are closed or *set down* on a *setting-down machine*, Fig. 670. (See Fig. 656.) If a setting-down machine is not available, seams may be set down with the use of a setting hammer and a stake.

824. Double-Seaming Machine

After the burrs have been made on the *burring machine* and set down on the *setting-down machine*, the seam or edge can be turned up against the sides of the can with a *double-seaming machine*, Fig. 671, thus making a *double seam*. (See Fig. 656.) If a double-seaming machine is not available, the seam or edge can be turned up against the sides of the can with a hammer and stake.

825. Crimping and Beading Machine

The making of the wavy end on a stove or furnace pipe is called *crimping*. It makes the end of the pipe smaller so that it will fit into another pipe.

A *bead* is made as an ornament and in order to stiffen the object. Stove and furnace pipes are beaded on one end.

Crimping and beading are done on a *crimping and beading machine*, Fig. 672, or crimping may be done in a *crimping machine* which does only the crimping; beading may be done on a *beading machine* which only does beading.

Review Questions

1. What is the difference between a single hem and a double hem?
2. What is a wired edge?
3. For what is a bench plate used?
4. For what are stakes used?
5. For what is the hand groover used?
6. For what is the grooving machine used?
7. For what is the bar folder used?
8. What is the difference between a bar folder and a brake?
9. How can moldings be made?
10. For what is the forming machine used?
11. For what is the turning machine used?
12. For what is the wiring machine used?
13. For what is the burring machine used?
14. For what is the setting-down machine used?
15. For what is the double-seaming machine used?
16. For what is the beading machine used?
17. For what is the crimping machine used?

Coordination

Words to Know

bar folder	grooved seam
beading machine	grooving machine
beakhorn stake	hand grooving
bench plate	hatchet stake
blowhorn stake	hem
brake	hollow mandrel stake
burring machine	Manufacturers
corner fold	Standard Gage
crimping and	for Steel Sheets
beading machine	molding
crimping rolls	needle-case stake
countersunk grooved	open fold
seam	setting-down machine
double hem	single hem
double-seaming	stake
machine	turning machine
double-seaming stake	wired edge
forming machine	wiring machine

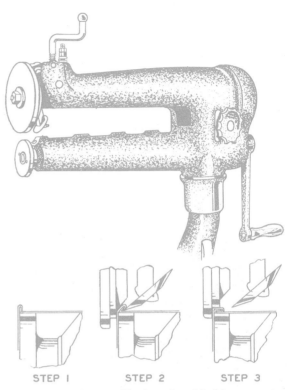

Fig. 671. Double Seaming Machine

STEP 1   STEP 2   STEP 3

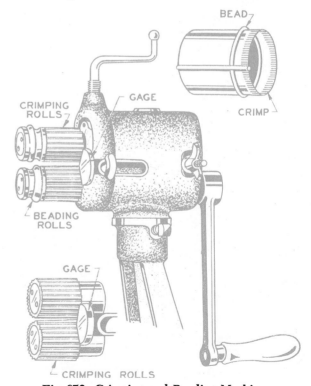

Fig. 672. Crimping and Beading Machine

Aluminum Foil Is Printed for Many Packaging Uses
— This Is an Eight-Color Roll-Fed Gravure Press
(Courtesy Reynolds Metals Co.)

Hammered Art Metalwork

831. Hammered Art Metalwork

Copper, brass, aluminum, pewter, monel metal, and silver can be used to form interesting bowls, trays, pins, etc., which even the beginner can make easily (see § 791). The material costs very little and much of the work can be done at home as very few tools are needed. Then, too, handmade articles show the character and spirit of the workman. Here is a chance to show your artistic workmanship. It is this that gives the work done by hand a real value, especially to the owner. These articles make excellent Christmas presents. Indeed, some boys earn money by making and selling them at a profit.

832. Who Does Hammered Work?

Hammered work is done by the *blacksmith, coppersmith, goldsmith, jeweler, ornamental ironworker, pewterer, sheet metalworker,* and *silversmith.* Some of the things that these tradesmen hammer are mentioned in Unit 2. The *auto mechanic* bumps kinks out of automobile bodies and fenders (see Fig. 540).

833. What Is Hammering or Peening?

Hammering or *peening* means to hammer a piece of metal with the small end of the hammer which is the *peen* (see Fig. 678).

This makes many small marks or dents in the metal, gives a rich, artistic finish, and adds beauty to the object. Many beautiful, useful, and valuable objects can be made by hammering flat pieces of soft sheet metal.

Hammering stretches and bulges the metal. It is this bulging which makes a bowl or dish. Sometimes the surface of an object is hammered only to give it a decorative or old appearance; this is called a *hammered finish.* If the hammered finish is desired on a flat piece of metal, as on a bookend, the bulges may be removed by placing the metal upon a large, flat surface and then laying a wooden block on the metal and striking heavily with a hammer on the wooden block.

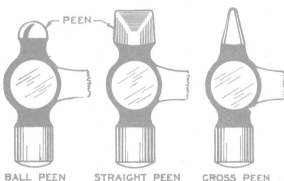

BALL PEEN   STRAIGHT PEEN   CROSS PEEN

Fig. 678. Hammers for Peening

BALL PEEN   STRAIGHT OR
                   CROSS PEEN

Fig. 679. Hammered Finishes

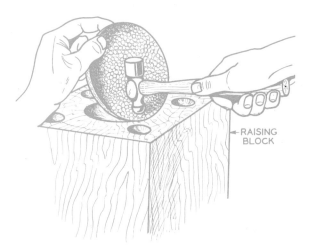

← RAISING
  BLOCK

Fig. 680. Raising a Bowl

834. Hammered Finish

Ornamental ironwork is often given a *hammered finish*. The *peening* on ornamental ironwork must be done before the pieces are bent into shape. Section 835 explains the kinds of marks that can be made. Punches with different points or rounded ends may be used to make various other marks.

Hammer marks are sometimes wanted on both sides of the metal. To do this, two hammers may be used. Fasten one hammer with the *peen* up in a vise, hold the metal on the peen, and strike it with the peen of the second hammer. (Planishing, a related operation, is explained in section 838.

After hammering, *wrought iron* (see § 302) or steel may be painted black or given a *smoke finish* (see § 1111). The high spots may be polished off with abrasive cloth. This leaves the dents black and the high places

polished. Give the entire work two coats of *wax* (see § 1113) or two coats of *clear lacquer* (see § 1102).

Hammered bowls or trays may be *buffed* (see § 1090) and then coated with clear lacquer.

835. Kinds of Hammer Marks

There are many kinds of hammers that are used for hammer work. The kinds of marks that can be made by peening depend upon the shape of the *peen* on the hammer, Fig. 678. The round marks in Fig. 679 are made with a *ball-peen hammer* which has a ball-shaped peen. The long, narrow marks are made with a *cross-peen hammer* or with a *straight-peen hammer*. Other marks may be made with different peens or blunt punches or chisels. *Planishing hammers* are shown in Fig. 681. (See § 60.)

836. Raising

Raising is the forming of a flat sheet of metal into a curved or hollowed shape, such as a saucer, bowl, tray, or spoon, Fig. 680. Many beautiful and useful things can be made of soft metals such as copper, brass, aluminum, pewter, monel metal, or silver. (See § 791). This is done by hammering, thus thinning out or stretching the metal (see § 833).

Pick out a piece of metal without scratches because they are hard to remove. The area of the flat metal should equal the area of the finished object. Small pieces of metal, such as scrap and waste pieces that are cut or trimmed off from articles should be saved until there are several pounds and then they can be sold.

If the object is to be *circular*,[1] it is well to lay out circles about ¼″ apart; they must be drawn lightly, not scratched. A fairly hard pencil may be used for drawing all other lines.

---

[1] *Circular* means in the form of a circle; round.

A *raising block,* a hollowed block of hardwood or metal, may be used; it should be held in a vise. The end of the wooden block may be hollowed out with a chisel or hammered with the *peen* of the *ball-peen hammer.* (See Fig. 678.)

Hold the metal over the raising block and hammer with a *raising hammer* or the *peen* of a ball-peen hammer. (See Figs. 638 and 680.) Begin by hammering lightly and evenly on the outside circle. Lift the hammer only about 2″. The marks should overlap one another. Striking harder in some places than in others will make the object lopsided. Evenly spaced hammer marks add beauty to the object. If wrinkles form at the edge, hammer them out carefully at once. After the first circle has been hammered, continue by hammering the second circle, then the third, and so on until the object is the desired shape.

Hammering makes *copper* and *brass* hard, stiff, and stubborn so that it is hard to work; it will even crack. It must be softened or *annealed* as explained in the next section. *Aluminum* hardens a little; *pewter* does not harden.

837. Annealing Copper or Brass

Copper and brass become hard and stiff from hammering, stretching, pressing, and bending. They may be *annealed* to make them soft again. This is done by heating the metal until rainbow colors begin to show and then cooling it quickly in water. Or, before heating, the copper or brass may be wiped with an oily cloth, heated until the oil burns off the metal, and then quickly cooled in water.

Annealed copper or brass is dark and dirty and should be cleaned as explained in section *1097* to get a nice, bright finish.

838. Planishing

Planishing means to make smooth. This may be done with a hammer which has a smooth, flat (or almost flat) *face;* it is called a *planishing hammer,* Fig. 681. It removes the bad lumps made by *raising* (see § *836*), closes the grain of the metal, stiffens it, hardens it, and makes a beautiful *hammered finish.*

The finely polished surfaces on planishing hammers and stakes should be carefully protected against nicks because they show on the work and spoil its appearance. (See § *834*).

To planish a raised bowl, place it over a *planishing stake,* Fig. 682, and hammer lightly with a planishing hammer, Fig. 683.

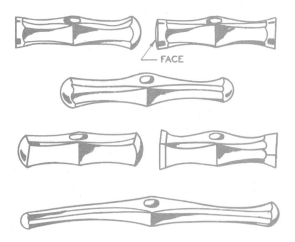

Fig. 681. Planishing Hammers

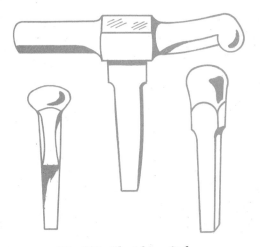

Fig. 682. Planishing Stakes

839. Fluting

Making grooves as, for instance, on the sides of plates, trays, and bowls, is called *fluting*, Fig. 684.

First, divide the sides into 5, 6, or 7 parts and draw lines with a pencil to show where the *flutes* are to be made. Then make a *fluting block*: Cut the shape of the flute into the end of a block of hardwood with a *coarse file*; a *rasp-cut file* is best (see §§ 233-234). All edges on the fluting block must be rounded. Next, hold it in a vise with the fluted end up and hammer the metal into the flute, using a tool with a round end which is very well polished.

Fluting helps to curve the top of the dish inward, thus making it smaller in diameter at the top and adding beauty to the design.

840. Chasing

Deepening the outline of a design on metal is called *chasing*, Fig. 685; it is also called *repoussé work*, which is a French word. Much of it is done as a hobby and as such is called *metal tapping*. It is done with *chasing tools*, also called *tracers*, which look like small cold chisels and punches with blunt, rounded, highly polished ends and edges, Fig. 686. Simple chasing tools may be made of large nails by rounding off and polishing the points.

The design to be chased is first drawn on paper, and then transferred to the sheet metal by using *carbon paper* (see § 792). Another way is to paste the paper with the design on the metal with *rubber cement* or *shellac* (see § 61). The metal with the design drawn on it is then tacked or screwed on a board of

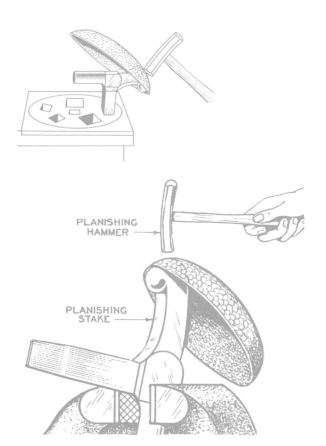

Fig. 683. Planishing a Raised Bowl

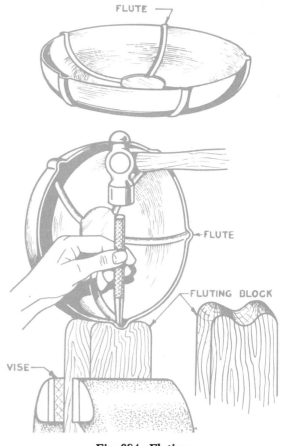

Fig. 684. Fluting

softwood; small screws placed about 1″ apart are better because tacks and small nails pull out when the metal is hammered. Another way to hold the metal is with *pitch* as explained in section *841*.

It is important to note in Fig. 686 how the chasing tool is held. Chasing is fine work and great care must be taken to see that the marks are made in the right places on the metal. The tool is held firmly between the thumb and the first and middle fingers. The ring finger and the little finger are pressed on the metal. This manner of holding the tool helps to guide it.

When a line is made, the chasing tool is held on the metal all the time, even between hammer blows. It is important that you have good light; there must be no shadow on the part to be chased. Light should come from over the right shoulder. The line to be chased should be between you and the chasing tool. Move the tool a very small distance toward you on the line between blows without lifting it. First chase the entire outline lightly, using a light hammer weighing about 2 ounces. Deepen the grooves by lightly going over and over again, a little at a time.

841. Pitch

Another way to hold the metal for *chasing*, besides the method explained in section *840*, is with a *pitch* made of:

> *Rosin* (see § *852*) − 1 lb.
> *Plaster-of-paris* (see § *983*) - 1 lb.
> Beef *tallow* (see § *401*) - 2 oz.

Mix as follows:

Step 1: Using a low flame, melt a little rosin slowly in an old coffeepot (easy to handle, pour, and store away).

Step 2: Add plaster-of-paris, a little at a time, and stir until well mixed.

Step 3: Add melted beef tallow and stir thoroughly.

Fig. 685. Chased Articles
(Courtesy Fellowcrafters, Inc.)

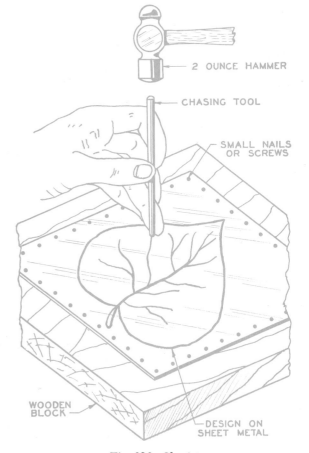

2 OUNCE HAMMER

CHASING TOOL

SMALL NAILS OR SCREWS

WOODEN BLOCK

DESIGN ON SHEET METAL

Fig. 686. Chasing

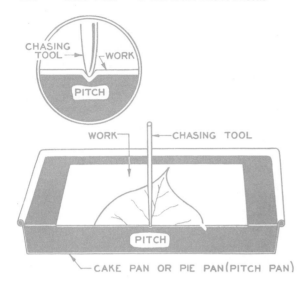

Fig. 687. Using Pitch for Chasing

Rosin, when cold, is brittle. Tallow softens it; plaster-of-paris hardens it. The whole mixture should be like rubber when cold. If it is crumbly, add tallow; if sticky, add rosin and plaster-of-paris. In warm weather, more plaster is needed; cold weather calls for more tallow. *Linseed oil* or *turpentine* (see §§ *403* and *405*) may be used instead of tallow.

Now, suppose that the pitch is to be used to hold the metal and to chase the design in Fig. 686. First, heat the pitch and pour it into a pie pan or a cake pan, then called a *pitch pan.* Next, rub oil on the back of the metal; this will cause it to stick to the pitch better and to be more cleanly removed later. Warm the metal and place face upward on the pitch. Press the metal down evenly to remove air pockets. The work is now ready for chasing. Fig. 687 shows how the pitch forms a perfect support for different shapes when chasing.

Review Questions

1. What does peening mean?
2. What is meant by raising a bowl?
3. Does hammering harden copper? Brass? Aluminum? Pewter?

4. How can copper and brass be annealed?
5. What is meant by planishing?
6. What kind of hammer is used for planishing?
7. What is a planishing stake?
8. What is meant by fluting?
9. What is meant by chasing?
10. What is metal tapping?
11. How is pitch prepared for use in chasing?
12. What should be done if the pitch is crumbly?
13. What should be done if the pitch is sticky?
14. Why should oil be put on the back of the metal before placing it on the pitch?

Coordination

Words to Know

art metalwork	pitch
chasing tool	planishing hammer
circular	planishing stake
clear lacquer	plaster-of-paris
cross-peen hammer	raising block
fluting block	repoussé
hammered finish	rubber cement
hammer mark	straight-peen hammer
metal tapping	tracer
ornamental ironwork	wax

Mathematics

1. If copper costs 42¢ a pound and a square foot of sheet copper weighs a pound, how much will a piece 3″ x 8″ cost?

Drafting

1. Design an object which you can hammer out of metal in the shop.

Occupational Information

1. Visit a store where hammered art metalwork is sold; then describe in writing some of the articles which you saw.

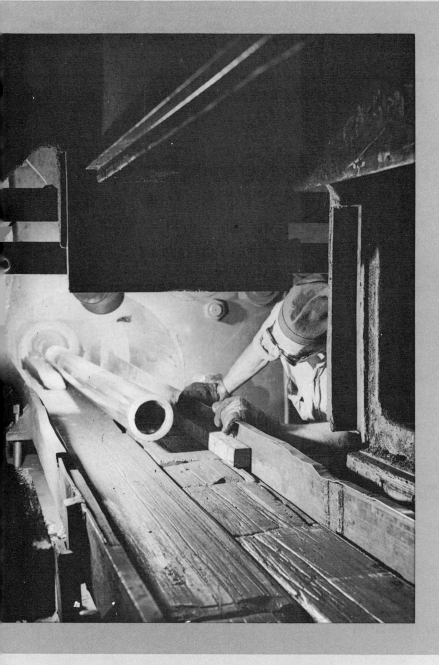

Extruded Aluminum Pipe Emerges from a Die of Hydraulically Operated Press (Courtesy Aluminum Company of America)

Hot Metalworking Processes

Part *IX*

Soldering
and Brazing

847. What Is Soldering?

Soldering is the joining of metal surfaces or edges with *solder*.[1] When the solder melts *below the red heat* temperature of iron, it is called *soft soldering;* when the solder melts at or above red heat it is called *hard soldering* or *brazing*. Brazing differs from *welding* because welding is the fusion of the pieces being joined. The filler rod for welding is basically the same as the pieces being joined, which is not true in soldering and brazing. The colors of hot iron and steel are explained in section 936.

848. Who Solders and Brazes?

The *electrician* solders wire joints. The *sheet metalworker* solders eave troughs, etc. The *tinsmith* solders cans, pans, pots, pails, etc. The *coppersmith* solders tanks, boilers, kettles, etc. A *radio serviceman* must solder

[1]The *l* is silent in solder; it is pronounced sod-er.

connections when repairing radios. The *jeweler* repairs ornaments, solders rings, jewelry, etc. The *auto mechanic* solders or brazes broken parts on automobiles. Soldering is also useful for mending broken articles at home or on the farm.

849. Tools and Materials Needed for Soft Soldering

A *soldering copper, soft solder, flux,* and heat are needed for soft soldering. These are explained in the following sections.

850. Soldering Copper

The tool used for soldering is the *soldering copper,* Fig. 693, often called a *copper* or *copper bit.* It is a square piece of copper pointed at one end and fastened to a steel bar with a wooden handle on the other end.

Soldering coppers are made in different weights from 1 ounce to 3 pounds. The weight is usually given per pair of coppers. For example, a 2-pound copper means that a pair weighs 2 pounds and that each copper weighs 1 pound. The size of the copper to use depends upon the work; use a heavy copper on heavy work and a light copper on light work.

An *electric soldering copper* and instant heating soldering guns are heated by electricity; they connect to any electric outlet.

851. Solder

The best *soft solder* is an *alloy* or metal made of *lead* and *tin.* (See § 343.) For gen-

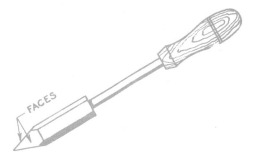

Fig. 693. Soldering Copper

eral work, a solder made of one-half lead and one-half tin is used; it is called *half-and-half* or *fifty-fifty* solder and melts at about 400° F. The solder must have a lower *melting point* than the metals to be joined. (See Table 12, p. 161.)

Solder comes in bars 12″ long and also in the form of wire on spools. A handy way to buy solder is in the form of hollow wire, the center of which is filled with *rosin* or *acid flux*.

Special solders are made for soldering *aluminum*. It takes more heat to melt *aluminum solder* than solder made of lead and tin.

Many commercial *paste-type solders* are available for use on various metals. Plumbers use them to sweat solder joints and fittings on copper tubing.

Other special kinds of soft solder are available. One is a silver-tin alloy with a low melting point for use on stainless steel. It will make solder joints up to ten times stronger than lead-tin solder.

852. Fluxes for Soldering

Flux cleans the metal and helps the solder to flow. Table 26 gives the kinds of fluxes that are used for soldering different metals. Ready-made fluxes in liquid, crystal, and paste forms are commercially available and can be used for ordinary soldering. Some of these fluxes are for general-purpose use on all common metals, and they produce good results. Flux makes the metal surface chemically clean and stops corrosion, permitting the solder to stick tightly and make a good joint.

The common name for *hydrochloric acid* is *muriatic acid* or *raw acid*. It is colorless and poisonous. An open bottle of hydrochloric acid gives off fumes which rust tools and machines. *Zinc chloride* is made *by adding zinc* (see § 371), a little at a time, to hydrochloric acid until it stops eating the zinc; the acid is thus "killed" or "cut"; hence it is also called *killed acid* or *cut acid*. This should be done in the fresh air and kept away from flames or an explosion will result. When water is added to

Table 26
FLUXES FOR SOFT SOLDERING
(See Section 852)

Metal to be Soldered	Flux	Chemical Name of Flux
Brass Copper	Cut acid Rosin Sal ammoniac[2]	Zinc chloride Colophony Ammonium chloride
Zinc Galvanized iron (zinc coated)	Cut acid Raw acid (muriatic acid)	Zinc chloride Hydrochloric acid
Iron Steel	Cut acid Sal ammoniac	Zinc chloride Ammonium chloride
Tin Tin plate	Rosin Cut acid	Colophony Zinc chloride
Pewter	Rosin Tallow	Colophony
Nickel Silver	Cut acid	Zinc chloride
Aluminum	Special fluxes by different manufacturers	

zinc chloride, it is slightly acid and may be used for all ordinary soldering. After soldering, the article must be washed with water to stop the acid from eating the metal.

Soldering salt makes water slightly acid when the commercial crystals are added to water. For bright, tinned parts, mix 1 ounce in 8 ounces of water. For bright copper and brass, mix 1 ounce in 4 ounces of water. For galvanized iron, mix 1 ounce in 2 ounces of water. Various kinds of soldering salts are available. It is best to follow the manufacturer's recommendations when preparing soldering flux solutions with soldering salts. The flux must not be stronger than necessary.

[2]*Sal ammoniac* is *ammonium chloride*. It is a white solid substance that looks like rock salt or rock candy; it is used as a soldering flux. Sal ammoniac changes directly from a solid to a gas.

Powdered *rosin*[3] may be used as a flux for soldering tin or copper; it is sprinkled in the joint and when heated flows into the seam. Rosin should be used for soldering *electrical joints*. (See § 448.)

A mixture of 1 ounce of glycerin (see § 402) and 5 drops of hydrochloric acid can be used as flux for soldering *pewter*. (See § 378.) The *tallow* from a tallow candle may also be used for soldering pewter.

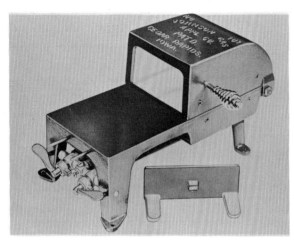

Fig. 694. Bench-Type Gas Furnace
(Courtesy Johnson Gas & Appliance)

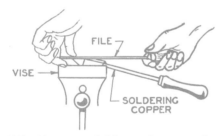

Fig. 695. Cleaning a Soldering Copper with a File

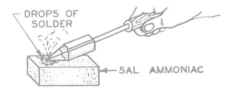

Fig. 696. Tinning a Soldering Copper on a Block of Sal Ammoniac

Special fluxes are made for soldering aluminum.

853. Heat for Soldering

Gas furnaces are often used in shops to heat *soldering coppers*, Fig. 694. The gas and air must be mixed to give a blue flame. Burning gas alone gives a yellow flame. The blue flame is hotter than the yellow flame. A portable gasoline torch or small, portable bottle-gas torch is used for outside work.

An *electric soldering copper* may be used; it can be connected to any electric light socket.

854. Tinning the Soldering Copper

A well-tinned soldering copper will hold a drop of solder on the point and make soldering easier. The *faces* on the point of the soldering copper (see Fig. 693) must be cleaned and coated with solder before the copper can be used for soldering. This is called *tinning* (see § 376).

To tin the copper, clean the four faces of the point with a file, Fig. 695. Keep the point bright. Always remember that dirt and rust are enemies of good soldering. Heat the copper until it melts solder. It does not need to be red hot. Rainbow colors show up when the copper begins to overheat; this is the danger sign. Continue with one of the following three ways, depending upon the materials that are handy:

(1) Dip point quickly into and out of a jar of *zinc chloride;* then melt solder on the faces and wipe with a dry cloth.

(2) Rub points in drops of solder on a block of *sal ammoniac* (see § 852). The solder will melt, run on the sal ammoniac, and then stick to the copper, Fig. 696.

---

[3]*Rosin,* also called resin, is a sticky hard substance. It is made from turpentine obtained from pine trees. Rosin is used in making varnish. Musicians use rosin on the bows of violins, cellos, etc. Baseball pitchers rub a finely ground rosin on their hands.

(3) Rub the point in some solder and powdered *rosin*.

855. Joints for Soldering

Sheet-metal joints to be soldered are usually *lock joints, lap joints,* or *butt joints,* Fig. 697. The parts to be joined should fit each other exactly; the better the fitting, the stronger will be the soldered joint. (See Figs. 656 and 663.)

856. Cleaning Surfaces

The surfaces to be soldered must be very clean. Rust, dirt, and grease must be removed. The black surface on some metal is *oxide*. It is formed by the surface of the metal uniting with the *oxygen* in the air. (See § 321.) It may be removed by polishing with *abrasive* cloth. (See § 283.) Where the surface cannot be cleaned with abrasive cloth, wash it with *hydrochloric acid*. Wash off the acid with water to stop the action of the acid. Any metal surface that has just been cleaned immediately begins to join with the oxygen in the air and form oxide on the metal surface. No matter how thin the oxide, it makes soldering impossible. The surfaces are made still cleaner by putting on a *flux* which thoroughly removes all oxide. (See §§ 852, and 1096-1097.)

A soft-lead (pencil) coating or a thin film of grease or shoe polish on the surface where the solder is *not wanted* will allow the solder to flow only where it is needed, producing neater work.

857. Holding Work

Place the parts together ready for soldering, and fasten them so that they cannot move while being soldered. If possible, clamp them together in a vise or C-clamp. The joint to be soldered should not touch the vise or other metal because the heat will be carried away from the joint and make soldering impossible.

858. Heating Soldering Copper

The soldering copper must be *tinned* and heated; this heat is to be used to melt the solder and to heat the pieces which are to be joined. If the point of the soldering copper is red hot, the tinning will burn off, and then the copper must be retinned. It is best to place the large part of the copper in the flame with the point out of the flame. By heating it this way, it will remain hot longer and also keep the point from becoming *pitted*, that is, full of small holes. The copper should be heated until it melts solder but should not be hot enough to burn off the tinning.

859. Soldering a Seam

The surfaces to be soldered must be clean and must be held together. Hold the soldering copper in the right hand and the solder in the left hand. *Tack* the seam together; that is, connect the parts in several places with the hot copper and a few drops of solder, Fig. 698, so that the parts will not buckle. Note that a well-tinned copper will hold a drop of solder on the point and make soldering easier.

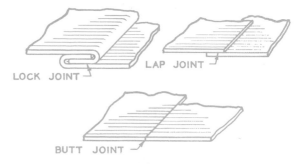

Fig. 697. Joints

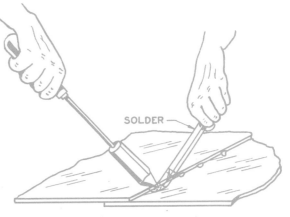

Fig. 698. Tacking a Seam with Drops of Solder While Holding the Lap Down Firmly

Next, hold the hot, tinned copper on the edge of the seam and touch the copper with the solder, Fig. 699. Move the copper slowly along the seam, a short distance at a time. As the copper melts the solder, put a little along the edge of the seam.

Remember, for neat work use only a little solder; too much solder on a joint is hard to remove. Also, the thinner the film of solder, the stronger will be the joint. The solder must be between the surfaces, to be joined, not around them. Then, move the copper back to the starting point and hold one of its flat *faces* on the seam until the metal gets hot enough to cause the solder that was put along the edge to flow into the seam. Give it time to harden before going ahead.

860. Sweat Soldering

In sweat soldering, the heat is applied to the pieces to be joined and the solder is melted by this heat. As it melts, the pieces of solder form balls, then flow along the joint. First, clean the surfaces or edges to be joined, put on a little flux, add small pieces of solder, and then press the parts together. Heat until the solder melts and joins the parts together.

861. Soldering Steel

Carbon steel (see § 319) can often be soldered by first putting a thin layer of copper on the surface. This is done by rubbing on some *copper sulfate solution* (see §§ 101-

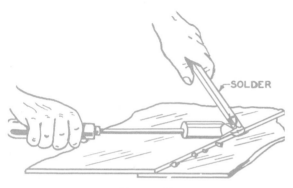

Fig. 699. Holding Soldering Copper on Edge of Seam

102); when the surface is dry, it may be soldered.

862. Cleaning Joint After Soldering

When zinc chloride, sal ammoniac, an acid, or any corrosive-type paste flux has been used as a flux for soldering, it is necessary to wash the joint in cold, running water. This is done to wash away all traces of the flux. If this is not done, the joint and the metal touched by the flux will turn to a black, dirty color.

863. Reasons for Hard Soldering

Hard soldering (silver brazing) is used where a strong joint is needed or where the parts will afterwards have to be in greater heat than the *melting point of soft solder*.

The most widely used hard solders are the *silver* and *silver-alloy solders*. Most of them melt at temperatures from 1100° to 1300° F. Hard soldering is used for joining such metals as copper, silver, gold in jewelry and art metal work. It can also be used on all carbon and alloy steels. It is often used to join band saw blades.

864. How to do Hard Soldering

The parts to be joined must be carefully cleaned, fitted snugly together, and then coated with the proper flux. For best results, use a *commercial flux* which is recommended for silver soldering. When a commercial flux is not at hand, powdered *borax* can be used as a flux. Pieces of silver solder are then placed on the joint; the parts are heated until the solder melts, runs into the joint, and fastens the parts together.

Heat for hard soldering is applied directly from a flame or torch. Gas-air torches usually have only one hose furnishing a gas. Natural, propane, or acetylene gas may be used, but each requires a different tip. Air is drawn from the room. Some may use a small pump to furnish low-pressure air through a second hose. This raises the melting temperature above the 1300°F. which is possible without air pressure. Fig. 700 shows a gas-air torch with an acetylene tank as commonly used by plumbers and jewelers. The oxyacetylene torch (with heat to 6000°F.) can be used with care. (See §§ 878 and 885.)

865.   Brazing and Its Applications

Brazing is defined by the American Welding Society as a group of welding processes which use a filler rod of a nonferrous metal or alloy with a melting point above 1000° F., but lower than the melting point of the metals being joined. Hence, brazing and hard soldering really mean the same thing because they are performed with nonferrous filler rods above a red heat (see Table 29). There is no fusion or melting together of the metals being joined in brazing, but there is a very strong bond between them. Bronze welding rods are used in brazing and *bronze welding*. Silver solder and silver alloys are used in silver brazing or hard soldering. Brazing is done where a strong joint is needed or where the parts will afterwards be in a greater heat than the melting point of soft solder. Brazing is widely used to repair gray iron and malleable iron castings. The high heat of fusion welding destroys the heat-treatment properties of malleable iron castings, and it makes gray-iron castings very brittle. Brazing can also be used to join thin sheet metal and thin pipe with less skill than is usually required to weld them.

866.   Brazing and Welding Fluxes

Many different fluxes have been scientifically developed for specific types of brazing and welding of various metals. They are available commercially from welding supply dealers. Because of the development of these fluxes, many of the metals which were formerly difficult to braze or weld may now be brazed or welded with comparative ease.

867.   Rods for Brazing
and Bronze Welding

Spelter is an old name for *zinc*. (See § 371.) *Spelter solder* or *spelter* for short was made of approximately 60% copper and 40% zinc. Brass is also made of copper and zinc. Many years ago spelter was used for *brazing*. The term spelter is now obsolete.

Today, *bronze rods* are used for *brazing* and *bronze welding* because they make stronger joints. These rods are copper alloys which have as basic elements about 60% copper and 40% zinc. In addition, other elements such as iron, tin, manganese, and silicon are included in small amounts to give them better brazing and bronze-welding characteristics. Most of the modern bronze welding rods melt at approximately 1600°F. Bronze joints with some of these types of rods produce a bond with a tensile strength of more than 50,000 pounds per square inch on steel and cast iron. Bronze welding rods are available with or without flux coatings. Coated rods are widely used because they simplify brazing and produce better joints.

868.   How to Braze

The parts to be brazed must be carefully cleaned, fitted snugly together, and then sprinkled with the proper flux. For best results, use a flux-coated rod or a commercial flux recommended for the type of metal being brazed. A different flux is usually recommended for brazing cast iron than for brazing steel. The joint is heated to a dark red color

**Fig. 700. Gas-Air Torch with
Small Acetylene Tank**

with an oxyacetylene torch (see §§ 878-885), and bronze brazing rod is melted and flowed over the joint in a thin layer until it is thoroughly *tinned* or coated with bronze. In adding additional flux, if the hot end of the brazing rod is dipped into the flux, the flux will adhere to the rod. Continue applying heat to the joint and the rod, forming a puddle of molten bronze, until the joint is built up.

Review Questions

1. What is meant by soft soldering?
2. What is meant by hard soldering?
3. What tools and materials are needed for soft soldering?
4. Describe a soldering copper. Make a sketch.
5. What is an alloy?
6. Of what is solder made?
7. Why is flux used?
8. Name some of the fluxes used for soft soldering. For hard soldering. For electrical joints.
9. What is meant by tinning?
10. How should a copper be tinned?
11. Tell how to solder two pieces together.
12. What is meant by sweat soldering?
13. What is meant by brazing?
14. What is spelter?
15. Why should a soldered joint be cleaned after a corrosive-type flux is used?
16. For what applications is hard soldering used?
17. What is the melting temperature range for most hard solders?
18. What is the basic material in most hard solders?
19. Explain how hard soldering is done.
20. What kinds of filler rods are generally used for brazing and bronze welding? What is their approximate melting temperature?

Coordination

Words to Know

acid flux	killed acid
aluminum solder	muriatic acid
ammonium chloride	oxide
borax	paste-type solder
bronze welding rods	pitted
brazing	raw acid
cut acid	riveted
electrical joint	sal ammoniac
electric soldering	soft soldering
copper	soldering copper,
50-50 solder	or copper bit
flux	soldering furnace
half-and-half solder	soldering salt
hard solder	sweat soldering
hard soldering	tinning
hydrochloric acid	zinc chloride

Mathematics

1. What does 60-40 solder contain? How many ounces of each in a pound of solder?

Occupational Information

1. What dangers are involved in soldering?

Oxyhydrogen Torch Welding on Device to Produce Parallel Air Flow in a Wind Tunnel (Courtesy Aluminum Company of America)

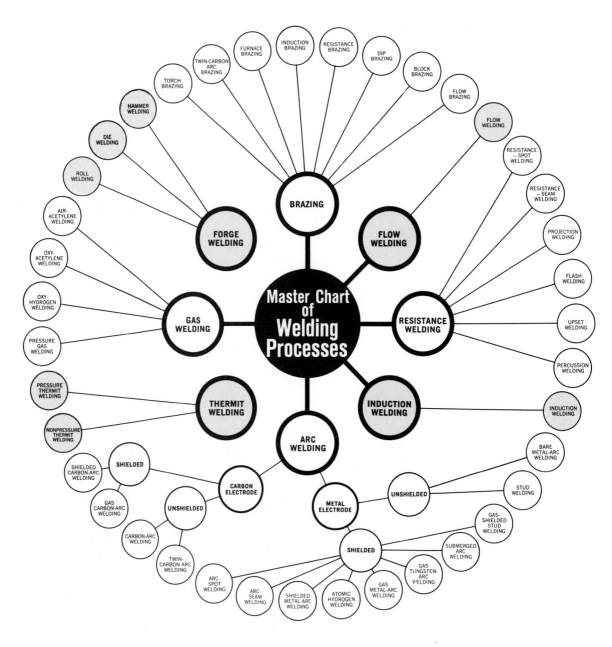

Fig. 705. Master Chart of Welding Processes
(Courtesy American Welding Society)

Welding

874. What Is Welding?

Pieces of metal may be fastened or joined together with *mechanical fasteners,* such as nuts and bolts, screws, clips, and rivets. (See Units 36 and 37.) They may be joined by soldering and brazing. (See Unit 42.) Sometimes pieces of metal are held together with gluelike materials called *adhesives.*

Another way to join pieces of metal is to *weld* them together. One kind of weld is made by heating the edges of the pieces to be joined. The metal from the edges melts and blends or *fuses* together. It is then allowed to cool and become solid. When heat is used to fuse metal to make a weld, the weld is called a *fusion weld.* The heat may be produced by burning gases and with an electric current.

Another kind of welding process is the *pressure weld.* The areas to be welded are heated to a plastic state and forced together by pressure (usually hammering). At one time, this was about the only way a blacksmith could fuse metals together. Today, there are many other welding processes—usually faster and better suited to our needs.

Fig. 705 shows how the *American Welding Society* has classified the welding processes in use today. Find each of the following terms on the chart.

Brazing is the joining of metals by melting a nonferrous filler rod at a temperature above 1000° F. but below the melting point of the metals being joined. Brazing is explained in sections 865 to 868.

Forge welding, pressure welding by heating and hammering pieces together, is explained in section 946.

Oxyacetylene welding, the most common form of *gas welding* is explained in sections 877 to 888.

Shielded Metal-Arc Welding, the most common form of *arc welding,* is explained in sections 889 to 905.

Resistance welding uses the heat generated by electric current passing through a small area of the metals being joined. Pressure forces the heated areas together until they have fused. *Spot welding,* a common form of resistance welding, is covered in section 907.

The other three central circles name processes not explained elsewhere in this book. *Thermit welding* processes use the intense heat of a chemical reaction to fuse metals. *Induction welding* uses high-frequency current as the source of heat.

Inert gas, such as helium or argon, is used in several processes to prevent the weld from becoming contaminated by scale, oxidation or other impurities. The gas keeps air away from the weld much like a CO_2 fire extinguisher puts out a fire by keeping air away. Most arc welding is shielded by a gas formed when the coating on the electrode is heated. (See § 900.)

The processes listed in the outer circle make interesting topics to read about in reference books in the library. Most of the processes have important industrial uses.

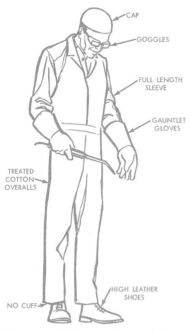

Fig. 706. Proper Clothing for Oxyacetylene Welding

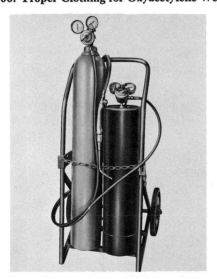

Fig. 707. Equipment for Oxyacetylene Welding
(Courtesy Linde Air Products Co.)

875. Who Welds?

A person that earns his living by welding is a welder; usually he also brazes. (See §§ 865-868.) Welders are found in most manufacturing plants, foundries, construction sites, boiler and tank shops, welding shops, railroad shops, and shipyards. Welding processes are probably used in every metal industry in some manner.

876. Learning to Weld

Learning to weld is not difficult. Anyone with average intelligence, a steady hand, and a real desire to learn can be a good welder.

877. Oxyacetylene Welding

The *oxyacetylene weld* is a *fusion weld*. (See Fig. 705.) The heat is produced by burning *acetylene gas* with *oxygen gas*, giving a temperature of about 6000° Fahrenheit. The edges of metal to be welded melt and fuse together. When the heat is taken away and the metal becomes solid, the pieces are welded together. The weld may be made so strong that the two pieces are like one piece.

Often, metal is added to the joint by being melted from a *filler rod*. This rod is usually made of the same metal as the pieces being welded. The pieces of metal to be joined are called the *base metal*. All of the melted metal, from both the base metal and filler rod, is called the *weld metal*.

878. Proper Clothing

Protective clothing should be worn by the welder using oxyacetylene equipment, (see Fig. 706). This includes the following items:
(1) A cloth or leather cap.
(2) Goggles with colored lenses.
(3) Coveralls of treated cotton or a full-length apron.
(4) Trousers without cuffs and a shirt with full length sleeves.
(5) Leather shoes.
(6) Gloves with cuffs that overlap the sleeves.

879. Oxyacetylene Welding Equipment

Oxyacetylene welding requires some special equipment (see Fig. 707). The pieces of equipment are:

(1) A cylinder of *oxygen*.
(2) A cylinder of *acetylene*.
(3) Special valves called *regulators* for the cylinders.
(4) A *welding torch*, sometimes called a *blowpipe*, and various sizes of *torch tips*.
(5) *Hoses* to carry the gases from the cylinders to the torch.
(6) A *lighter* that can make a spark to ignite the mixture of gases.
(7) A pair of *tongs* or *pliers* to handle pieces of hot metal.

880. The Welding Torch

The welding torch mixes the gases from the oxygen and acetylene cylinders. It is made so that it can control the flow of each gas to produce the size and type of flame needed. With the welding torch, the welder can direct a maximum amount of heat to a small spot or area.

Table 27
TIP SIZES, REGULATOR PRESSURES, AND ROD SIZES FOR WELDING

Tip Size No.	Gas Pressure psi[1]		Metal Thickness, Inches	Filler Rod dia., Inches
	Oxygen	Acetylene		
1	1	1	. . .	. . .
2	2	2	$\frac{1}{32}$ (22 gage)	$\frac{1}{16}$
3	3	3	$\frac{1}{16}$ (16 gage)	$\frac{1}{16}$
4	4	4	$\frac{3}{32}$ (13 gage)	$\frac{1}{16}$, $\frac{3}{32}$, or $\frac{1}{8}$
5	5	5	$\frac{1}{8}$ (11 gage)	$\frac{3}{32}$ or $\frac{1}{8}$
6	6	6	$\frac{3}{16}$	$\frac{1}{8}$
7	7	7	$\frac{1}{4}$	$\frac{3}{16}$
8	8	8	$\frac{5}{16}$	$\frac{3}{16}$
9	9	9	$\frac{3}{8}$	$\frac{3}{16}$
10	10	10	$\frac{7}{16}$	$\frac{3}{16}$ or $\frac{1}{4}$

[1] psi means pounds per square inch.

881. Torch Tips

There is a certain size and kind of flame that is best for welding each thickness of metal. Since the *tip of the torch* controls the flame, welding torches are made so that the tips can be easily changed. (See Fig. 708.)

Be sure to use the correct size wrench when changing tips. Some tips with rubber gaskets must be screwed only finger tight. Table 27 gives information that will help in selecting some brands of tips. Follow the manufacturer's recommendations. Each tip has the size number marked on it.

Sometimes the hole in the torch tip (called the *orifice*) becomes partly clogged with a small piece of carbon, dust, dirt, etc. The gases passing through the tip may make a different kind of hissing sound and the flame may have an odd shape. When this happens it is important that a special tip cleaner be used to clean the tip. (See Fig. 709.) Do not try to use a piece of wire, wood, or a wire

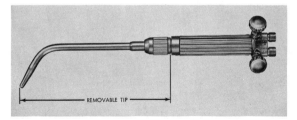

Fig. 708. Removable Tip of Welding Torch
(Courtesy Linde Air Products Co.)

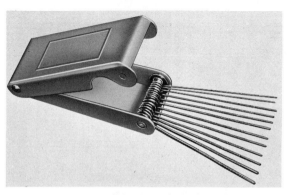

Fig. 709. Tip Cleaners
(Courtesy Linde Air Products Co.)

Fig. 710. Oxygen Cylinder Pressure Regulator

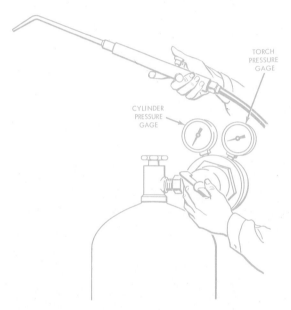

Fig. 711. Setting the Gas Pressure Regulators

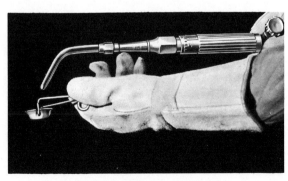

Fig. 712. Lighting the Torch
(Courtesy Linde Air Products Co.)

brush to open the hole because the tip may be damaged. Some tip cleaners carry the same number as the tip. Clean the tip by inserting a tip cleaner of proper size in the hole in the torch tip.

882. Gas Pressure Regulators

In the acetylene cylinder the pressure of the acetylene gas can vary from about 15 pounds per square inch (when it is almost used up) to 250 psi (when it is full). The pressure in the oxygen cylinder can vary from about 15 psi (almost used up) to 2200 psi (full).

The welder works with only from 1 to 10 psi of each gas supplied to the welding torch. Therefore, he needs a device on each cylinder that will deliver a constant supply of gas at a reduced pressure. The device that does this is a *gas-pressure regulator*. (See Fig. 710.) Many welders shorten the name to *regulator*.

883. Setting the Regulators

Open the oxygen cylinder valve — slowly at first — until the pressure gage stops increasing, then more quickly until the valve is fully opened. (See Fig. 711.) Open the acetylene cylinder valve ¼ to ¾ of a turn. Keep the wrench on the valve so that in an emergency the valve can be closed quickly. If either cylinder gage shows less than 15 psi, the cylinder should be replaced.

Open the oxygen *needle valve* on the torch about one turn. The oxygen hose is the green hose. Turn the oxygen regulator handle clockwise until the gage shows the proper working pressure (see Table 27); then close the needle valve on the torch.

Open the acetylene needle valve on the torch about one turn. The acetylene hose is the red hose. Turn the acetylene regulator handle clockwise until the gage shows the proper working pressure. Close the needle valve on the torch.

884. Lighting the Torch

Before lighting the torch be sure the proper clothing is being worn. (See § 878.) This includes goggles with colored lenses.

A *torch lighter*, also called *spark lighter* and *friction lighter*, should be kept with or near the welding equipment. The torch lighter is used to make a spark that will *ignite* the acetylene gas.

Open the acetylene needle valve on the torch about a half turn. Point the tip of the torch away from the body and away from the gas cylinders. Ignite the acetylene gas with the torch lighter. (See Fig. 712.) Do not use matches or a cigarette lighter to light the torch. The acetylene will burn a dark orange color and may give off a black soot. The acetylene valve is adjusted properly when the flame almost separates from the torch tip.

Open the oxygen needle valve. Adjust each needle valve to obtain the desired size and kind of flame.

885. Adjusting the Flame

Once the torch is lighted, the oxyacetylene flame can be adjusted to:

(1) A *neutral flame* — the proper mixture of oxygen and acetylene for most welds. (See Fig. 713.)

(2) A *carburizing flame* — a low temperature flame for torch brazing, it has too much acetylene (or too little oxygen) for welding. (See Fig. 714.)

(3) An *oxidizing flame* — this flame has an excess of oxygen (or insufficient acetylene). It will not make a strong weld—always harmful. (See Fig. 715.)

886. Tacking

In welding, a *tack* is a weld at one spot. (See Fig. 716.) Form a puddle of melted metal from the edges of both pieces to be welded. Put the end of the filler rod into the puddle and melt it to fill the gap between pieces. Remove the rod and flame. Tack two ends to hold the pieces in position for welding.

Fig. 713. Neutral Flame — Equal Volumes

Fig. 714. Carburizing Flame — Excess Acetylene

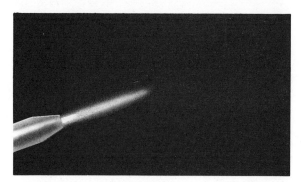
Fig. 715. Oxidizing Flame — Excess Oxygen

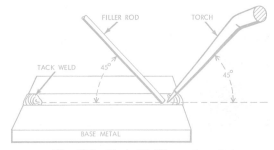
Fig. 716. Tack Welding a Butt Joint

887. Welding with an Oxyacetylene Flame

Adjust the colored goggles over the eyes to fit comfortably. Put on the welding gloves; light the torch and adjust flame to neutral. Tack each end of the weld to be made.

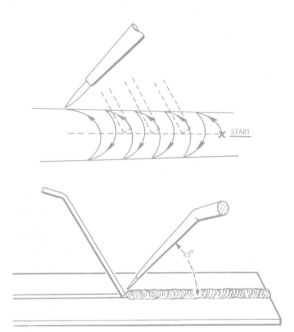

Fig. 717. Forehand Oxyacetylene Welding

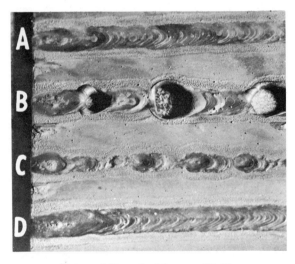

A and D — Satisfactory Welds
B — Excessive Heat. Torch Moved Too Slowly.
C — Insufficient Heat. Torch Moved Too Fast.

Fig. 718. Appearance of Oxyacetylene Welds
(Courtesy Linde Air Products Co.)

The problem now is to trace a path with the flame that will (1) melt the edges of the pieces to be welded, and (2) melt just enough metal from the filler rod to fill the gap between the pieces. Starting at the right, hold the torch so that its tip forms an angle of about 45° with the work. (See Fig. 717.) The tip of the inner cone of the flame should almost touch the work.

Play the flame over both pieces to be welded, moving it in a small circle until each edge just begins to melt and a puddle forms. Put the end of the filler rod into the puddle. Now start moving the flame around three sides of the rod so that a half circle or U-shape is traced with the flame. At the same time, begin to move the rod and the flame slowly to the left along the gap. Continue the movement until the weld is finished. If the torch and rod are moved too rapidly, the gap will not be filled. If the movement is too slow, the flame will melt a hole through the metal. It takes a lot of practice and experimenting to become good at this movement.

Welding from right to left or front to back as in Fig. 717 is called the *forehand technique.* It is commonly used on thin metals. On thick metals the *backhand technique* is used. In this, the rod is moved from side to side and the flame held steadily, welding from the opposite end — left to right or back to front.

If the welding must be stopped for only a few minutes, it is all right to shut off the flow of gases at the torch. When the welding is to be stopped for a longer time, as for lunch, end of the class period, or overnight, the acetylene and oxygen tank valves must be closed.

888. Inspecting the Oxyacetylene Weld

When the weld is finished, remove the scale (see § 252) with a wire brush or tool. Look for errors that can be corrected when making the next weld. Study Fig. 718 for examples of good and bad welds.

889. Welding with Electric Current

There are many welding processes that use electricity. The names of some are *shielded metal-arc, carbon-arc, atomic-hydrogen arc, tungsten inert gas-arc* (TIG), *and spot weld.* (See Fig. 705.) Each process has advantages over the others for a particular type of work.

Only the shielded metal-arc weld will be discussed in this book. Some of the techniques, however, do apply to other kinds of arc welding. The shield is a vapor formed when the flux coating on the electrode is heated. Manual shielded-arc welding is widely used in constructing machinery of all kinds, structural steel work, and all types of maintenance and repair welding.

890. Current for Arc Welding

Either of two kinds of electrical current may be used for electric welding: direct current or alternating current. (See § *469.*) Direct current means that the current always flows in one direction. Alternating current means that the current rapidly changes its direction again and again.

Direct current is often shortened and called DC. Alternating current is often abbreviated AC.

891. Types of Machines for Electric Arc Welding

There are three types of arc welding machines in common use:

(1) The direct current generator, driven by an electric motor or gasoline engine. (See Figs. 719 and 720.)

(2) The alternating current transformer-type welder, which operates from a powerline with a built-in transformer.

(3) The direct current transformer-type welder, which operates from a power line with built-in transformer and rectifier.

To produce the heat necessary to melt metal, the electric current must be changed from the 110 or 220 volts provided by power companies. The voltage must be reduced or stepped-down, allowing the amperage to be increased or stepped-up. A typical small arc welding machine will produce 150-250 amperes at 20 to 40 volts.

Each type of welding machine has controls for adjusting the amperage, which is deter-

Fig. 719. Motor Driven Generator
(Courtesy Hobart Brothers Co.)

Fig. 720. Engine Driven Generator
(Courtesy Hobart Brothers Co.)

mined by the size of electrode being used and the thickness of the metal being welded. When the current setting is too high, the melted puddle is too large, the electrode melts too rapidly, and there is considerable spatter. When the current setting is too low, the puddle is too small, it is difficult to maintain the arc, and the electrode is likely to stick to the base metal. In general, an amperage setting equal to the decimal equivalent

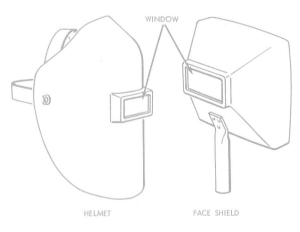

Fig. 721. Helmet and Face Shield for Arc Welding

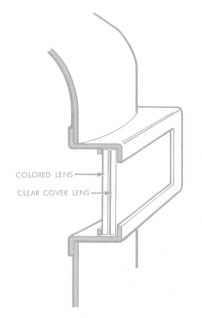

Fig. 722. Cutaway Showing Typical Construction of Helmet Window

of the diameter of the rod being used will be found to be on the high side of an acceptable range. For example, with ⅛″ rod this would mean 125 amperes; with ³⁄₁₆″ rod, 185 to 190 amperes. These should be considered as trial settings.

Some welders have a low and a high welding range with overlapping current ranges. For example, a 180 ampere welder may have a low current range of 20 to 115 amperes, and a high current range of 60 to 180 amperes. One could weld with a ³⁄₃₂″ diameter electrode on either current range using 60 to 80 amperes. The low current range provides a higher open-circuit voltage and a more stable arc thus making it easier to weld thin metals. The high current range provides a lower open-circuit voltage which produces better quality welds with thicker rods on thicker metals.

892. The Welding Arc

In some ways the welding arc is like the sun. The arc gives off heat, a brilliant white light, infrared rays, and ultraviolet rays. If the body is not properly protected from the arc, it can be burned in much the same manner as sunburn. The eyes, arms, legs, and feet should be protected.

893. Helmet and Face Shield

The *helmet* and *face shield* are made from lightweight, pressed-fiber material. (See Fig. 721.) Their black color reduces reflection. They have a window made of special dark-colored glass, called a lens, through which the welder looks at the welding arc. The special lens absorbs infrared and ultraviolet rays. It should be a number 10 lens for electric welding. This is much darker than the number 5 or 6 lens used in oxyacetylene goggles. To protect the more expensive, colored lens from the spatter of the weld, a clear, easily replaceable cover lens is used over the dark lens. (See Fig. 722.)

Looking at the arc without a shield will burn the eyes. This will depend on the length of time the eyes are exposed to the arc light. Spatter from an arc can also cause serious damage. *Caution:* Always wear clear, safety goggles underneath the welding helmet. This protects the eyes when chipping and brushing the weld flux or *slag*, Fig. 726.

894. Clothing for Electric Welding

Heavy, long-sleeved, fire-resistant cotton coveralls should be worn. Pay special attention that the sleeves and legs are not turned up to form cuffs. Clothing having no front pockets, or pockets with button cover flaps, is recommended. Pieces of hot metal from the weld often catch in cuffs and sometimes cause painful burns before they can cool or be removed. Some welders like to wear leather aprons, sleevelets, leggings, and spats. Most welders use a glove that overlaps the sleeve for protection from spatter of melted metal and the arc. Gloves also help to handle hot metal. (See Fig. 723.)

895. Welding Shop Tools

The commonly used welding shop tools are shown in Fig. 724. They are:

(1) Wire brush — for cleaning the work and the weld.
(2) Chipping hammer — to remove burrs and slag.
(3) Hammer — for bending and shaping metal.
(4) Wedges — to position the work for welding.
(5) Clamps — to hold the work for welding.
(6) Pliers or tongs — for handling pieces of hot metal.

896. The Electric Circuit for Arc Welding

An electric circuit is a path over which electric current can flow. If the path is interrupted or incomplete at any point, the circuit is said to be open. Current will not flow in an *open circuit*. Current will only flow in a com-

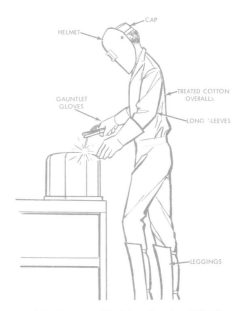

Fig. 723. Proper Clothing for Arc Welding

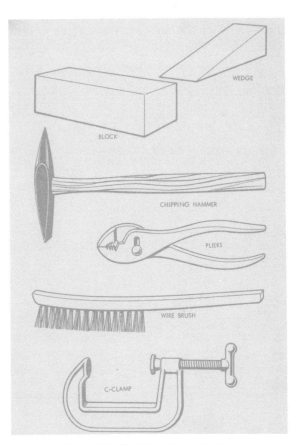

Fig. 724. Welding Shop Tools

pleted or *closed circuit*. The diagram in Fig. 725 is an electric arc welding circuit. The circle with a positive (+) on one side and a negative (−) on the other is a symbol for the welding machine (see § 891.) Starting from the − side, trace the path of the current. From the machine, it leads to the electrode holder. The current goes through the electrode, the *arc, the material being welded,* and then back to the + side of the welder. If the arc is broken, the path is interrupted and current will not flow. One cable (−) is connected to the electrode; the other (+) to the work. The cable connected to the work is called the ground cable.

897. Polarity

Look at Fig. 725 again. The path from the + side of the welder leads to the work. The path from the electrode leads to the − side of the welder. When the electrode leads to the − side of the welder, the circuit is said

to have *straight polarity*. Straight polarity is sometimes called *electrode negative*.

If the + and the − are changed around, Fig. 725, the polarity is reversed and the circuit is said to have *reverse polarity*. Reverse polarity is sometimes called *electrode positive* because the electrode leads to the positive side of the welder.

Straight polarity is the normal set-up for DC welding, but some types of welds can be made more easily with reverse polarity.

Straight polarity and reverse polarity refer only to direct current circuits (DC). If an AC machine is being used, the polarity reverses with each cycle of the current.

898. Welding Arc Temperatures

When electricity flows continuously through the air gap between a welding electrode and metal to be welded, the flow is called a *welding arc*. (See Fig. 726.) Such an arc gives off a brilliant white light and extreme amounts

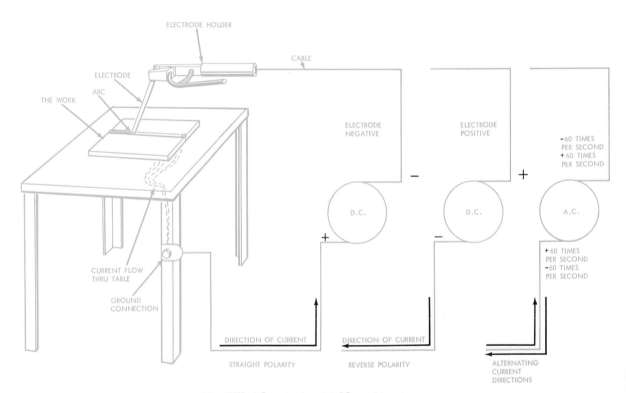

Fig. 725. Electric Arc Welding Circuits

of heat. Temperatures of 10,000° Fahrenheit have been measured in the welding arc.

899. The Electrode

As shown in Fig. 726, the *electrode* is a rod that carries current between the electrode holder and the welding arc. The welder can make the welding arc long or short by moving the electrode up or down. Electrodes are widely used in 14″ lengths and in a range of diameters from 1/16″ to 3/8″.

The electrode is also used to supply additional metal to the weld. Because it supplies metal to the weld, the electrode is used up (consumed) and must be replaced frequently.

Electrodes of carbon or tungsten are used for metal cutting and for welds which do not need additional metal.

900. The Coated Electrode

When melted metal is exposed to the air, it has a tendency to combine with nitrogen and oxygen from the air. These *nitrides* and *oxides*, called impurities, make the weld metal *brittle*. Brittle metal is not strong. For most welds it is best to have the weld as strong or stronger than the metal being welded. *Shielded arc welding* is very popular for making strong welds that are not brittle.

To shield the arc means to protect it (and the melted metal) from the surrounding air. This is done by using a special electrode, called a *coated electrode*, in the electrode holder. As the coating burns off in the arc, it forms gases that surround the arc and protect the arc from the air. The electrode coating is also a *flux*. A flux is a material that will quickly combine with the nitrides, oxides, and other undesirable impurities in the melted metal. These impurities are lighter than the melted metal. They float on top of the weld metal. When the metal cools, the impurities form a crust on top of the weld. This crust is called *slag*, (see Fig. 726), and can be easily chipped away with a chipping hammer, Fig. 724.

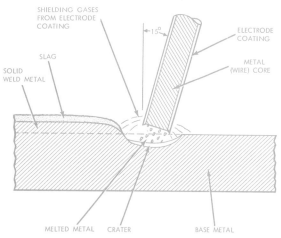

Fig. 726. The Welding Arc

901. Electrode Numbering System

E6013, E7025, and E9030 are examples of numbers that identify welding electrodes. They belong to a system developed by the *American Welding Society*. The system uses a letter followed by four digits.[2] (See Table 28.) Numbers in which the first digit is 6 (as E6013) are mild steel; other numbers (as E7025, E9030, etc.) are alloy steels.

Features and traits of welding electrodes vary from one manufacturer to the next even though they have identical numbers under the AWS numbering system. Therefore, it is always best to use the current and usage recommendations of the individual manufacturer. Most dealers can supply electrode selection charts and handbooks which list the characteristics and uses of their electrodes.

A good electrode for the beginner who is learning to weld is the 1/8″ diameter E6013 rod. It is a mild steel electrode which can be used to weld in all positions, on AC or DC, and on light or heavy gage mild steels. It has a steady arc, a smooth bead, high tensile strength, and it starts and restarts easily. The same electrode in a 3/32″ diameter can be used on sheet metal and other thin steels.

[2] Digit means any of the ten figures 0, 1, 2, 3, 4, 5, 6, 7, 8, 9, by which all numbers may be expressed.

Table 28
AMERICAN WELDING SOCIETY (AWS) NUMBERING SYSTEM
FOR COATED ELECTRODES

LETTER OR DIGIT	DESCRIPTION
E	The electrode is made for electric arc welding.
1st and 2nd Digits	These indicate the minimum tensile strength of the wire used to make the electrode. (60 means 60,000 pounds per square inch.)
3rd Digit	This shows the welding position for which the electrode can be used. If the 3rd digit is: 1 — the electrode may be used for any welding position: for flat welds (See Fig. 727), for vertical welds (See Fig. 728), for horizontal welds (See Fig. 729), for overhead welds (See Fig. 730). 2 — the electrode may be used for flat or horizontal welds. 3 — the electrode may be used for flat welds only.
4th Digit	This indicates the kind of current and type of coating.

Fig. 727. Flat Welding

Fig. 728. Vertical Welding

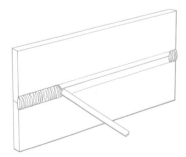

Fig. 729. Horizontal Welding

Fig. 730. Overhead Welding

902. Starting the Arc

Select the proper electrode for the job, (see section *901*), and clamp it in the electrode holder. If using a DC welder set the polarity to straight or reverse. (See section *897*.) Make an approximate current setting — low for welding thin metal, higher for thicker metal. Take notice that you are wearing the proper clothing. (See section *894*.) Put on the welding gloves and have a helmet or face shield ready. Turn on the welding machine.

Either of two methods can be used to start the arc. With a relaxed but firm grip on the electrode holder, put the end of the electrode near the spot where the weld will start. Before the arc is started, protect your eyes with the helmet or face shield. Experienced welders learn to put the shield over their faces and start the arc at the same time.

Method 1 — Down-Up Method

(See Fig. 731.) Lower the electrode straight down and touch the plate lightly. Quickly pull the electrode up and away — a distance about the diameter of the electrode. The contact should be for only a fraction of a second. The action resembles a quick pecking motion. Now, lower the electrode a little until the proper arc length is held.

This method is best. It is used by many experienced welders. At first, it is more difficult to start the arc by this method on a cold metal workpiece. With some practice it becomes easy.

Method 2 — Scratch Method

(See Fig. 732.) This method of starting the arc is something like striking a match. Hold the end of the electrode near the plate. With a sweeping motion, scratch the plate lightly with the electrode. Follow through by moving the electrode slightly away from the plate, stopping at the spot where the weld is to start. Adjust the length of the arc.

This method is usually a little easier to learn, particularly when striking an arc on a cold metal workpiece. It is not as good as the down-up method because it is harder to find the spot where the weld is to start. It also puts arcing scars on the plate.

Need for Practice

Starting the arc (sometimes called *striking the arc*) requires much practice. The welder must learn to adjust the setting on the current generator, test the polarity, move the electrode, handle the helmet and face shield, and break the electrode away from the plate when it sticks. He must learn to handle himself and the equipment safely.

903. Welding with the Arc

The beginner must experiment with different kinds and sizes of electrodes, various current settings, straight and reversed polar-

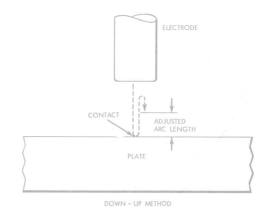

Fig. 731. Starting the Arc — Down-Up Method

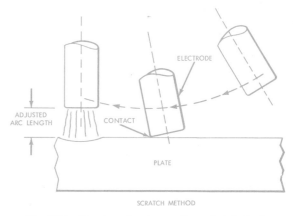

Fig. 732. Starting the Arc — Scratch Method

ity, the length of the arc, and movement of the electrode before he can expect to make good welds.

A weld should not be made over another weld until the slag has been thoroughly chipped away.

904. Joints Used in Welding

The basic joints used in gas and arc welding are the *butt joint, tee joint, corner joint, lap joint,* and *edge joint.* (See Fig. 733.) There are many variations of these.

905. Inspecting the Arc Weld

After making the weld, chip the slag away with a chipping hammer. Be sure to wear safety glasses with clear lenses while chipping. Carefully inspect the weld. Fig. 734 shows an example of a good weld. It also

shows some bad welds and tells why they are bad.

Always inspect each weld before going on to the next. Try to determine the reasons for defects and improve the next weld.

906. Cutting Metal with Welding Equipment

Metal may be cut by the oxyacetylene process and with the electric arc process. Plates of steel are often shaped in this way, since it is faster than sawing. With specialized equipment, elaborate contours are formed easily and the edge produced requires little more finishing than if it were made by sawing.

When cutting with the electric arc, a carbon or tungsten electrode is used. Much more current is used for cutting than for welding.

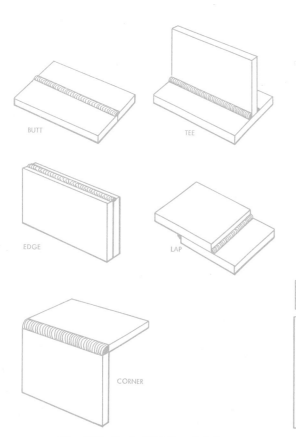

Fig. 733. Basic Welding Joints

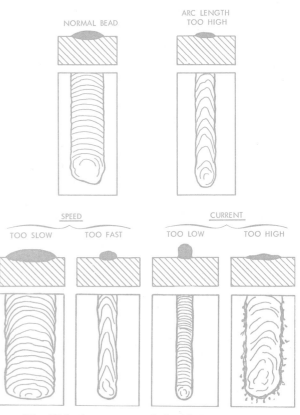

Fig. 734. Appearance of Shielded Arc Welds

907. Electric Spot Welding

Electric *spot welding* is a form of *resistance welding*. Spot welding is done by passing high current at a low voltage through a small spot on two pieces of metal, usually sheet metal, for a short period of time. It is done with a spot welder, Fig. 735 and 736. Resistance to the flow of current through the metal at the spot causes heat which makes the spot weld. The pieces of metal must be held together under moderate pressure during the weld and for a few seconds after, while the weld cools.

The welding time is controlled by a timer which is usually built into the spot welder. Welding time commonly varies from *3 cycles* to *120 cycles*. With 60- cycle current, 120 cycles means 2 seconds of time. Two pieces of 20-gage sheet steel may be spot welded in approximately a 15- to 20-cycle period. If the welding time is too long, the weld will be pitted from excess heat. If the time is too short, the weld will come apart. The points on the welding tongs should be properly dressed to shape with a file, and they should be replaced when badly worn or burned. The tongs should also be adjusted for the correct pressure for the thickness of the weld desired. Too much pressure will cause pitting of the weld.

Although spot welding is most frequently used to weld sheet metal joints, it may also be used to spot weld sheet metal to small diameter rods or flat bars.

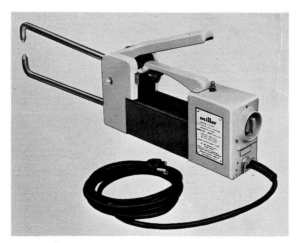

Fig. 735. Portable Spot Welder
(Courtesy Miller Electric Mfg. Co.)

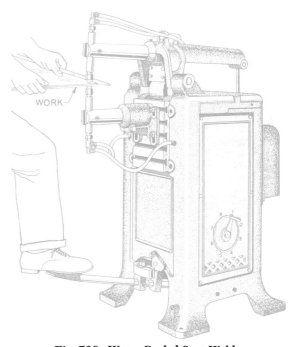

Fig. 736. Water-Cooled Spot Welder

Review Questions

1. How can pieces of metal be fastened together?

2. List three ways to make a weld.

3. Where are welders employed?

4. What temperature can the oxyacetylene flame produce?

5. Why is a filler rod used in oxyacetylene welding?

6. What is the difference between "base metal" and "weld metal?"

7. What kind of clothing should the oxyacetylene welder wear?

8. What does the welding torch do?

9. Why are there different sizes of torch tips?

10. What tip size, regulator settings, and

filler rod diameter should be used to weld 11 gage steel?

11. Why is it necessary to use a gas-pressure regulator?

12. Why should the wrench be kept on the acetylene cylinder?

13. What kind of flame should be used to make most welds?

14. What is the purpose of a "tack?"

15. What can happen if the weld is made too slowly?

16. Describe the appearance of a good oxyacetylene weld.

17. In what ways is the welding arc like the sun?

18. How can the eyes be protected from the welding arc?

19. Will the light from the welding arc permanently hurt the eyes?

20. Why should the welder wear clothing without cuffs?

21. What are some of the welding shop tools? For what are they used?

22. Describe the arc welding circuit.

23. How can the welder change the polarity of the DC generator?

24. Approximately what temperatures are attained in the welding arc?

25. What is the purpose of the electrode coating?

26. What becomes of the coating as the electrode burns off in the arc?

27. Are all E6013 electrodes exactly the same?

28. What kinds of joints are used in welding? Sketch them.

29. Why should the welder wear safety glasses while chipping slag from his welds?

30. Why should you inspect each weld?

Coordination

Words to Know

alternating current	arc
American Welding Society	backhand technique
	base metal
brittle	neutral flame
butt joint	nitrides
carburizing flame	oxides
closed circuit	oxidizing flame
coated electrode	oxyacetylene weld
corner joint	polarity
direct current	pressure weld
edge joint	rectifier
electrode	resistance welding
filler rod	reverse polarity
flux	shielded-arc welding
forehand technique	slag
forge welding	spot welding
fusion	straight polarity
fusion weld	striking the arc
gas-pressure regulator	tack
	tee joint
ignite	torch lighter
inert	transformer
lap joint	weld metal
needle valve	

Mathematics

1. What is the weight of a 3′ x 6′ bench top made from ¼″ thick steel? (Steel weighs 0.283 pounds per cubic inch.)

2. How many ³⁄₁₆″ diameter steel electrodes are there in a 50 pound box? They are 14″ long. (Neglect the weight of the electrode coating.)

Drafting

1. Design an all-welded work bench.

2. Draw a DC arc welding circuit having reverse polarity.

3. Draw the basic joints used in welding.

Occupational Information

1. What abilities are needed to learn to weld?

2. What hazards must the welder guard against?

3. How much are welders paid in your area?

4. Are welders required to be licensed in your state?

Tools for
Hand Forging

912. What Does Hand Forging Mean?

The forming by hammering of hot or cold metal into a certain shape is called *forging*. When the hammering is done by hand, it is called *hand forging*. *Machine forging* is done with large forging presses, as in Fig. 787. Machine forging is performed with large machines called *drop hammers*. These parts generally require some machining before use. Examples of drop-forged parts on an automobile include blanks for making gears, connecting rods, spring shackles, and parts for the steering mechanism. Tools such as pliers, wrenches, and hammers are drop forged into shape. Large items such as railroad car wheels are also drop forged. Forging improves the grain structure and relieves internal stresses, thus improving its strength. Principles involved in drop forging and in methods of machine forging are also involved in hand forging. An example of the hand forging technique applied with a large forging press is shown in Fig. 787. (See also *diesinker* and *hammerman* in § 19.)

913. Hand Forging Is an Art

Great skill is needed in hand forging. Many beautiful and useful iron ornaments, such as lamps, lanterns, door knockers, fireplace tools, railings, fences, gates, and hinges, are made by hand forging. (See *hammered finish* in § 834.)

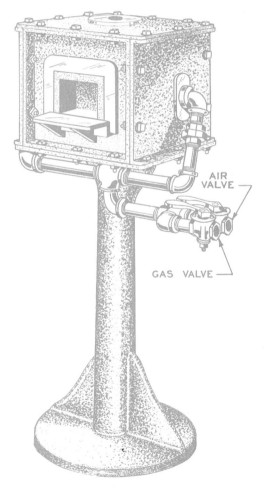

Fig. 745. Gas Forge

914. Who Does Hand Forging?

Hand forging is done by the *blacksmith* and the *ornamental ironworker*. The *maintenance machinist* sometimes forges cutting tools and special parts for machines. The *millwright* must forge brackets, braces, etc.

915. Gas Forge

There are many types of gas furnaces; one is shown in Fig. 745. One pipe supplies gas, and another supplies air from a blower. An automatic lighting system with a pilot light and electrical controls is the safest. If lighted manually, use extreme caution and follow the furnace manufacturer's instructions carefully. Know which valve is for gas and which is for air. Ask your instructor to show you how to light the forging furnace.

916. Anvil

Metal is hammered and bent into shape on an *anvil*, Fig. 746. Its shape has been the same for hundreds of years.

The *body* is made of soft steel.

The *face* is made of *hardened steel* and *welded* to the body (see Unit 43 and §§ 946 and 952). It is smooth and should be kept free from dents and marks.

The *horn* is shaped like a cone. It is tough and unhardened. Rings, hooks, and other curved parts are formed on it.

The *cutting block* is between the face and the horn. Its surface is not hardened. Metal may be cut or chipped upon it with a cold chisel; the face should not be used for chipping.

The *hardy hole* is a square hole in the face of the anvil. Various tools are held in the hole for different kinds of work.

The *pritchel hole* is the small, round hole in the face of the anvil. It is used for bending small rods and punching holes in metal.

Anvils weigh from 100 to 300 pounds. One weighing from 100 to 200 pounds is suitable for school use. It is necessary to fasten it upon a metal or wooden foundation. The face of the anvil should be at the height of the

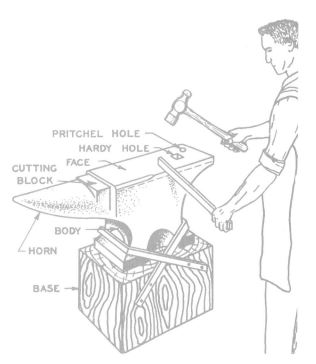

PRITCHEL HOLE
HARDY HOLE
CUTTING FACE
BLOCK
BODY
HORN
BASE

Fig. 746. Anvil

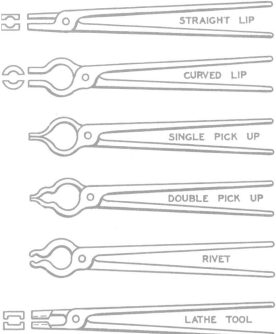

STRAIGHT LIP

CURVED LIP

SINGLE PICK UP

DOUBLE PICK UP

RIVET

LATHE TOOL

Fig. 747. Tongs

knuckles when a person stands beside it with his hands at his sides. The anvil should be placed so that the horn will be at the left of the worker (see Fig. 746).

917. Tongs

Tongs are made in a number of shapes; some of these are shown in Fig. 747. They are used to hold and handle hot metal. Some of the types of tongs are:

Straight-lip tong, also called *flat-jawed tong* — used to hold flat work.

Curved-lip tong, sometimes called *bolt tong* — used to hold round work, such as bolts or rivets. The opening behind the jaws allows space for the head of a bolt.

Single-pickup tong — used to pick up either flat work or round work.

Double-pickup tong — used to pick up either flat work or round work.

Rivet tong — used to hold square or round work, such as rivets or bolts.

Lathe-tool tong — used to hold about ½″ x 1″ steel which is used for making special cutting tools for *lathes, shapers,* or *planers.* (See § 1186.)

918. Holding Work with Tongs

Always use tongs that will grip the work firmly, Fig. 748. A ring, or *link*, may be slipped over the handles to hold them together and thus hold the work firmly and relieve the hand of the strain. The job is slowed up if the tongs do not fit the work. There is also danger of the hot work slipping out of the tongs, thereby injuring workers. Never leave the tongs in the fire with the work.

919. Hammers and Sledges

Hammers and sledges with many types of heads are used in hand forging. The hammers used for light forge work are shown in Fig. 678.

A *blacksmith hand hammer* is shown in Fig. 749. A *sledge* is a large, heavy hammer with a long handle. It is swung with both hands. Sledges weigh from 8 to 20 pounds.

920. Set Hammer

The set hammer has a smooth, flat face, about 1¼″ square, Fig. 750. It is used to make square corners and shoulders by placing it on the work and then striking the other end with a hammer or sledge.

921. Flatter

The flatter has a flat, smooth face about 2½″ square, with rounded edges. (See Fig. 750.) It is used for the same kind of work as the *set hammer* except that the flatter has a larger face. It is used to make hammered surfaces flat and smooth by placing it on the work and then striking the other end of the flatter with a hammer or sledge.

922. Hardy

The hardy is a tool similar to a chisel, Figs. 751 and 752. It has a square shank and is used to cut hot and cold metal. The square

Fig. 748. Holding Work with Tongs

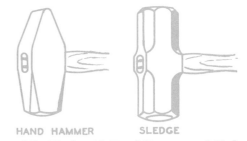
Fig. 749. Blacksmith Hand Hammer and Sledge

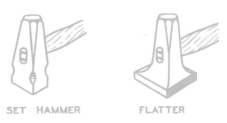
Fig. 750. Set Hammer and Flatter

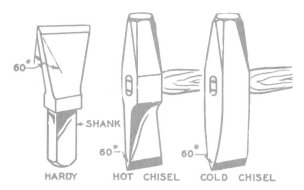

Fig. 751. Hardy and Blacksmith Chisels

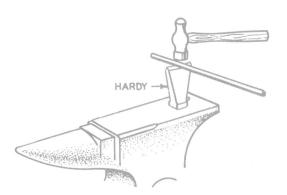

Fig. 752. Cutting Metal with a Hardy

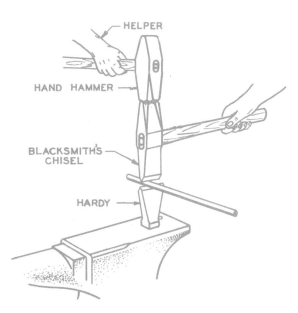

Fig. 753. Cutting Metal with a Blacksmith
Chisel and Hardy

shank is placed in the *hardy hole* of the anvil. The metal to be cut is then laid on the *cutting edge* and struck with a hammer.

Metal under ⅜″ thick may be cut cold by laying it on the hardy and nicking it on both sides, Fig. 752. When the cut is almost finished, bend the two parts back and forth until they break. Metal over ⅜″ thick should be heated before it is cut.

923. Blacksmith Chisels

Blacksmith chisels (see Fig. 751), often called *cutters,* are fitted with handles. There are two kinds: One is used to cut cold metal and is called a *cold chisel* or *cold cutter;* the other is used to cut hot metal and is called a *hot chisel* or *hot cutter.* Note that the one used to cut hot metal is much thinner than the one used to cut cold metal; one should not be used in place of the other. Both sides of the metal should be cut or nicked only part way through with a blacksmith chisel and hardy, Fig. 753, and then broken.

Thin metal may be cut on the *cutting block* of the anvil. (See Fig. 746.)

924. Blacksmith Punches

Blacksmith punches, Fig. 754, are used to punch holes in hot metal. They are made in different sizes and shapes, and are tapered.

To use a punch, heat the metal to a bright red color, lay it flat on the anvil, place the punch on the spot where the hole is to be made, and strike a heavy blow with the hammer. Continue striking the punch until it goes

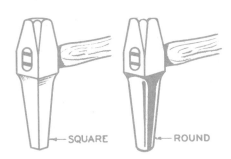

Fig. 754. Blacksmith Punches

into the metal with difficulty, Fig. 755. Quickly remove the punch, cool it, and turn the metal over. Lay it so that the punched part will be exactly over the *pritchel hole*. (See Fig. 746.) Place the punch on the bulge made by the punch and drive it through. (See § 797.)

925.   Fullers

Forming tools of different shapes, used to make grooves or hollows, are called *fullers*, Fig. 756. They are often used in pairs. The *bottom fuller* has a square *shank* that fits into the hardy hole in the anvil. The *top fuller* has a handle.

Fullering is the using of fullers. The work is placed on the bottom fuller; then the top fuller is placed on the work and struck with a hammer, Fig. 757. The top fuller is also used as in Fig. 758 and for stretching or spreading metal just the same as when *peening* with a *cross-peen* or *straight-peen* hammer. (See § 834.)

926.   Swage Block

A swage block, Fig. 759, is a heavy block of cast iron or steel, about 4″ thick and from 16″ to 20″ square. It has many different grooves and holes which are used to form metal into different shapes. The swage block can be set up in any position and often takes the place of *bottom swages*.

927.   Swages

Swages are grooved tools used to smooth or finish round bars or surfaces, Fig. 760. They are often used in pairs. The *bottom swage* fits into the *hardy hole* in the anvil. The work is laid in the groove of the bottom swage. The

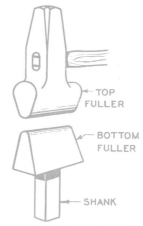

Fig. 756. Fullers

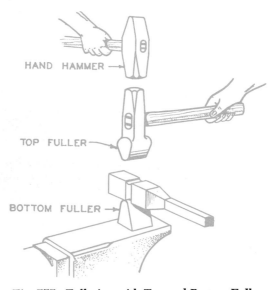

Fig. 757. Fullering with Top and Bottom Fullers

Fig. 755. Punching

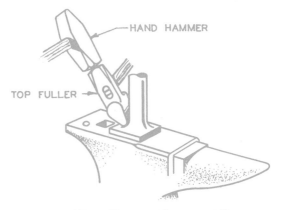

Fig. 758. Fullering with a Top Fuller

top swage, which has a handle, is next placed over the work and struck with a hammer, thus making a smooth, round surface. Each swage is made for a round bar of a certain size. Swages are also made for other shapes besides round.

Review Questions

1. What is forging?
2. What is machine forging?
3. List several kinds of products that generally are machine forged.
4. What is hand forging?
5. In what position should the anvil be mounted?

6. Name the parts of an anvil.
7. Name six kinds of tongs. For what is each used?
8. For what is a set hammer used?
9. For what is a flatter used?
10. For what is a hardy used?
11. Name the two kinds of blacksmith chisels. For what is each used?
12. For what are blacksmith punches used?
13. What is meant by fullering? How is it done?
14. For what is a swage block used?
15. What is meant by swaging? How is it done?

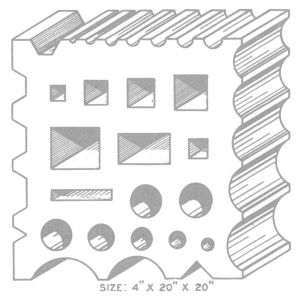

Fig. 759. Swage Block

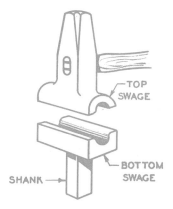

Fig. 760. Swages

Coordination

Words to Know

air valve	flatter
anvil	forging
body	forging press
cutting block	fullering
face	gas forge
hardy hole	hand forging
horn	hardy
pritchel hole	hot chisel or
blacksmith chisel	hot cutter
or cutter	rivet tong
blacksmith hand	set hammer
hammer	single-pickup tong
blacksmith punches	sledge
bottom fuller	straight-lip tong
bottom swage	or flat-jawed
cold chisel or	tong
cold cutter	swage block
curved-lip tong or	swaging
bolt tong	tong
double-pickup tong	top fuller
drop forging	top swage

Mathematics

1. If a cubic inch of iron weighs ¼ lb., how much will a block 4″ thick and 20″ square weigh?
2. How much does a bar of steel 4″ square by 12′ long weigh?

Hand Forging and Bending

935. Ways to Cut Metal

The cutting tool must always be harder than the material to be cut. The hardness of steel should be tested with the *point* or *arris* of a file before trying to cut it. (See Fig. 979.) If the file cuts the steel, it is *soft*. If the file does not cut, but slips over the steel, it is *hard* and should be cut with an *abrasive wheel*. (See § *1015*.)

In forging, metal may be cut with a *hand hacksaw* or a *power saw*. (See Units 11 and 12.) Cutting thin sheet metal is explained in section *799*. Thick sheet metal and small rods may be *sheared* or cut in a vise with a *cold chisel* and hammer. (See §§ *220* and *221*.) Flat metal may be sheared in a vise by placing a wrench on the metal next to the vise jaws and then pulling the wrench around, Fig. 767.

Metal may also be cut with a *hardy* or with a *blacksmith's chisel* and hardy. (See Figs. 752 and 753.)

Wrought iron and steel may also be cut with the *oxyacetylene flame*. (See § *906*.) Small, soft wire may be cut with *pliers*. (See § *684*.)

936. Colors of Hot Iron and Steel

Iron and steel change color as they are heated. An experienced workman can tell the temperature of the metal by its color.

If the iron is a dark red color when held in a dark place, but black in daylight, it is called *black red*. The first redness that can be seen in daylight is called *dark red, blood red,* or *low red*. The next color is *cherry red* or *bright red* in daylight. It next turns to a *lemon color* and then becomes *white hot*. Then it begins

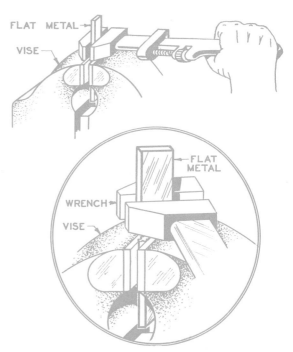

Fig. 767. Cutting (Shearing) Flat Metal with the Vise Jaws and a Wrench

to throw off sparks which is *welding heat.* (See § 946.)

The temperatures of the different colors are given in Table 29, page 363.

937.   Strike While Metal Is Hot

In forging hot metal, the metal must be hammered only while *bright red* or hotter.

Fig. 768. Drawing Out Metal

Fig. 769. Steps in Drawing a Round Bar
to a Point

Fig. 770. Offsets

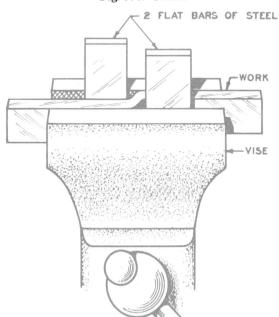

Fig. 771. Making an Offset in a Vise

(See § 936.) If hammered at a lower temperature, it will crack or split. Also, all forging must be done with as little heating as possible because too much heating spoils the steel. It is, therefore, necessary to have all tools handy so that the hammering and forming can be done quickly while the metal is hot.

938.   Drawing Out Metal

In forging, *drawing out* metal means stretching or lengthening it by hammering. The *tapered* part of a *flat cold chisel* is an example of drawing out metal. (See Fig. 186.)

First, heat the metal until it is bright red; otherwise, it will tear. To draw or stretch the metal quickly, lay it on the horn of the anvil and strike with the hammer, Fig. 768. This makes a number of notches and makes the piece longer without making it much wider. The notches can then be flattened on the face of the anvil.

When drawing out metal to a round point, as on a *center punch*, it is best to make a small point first and then lengthen it. The point must be hammered only while red hot, otherwise it will tear. It should be drawn out as in Fig. 769:

Step 1: Square.

Step 2: Octagonal.[1]

Step 3: Round.

Compare drawing out metal with *drawing* in section *331.*

[1] *Octagonal* means eight-sided.

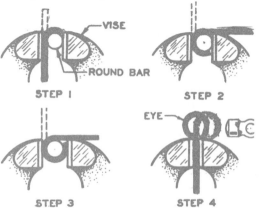

Fig. 772. Bending an Eye in a Vise

939. Offsetting

An *offset* is made of two bends; a *double offset* has four bends, Fig. 770. The bends may be made over the edge of the anvil or in a vise, Fig. 771. (See offset screwdriver in Figs. 541 and 545.)

940. Bending

Making an Eye on the Anvil

The steps for bending an *eye* in a vise are shown in Fig. 772. The steps for making an *eye* on the anvil are shown in Fig. 773.

Step 1: Measure the length of metal it will take to make the eye. Heat and bend this part over the edge of the anvil to a *right angle* (90°).

Step 2: Heat and begin at the end to form the eye.

Step 3: Form the eye by heating and bending over the horn.

Step 4: Close the eye by holding over the edge of the anvil and striking it with a hammer.

Making a Ring on the Anvil

Step 1: Measure and cut off the length of metal it will take to make the ring.

Step 2: Heat and bend both ends on the horn of the anvil, Fig. 774.

Step 3: Finish on top of the anvil.

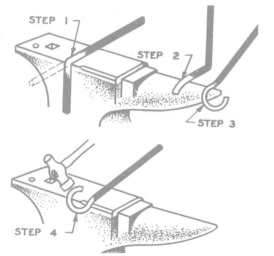

Fig. 773. **Bending an Eye on an Anvil**

Making a Number of Rings

Many *rings* of the same size may be made as shown in Fig. 775.

Step 1: Bend the metal into the form of a *spring*.

Step 2: Cut one side of the spring.

Step 3: Bend so that the ends of each ring come together.

Step 4: Ends may then be *brazed* or *welded*. (See §§ 867-868 and Unit 43.)

A *chain* may be made by hooking or *linking* the rings together before the ends of the rings

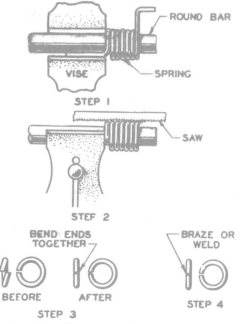

Fig. 774. **Bending a Ring on an Anvil**

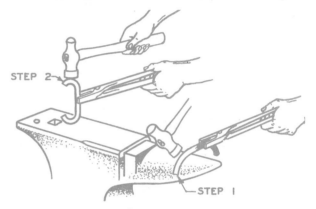

Fig. 775. **Making Rings from a Coil or Spring**

are bent together as shown in Step 3 in Fig. 775. The ends may afterwards be brazed or welded.

Small rods can be bent in the *hardy hole* or *pritchel hole* of the anvil as shown in Fig. 776. Bars and rods can often be bent in a vise, Fig. 777. If the metal is thin it can be bent

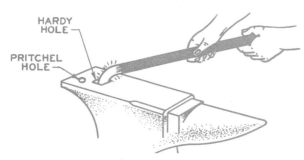

Fig. 776. **Bending a Rod in the Hardy Hole**

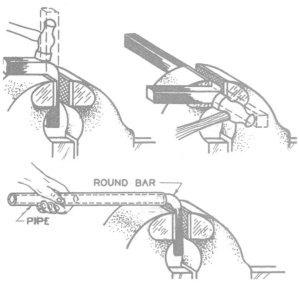

Fig. 777. **Bending Bars or Rods in a Vise**

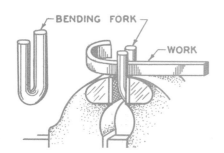

Fig. 778. **Bending with a Bending Fork Held in a Vise**

cold; if thick, it must first be heated evenly where the bend is to be made. Cold metal will break if bent back and forth. A rod may also be bent quickly by slipping a piece of pipe over it while the rod is held in a vise and then bending it. (See Fig. 777.)

A good way to make curved bends in a vise is to first bend a ¾″ or 1″ round rod in the shape of a U. This is called a *bending fork*. Clamp it tightly in the vise and use it for bending as shown in Fig. 778. Bends can also be made on a *bench anvil*, Fig. 779.

941. Making Scrolls

A *scroll* is a graceful, pleasing curve or curl like a watch spring, Fig. 780. It is used to decorate and beautify objects. A good scroll is tightly curved at the inside, gradually widening toward the outside. The curve must

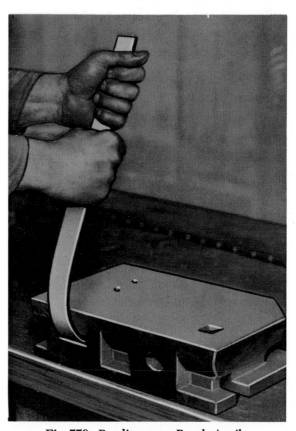

Fig. 779. **Bending on a Bench Anvil**
(Courtesy The Cincinnati Tool Co.)

be smooth and free from kinks. Fig. 780 shows two scrolls forming an *S-scroll*. The scrolls which make up an S-scroll may both be the same size or one may be larger than the other. The connecting line of the S-scroll, between the two scrolls, should be a gracefully curved line rather than a straight one.

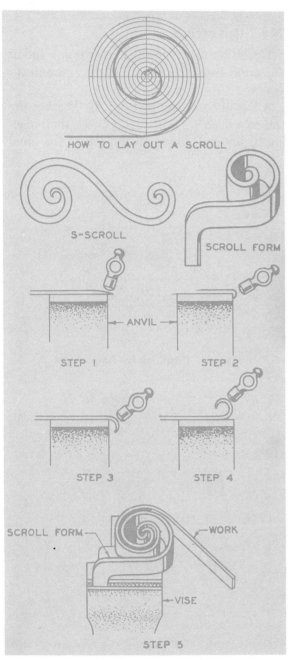

Fig. 780. Forming a Scroll

The length of the metal needed to make a scroll may be measured by first making the scroll out of soft wire, then straightening it out and measuring the length. Or, if you have a sample of the scroll that you wish to make, the length may be measured with a divider as explained in section *109.*

A simple way to make a scroll is to use a *bending fork* with narrow jaws. (See Fig. 778.) A beautiful scroll may be made with a *scroll form* by following the steps shown in Fig. 780:

Step 1: Heat and draw out the end of the bar. (See § 938.)
Step 2: Heat and bend ⅛″ to ¼″ of the end over the edge of the anvil.
Step 3: Continue bending by moving and hammering the bar over the edge of the anvil about ⅛″ at a time.
Step 4: Turn the bar over and continue forming with the hammer.
Step 5: Heat, fit into *scroll form,* hold in place with tongs, and finish bending.

Thin metal may be bent cold. Thicker metal should be heated red hot.

942. Making Spirals

A *spiral* is a graceful, screwlike twist, Fig. 781. Many springs are made in this shape, and it is used to decorate and beautify the ends of some objects. The length of the metal

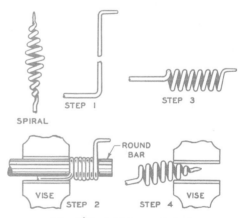

Fig. 781. Making a Spiral

needed to make a spiral may be measured by first making the spiral out of soft wire, then straightening it out and measuring the length.

A simple spiral can be made by following the steps shown in Fig. 781:

Step 1: *Draw out* the end of heavy wire to a point (see § 938) and bend the point, a short distance from the end, to a 90° angle. Measure out enough wire to make the spiral and make another 90° bend in the opposite direction.

Step 2: Fasten the thick end against a proper size pipe or round bar in a vise. Wind the wire tightly and closely on the pipe. If necessary, use pliers or tongs.

Step 3: Remove the pipe and spread the *coils* evenly with a screwdriver, a little all around.

Step 4: Gradually make the coils smaller toward the point by pressing in a vise and tapping with a hammer.

943. Twisting

Flat or square pieces of metal may be twisted in the vise with a *monkey wrench*, Fig. 782; a *tap wrench* (see Fig. 510) may be used if it fits the metal. Thin metal may be twisted cold but thick metal must be hot. Metal up to ½″ square can be twisted cold.

The beginning and the end of the twist should first be marked with chalk or a *center punch*. (See Fig. 41.) Clamp the bar in the

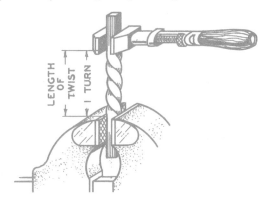

Fig. 782. Twisting

vise with one mark even with the top of the vise jaws. Place the wrench at the other mark. The length of the twist will equal the distance from the wrench to the vise jaws.

To make a long twist, slip a pipe, the length the twist is to be, over the metal. Then twist. It is thus kept from bending out of shape while twisting.

944. Upsetting

Upsetting means to thicken or bulge and at the same time shorten. It is the opposite of *drawing out*. (See § 938.)

A bar of iron may be upset by heating the end to a *welding heat* (see § 936), then placing it, hot end down, on the top of the anvil

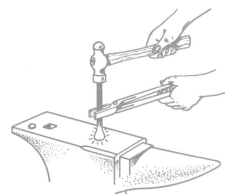

Fig. 783. Upsetting by Hammering

Fig. 784. Upsetting by Ramming

and striking the other end with a hammer, Fig. 783. If the bar is long, it may be grasped with both hands and the end bounced or *rammed* upon the anvil, Fig. 784. If the bar bends or kinks, straighten it before going ahead. Light blows only upset the very end of the bar while heavy blows upset it further back.

945. Heading

Heading means to form a *head* on something, as on a rivet or bolt. It is done with a *heading tool*, Fig. 785. This has a hole which is slightly *tapered*. There should be a heading tool for each size of rod. The hole should be about $\frac{1}{32}''$ larger than the rod for rods up to $\frac{1}{2}''$ in diameter, and a little larger as the diameter is increased.

The steps for heading are:

Step 1: *Upset* the end of the bar from which the bolt or rivet is to be made. (See § 944.)

Step 2: Slip the body of the bolt into the small end of the hole in the heading tool and into the *hardy hole*.

Step 3: Strike heavy blows on the heated, upset end with the hammer until the head is the right thickness.

Step 4: Finish the sides of the head on the face of the anvil with a hammer.

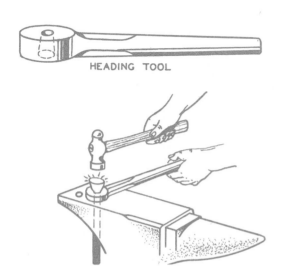

Fig. 785. Heading

946. Forge Welding

Forge welding is the joining of two pieces of metal by making them soft and pasty with heat and then pressing, hammering, or melting them together. A *forge welder* needs the experience which comes only with practice. Wrought iron and steel containing up to .50% carbon can easily be welded. (See §§ *302, 320-321,* and *326-327.*)

It must be remembered that *scale* (see section 252) must be kept from forming if a good weld is to be made. *Flux* is used for this purpose. (See § 852.) There are many kinds of fluxes. Clean *sharp sand* is a good flux for wrought iron; powdered *borax* (see § 865) is good for steel. The flux may be sprinkled with a long-handled spoon on the place where the weld is to be made. In heating, it melts and keeps the air, which combines with the metal to form the scale, away from the hot metal.

There are different kinds of forged welds. Only the *fagot*[2] *weld* is described here, Fig. 786. It is good for practicing how to weld. A fagot weld is made by laying pieces of iron on top of each other and welding them into one piece as follows:

Step 1: Heat two pieces to a bright red and put on the flux.

Step 2: Heat to a *welding heat.* (See § 936 and Table 29 on page 363.) The pieces must be heated evenly so that the inside will be as hot as the outside.

Step 3: Lay them on top of each other on the anvil and quickly strike a few light blows in the center to make them stick. Continue hammering until they are welded together.

[2] *Fagot* means to make a bundle; to tie together in a bundle as a bundle of sticks.

Fig. 786. Forged Welds (Fagot Welds)

Remember that the more often the metal is heated the harder it is to weld. More pieces may be welded on, one at a time. Another way to make a fagot weld is to bend or fold the end of a piece of metal once or twice and weld it into a solid lump.

Review Questions

1. Tell three ways by which metal may be cut in hand forging.

2. What is meant by drawing out metal? How is it done?

3. What is an offset?

4. Tell how to make a ring. A chain.

5. Describe a scroll.

6. Describe a spiral.

7. Tell how to twist metal.

8. What is meant by upsetting? How is it done?

9. What is meant by heading? How is it done?

10. What is a fagot weld?

Coordination

Words to Know

bench anvil	black red
bending fork	chain
cherry red or bright red	linking
	octagonal
coil	offsetting
dark red, blood red, or low red	ramming
	scroll form
double offset	sharp sand
drawing out	spring
eye	S-scroll
fagot	twisting
fagot weld	upsetting
heading tool	welding heat
lemon color	white hot

Mathematics

1. How long a bar of ⅜" round steel will it take to make a ring with 2" inside diameter?

2. How many feet of ¼" round steel will it take to make a 19-foot chain, using rings with 1" inside diameter?

Occupational Information

1. Of what value is a knowledge of hand forging to any mechanic?

2. In what trades is a knowledge of hand forging important?

3. Read Longfellow's "The Village Blacksmith."

Fig. 787. Hand Forging Aluminum on a 15,000 Ton Forging Press Using Simple Flat Dies
(Courtesy Aluminum Co. of America)

Heat Treatment
of Steel

948. What Does Heat Treatment of Steel Mean?

Heat-treatment processes involve heating and cooling of metals, in their solid states, for the purpose of changing their *properties*. The common properties of metals are explained in section 358. The principal properties of steel which can be changed by heat-treatment processes include hardness, brittleness, toughness, tensile strength, ductility, malleability, machinability, and elasticity.

Steel may be made harder, tougher, stronger, or softer through various kinds of heat-treatment processes. Every tool must have a certain hardness, strength, toughness, brittleness, or *grain* to do its work. All metals have a *crystalline* grain structure while in the solid state. The *grain structure* in steel may be changed in several ways with heat-treatment processes. To bring about the proper grain structure, and thus develop the desired properties, the steel is heated and then cooled in different ways. This is called *heat treating*. The following are the principal kinds of heat-treatment processes:

(1) Hardening (See § 951)
(2) Tempering (See § 954)
(3) Annealing (See § 955)
(4) Normalizing (See § 956)
(5) Case Hardening (See §§ 957 and 958)
(6) Flame Hardening (See § 959)
(7) Induction Hardening (See § 959)

All heat-treatment processes involve heating and cooling metal according to a *time-temperature cycle* which includes the following three steps:

(1) Heating the metal to a certain temperature.
(2) Holding the metal at an elevated temperature for a certain period of time. (This is called soaking.)
(3) Cooling the metal at a certain rate.

The procedure used in the above three steps varies for each kind of heat-treatment process.

949. Furnaces and Temperature Control

The various heat-treatment processes require that steel parts be heated to certain temperatures. These temperatures must be determined and controlled accurately for best results. The parts generally are heated in furnaces. However, they may also be heated with other sources of heat such as a portable gas torch Fig. 700, an oxyacetylene welding torch Fig. 707, or even a small bunsen-type burner.

Several kinds of furnaces may be used. They are heated by gas, oil, or electricity. Large industrial-type furnaces are shown in Figs. 800 and 801. Smaller furnaces are used in metallurgical laboratories, small heat-treating shops, and in school metalwork laboratories.

Kinds of Furnaces

An *electric heat-treating furnace,* which heats to temperatures within a range from 300° to 2300° F., is shown in Fig. 790. A gas-fired, heat-treatment furnace which heats to temperatures up to 2300° F. is shown in Fig.

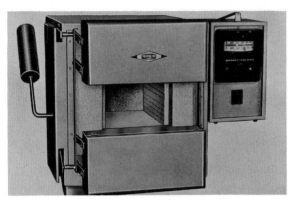

Fig. 790. Electric Heat-Treatment Furnace with Temperature-Indicating Control Unit (Courtesy Thermolyne Corp.)

Fig. 791. Gas-Fired Heat-Treatment Furnace Equipped with Indicating Temperature Controls (Courtesy Johnson Gas Appliance Co.)

791. The gas-fired *hardening furnace,* at the left in Fig. 792, is used for hardening carbon steels and high-speed steels in the temperature range from 1300° to 2350° F. The gas-fired furnace, at the right in Fig. 792, is a *drawing (tempering) furnace* which is used for tempering in the range from about 400° to 1150° F. A gas-fired, pot-type, liquid-hardening furnace is shown in Fig. 793. This kind of furnace heats salt, lead, and cyanide baths for liquid case hardening processes and for other special heat-treating processes. An ordinary *bench-type* gas furnace, such as the kind which is often used for heating soldering coppers, Fig. 694, may be used to heat steel for either hardening or tempering. A gas-fired forging furnace, Fig. 745, may also be used for heat-treatment processes.

Temperature Control

For best results, heat-treatment furnaces should be equipped with temperature-indicating and control devices, Fig. 794. With controls of this type and similar types, the desired temperature is set with a control knob. The

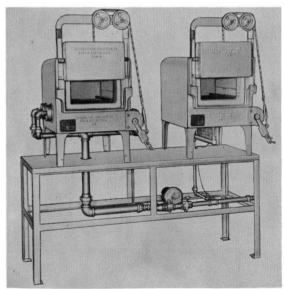

Fig. 792. Duo Furnace Unit:(Left) Hardening Furnace; (Right) Drawing or Tempering Furnace (Courtesy Johnson Gas Appliance Co.)

furnace then heats to the desired temperature and maintains this temperature within a few degrees. It turns the gas or electric current on or off, intermittently, as necessary to hold a steady temperature. The furnaces in Figs. 791 and 790 are equipped with heat-indicating and temperature controls.

Temperature Colors

When clean, bright steel is heated, various colors appear at different temperatures, as shown in Table 29, page 363. If the furnace used for heat treating is not equipped with a temperature-indicating and control device, the temperature can be estimated by observing the color of the steel as it is heated. This is the way blacksmiths used to determine the temperature of steel for heat-treatment purposes. This method, however, is not very accurate. Without skill and experience the temperature can easily be off 20° to 30° in the range from 375° to 600° F. In the red-heat range the temperature can easily be in error several hundred degrees.

Temperature-Indicating Material

An inexpensive way to determine temperatures of heated steel is through the use of temperature-indicating pellets, crayons, or paints, see Fig. 795. These materials are made to melt at various temperatures from 100° to 2500° F. Simply select the crayon or other material which is designed to melt at the desired temperature. Rub the crayon or other identifying material on the workpiece. When it is heated to the desired temperature, the identifying material will melt, thus indicating the temperature of the workpiece.

A *magnet* may be used as an aid in identifying the hardening temperature of steel. (See § 952.)

950. Carbon Content Affects Hardening

Plain carbon steel is composed principally of iron and carbon (see §§ 317-319). The carbon content in steel enables the steel to become hardened. Hence, pure iron cannot be

Fig. 793. Pot-Type Liquid Hardening Furnace (Courtesy Johnson Gas Appliance Co.)

Fig. 794. Temperature-Indicating and Control Equipment for Gas Heat-Treatment Furnace (Courtesy Johnson Gas Appliance Co.)

Fig. 795. Temperature-Indicating Products: Pellets, Crayons, and Liquid (Courtesy Tempil°)

hardened by heat treatment. Whether steel is plain-carbon steel or alloy steel, it is the amount of carbon content which largely determines the maximum hardness obtainable by heat treatment.

The plain carbon steels may be classified in the following three general classifications according to carbon content:

Low-carbon steel, 0.05 to 0.30% carbon
Medium-carbon steel, 0.30 to 0.60% carbon
High-carbon steel, 0.60 to 1.50% carbon

The high-carbon steels can be made very hard, brittle, or tough by heat treatment. Metal-cutting tools, such as drills, milling cutters, taps, and dies, are made of high-carbon steel with carbon content ranging from approximately 0.90 to 1.10%. (See Table 6, page 142.)

The medium-carbon steels can be made relatively hard by heat treatment. However, they cannot be hardened sufficiently to make drills, taps, threading dies, or similar metal-cutting dies. Some uses of medium-carbon steels are shown in Table 6, page 142.

The hardness of metals can be measured with instruments, as explained in Unit 56. The Rockwell-C scale may be used to indicate the hardness of hardened steel. The Rockwell-B scale may be used to indicate the hardness of soft steels and nonferrous metals. These hardness values can be converted to equivalent values on other kinds of hardness scales. (See Table 35, page 457.)

A comparison of the maximum obtainable hardness for one kind of medium-carbon steel (1045 steel) and one kind of high-carbon steel (1095 steel) is shown in Fig. 797. Before tempering, the 1095 steel was hardened to a Rockwell hardness of C-66. The 1045 steel was hardened to Rockwell C-59. A hardness of Rockwell C-60 or higher, after tempering, is generally required for metal-cutting tools such as drills and files.

Low-carbon steels can be hardened only a small amount by direct hardening. However, the skin layer, the thin outside case on these steels, can be hardened by the heat-treatment process called case hardening.

951. Hardening

Hardening is a heat-treatment process which makes steel harder. Files, drills, and taps are examples of steel which is *hardened* by heat-treatment. Hardened cutting tools keep their edges longer. High-carbon steels, particularly those with more than about 0.75% carbon, become very hard and very brittle when hardened, see Fig. 797.

Medium-carbon steels and high-carbon steels are hardened by heating slowly to the proper *hardening temperature* (see Fig. 796), and then cooling them rapidly. They are cooled rapidly by *quenching* in water, brine, or oil. Some alloy steels are hardened by using special procedures.

The maximum hardness obtainable by heat treatment depends upon:

(1) The amount of carbon in steel.
(2) The speed of heating.
(3) The temperature at which the steel is quenched for hardening, called the hardening temperature.
(4) The speed of cooling.

When high-carbon steel has been hardened, it becomes very brittle due to internal stresses which result from rapid cooling. In fact, it is frequently so brittle that if struck by a hammer it would crack or shatter. Hence, a hardened piece of high-carbon steel requires an additional heat-treatment process, called *tempering*, before it may be used. Hardened steel should be tempered immediately or as soon as possible after hardening. Occasionally, hardened steel will crack if cooled improperly or if allowed to remain in a hardened condition without tempering for a prolonged period.

Cold metals may be *work hardened* by hammering, pressing, or rolling. (See §§ 837 and 1222.)

952. Hardening Temperature

The *hardening temperature* is the temperature at which a piece of steel should be quenched for *hardening*. The hardening temperatures for various plain carbon steels are in a range indicated by a shaded area on the chart in Fig. 796. The hardening temperature is within a range from about 50° to 100° F. above the AC_3 line which represents the *upper-transformation temperature*, also called the *upper-critical temperature*. The AC_1 line on the chart represents the *lower-transformation temperature*, also called the *lower-critical temperature*. The AC_2 line on the chart represents the *magnetic point*. When heated above the magnetic point, steel loses its magnetic properties and is no longer attracted to a magnet. *Note* that lines AC_3 and AC_2 join with line AC_1 on the right-hand portion of the chart, as far as hardening and annealing temperatures are concerned, for steels with more than 0.80% carbon.

When steel is heated through the upper-transformation temperature, the grain becomes very fine, that is, the crystals get smaller. If suddenly cooled, this fine grain is trapped and the steel becomes very hard. Fine-grained steel is very strong after tempering.

At temperatures of more than 100° F. above the upper-transformation temperature, the grain again starts to coarsen, and it becomes very coarse at higher temperatures. If the steel is cooled rapidly in this condition, it will be very hard and brittle and may crack. It also will lack the desired toughness after tempering. Hence, it is important to select a hardening temperature which is within the proper hardening temperature range.

The hardening temperature varies for different kinds of steel. It depends upon the amount of carbon in the steel. The more carbon the steel contains, the lower its hardening temperature. In other words, high-carbon steels need less heating for hardening. Of course, you must know the approximate carbon content of the steel in order to determine the hardening temperature.

The hardening temperature can be tested and estimated with a magnet. Medium-carbon and high-carbon steels are not attracted by a magnet at the hardening temperature. Thus, a piece of steel to be hardened may be heated until a magnet no longer attracts it; it should then be cooled rapidly by quenching.

953. Quenching Solutions

Steel is hardened by heating it slowly and uniformly to the hardening temperature (see Fig. 796), followed by rapid cooling in a *quenching solution*. Steel may be quenched in water, brine, or oil. Special kinds of tool steel may be quenched merely by allowing them to cool in the atmosphere.

Some quenching solutions cool more rapidly than others. The rate of cooling is most rapid with brine, less rapid with water, slow with oil, and slowest in air. If steel is quenched and

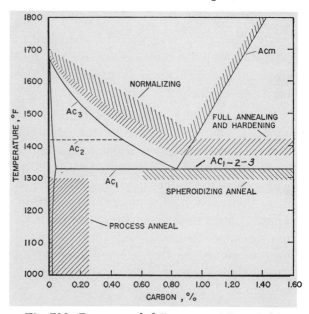

Fig. 796. Recommended Temperature Ranges for Heat-Treating Plain Carbon Steels*

*Adapted from Thomas G. Digges, Samuel J. Rosenberg, and Glenn W. Geil, *Heat-Treatment Properties of Iron and Steel*, National Bureau of Standards Monograph 88. Washington, D. C.: U. S. Government Printing Office, 1966.

cooled too rapidly, it will crack. Brine or water should be at a temperature of about 60° F. for quenching purposes. Oil, unlike water, cools best when it is at a temperature of about 100° to 140° F. Several kinds of oils are used as quenching solutions. A light grade of straight mineral oil is often recommended.

Plain-carbon steels are usually quenched in water or brine. Although brine cools about twice as rapidly as water, it tends to *throw* the scale away from the steel during quenching. This causes the steel to cool more uniformly. If small carbon steel parts vary in thickness, such as screwdriver blades or cold chisels, they often crack when quenched in water. This is due to the uneven rate of cooling for thick and thin sections. Parts of this type may be quenched in oil. However, it should be remembered that the parts will not be as hard after quenching in oil which cools slower than water.

It is best to follow the steel manufacturers' recommendations when selecting quenching solutions for alloy steels or expensive tool steels. Most alloy steels must be quenched in oil to prevent cracking. Some special tool steels are classified as *air hardening* and are hardened by cooling in air.

When quenching steel, the parts should be *agitated* (moved about) in the solution. Either an *up-and-down* or a *figure-eight* movement should be used. Vaporized gas bubbles will form on the surface of the hot metal when it is immersed in the quenching solution. These bubbles form a temporary insulation on the surface of the metal and cause the metal to cool slower in that area. The agitation causes the steel to cool evenly, thus preventing cracks because the gas bubbles do not have time to form on the metal's surface. Rapid agitation speeds up the rate of cooling. In fact, very rapid agitation can double the cooling speed. Excessive agitation of small parts may cause cracking with a water or brine quench.

954. Tempering

Tempering is often called *drawing* or *drawing the temper*. It is a heat-treatment process which relieves internal strain in hardened steel and thus increases its toughness. (See § 358.) Tempering is done by slowly reheating steel parts to a certain tempering temperature which is below a red heat, see Table 29. The parts are then allowed to cool in air, or they may be quenched. The method of cooling generally is not important.

Tempering is a stress-relieving process which relieves internal stresses created within the grain structure of steel during the hardening process. The internal stress is produced when the exterior surface of the metal cools quicker than the internal portion.

Tempering makes hardened steel tougher and also softer. The purpose of tempering, however, is to make the steel tougher, not softer. If it were possible to make steel tougher without softening it, this would be ideal, but this is not possible. Therefore, the ideal heat treatment of steel tools or parts is a combination of the right amount of hardness and toughness to do the job for which they were designed.

Hardened steel is tempered to increase its toughness so that it will not crack or fracture under heavy stress, vibration, or impact. The toughness of steel can be measured with special impact-testing machines in research laboratories. These machines measure the amount of energy, in terms of foot-pounds, required to fracture a standard size metal specimen.

Since most school shops do not have toughness-testing machines to determine the toughness of steel, another method may be used. The hardness and toughness of steel are related to each other, but in opposite order. The harder the steel, the more brittle it is; the softer the steel, the tougher it is. Hence, the toughness of *hardened and tempered* steel parts may be estimated, indirectly, by determining the hardness of the steel. Hardness testing is explained in § 1159. The hardness of one kind of medium-carbon steel and one kind of high-carbon steel which were hardened and then tempered at various tempering temperatures is shown in Fig. 797.

The problem in tempering is to determine the correct tempering temperature. The temperature to which steel is heated for tempering depends on the following factors:

1. The type of steel (carbon steel or special alloy steel).
2. The carbon content.
3. The hardness required.
4. The toughness required.

Recommended tempering temperatures, and the color of polished steel at these temperatures, are shown on Table 29. Tempering temperatures range from about 300° to 1100°

F. Most carbon-steel tools, however, are tempered in the range from 380° to 600° F. Temperatures above 800° F. are used for tempering items which require extreme toughness and little hardness, such as medium-carbon steel parts for the steering mechanism on automobiles.

Tempering Procedure

Tempering should follow as soon as possible after hardening. The steel should be heated slowly and uniformly to the tempering temperature selected, see Table 29. The parts should be held at the tempering temperature (this is called soaking) for a period of 1 hour per inch of part thickness. This provides time for necessary atomic rearrangement (internal changes) within the grain structure of the steel. Parts ¼″ or less in thickness *do not require soaking* to obtain the required temperature. After the required soaking period, the parts may be allowed to cool in the atmosphere or they may be quenched in water.

Table 29
TYPICAL TEMPERING TEMPERATURES FOR VARIOUS TOOLS

Degrees Fahrenheit	Temper Color	Tools
380	Very light yellow	Tools which require maximum hardness: lathe centers and cutting tools for lathes and shapers
425	Light straw	Milling cutters, drills, and reamers
465	Dark straw	Taps, threading dies, punches, dies, and hacksaw blades
490	Yellowish brown	Hammer faces, shear blades, rivet sets, and wood chisels
525	Purple	Center punches and scratch awls
545	Violet	Cold chisels, knives, and axes
590	Pale blue	Screwdrivers, wrenches, and hammers

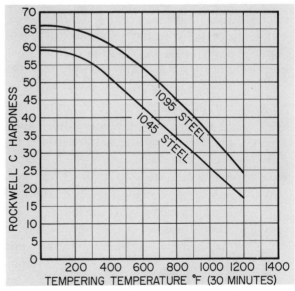

Fig. 797. Effect of Various Tempering Temperatures on the Hardness of Carbon Steel Note: Surface hardness of carbon-steel bars, SAE 1045 steel ¾″ square, and SAE 1095 steel ½″ diameter, after tempering at various temperatures. Both steels were hardened in water quench, the 1045 steel at 1500° F., and the 1095 steel at 1450° F.

955. Annealing

Annealing is a heat-treatment process which is used to produce softening and to improve machinability of hard or hardened steel. It relieves internal stress and strain which may be caused by machining, previous heat treatment, or by cold-working operations; some cold-working operations include rolling, stamping, or spinning. Annealing, therefore, is the opposite of hardening. Three kinds of annealing may be done:

(1) Full annealing
(2) Process annealing
(3) Spheroidizing anneal

Full Annealing

This process relieves internal stress, produces maximum softness in steel, and improves machinability. It is used to soften hardened steel for remachining. If a file is fully annealed, a hole can be drilled through it. It could then be rehardened if desired. The following procedure is used for full annealing:

(1) Heat the steel uniformly to the full-annealing temperature. This temperature is 50° to 100° F. above the upper-transformation temperature represented by line AC_3 in Fig. 796. The full-annealing temperature range is within the same range of temperature as the hardening-temperature range. It varies according to the carbon content of the steel.

(2) Allow the steel to soak at the full-annealing temperature for about 1 hour per inch of part thickness.

(3) Allow the steel to cool very slowly. It may be removed from the furnace and packed in ashes or lime for slow cooling, or the furnace may be shut off and the part allowed to cool in the slowly cooling furnace.

Process Annealing

This process is often called *stress-relief annealing*. It is used for relieving stresses in steel due to cold-working processes such as machining, punching, or rolling. It is most frequently used with low-carbon steels. The following procedure is used for process annealing:

(1) Heat uniformly to a temperature ranging from 1000° to 1300° F. (see Fig. 796).

(2) Allow the part to soak at the desired temperature for a period of about 1 hour per inch of part thickness.

(3) Remove the part from the furnace and allow it to cool in air.

Spheroidizing Anneal

This process involves heating steel to relatively high temperatures, usually from 1300° to 1330° F., see Fig. 796. The steel is soaked at this temperature for several hours in order to develop a special kind of grain structure in steel. The grain thus formed is very soft and machinable. This process generally is applied to high-carbon steels. Steel annealed by this process should cool slowly to about 1000° F. Below that temperature it may cool at any rate of speed.

956. Normalizing

Normalizing is a heat-treatment process which involves heating steel to the *normalizing temperature*, soaking it at this temperature for a period of time, and allowing it to cool in air. Normalizing relieves internal stresses in steel due to forging, machining, or cold-working. It also removes the effects of other heat-treatment processes. It softens hardened steel and improves its machinability. It is somewhat similar to annealing, except that steel which is normalized is not as soft as when fully annealed. The following procedure is used for normalizing:

(1) Heat the steel uniformly to the normalizing temperature. This temperature varies for steels of different carbon content and is shown in Fig. 796.

(2) Allow the steel to soak at the normalizing temperature for a period of about 1 hour per inch of thickness.

(3) Remove the steel from the furnace and allow it to cool in air.

957. Case Hardening

Case hardening is a *surface hardening* process which involves hardening the thin surface layer on steel, while the inner core remains quite soft, see Fig. 799. The surface layer forms a hardened *case* over the softer steel; hence the term case hardening. This process generally is applied to low-carbon steels. Occasionally, it is applied to medium-carbon steels.

The case hardening process actually involves two important heat-treatment phases or steps, first *carburizing* then *hardening*. It will be recalled that low-carbon steel hardens very little because it does not possess enough carbon content (see § 950). Suppose that more carbon could be absorbed into the surface layer of low-carbon steel. This would cause the surface layer to become high-carbon steel. This is what carburizing does. It causes carbon to be absorbed into the surface layer of steel, thus transforming it into high-carbon steel.

During the second important phase in the case-hardening process, the carburized steel is actually hardened. It is hardened by using the same procedure used for hardening high-carbon steel, see Fig. 951. Thus the case-hardening process produces a hardened case layer of steel over a softer inner core. The surface hardness value, before tempering, is usually from Rockwell C-60 to C-66. The core hardness for case hardened low-carbon steels usually ranges from about Rockwell C-20 to C-30. Since the inside core of the steel possesses some carbon content, it does harden to the degree made possible by the amount of carbon content.

Tools and parts which need increased strength or a hard-wearing surface are case hardened. Wrenches, pliers, and hammers are often case hardened. Gears, screws, bolts, and other parts which wear only on the surface are case hardened.

Carburizing is a relatively slow process. Steel must be soaked at the *carburizing temperature* for about 8 hours to carburize to a surface depth of $\frac{1}{16}''$ and about 24 hours for a depth of $\frac{1}{8}''$. Case-hardened products generally are carburized to a surface depth of from 0.020'' to 0.030'' during a period of about 2 to 4 hours. The length of time required for penetration of carbon during the carburizing process varies with the (1) carburizing tem-

Fig. 798. Packing Parts to be Case Hardened in Carburizing Compound (Courtesy Chrysler Corp.)

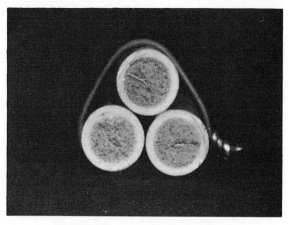

Fig. 799. Case Hardened Steel (Courtesy American Gas Furnace Co.)

perature, (2) the carburizing substance used, and (3) the depth of penetration desired.

Several kinds of carbonaceous substances may be used to introduce carbon into steel at the carburizing temperature. These materials include solid materials, liquids, and gases. Hence three kinds of carburizing processes are named according to the kind of carburizing material used. Solid materials are used for *pack carburizing*, Fig. 798. Gases such as liquid gas or natural gas are used for *gas carburizing* in special furnaces, Fig. 800. Special kinds of salt are heated to form a molten salt bath for *liquid carburizing* in liquid heat-treatment furnaces of the types shown in Figs. 801 and 793.

Carburized parts may be hardened by quenching directly from the carburizing temperature, or they may be allowed to cool first. When the latter procedure is used, the parts are reheated to the hardening temperature and quenched. When quenched directly from the carburizing furnace, less scale is built up on the parts, due to oxidation. Hence, there is less difficulty in surface cleaning the parts.

Case-hardened parts may be tempered or not, as desired. Since the inner core is relatively soft, and the hardened surface layer is very thin, there is little danger of cracking or fracturing. When deeply case hardened, the parts should be tempered as explained in § 954. Low tempering temperatures, 300° to 400° F., generally are used.

Pack Carburizing

With this method, steel parts are packed in a metal box containing material which has much carbon in it. Either a special carburizing compound or a special kind of charcoal developed for carburizing may be used, § 798. The container is then sealed and heated to the carburizing temperature, ranging from 1700° to 1800° F. The container of parts is soaked at this temperature until the parts are carburized to the desired depth. With this method, the parts are allowed to cool and are removed from the container. They are then hardened as explained in § 951.

958.   How to Case Harden Steel

One of the safest methods for case hardening in the school metalwork laboratory involves the use of a special type of carburizing

Fig. 800. Gas-Carburized Roller Races Ready to be Discharged from Carburizing Furnace (Courtesy American Gas Furnace Co.)

Fig. 801. Liquid Carburizing of Gears in a Salt Bath (Courtesy AJAX Electric Co.)

compound. A nonpoisonous, noncombustible, carbonaceous substance, such as *Kasenit* (trade name), is recommended as the carburizing material. Pack carburizing with this type of material is done in an open or well-vented container. The container may be made of heavy-gage sheet steel or plate steel. The following procedure is generally used:

Pack Method

For case depths up to 0.015″:

(1) Place the steel part in an open, well-vented, shallow container. Cover the part with Kasenit or other equivalent carburizing compound. A vented cover may be placed on the container if desired.

(2) Place the container in a heat-treatment furnace and heat to 1650° F. Soak the part at this temperature for 15 to 60 minutes, depending on the depth of case desired. With this procedure a case depth of 0.005″ to 0.020″ can be obtained.

(3) Remove the part from the molten compound with dry tongs and quench in clean water immediately.

(4) Temper the part if desired. A tempering temperature of 300° to 400° F. is satisfactory for most applications.

Dip Method

For a shallow case, several thousandths of an inch in depth:

(1) Heat the part uniformly to 1650° F. This will be a bright red color.

(2) Dip or roll the part in Kasenit or a similar case hardening compound, and continue to heat the part for several minutes. The coating of compound will bubble and form a crust as it is absorbed into the steel.

(3) With the part heated to 1650° F., quench in clean cold water.

(4) To increase the depth of the carburizing, repeat Step 2 one or more times, as desired.

(5) Temper if desired. Parts which are case hardened to very shallow depths are not often tempered.

959. Other Methods of Heat Treatment

Flame hardening is a surface-hardening process which is used on steels which have hardening properties. It hardens the surface to depths ranging from 1/32″ to 1/4″ deep. It is done by heating the surface layer of steel very rapidly with an oxyacetylene flame to the hardening temperature, Fig. 802. The surface is immediately flush quenched with a spray of water or other coolant. It is then tempered. Flame hardening is used on gear teeth, lathe parts, and other surfaces which must wear longer. They have the advantage of exterior hardness without being brittle because of the softer tough core.

Induction hardening also is a surface-hardening process which is used on steels which have hardening properties. It hardens to depths ranging up to 1/4″. It is similar to flame hardening except that high-frequency current is used as a source of heat for hardening. The steel is rapidly heated to the hardening temperature with high-frequency current which passes through a coil surrounding the object being heated. It is immediately

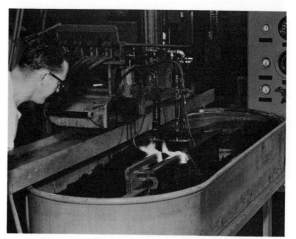

Fig. 802. Flame Hardening the Ways on a Lathe Bed (Courtesy Clausing Div., Atlas Press)

flush quenched with water or other coolant, Fig. 803.

960. Testing Hardness of Metal

The methods used for testing the hardness of metal are explained in Unit 56. This inspection operation can follow heat treatment of steel.

Review Questions

1. What is meant by heat treatment?

2. List the principal properties of metal that can be changed by heat treatment.

Fig. 803. **High-Frequency Induction Hardening of Four Track Rollers Simultaneously**
(Courtesy Tocco Div., Park Ohio Industries, Inc.)
  A. Assembly Setup
  B. Parts Being Heated
  C. Parts Being Water Quenched

3. List the principal kinds of heat treatment processes.

4. A time-temperature cycle involving three principal steps is included in all heat-treatment processes. List the three steps.

5. What is meant by *soaking* during heat-treatment processes?

6. What types of furnaces may be used for heat treating steel parts?

7. What purpose does a temperature-indicating and control device serve on a heat-treatment furnace?

8. What is meant by temperature colors on steel? How can you make use of them?

9. List several kinds of temperature-indicating materials, and explain how they may be used.

10. Of what importance is the carbon content of steel?

11. List three general classifications for plain-carbon steels.

12. To what extent can medium-carbon steels be hardened?

13. List several kinds of hardness scales which may be used to indicate the hardness of steel.

14. What heat-treatment process is often used on low-carbon steels?

15. What is meant by hardening; how is it done?

16. List four factors which help determine the maximum hardness obtainable for a piece of steel.

17. Can high-carbon steel parts be used without further heat treatment after hardening? Why?

18. What is meant by the hardening temperature?

19. Is the hardening temperature the same for all steels? Why?

20. What kind of grain structure is in steel which is quenched at the proper hardening temperature?

21. How can you use a magnet to estimate

the hardening temperature of medium- and high-carbon steels?

22. List four kinds of quenching solutions.

23. Which quenching solution cools most rapidly?

24. What kind of quenching solutions may be used for hardening plain-carbon steels?

25. In what kind of quenching solution are most alloy steels quenched?

26. How should steel parts be agitated when quenching?

27. What is the purpose of tempering; how is tempering done?

28. How can the toughness of steel be estimated indirectly?

29. What factors must be considered in deciding what tempering temperature to use on a steel part?

30. In what range of temperatures are most carbon-steel tools tempered?

31. When and how is carbon steel tempered?

32. What purpose does the soaking period serve during the tempering process?

33. What is annealing, and what is its purpose?

34. List three kinds of annealing processes.

35. Explain how full annealing is done.

36. What is normalizing and what is its purpose?

37. Explain how normalizing is done.

38. What is meant by case hardening; for what purpose is it used?

39. On what kinds of steel are case-hardening processes applied?

40. What two important phases or steps are involved in case hardening?

41. What is meant by carburizing?

42. Indicate the Rockwell hardness range for case-hardened surfaces and for the core of case-hardened parts.

43. How long does it generally take to carburize to a depth of 0.020″ to 0.030″?

44. List three kinds of case-hardening processes.

45. Must case-hardened parts always be tempered?

46. Explain how to case harden parts with Kasenit or a similar carburizing or case-hardening compound using the pack method.

47. Explain how to case harden parts with Kasenit or a similar carburizing compound using the dip method.

48. Explain the flame hardening process and its use.

49. Explain the induction hardening process and its use.

50. How can the hardness of metals be tested?

Coordination

Words to Know

annealing	lower-transformation
carburizing	temperature
carburizing	magnetic point
temperature	normalizing
case hardening	normalizing
crystalline grain	temperature
dip carburizing	pack carburizing
drawing temperature	process annealing
flame hardening	properties of steel
full annealing	quenching
gas carburizing	quenching
grain structure	solution
hardening	Rockwell hardness
hardening	scale
temperature	spheroidizing anneal
hardness	tempering
heat treatment	temperature
induction hardening	time-temperature
Kasenit	cycle
liquid carburizing	toughness
lower-critical	
temperature	

Occupational Information

1. What are the dangers involved in heat treating?

2. What diseases are prevalent in heat treating?

3. In which trades is a knowledge of heat treatment of steel important?

Molder is shown carefully setting cores into a finished mold. (Courtesy Link-Belt, Division of FMC Corporation)

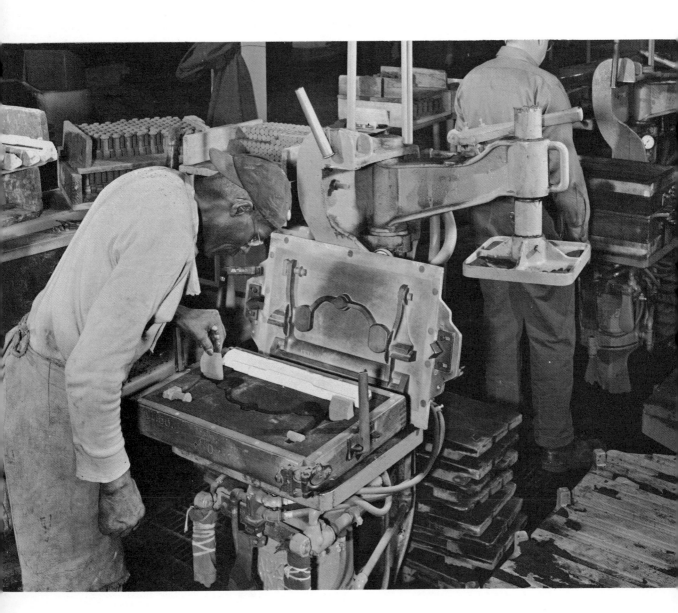

Molds and Molding

961. What Is a Mold?

When a baker makes muffins or cup cakes, he pours the batter into a muffin pan. The round forms are called *molds,* sometimes spelled *moulds.* He also makes waffles in a mold. Ice cubes are formed in molds. A form or shape into which melted metal is poured to make an object of a certain shape is also a mold. Most molds for shaping melted metal are made of sand, metal, or plaster.

962. What Is a Pattern?

Molds are made by shaping the mold material around a full-size model that is the shape of the casting (see § 990) to be made. The model is called a *pattern.* Patterns for models are made of wood, metal, wax, and plaster-of-paris.

Wood patterns are often made from mahogany. This wood is hard but is easy to shape by sawing, planing, carving, and sanding. It has a fine, smooth surface when finished.

A pattern made of metal is a *metal pattern.* It lasts longer and keeps its shape better than one made of other material.

A *wax pattern* may be made by cutting the wax with a thin, warm knife.

A *plaster-of-paris pattern* is made by mixing water with plaster-of-paris powder to make a paste. The paste is formed into the desired rough shape, leaving a little extra for finishing. When it is hard, it can be finished by scraping and sanding to a smooth surface.

A *solid pattern* is made in one piece. A *split pattern* is made in two halves. It can be removed from the mold in pieces.

A person who makes patterns is a *patternmaker.* A person who makes metal patterns is a *metal patternmaker.*

Finished castings can sometimes be used as patterns. If you look around at home you will probably find many articles that can be used as patterns for casting. Bookends, paper weights, small statues, etc., make good patterns. They can usually be used without being damaged.

963. Draft

In order that a pattern may be lifted easily from the mold (see § 961) without breaking the mold, the sides of the pattern must be *tapered.* The taper is also called *draft.* When the pattern is tapered so that it can be removed from the mold, it has *positive draft.* (See Fig. 804.) If however, the pattern is tapered so that it cannot be withdrawn from the mold without breaking the mold, it has *negative draft.* Negative draft is also called *back draft,* or *reverse draft.* When the sides of the pattern are straight, the pattern has *zero draft*.

A pattern with negative draft cannot be used to make a mold because it cannot be withdrawn. When a pattern has negative draft it can usually be repositioned. (See Fig. 804.) Sometimes, however, the pattern must be reshaped. (See Fig. 805.)

964. Shrinkage

Metal shrinks as it cools. (See §§ *671* and *721*.) Thus, a casting is larger when it is hot than after it has cooled. When making a pattern, the patternmaker makes the pattern a little larger than the finished casting to allow for shrinkage. He measures with a special ruler that is ⅛″ to ¼″ longer *per foot* than the standard rule. It is called a *shrink rule*.

The amount of allowance for shrinkage depends on the kind of metal being cast and on whether the mold will cool quickly or slowly. For small castings, the allowances for shrinkage are iron, ⅛″ per foot; steel, ¼″ per foot; aluminum, $\frac{5}{32}$″ per foot; and brass, $\frac{3}{16}$″ per foot.

965. Kinds of Molds

Molds can be classed as sand molds, metal molds, or special molds. Following are the popular names of various kinds of molds:

Sand Molds

Green-Sand Molds
Dry-Sand Molds
Shell Molds

Metal Molds

Permanent Molds
Die Molds

Special Molds

Investment Molds
Plaster Molds

Table 30 compares these molds.

966. Green Sand Molds

Molds made from a mixture of moist sand and clay are called green-sand molds. A large percentage of the castings made in the United States are made from these molds.

Small sand molds can be made by hand on the bench; this is called *bench molding*. Large sand molds are handmade on the floor; this is called *floor molding*.

967. Flask

A *flask* is a frame for a mold made from wood or metal. It holds the sand, Fig. 806. Flasks are made in two halves. The top is called the *cope*, and the bottom is called the

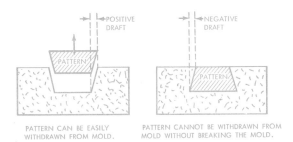

Fig. 804. Positive Draft and Negative Draft

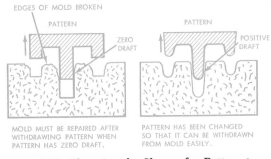

Fig. 805. Changing the Shape of a Pattern to Give it Positive Draft

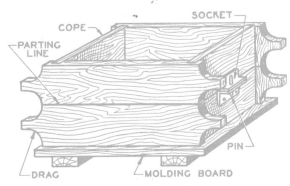

Fig. 806. Flasks and Molding Board

Table 30
COMPARISON OF MOLDS USED TO MAKE METAL CASTINGS

	SAND MOLDS			METAL MOLDS		SPECIAL MOLDS	
	GREEN SAND MOLD (SEE § 966)	DRY SAND MOLD (SEE § 976)	SHELL MOLD (SEE § 977)	PERMANENT MOLD (SEE § 979)	DIE MOLD (SEE § 980)	INVESTMENT MOLD (SEE § 982)	PLASTER MOLD (SEE § 983)
CHIEF MATERIALS FOR MOLD	Sand + Clay Binder + Moisture	Sand + Oil Binder + (Oven Bake)	Sand + Resin Binder + (Oven Cure)	Usually Steel	Hardened Steel	Silica Sand + Special Binder + (Air & Oven Cure)	Gypsum + Water
USUAL METALS CAST	Most Metals	Most Metals	Most Metals	Aluminum, Brass, Bronze, Some Iron	Alloys of Aluminum, Zinc, Magnesium	Special Alloys	Aluminum Brass Bronze Zinc (Metals that Melt Under 2000° F.)
SURFACE FINISH OF CASTING	Rough	Rough	Smooth	Smooth	Very Smooth	Very Smooth	Very Smooth
ACCURACY OF CASTING	Not Very Accurate	Not Very Accurate	Fairly Accurate	Fairly Accurate	Very Accurate	Very Accurate	Fairly Accurate
USUAL WEIGHT OF CASTINGS	Less than 1 Lb. to Several Tons	Less than 1 Lb. to Several Tons	½ Lb. to 30 Lb.	Less than 1 Lb. to 15 Lb.	Less than 1 Lb. to 20 Lb.	Less than 1 Ounce to 5 Lb.	Less than 1 Lb. to 20 Lb.
COST OF MOLD	Low	Low	Medium	High	High	High	Medium

drag. The halves are held together by *pins* and *sockets*. When they are put together, a *parting plane*[1] separates the cope and drag. The size of the flask depends upon the size of the pattern.

Wood flasks are inexpensive, but they char easily from the heat of hot, melted metal. They must be replaced often. Metal flasks last longer.

[1] In geometry, a plane is an imaginary flat surface that has length and breadth (two dimensions) but zero thickness. In molding and casting, the parting plane is sometimes called a *parting line*.

968. Molding Board

The board or plate upon which the pattern is laid while pressing the sand around the pattern is called a *molding board*. (See Fig. 806.) It should be slightly larger than the flask and strong enough that it will not bend while the mold is made.

969. Sand for Green-Sand Molds

Sand for green-sand molds is not sand alone, but a mixture of sand, clay, and water. A *green-sand foundry* makes *molding sand* by mixing sand with special clays. Enough water is added to make the mixture moist. The damp, sticky clay makes the grains of sand cling together. The mixture is called "green" because the mold is not dried, baked, or cured before it is used. Other ingredients are also mixed with the clay, sand, and water. Some of these make the mixture black.

Fig. 807. Testing Temper of Green Sand

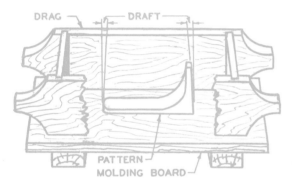

Fig. 808. Pattern and Drag Placed on Molding Board

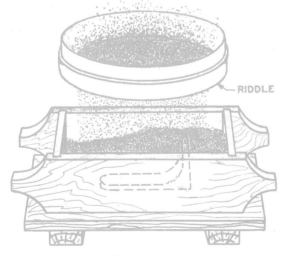

Fig. 809. Riddling Sand Over Pattern

In molding, *tempering* means to mix sand with water to a certain dampness. When the proper amount of moisture has been added, the sand is said to have good temper. It will pack or squeeze in the hand somewhat like snow and break with even, square edges, Fig. 807. Also, the sand will not cling to the hand when pressed into a lump. It will fall away leaving the hand almost clean.

When sand has poor temper it has too little or too much water. If the sand is too dry, some of the sand will be "washed" away from the inside of the mold by the melted metal and the casting will not be the right size. Also, the casting may have some of the washed-away sand imbedded in the metal. If the sand is too damp, the hot metal changes the excess moisture into steam. The steam causes holes in the casting.

Waterless Sand: This is another type of molding sand. It is used to make molds in the same manner as the water-moistened sand in green-sand molding. It is called waterless sand because a special oil and a formulated bonding material is mixed with pure silica sand to hold it together.

Waterless sand has many advantages and some disadvantages for use in schools. It may be used in casting aluminum, magnesium, bronze, and brass. Its advantages include greater precision, less gases formed, the use of finer sands with lower permeability, finer finishes, molds may be set aside for several days without evaporation before pouring the casting, molds may be rammed tighter and with less even pressures, gates may be made smaller, and fewer vent holes and risers are needed in the mold.

Waterless sand must be conditioned and thoroughly mixed in a *mulling machine* before its initial use. If the sand is riddled carefully and turned over frequently with a shovel, it will need to be reconditioned and remulled about once a year for school use. This service may be performed by a nearby foundry or by the dealer. Casting in waterless sand molds requires good ventilation to carry away fumes and odors.

One should follow the manufacturers' recommendations carefully in mixing the ingredients and in mulling waterless sand. Information concerning these materials and procedures is available from many foundry supply dealers.

970. Parting Compound

When packing sand around the pattern to make a mold, the sand sometimes sticks or clings to the pattern. When this happens, it is difficult to remove the pattern from the mold. *Parting compound*, also called *parting sand* or *parting*, is a fine sand or powder used to keep the molding sand from sticking to the pattern. It must be kept dry to work well. *Charcoal dust* or *brick dust* may be used for parting compound. It is usually put into a bag and "dusted on." (See Fig. 816.)

971. Riddle

A *riddle* (See Fig. 809) is like a kitchen flour sieve except that it is larger. It is used to sift sand. It breaks up lumps and leaves the sand "fluffy" so that it will pack properly around the pattern. The *meshes* of some riddles are very fine; others have coarse meshes. Sifting sand with a riddle is called *riddling*.

After using a riddle, it should be cleaned and hung up in a dry place so that the wires will not rust.

972. Mold Vents

Air, steam, and gas must be allowed to escape from the mold. These cause blowhole defects in the casting. *Blowholes* are holes in castings caused by small explosions of steam and hot gases from the molding sand. *Vent holes* are made over the pattern by pushing a wire or rod into the mold. They allow the steam and gases to escape. (See Fig. 819.)

973. Making a Green-Sand Mold, Using a Solid Pattern

Suppose that a mold for a *bookend* with a flat back is to be made. A *solid pattern* (see § 962) is to be used and the flat back of the pattern will be at the *parting line*. (See § 967.) The surfaces of the pattern must be clean, smooth, and dry; otherwise, sand will stick to them. The steps for making a sand mold are as follows:

Step 1: Put the flat side of the pattern, which is also the wider side, on the *molding board*, Fig. 808. Put the *drag* around the pattern with the *pins* pointing down, and shake some *parting* over the pattern. (See § 970.)

Step 2: Set the *riddle* (see § 971) on top of the drag, fill it with sand, and sift the sand over the pattern, Fig. 809, until it is at least 1″ thick. Press the sand around the pattern with the fingers.

Step 3: Dump the rest of the sand that is in the riddle into the drag. Fill the drag with sand until it is piled up in a heap above the drag, Fig. 810. Press the sand down in the drag and around the pattern with the shovel handle and with *rammers*, Fig. 811. The small end of the rammer is the *peen* and the large end is the *butt*. Be careful not to strike the pattern or the edges of the drag.

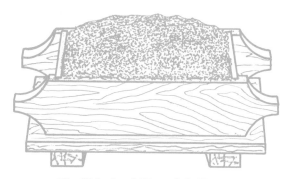

Fig. 810. Sand Heaped in Drag

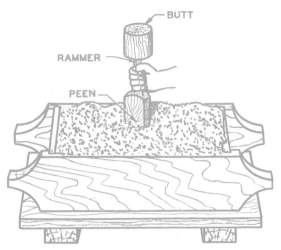

Fig. 811. Ramming

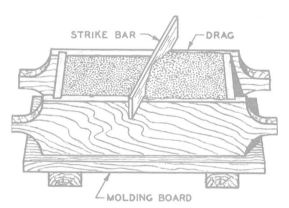

Fig. 812. Striking Off Sand with Strike Bar

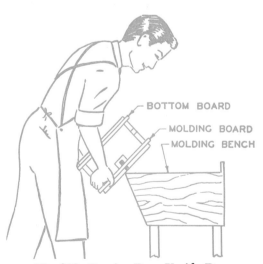

Fig. 813. Turning Drag Upside Down

Step 4: Smooth the top of the mold with a *strike bar,* which is a board or strip of iron with a *straight edge,* Fig. 812.

Step 5: Sprinkle a handful of molding sand over the top, lay the *bottom board* on, and move it back and forth until it rests firmly on the drag.

Step 6: Hold the drag, molding board, and bottom board tightly together at the sides. Slide them to the front of the bench until they begin to drop toward you. At this moment, turn it over to rest on the bottom board, Fig. 813. The pins are now pointed up, the molding board is on top, and the bottom board is at the bottom.

Step 7: Remove the molding board; the flat side of the pattern is now up.

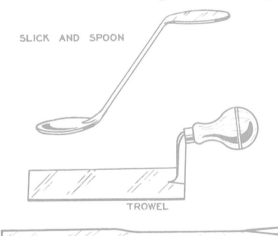

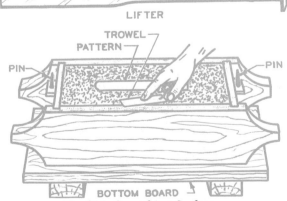

Fig. 814. Smoothing Surface

Make the surface smooth with the *slick, spoon, trowel,* and *lifter,* Fig. 814, and see that the sand is packed around the edges of the pattern.

Step 8: Blow off all loose sand with a *bellows,* Fig. 815. Shake some *parting sand* over the pattern and mold to keep the two halves from sticking together, Fig. 816.

Step 9: Set the *cope* part of the flask on the drag, Fig. 817. Also, set the *sprue pin.* This is a *tapered* wooden or metal pin which is used to make a hole in the cope through which the metal is poured into the mold. Place it on the drag about 1″ from the pattern. The hole is called a *sprue.*

Also set the *riser pin* in place; it is used to make a hole to tell when the mold is full of melted metal. The hole, which is called a *riser,* also allows the air and gases to escape and the dirt from the melted metal to rise; this makes a cleaner casting. The riser should be a little larger than the sprue.

Step 10: Riddle sand into the cope and *ram*

as before. The sand in the cope should not be packed as tightly as in the drag in order to allow the gases to escape more easily.

Step 11: Smooth off the top. Lift out the sprue pin and riser pin. Round off the top of the sprue hole into the shape of a funnel with the fingers, Fig. 818. Make *vents,* which are explained in section 972 and Fig. 819. These holes are made by pushing a $\frac{1}{16}$″ round wire into the mold to about 1″ from the pattern.

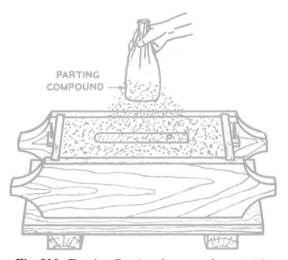

Fig. 816. Dusting Parting Compound on Mold

Fig. 815. Blowing Off Loose Sand with Bellows

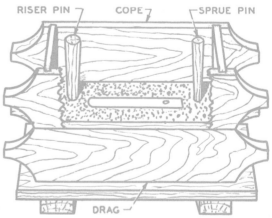

Fig. 817. Cope Set on Drag, Sprue Pin and Riser Pin in Place

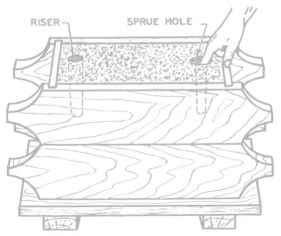

Fig. 818. **Enlarging Top of Sprue**

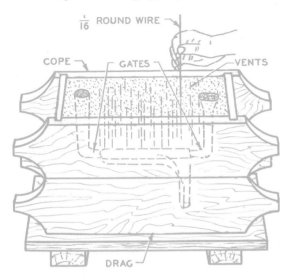

Fig. 819. **Making Vents in Mold**

Fig. 820. **Wetting Edges of Mold with Sponge**

Step 12: Lift the cope off, lay it on its side on the bench, and dampen the edges of the mold next to the pattern with a *sponge*. If a wire or nail is pushed through the sponge, it will keep from dampening the mold too much, Fig. 820. Dampening makes the sand around the pattern firmer so that the pattern can be lifted out without breaking the mold.

Step 13: Lift the pattern out with a *draw* pin, which is a piece of steel with threads on one end; the pin is screwed into a hole in the pattern. The draw pin can be *rapped* lightly on all sides to loosen the pattern, and thus it can be lifted easier, Fig. 821.

Step 14: Cut a small channel, called a *gate*, in the sand of the drag from the hole made by the pattern to the place where the *sprue* is located. It should be almost ¼″ deep and 1″ wide. This may be done with a *gate cutter*, made of 4″ x 4″ *sheet metal* bent into a "U." It should be a little deeper under the sprue than

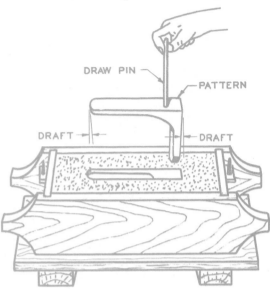

Fig. 821. **Lifting Pattern Out of Mold**

at the other end. Also, cut a gate between the riser and the hole made by the pattern. Patch up small breaks in the mold. Blow off all loose sand with the bellows. Replace the cope on the drag.

Step 15: Place a *flask weight* on top to keep the melted metal from lifting up the sand. All these are clamped together, if necessary, and set on the floor ready to receive the melted metal, Fig. 822.

After the mold is poured and cooled, the casting is removed from the mold. It looks like Fig. 842. The sand from a green-sand mold can be reused if it is reconditioned with more clay, water, and other ingredients. (See § 969.)

974. Making a Sand Mold, Using a Split Pattern

Making a sand mold with a *split pattern*, B in Fig. 823, is the same as explained in section 973, except that a split pattern is made so that one-half of the pattern is set in the drag (see § 967) and the other half is set in the cope. It is easier to remove a split pattern from the mold without breaking the mold.

Fig. 822. Molds Ready for Melted Metal
(Courtesy National Cash Register Co.)

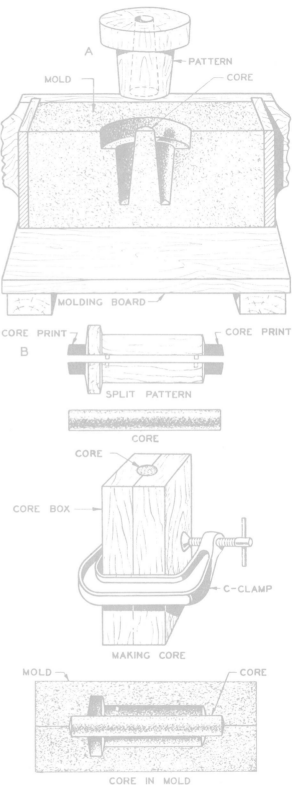

Fig. 823. Cores in Molds

975. What Is a Core?

In molding, a *core* is a separate, hardened sand shape put into a mold to form a hole or hollow in a casting, Fig. 823. This makes the casting lighter and less metal will have to be cut away later. One kind of core may be formed in the mold by simply lifting the hollow pattern out of the mold. (See A in Fig. 823.) The split pattern, B in Fig. 823, is made without a hole. Instead, it has *core prints* on the ends of the pattern that form hollows in the mold for the core. After the pattern is lifted out of the mold, the core is set in place. When melted metal is poured into the mold, it flows around the core, forming a hole in the casting.

A *core box* (Fig. 823) is a wooden or metal mold in which a core is shaped from sand. After removing the core from the core box, it is baked in a *core oven* to make it hard. A person who makes cores is a *coremaker*.

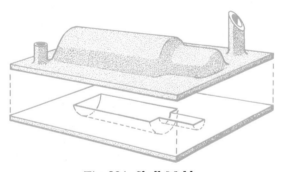

Fig. 824. Shell Mold

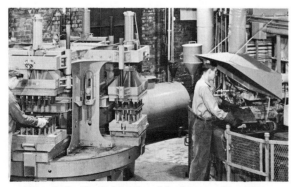

Fig. 825. Shell Molding Machine — Forming Half Shell (right) and Assembling Pairs (left) (Courtesy, Link-Belt Co.)

CO₂ Process: Another type of sand core (used both in schools and in industry) is made by the CO_2 *process* instead of baking it in an oven. Core sand is mixed with a commercial binder designed for use with the CO_2 (carbon dioxide) process. The core sand is pressed or blown into the core box. It is then hardened by blowing CO_2 gas through the sand for several seconds. The core is then ready for use without baking.

976. Dry-Sand Molds

A *dry-sand mold* is stronger than a green sand mold. It will not break as easily and can be handled more readily. It does not have to be used right away and can be stored. The surface of a dry-sand mold is hard and smooth. The sand will not wash away when the hot, melted metal is poured against it as easily as in a green-sand mold.

To make a dry-sand mold, special foundry oils are mixed with sand. These oils coat the the grains of sand and make them stick to each other. The sand is *rammed* into the cope and drag to shape the mold, just as with green sand. The flasks are removed and the mold is baked in an oven at 300° to 600° Fahrenheit. When the mold has finished baking, it is removed from the oven and allowed to cool. The parts of the mold are put together and the mold is ready for the melted metal.

The casting cannot be spoiled by pockets of steam, which can form in a green–sand mold, since there is no moisture in a dry sand mold.

977. Shell Molds

Another type of sand mold, called a *shell mold,* was developed in Germany in the 1940's. A fine powdered *resin*[2] is mixed with dry molding sand. The sand-resin mixture

[2]This *resin* is much the same as one type of those materials generally known as *plastics*. It softens when heated, then hardens with continued heating. Once it has been melted it will not melt again; therefore, this is called a thermosetting resin.

is poured onto a metal pattern that is already heated to 400° to 600° Fahrenheit. While standing on the hot pattern for a short time, the resin melts and coats the grains of sand. The resin is sticky when melted and causes the grains of sand to stick to each other. At the proper time, the pattern is turned upside down and the excess sand mixture falls off. Only ¼" to ½" of the sand-resin mix sticks to the hot pattern. The pattern is turned upright again and then put into an oven to cure (allow the resin to harden). When the sand mold is removed from the oven, it is hard and thin, thereby the name *shell* mold, Fig. 824.

The shell mold is usually made in two halves, Fig. 825. When the halves are put together, and the complete shell supported in a bed of sand, melted metal can be poured into the mold. Castings made in a shell mold are smooth and require less machining than castings made from a green-sand mold. Shell molds are being used more and more where accuracy and good finish on castings are important. The sand from shell molds cannot be easily reused.

978. Metal Molds

Metal molds are also used to make some castings. One kind of metal mold is called a *permanent mold*. Another kind is called a *die mold*. Unlike sand molds, metal molds can be used over and over again. Also, there is no sand to handle and no mold gases caused by the binder in the sand.

The *cavity* of any mold is the hole inside the mold that is to shape the melted metal into a casting. A pattern is used to make the cavity in a sand mold.

The cavity of a metal mold, however, is not made from a pattern, like a sand mold. Instead, the cavity must be cut (machined) into the metal with metal-cutting tools.

979. Permanent Molds

The *permanent mold*[3] is usually made from iron or steel. The cavity of the mold is cut (machined) into the metal. (See Fig 831.) Since the permanent mold cannot be destroyed to get the casting out, like the sand mold, only simple shapes can be made from the permanent mold.

Each time melted metal is poured into the permanent mold, it "washes" a little bit of the mold away and the mold becomes slightly larger. When the castings made from this mold become too large, the mold must be thrown away and a new one made to replace it.

The surface of castings made from permanent molds is very smooth.

The molds used to make the toy soldiers and cowboys in Fig. 833 are permanent molds.

980. Die Molds

A *die mold* is a metal mold. It is like a permanent mold except that the metal is forced into the cavity under pressure. The metal is said to be *injected* into the mold. Casting by forcing melted metal into a die mold is called die-casting. The casting made by this method is also called a *die casting*.

Zinc, lead, tin, aluminum, and their alloys are metals commonly used in die-casting. Metals that melt at higher temperatures, like iron and steel, cannot be die-cast easily.

A die mold is used with a machine that can hold the die and force the melted metal into the die, Fig. 826. The machine is called a *die-casting machine*, Fig. 827. Both the mold and the machine are very expensive. This expense is justified, however, when many die castings are to be made.

After being taken from the mold, the die casting needs very little work to make it a finished casting. (See § *1000.*) Often, only trimming the flash (see § *1000*) and buffing are required. Many die castings are plated with nickel and chrome.

---

[3]*Permanent molds* are usually made from metal, but not always. They are called metal molds here to simplify the classification of molds. For special reasons, permanent molds are occasionally cut from nonmetals like block graphite.

Much hardware is made by die-casting. Automobile door handles and hood ornaments, kitchen cabinet handles, and some lamp bases are examples of die castings.

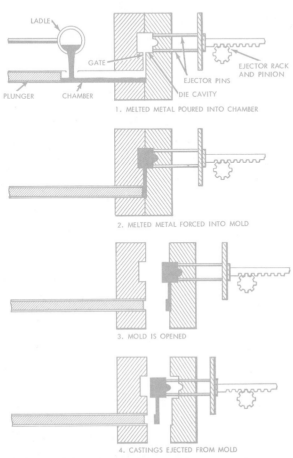

Fig. 826. **Die-Casting Process**

Fig. 827. Crane Setting a Die for Aluminum Die Casting (Courtesy Aluminum Co. of America)

981. Special Molds

Other kinds of molds are made for special purposes, but not used as much as sand and metal molds. Two important special molds are *investment molds* and *plaster molds*.

982. Investment Molds

Most molds are made from a pattern that has positive draft (see § 963) so that it can be withdrawn from the mold. An *investment mold* is made from a wax pattern. The wax pattern does not have to be tapered because it is melted out of the mold after the mold is made. Therefore, almost any shape of casting can be made from an investment mold. Often, some parts of the wax pattern have straight sides or sides that have negative draft.

Fig. 828 shows how to make an investment mold. A wax pattern is molded or cut with a warm knife. The pattern is put into a steel flask that looks like a can with its top and bottom removed. A slurry (watery paste) of *silica*[4] and hardener is poured around the wax pattern. The flask is put on a vibrating table which packs the slurry against the wax pattern and removes bubbles of air. Then it is set aside to dry and harden.

Several hours before the mold is to be used, it is turned upside down in a furnace and heated to about 1500° Fahrenheit. The wax melts and runs out, leaving the shape of the wax pattern in the mold. Because the wax is melted out of the mold, the mold is sometimes called a lost-wax mold and the process called the *lost-wax process*.

Investment mold comes from an old English word, "invest," meaning to enclose or surround. Thus, the wax pattern is *invested* in a slurry of silica.

The investment mold makes a casting that is very accurate and has a fine, smooth sur-

[4] *Silica* is silicon and oxygen combined. It is called silicon dioxide by the chemist. Silicon dioxide is found almost everywhere as sand, quartz, flint, etc. It is used to make molds because it melts at a high temperature and does not change shape or crack when heated. A slurry of silica handles and pours like newly mixed cement.

face. Since the mold is used while still hot from the furnace, it does not chill or cool the melted metal quickly. Therefore, the melted metal can flow into fine cracks and very thin parts of the mold before it becomes solid.

Industry uses investment molds to make castings of many sizes and shapes.

The dentist casts gold into investment molds to make fillings and other parts for teeth.

The jeweler uses investment molds to cast gold, silver, and platinum into rings, bracelets, pins, trophies, and parts for jewelry.

983. Plaster Molds

Plaster molds are sometimes used to make castings from alloys (see § 343) of copper, aluminum, and other metals that melt at low temperatures (400° to 1700° Fahrenheit). Since they are easy to make, plaster molds are especially useful when only a few castings are to be made, Fig 829.

The plaster is made by mixing water with plaster-of-paris.[5] The mixture is a thick, creamy paste that stirs and pours like hot, cooked breakfast cereal. The wet plaster is poured over a pattern and set aside to harden.

[5]*Plaster-of-paris* is soft, white powder like flour. It makes a paste when mixed with water. When allowed to stand in the air, the paste sets (dries) quickly and becomes hard. It is called plaster-of-paris because it was first mined near Paris, France.

Fig. 829. (Top) Pouring Plaster into Core and (Bottom) Assembling Plaster Cores for Casting an Aluminum Tire Tread Mold (Courtesy Aluminum Co. of America)

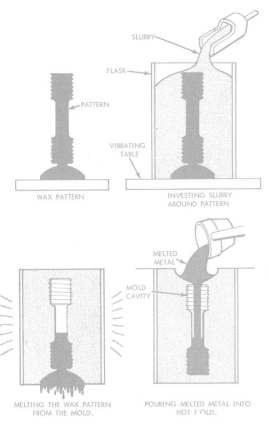

Fig. 828. Making and Pouring an Investment Mold

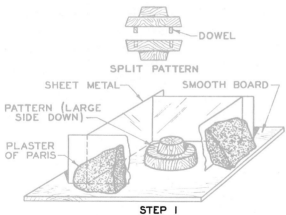

DOWEL

SPLIT PATTERN

SHEET METAL

PATTERN (LARGE
SIDE DOWN)

SMOOTH BOARD

PLASTER
OF PARIS

STEP 1
LAY PATTERN ON BOARD AND FORM A BOX

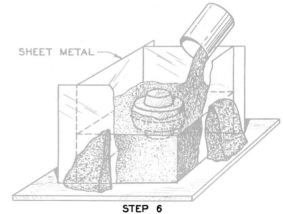

SHEET METAL

STEP 6
PLACE WHOLE PATTERN IN MOLD, BUILD
HIGHER BOX, AND FILL WITH PLASTER OF PARIS

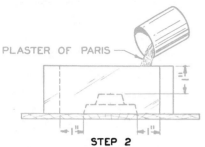

PLASTER OF PARIS

STEP 2
POUR PLASTER OF PARIS INTO MOLD

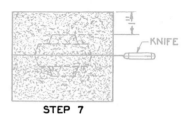

KNIFE

STEP 7
REMOVE BOX AND SEPARATE HALVES

STEP 3
REMOVE SIDES AND SLIDE MOLD OFF BOARD

STEP 4
TURN MOLD UPSIDE DOWN, LIFT PATTERN
OUT, AND REPAIR MOLD

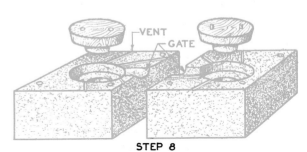

VENT

GATE

STEP 8
REMOVE PATTERN, REPAIR MOLD, CUT GATE,
AND MAKE VENTS

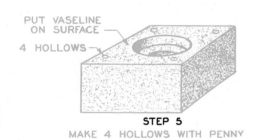

PUT VASELINE
ON SURFACE

4 HOLLOWS

STEP 5
MAKE 4 HOLLOWS WITH PENNY

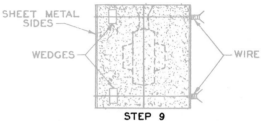

SHEET METAL
SIDES

WEDGES

WIRE

STEP 9
MOLD READY FOR MELTED METAL
(BE SURE THAT THE PLASTER OF PARIS IS DRY
BEFORE POURING THE METAL IN)

Fig. 830. Making Plaster of Paris Mold

The pattern is then taken out of the mold. The mold must be thoroughly dried before melted metal is poured into it. Otherwise, the moisture will turn into steam that cannot get out of the mold. When this happens, the casting will have holes or a rough surface.

Wood patterns can be used to make plaster molds, but they are not as good as patterns made from metal or plastic. Wood patterns will absorb moisture and swell.

Castings made from plaster molds have a very smooth surface. The sculptor uses plaster molds to cast bronze into statues and fine ornamental work. Special foundries also use plaster molds.

984. Making a Plaster of Paris Mold

The steps for making a plaster-of-paris mold, as shown in Fig. 830, are as follows:

Step 1: Place one half of the *split pattern* (see § 974) on a smooth board; the larger side of the pattern must be against the board, and the smaller side must be upward so that when the mold is afterward turned upside down, the pattern can be lifted out of the mold. Form a sheet metal box around the pattern, leaving about 1″ between the sides of the pattern and the box. The sides of the box should also be about 1″ higher than the pattern.

Step 2: Make a paste by mixing water and plaster-of-paris. Pour this paste into the mold until it is filled.

Step 3: After the plaster has hardened enough to stand alone, remove the sides of the box and slide the mold carefully off the board.

Step 4: Turn the mold upside down. Lift the pattern out and make small repairs with wet plaster.

Step 5: Make four hollows near the corners in the top of the wet mold with a penny. Half of the mold is thus finished. Put *vaseline* on the surface of the mold; it will keep the two halves of the mold from sticking together.

Step 6: Place the whole pattern in the mold. Build a box against the sides of the mold; again the sides should be about 1″ higher than the pattern. Pour plaster-of-paris into it, thus forming the other half of the mold.

Step 7: After the plaster has hardened, remove the sides of the box and with a thin knife carefully separate the two halves.

Step 8: Remove the pattern and make any necessary repairs to the mold. Cut the *gate* which is the hole through which the hot metal is to be poured; it is sometimes called a *sprue*. Also, make the *vents* (see § 972) with the point of a pin to allow the trapped air to escape from the mold.

Step 9: The mold must be well dried; pouring hot metal into a wet mold will cause an explosion. Put the mold together and replace the sheet metal sides and fasten the wires and wedges. The mold is now ready for the melted metal.

Review Questions

1. What is a mold?
2. What is a pattern?
3. Name some materials that are used to make patterns.
4. What is draft?
5. What is shrinkage? How does the patternmaker allow for shrinkage?
6. Make a list of the different kinds of molds.
7. What is bench molding?
8. What are flasks?
9. Name the materials used to make green sand.

10. Why is green sand called green?

11. What does sand temper mean?

12. Why is parting compound used in molds?

13. What is a riddle?

14. Why are molds vented?

15. What does ramming mean?

16. Why are cores used in molds?

17. What advantages do dry-sand molds have over green-sand molds?

18. Explain shell molding.

19. What is a permanent mold?

20. What is die-casting?

21. Describe how investment molds are made.

22. Describe how plaster molds are made.

Coordination

Words to Know

back draft	bench molding
bellows	blowholes

bottom board	parting compound
cavity	parting line
CO_2 process	pattern
cope	permanent mold
core box	plaster mold
core oven	positive draft
core prints	ram
die casting	resin
die mold	reverse draft
draft	riddle
drag	riser
draw pin	shell mold
dry-sand mold	shrink
flask	shrink rule
gate	slick
gate cutter	solid pattern
green-sand mold	split pattern
investment mold	sponge
lost-wax process	spoon
mesh	sprue
metal pattern	sprue pin
metal pattern-	strike bar
maker	taper
mold	temper
molding	trowel
molding board	vent holes
molding sand	waterless sand
mulling machine	wax pattern
negative draft	zero draft

Fig. 831. Aluminum Being Cast in a Large Permanent Mold (Courtesy Aluminum Co. of America)

Mathematics

1. 250 pounds of dry sand are to be mixed to make green–sand molds. If the moisture content of the sand is to be 3%, how many pounds of water must be added?

Occupational Information

1. Arrange a field trip through a foundry.

2. Write a report on the ingredients used to make green sand.

3. What kind of machines are used to test the quality of sand?

4. Make a list of occupations and industries which might mold and cast metal.

5. Make a list of the kinds of molds used in making type and printing plates.

Casting

990. What Is a Casting?

To *cast* means to pour melted metal into a mold (see § 961) to form it into a shape. On cooling, the metal becomes solid and takes the shape of the mold. The object made by this method is called a *casting*.

After the casting is removed from the mold, it is called a *raw casting*. It needs cleaning and finishing before it is a *finished casting*. (See § 1000.)

991. Who Makes Castings?

A person who casts, makes castings, or does casting is a *caster* or *founder*. They are described in Unit 2. The founder works in a foundry. A *foundry* is a place that has the equipment to melt metal and make molds. The products of a foundry are castings.

The dentist casts gold into molds for fillings for teeth. Many of the jeweler's wares are made by casting. The modelmaker sometimes makes metal models by casting them. The sculptor casts statues and other fine ornamental work.

992. Why Cast?

The casting process is used to shape metal because the casting is almost the finished size and shape when it is removed from the mold. There is little metal wasted. Often, very little finish machining is required to make the casting into the final product. Holes and other shapes can also be put into the casting that would be very difficult to form otherwise. Look at the lead castings (toy soldiers and cowboys) in Fig. 833. Many hours of work would be required to make these shapes by cutting them from a solid block of metal.

In the school shop, a number of castings can be easily made by using an existing model as a pattern, see § 962. In the foundry, thousands of pieces can be cast from a single pattern.

993. Casting Lead

Lead (see § 375) is a good metal to use to practice casting. It can be melted over the ordinary gas flame at the low temperature of 621° F. The proper pouring temperature of lead can be quickly learned by trial and error. If the melted metal became solid (or *frozen*) before it completely filled the mold, it was poured too cold. If this happens, the workman knows that, for the next pouring, the melted metal must be heated to a higher temperature.

A thin scum forms over the surface of melted lead (and most other metals). With practice, the melter can judge the temperature of the melted lead by scraping away the scum and looking at the clean metal. Lead that is too cold to pour has a dull appearance. As the melted lead becomes hotter, the metal under the scum becomes bright and shiny.

Fig. 833 shows melted lead being poured into a metal mold (see § 978). Section *687* tells how to cast a lead hammer using a *combination hammer mold.*

994. Melting Furnaces

There are several kinds of furnaces for melting metals. Some foundries make many large castings and so must have large furnaces. One kind, a cupola, is used in an *iron foundry* (a foundry that specializes in making castings from iron). The cupola (see § *300*) is like a blast furnace (see § *299* and Fig. 260), but it is smaller. Other foundries specialize in making castings from other metals and use furnaces suitable for those metals.

In small foundries and in the school shop where only a little casting is done, a *gas-fired furnace*, like the one shown in Fig. 834, might be used. With this type of furnace, natural or manufactured gas[1] and air are mixed and burned inside the furnace. The hot gases flow around a pot containing the metal to be melted. A gas furnace of this type is good for melting such metals as lead, brass, aluminum, and zinc, which can be cast at relatively low temperatures.

Where higher temperatures are needed to melt metal, electricity is sometimes used. One

---

[1] Natural gas is found in the earth, usually in areas which also have oil wells. Manufactured gas is made from coal, coke, or petroleum products.

Fig. 834. Gas-Fired Furnace with Ultraviolet Safety System and Automatic Spark Ignition (Courtesy McEnglevan Heat Treating and Mfg. Co.)

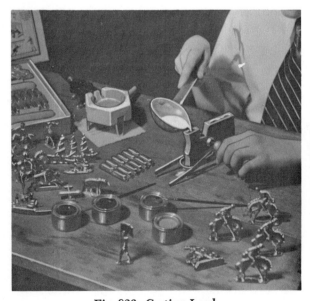

Fig. 833. Casting Lead

type of electric furnace is called an *arc furnace*. (See Fig. 835.) It operates, in principle, like a giant electric arc welding machine. Inside the furnace, electricity is made to jump from a rod made of carbon, called an "electrode," and through an air space, called "the gap." When the electricity jumps this gap, an arc is made which gives off a brilliant white light and large amounts of heat. (See §§ 896-899.) The heat is used to melt the metal.

995. Clothing for Melting and Pouring

Without the proper clothing, melting and pouring can be dangerous. Metal may be spilled from the ladle. Also, gas pockets in the mold and moisture in the ladle or mold can cause explosions. These explosions can spray melted metal and cause body burns and injury to the eyes.

A cap, goggles, heavy leather or asbestos apron, asbestos leggings which cover the shoes, and heavy asbestos gloves should be worn to guard against these dangers. (See Fig. 836.)

996. Melting Metal

Put pieces of the kind of metal to be cast into the furnace. Before starting the furnace make a check of what will be needed.

First of all, be sure the mold will be finished when the metal is melted and ready for pouring. Place the mold near the melting furnace so that the melted metal can be poured quickly and will not have to be carried far. See that there is a clear path from the furnace to the mold. There should be nothing to stumble over or bump into while carrying the hot metal.

Some means to measure or gage the temperature of the melted metal should be available. An instrument that measures the temperature of melted metal is called a *pyrometer*, Fig. 843. *Pyro* means heat; thus a pyrometer

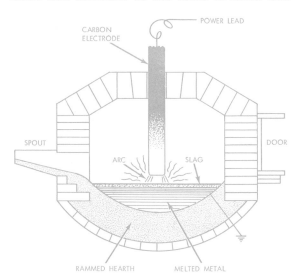

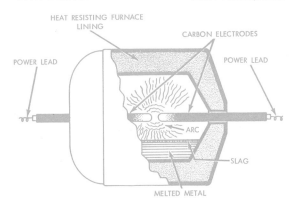

Above: Direct Arc   **Below: Indirect Arc**

Fig. 835. Two Types of Electric Arc Furnace —
Direct and Indirect Arc

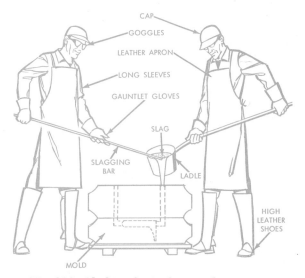

Fig. 836. Clothing for Melting and Pouring

is a heat or temperature meter. There is a number of kinds of pyrometers used. Your instructor will show you how to determine the temperature of the metal.

Get a metal bar at least 3′ long to use as a *slagging bar*. The *slagging bar* is used to keep slag from running into the mold while the metal is being poured. (See Fig. 836.) *Slag* is a waste material that floats on the melted metal. It contains impurities from the pieces of metal that were put into the furnace to be melted. These impurities are sand, scale, and dirt. The slag also includes the metal that has combined with oxygen and nitrogen from the surrounding air during melting. Slag looks like scum and has a dull appearance. It acts like a blanket and keeps more of the melted metal from com-

Fig. 837. Molten Aluminum Being Moved Directly from Nearby Reduction Plant to Foundry (Courtesy Reynolds Metals Co.)

Fig. 838. Hand Pouring Aluminum into a Sand Mold (Courtesy Aluminum Co. of America)

bining with the oxygen and nitrogen in the air. It must not be poured into the mold. It can be scooped off the top of the melted metal before pouring, or held in the ladle with the slagging bar.

997. Pouring Temperature and Superheat

If melted metal is poured into the mold before it has reached the proper temperature it may solidify before it has completely filled the mold cavity. When this happens the metal is said to have been "poured cold." This is more likely to happen with molds that have thin or small sections through which melted metal must flow to fill the mold. On the other hand, if the metal is heated above the proper temperature, time and heat are wasted, the mold is more likely to be damaged when the metal is poured, and the metal becomes more dangerous to handle.

The proper temperature to pour metal is called the *pouring temperature*. The pouring temperature depends on the kind of metal being used, the shape of the mold, and how many molds are to be poured. If several molds are to be poured, the melted metal may be hot enough for the first molds, but too cold for the last mold. If the last mold is poured cold, it will "freeze off"; and the mold will be wasted.

The pouring temperature of a metal is often given in terms of its *superheat* or *degrees of superheat*. Superheat is the number of degrees above the melting temperature. For example, aluminum melts at 1218° F. If it is poured into the mold when it reaches 1418° F., it is said to have 200° of superheat.

998. The Ladle

A *ladle* is used to transfer melted metal from the furnace to the mold and to pour the melted metal into the mold. Some ladles look like big water dippers. (See Fig. 836.) Unlike a water dipper, care must be used to keep the ladle free from moisture. If there is water or moisture in the ladle, it will suddenly turn to steam when melted metal touches it. When moisture *flashes* to steam in the presence of melted metal, an explosion results and the melted metal splatters. The proper clothing should always be worn by the melter and pourer.

Sometimes the ladle is heated separately in an oven or with a gas flame. This is done to dry out the ladle and be sure all moisture is driven away. Heating the ladle also reduces the amount the melted metal will cool as it is poured from the furnace into the ladle.

Fig. 839. Sewing Machine Castings Move on Conveyor into Cooling Tunnel (Courtesy Link-Belt Co.)

999. Pouring the Mold

Before the melted metal reaches the pouring temperature, it should be decided who will read the pyrometer (to know when the pouring temperature is reached), who will operate the furnace and turn it off, who will handle the ladle, and who will direct the pourer.

When the melted metal reaches the pouring temperature, the furnace is shut off and the metal is poured from the furnace into the ladle. The pourer will be wearing goggles and may not be able to see well after watching the hot metal being poured from the furnace. The person directing the pouring, therefore, should "talk" the pourer over to the mold. Since there may be more than one mold, point to the pouring cup of the mold to be poured first. The pourer should pour the melted metal smoothly and steadily, keeping the *pouring cup* of the mold full. The stream of metal should be continuous and uninterrupted until the mold is full. The pourer can tell when the mold is almost full by watching the metal fill up the *riser* of the mold.

During the pouring someone should keep the slag in the ladle with the slagging bar (see Fig. 836) so the slag will not run into the mold and cause a defect in the casting. It is a good idea to take temperature readings while the metal is in the ladle, just before

Fig. 840. Automatic Casting Shake-out from Conveyor Trucks (Courtesy Link-Belt Co.)

Fig. 841. Castings Emerging after being Cleaned by Tumbling (Courtesy Link-Belt Co.)

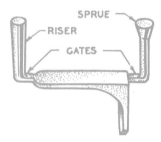

Fig. 842. Castings as Taken from Mold

pouring, and during the pouring. Several persons should be waiting with shovels of sand to throw on any melted metal that spills on the floor. Also, there are often special tasks that come up that these persons can do. Should the mold break and the melted metal run out onto the floor (called a *runout*) enough sand should be on hand to cover all the metal that was in the mold.

1000. Cleaning and Finishing the Casting

After the mold has cooled so that it can be handled with gloves and *tongs* (see Fig. 747), it can be broken apart and the casting removed. This is called the *shakeout operation*. In large foundries, the mold is put on a vibrating conveyor. The sand falls through the conveyor leaving the casting on the conveyor, Fig. 840.

When the casting has been shaken out of the mold, it still has much sand and dirt clinging to it. Before the casting can be machined, the sand must be removed or the cutting tools will become dull very quickly. This is called the *cleaning operation*. Several methods are used to clean castings. Among them are *sand blasting, shot blasting*, and *tumbling*.

In sand blasting, sand is blown at high speed against the casting. The sand, dirt, and scale on the casting are rubbed and blown away.

In shot blasting, pieces of metal about the size of an air rifle BB, called *shot*, are hurled against the casting. Again, the sand, dirt, and scale on the casting are rubbed and blown away.

In tumbling, the castings if they are small, are put into large, metal barrels and the barrel is turned and tumbled. The castings knock against and rub each other removing the sand, dirt, and scale, Fig. 841.

Before the casting is a *finished casting*, the *sprues, gates,* and *risers* (see Fig. 842) are sawed off or knocked off with a sledge. Also, the *flash*[2] and sharp edges that occur at the parting line (see Fig 806 and § 967) must be removed with a grinder or file. The casting is now a finished casting. It is ready for machining.

Review Questions

1. What is a casting?
2. How is a casting made?
3. What is a foundry?
4. List some advantages that casting has over other ways to shape metal.
5. What is a cupola?
6. What is a **gas-fired furnace**?
7. What is an electric arc furnace?
8. Why should special clothing be worn when melting metal and pouring metal?
9. What is slag? How is it useful?
10. Why is it important to pour melted metal at the proper temperature?
11. What is superheat?
12. What is a ladle? Why should it be kept dry?
13. Describe how the pourer should fill a mold with melted metal.
14. What is a runout?
15. What is the shakeout?
16. How can castings be cleaned?
17. How is a raw casting made into a finished casting?

[2] A small open crack occurs at the parting plane of a mold because the cope and drag do not fit together perfectly. When the mold is poured, melted metal fills the open crack. As the metal becomes solid, a thin, sharp edge of metal *flash* occurs all around the casting at the parting plane.

Coordination

Words to Know

arc furnace	pouring cup
cast	pouring temperature
caster	pyrometer
casting	raw casting
clean casting	riser
cupola	runout
finished casting	sand blasting
flash	shakeout
founder	shot blasting
foundry	slag
frozen metal	slagging bar
gas-fired furnace	sprue
gate	superheat
iron foundry	tongs
ladle	tumbling

Mathematics

1. Seventeen pounds of sand are used in a mold to make a casting that weighs 5 pounds. How much sand must a foundry handle to make 600 castings? What is the weight ratio of casting to mold?

2. A certain casting is 30″ long at room temperature (70° F.). How long will it be when it is heated to 1270° F. if it enlarges $\frac{1}{16}$″ per foot for each 100° of heating?

Occupational Information

1. Write a short report on furnaces used to melt metal.

2. Describe different kinds of pyrometers.

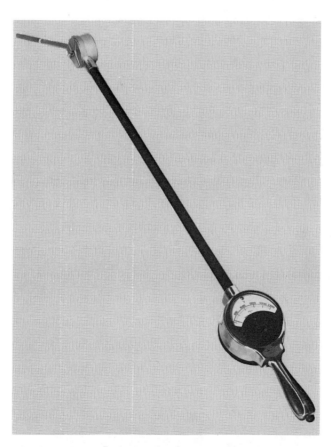

Fig. 843. Portable Lance Pyrometer for Measuring Temperature of Molten Nonferrous Metals

Using a Small Grinding Wheel
on a Flexible Shaft
(Courtesy Aluminum Company of America)

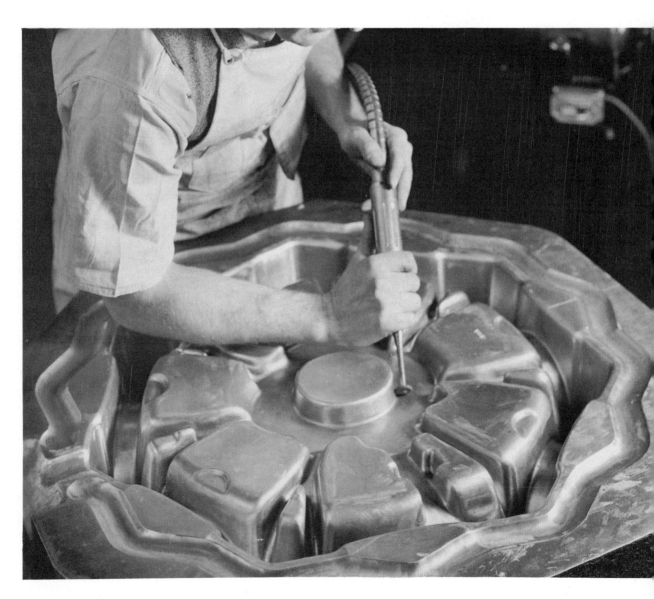

Regrinding the Flutes
of a Tap
on a Universal Tool
and Cutter Grinder
(Courtesy Norton Co.)

Tool Sharpening

Part X

Fig. 844. Common Types of Tool Grinding Wheels
(Courtesy Norton Co.)

Grinding Wheels

1006. What Does Grinding Mean?

Grinding means polishing or cutting metal with an *abrasive* (see § 278). Some abrasives are made into stones and wheels. Many interesting booklets about grinding, abrasives, and *grinding wheels* are published by the makers of grinding wheels.

1007. Reasons for Grinding

Cutting tools must be harder than the material to be cut. Hardened steels that are as hard or harder than cutting tools must be ground to shape. Grinding is done to:

(1) Remove metal from work that is oversize.

(2) Make *cutting edges* on chisels and other cutting tools.

(3) Make points, as on prick punches or scribers.

(4) Make smooth, polished surfaces.

1008. Abrasives

Grinding is done with grinding wheels which are made from grains of hard material called *abrasive*. (See § 278.) Most grinding wheels are manufactured from two kinds of artificial abrasive materials:

(1) Aluminum oxide (see § 279).

(2) Silicon carbide (see § 279).

The properties and kinds of abrasives used in manufacturing grinding wheels and the materials which may be ground with each kind of abrasive are explained in section 280. If

you have not read these sections, you should read them before studying this unit further.

1009. How Does a Grinding Wheel Cut?

The *grinding wheel* is made of abrasive grains which have small cutting edges and points. Examine any grinding wheel with a magnifying glass and you will discover many small cutting edges just like the teeth of a file. Thus, the grinding wheel is a *cutting tool*. The *cutting edge* on each grain *cuts* a tiny chip from the metal. These chips are very small indeed, but the wheel turns at a high speed and many small cutting edges cut many small chips in a very short time; thus, much metal is cut away quickly.

1010. Grain Sizes of Abrasives

The beginner should study the *grain sizes* of abrasives. All grinding abrasives are first crushed and ground, then passed through sieves of different mesh size and graded accordingly. The grains are numbered according to their sizes, Fig. 849. The grain sizes of abrasives are explained in section 282.

1011. Bonds

The bond is the cement which binds or holds the abrasive grains together in the form of a grinding wheel, Figs. 844 and 845. Several different kinds of bonding materials are used in manufacturing grinding wheels. The basic kinds of bonding materials are:

397

vitrified

silicate[1]

rubber

rubber reinforced

resinoid

resinoid reinforced

shellac

oxychloride

A number of additional bonding materials which are modifications or combinations of the above bonding materials are also available. The type of bonding material used in a grinding wheel is identified by a code letter or letters, see Fig. 849.

The best bond is one which is not softened by heat when grinding and which holds the cutting points of the abrasive until they are dull. The dull grains are then pulled away from the bond because more pressure is used

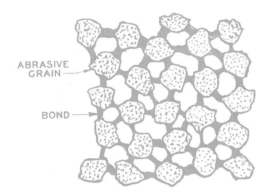

Fig. 845. Grains Held Together by Bond (Enlarged)

Fig. 846. Cutting Off the End of a Drill with an Elastic Grinding Wheel (Courtesy Norton Co.)

to grind, and new, sharp points are uncovered to begin cutting.

1012. How Grinding Wheels Are Made

A grinding wheel is made of abrasive grains cemented or *bonded* together to form a wheel. It is then baked, Figs. 844, 845. Such wheels are called *abrasive wheels*. Three common methods of manufacture produce:

(1) Vitrified wheels.

(2) Silicate wheels.

(3) Elastic wheels.

1013. Vitrified Wheels

To *vitrify* means to make glassy by burning. The *bond* used in vitrified wheels is a kind of earth or clay. The wheels are baked in an electric furnace at about 3000° F. for about 100 hours. Most wheels are made this way. They have large pores, cut easily, and do not *glaze* (see § 1053) easily when grinding is done. Heat, cold, water, oil, or acids do not hurt them. About 75% of all grinding wheels produced are the vitrified or modified-vitrified types. These wheels, however, are not *elastic* (see § 345); thin wheels made this way break very easily. Vitrified wheels are made up to 36″ in diameter.

1014. Silicate Wheels (Semivitrified)

The bond of silicate wheels is *silicate* or water-glass bond. The manufacturing time is less and a thinner-sized wheel can be constructed as compared to the vitrified process. Hard silicate wheels are used for grinding fine edges on tools and knives. They are not recommended for rough grinding. Silicate wheels are made up to 60″ in diameter.

1015. Elastic Wheels

The bond of elastic wheels is *rubber, shellac* (see § 61), or *Bakelite.* (See § 443.) Very thin, strong wheels are made this way. They can be run faster than vitrified wheels. Elastic

[1]*Silicate bond*, also known as *water-glass bond*, is made by melting sand, charcoal, and soda.

wheels can be made as thin as ¼₄″ and are used for sharpening saws, grinding in narrow spaces, making narrow cuts, and cutting off metal, Fig. 846.

1016. Grades of Wheels

Grinding wheels are available in a variety of grades ranging from soft to hard. On a soft wheel, the dull grains are released or torn off the wheel easily while grinding. On a hard wheel, the grains are held tightly and do not tear off easily. Hence the *grade* of a grinding wheel refers to the looseness or tightness with which the abrasive grains are held together.

Softer grades of grinding wheels are generally used for grinding very hard materials, such as hardened tool steel. The abrasive grains dull more easily on hard materials, and they must, therefore, be torn away more easily. When they tear away, new sharp grains are exposed. Harder grades are used for grinding softer materials. Hence, the terms *hard* or *soft*, as related to the *grade* of grinding wheels, have no relationship to the abrasive grain itself. One kind of abrasive grain, such as aluminum oxide, may be used to manufacture either hard-, medium-, or soft-grade grinding wheels. With any given bonding material, it is the amount of bonding material which determines the grade. The grade of a grinding wheel is identified by a letter of the alphabet as shown in Fig. 849.

1017. Structure of Wheels

The structure of a grinding wheel refers to the spacing between the abrasive grains. Some wheels have abrasive grains which are more *dense* or closely spaced. *Open-grain* wheels have grains spaced farther apart or less dense. Open-grain wheels grind more rapidly than close-grain wheels. Manufacturers identify the structure of grinding wheels by a number from 1 to 15. The number 1 is most dense while the number 15 is the least dense, see Fig. 849.

1018. Shapes of Grinding Wheels

Grinding wheels are made in a wide variety of shapes chosen by the Grinding Wheel Manufacturers Association of the United States and Canada. Their names describe their shapes. Some common shapes are shown in Fig. 847.

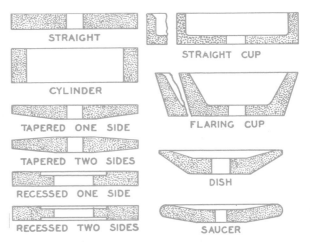

Fig. 847. Grinding Wheel Shapes

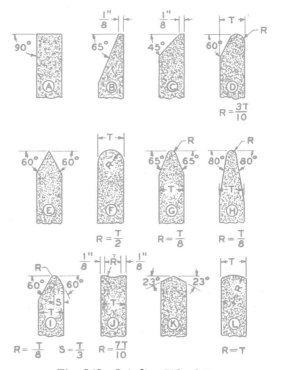

Fig. 848. Grinding Wheel Faces

1019. Wheel Faces

The shapes of grinding wheel faces are indicated by letters, Fig. 848.

1020. Wheel Holes

The hole in a grinding wheel should be about .002″ larger than the diameter of the *shaft*. (See § 261 and Fig. 858.) This allows the wheel to slide freely but not loosely on the shaft. If the hole is so small that the wheel has to be forced on the shaft, there is danger of the wheel cracking.

1021. Wheels for Different Kinds of Work

All materials cannot be ground equally well with one and the same wheel. The shape of the work and the kind of metal determine the *cutting edge* needed on the grinding wheel. Therefore, different *grain sizes* and *grades* of wheels are recommended for the various kinds of work. It is best to refer to manufacturers' catalogs for the kind of wheel to use. Recommended grinding wheels for various kinds of grinding operations, on various types of materials, are also listed in handbooks for machinists.

1022. Grinding Wheel Marking System

A standard marking system is now used by most grinding wheel manufacturers for identifying the following characteristics of grinding wheels, as shown in Fig. 849:

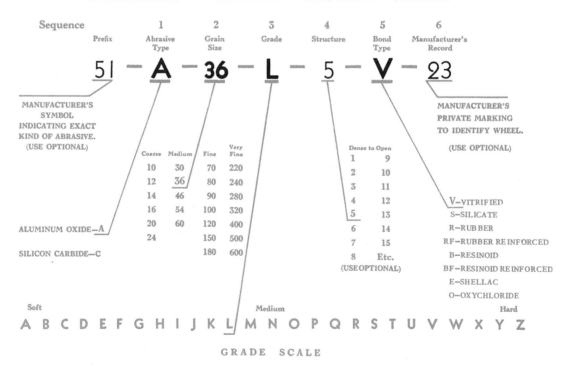

STANDARD MARKING SYSTEM CHART

*Extracted from American Standard (ASA B5.17-1958), with permission of the publisher, the American Society of Mechanical Engineers, 29 West 39th Street, New York 18, New York

Fig. 849. Standard Marking System Used for Identifying Grinding Wheels and Other Bonded Abrasives

1. Abrasive type.
2. Grain size.
3. Grade.
4. Structure.
5. Bond type.

The characteristics of a grinding wheel identified with the code number, 51A36-L5V23, is shown in Fig. 849. The information in the code number is listed in the following sequence:

1. Prefix: Manufacturer's symbol to indicate the exact kind of abrasive. (This is optional and may not be given.)
2. Abrasive type: by letters A or C.
3. Grain size: by grain-size number.
4. Grade: by code letter from A to Z.
5. Structure: by code number from 1 to 15.
6. Bond-type: by code letter.
7. Suffix: Manufacturer's private code to identify the wheel (optional).

1023. Ordering Grinding Wheels

Selection

The following factors must be considered in recommending or selecting a grinding wheel for a specific job:

(1) Type of grinding operation: hand grinding, surface grinding, tool grinding, cylindrical grinding, etc.
(2) Material to be ground: steel, cast iron carbide tools, etc.
(3) Amount of stock to be ground: heavy or light rate of stock removal.
(4) Quality of finish desired: rough or smooth finish.
(5) Area of wheel contact: a wheel with a wide face may require a softer grade.
(6) Wheel speed: wheel must be rated at or above the maximum rpm of the grinding machine.
(7) Whether grinding is done dry or with a cutting fluid.
(8) Abrasive type, grain size, grade, structure, and bond type.

Ordering the Wheel

When ordering a grinding wheel, always provide the following information:

(1) Shape of wheel
(2) Type of wheel face
(3) Diameter of wheel
(4) Width (or thickness) of wheel
(5) Diameter of hole
(6) Speed (rpm) of machine
(7) Identify the following information by using the standard marking system, Fig. 849:

   a. Abrasive-type: Use a prefix number if desired.
   b. Grain size.
   c. Grade.
   d. Structure.
   e. Bond-type.
   f. May specify the manufacturer's record number if desired.

Review Questions

1. What does grinding mean?
2. What are the reasons for grinding?
3. What is an abrasive?
4. Name some abrasives.
5. How is the grain size of an abrasive measured?
6. What is the bond of a grinding wheel?
7. Name the kinds of bonding materials used in grinding wheels.
8. What does vitrify mean?
9. What is meant by the grade of a grinding wheel?
10. How does a grinding wheel cut?
11. What should be the relation between the size of the hole in the grinding wheel and the diameter of the shaft?
12. What is meant by the structure of a grinding wheel?
13. List several common shapes of grinding wheels.
14. Where can you find a list of recommended kinds of grinding wheels for different grinding jobs?

15. Explain the kind of standard marking system which is now used by most grinding wheel manufacturers to identify grinding wheels.

16. Make out an order for a grinding wheel for your shop.

Coordination

Words to Know

bond	medium
elastic wheel	soft
grade	grinding wheel
hard	semivitrified wheel

shape	straight cup
cylinder	tapered one side
dish	tapered two sides
flaring cup	silicate bond
recessed one side	vitrified wheel
recessed two sides	wheel face
saucer	wheel hole
straight	

Occupational Information

1. Describe the manufacture of grinding wheels.

2. Describe the measuring of grain sizes of abrasives.

Hand Grinders

1026. What Is a Hand Grinder?

A hand grinder, called *grinder* for short, is a machine that has one or two grinding wheels on a shaft; it is run by a hand crank or an electric motor. The work is either held in the hand and pressed against the wheel or a machine with a wheel fastened to it is held by hand and moved over the work. A hand grinder is used to sharpen tools such as chisels, drills, scribers, and punches or to remove the roughness from a piece of metal.

1027. Portable Hand Grinder

The portable hand grinder, Fig. 854, is a small grinder which can be clamped to a

table or bench. Power is supplied by turning a crank by hand. A set of gears drives the wheel. This grinder is useful around the home for light grinding, Fig 855.

1028. Portable Electric Grinder

The portable electric grinder is a small grinder which can be taken from job to job, Fig. 856. It can be connected to any electric light socket. The grinder is held in the hands and moved over the work.

1029. Bench Grinder

A bench grinder, Fig 857, is a small grinder which can be bolted to the top of a bench. It usually has a wheel on each end of a *shaft* which extends through an *electric motor*.

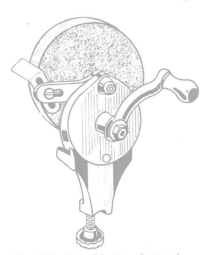

Fig. 854. Portable Hand Grinder

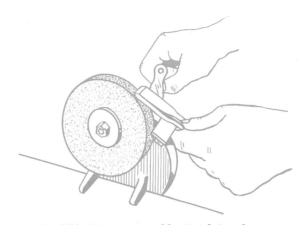

Fig. 855. Using a Portable Hand Grinder

This grinder is used to grind tools and for general light grinding.

1030. Pedestal Grinder

A pedestal grinder or *floor-type grinder* is shown in Fig. 858. It usually has a grinding wheel on each end of a *shaft* which extends through an *electric motor*. This grinder is used for sharpening tools and for other general grinding.

1031. Wet Grinder

The wet grinder, Fig. 862, has a pump to supply a flow of water or *coolant* to the wheel. (See § *1044*.) The water runs back into the tank and is used over and over again. It car-

ries off the heat caused by grinding and washes away bits of metal and abrasive. If not carried away, these bits of metal would fill up the pores of the wheel and cause what is known as a *loaded wheel*. (See § *1053*.)

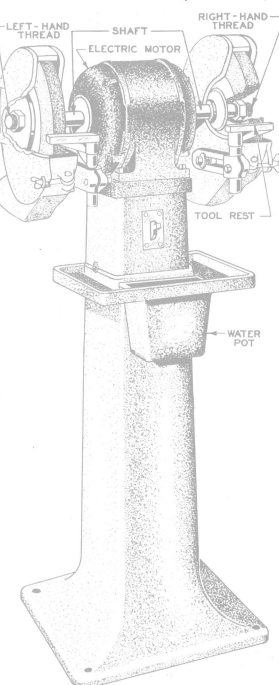

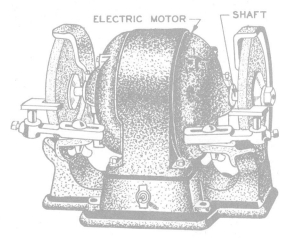

Fig. 856. Using Portable Electric Grinder to Smooth a Weld on a Truck Chassis (Courtesy *Today*, **International Harvester Co.)**

Fig. 857. Bench Grinder

Fig. 858. Pedestal Grinder

1032. Foundation of Grinder

A grinder should be bolted tightly to the bench, floor, or to something solid so that it does not shake.

1033. Why Do Wheels Break?

Many grinding wheels break because of:
(1) Flaws in the wheel (see § 1038).
(2) Wrong placing and fastening of the wheel on the shaft (see §§ 1019, 1035-1037, and 1039-1040).
(3) Too much speed (see § 1045).
(4) Work getting caught (see Fig. 860).

1034. Wheel Guards

The operator is protected from flying pieces by a *wheel guard* that nearly surrounds the wheel, Fig. 860. Just enough of an opening is left to do the grinding.

Proper wheel guards give complete protection against broken grinding wheels. In a series of tests, not once did a piece of the wheel leave the guard in a manner that could

Fig. 860. Wheel Guards Protect Against Danger from Broken Grinding Wheels
(Courtesy Norton Co.)

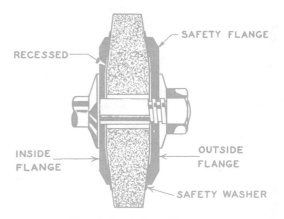

Fig. 861. Safety Flanges

have caused injury to the operator, Fig. 860. The wheels in the tests were broken by dropping a steel *wedge* between the *tool rest* (see § 1041) and the wheel. This is one of the most common causes of accidents.

1035. Safety Flanges

Safety flanges are large metal washers, Fig. 861, placed on each side of the grinding wheel. They clamp the wheel in place on the shaft and also hold the parts of the wheel together if it breaks, Fig. 862 and 863. They should be at least one-third of the diameter of the wheel; one-half is better. The flanges should be *recessed*; that is, the side that fits against the wheel should be cut deeper in the

Fig. 859. Wet Grinder

middle so that only the outer edge presses against the wheel. The *inside flange* should be *keyed* (see § 753) or otherwise fastened to the shaft.

1036. Safety Washers

Soft washers made of blotting paper, leather, or rubber should be placed between the wheel and the *flanges.* (See § 1035 and Fig. 863.) These washers should be a little larger

Fig. 862. Flanges Hold Broken Parts of the Grinding Wheel Together (Courtesy Norton Co.)

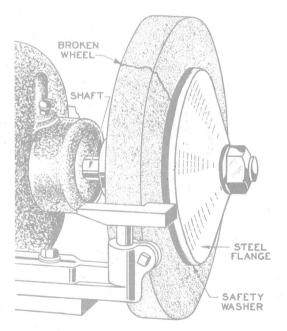

Fig. 863. Broken Wheel Held Together by Safety Washers and Flanges

than the flanges. The soft material is forced into the pores of the wheel, thus locking the wheel in place.

1037. Threads on Grinder Shaft

The ends of the *grinder shaft* on which the wheels are fastened are always *threaded* so that the *nuts* which tighten the wheels to the shaft will tighten as the shaft turns. For this reason, the left side of the grinder has *left-hand threads* on the shaft and nut while the right side of the grinder has *right-hand threads* on the shaft and nut. (See Fig. 858 and § 604.)

Be careful to turn the nuts in the right direction when removing or replacing them. To remove the nuts, turn them in the direction that the wheels turn when grinding.

1038. Inspecting Grinding Wheels
for Cracks

Before a new wheel is used it should be carefully inspected for cracks. Strike the wheel gently with a light object, such as the handle of a screwdriver for light wheels and a *mallet* (see Fig. 540) for heavy ones. Wheels must be dry and free from the sawdust in which they were packed when they are being tested in this way. The sound will indicate whether the wheel is cracked or not. A good wheel will ring clearly when struck.

1039. Mounting the Grinding Wheel

Grinding wheels sometimes break because of wrong *mounting* (placing and fastening on the shaft). The wheel should not be forced on the shaft as this may cause it to crack. (See § 1020.) *Safety washers* (see § 1036), a little larger than the diameter of the *flanges* (see § 1035), should be placed between the sides of the wheel and the flanges. The nut should be just tight enough to hold the wheel firmly.

1040. Starting New Wheels

After *mounting* a wheel (see § *1039*), stand to one side and let the wheel run at full speed for at least one minute. It should then be *trued* with a *grinding wheel dresser*. (See § *1061*.)

1041. Tool Rest

Every grinder should have a *tool rest* (see Fig. 858) upon which the work is rested while grinding, Fig. 864. (See also Figs. 401 and 881.) The tool rest should be set as close to the wheel as possible without touching it and should just clear the wheel. This is done to keep the work from catching between the wheel and the tool rest. (See Fig. 860.) Most grinding accidents are caused in this way. The tool rest must be moved closer as the wheel wears smaller to keep the proper space. This, however, must be done while the wheel is at a standstill.

1042. Glass Eye Shield

Some grinders have *glass eye shields* through which to look while grinding, Fig.

865. The shield, together with safety goggles, provides safe eye protection.

If a grain of *abrasive* (see § *1008*), which has rough, sharp edges and points, gets into the eye, it often has to be removed by a doctor. The eye may be swollen and very sore after the grain is removed and the worker may not be able to work for several days. (See § *1060*.)

1043. Water Pot

Some grinders have a *water pot* (see Fig. 858). It is filled with water and is used to keep the work cool (by dipping it into water often). If the grinder has no water pot, a small pail filled with water should be kept near the grinder.

1044. Coolant for Grinding

A *coolant* or *cutting compound* keeps the work cool and washes away bits of metal and loose abrasive, leaving the work and wheel clean and free-cutting. (See §§ *406* and *1031*.)

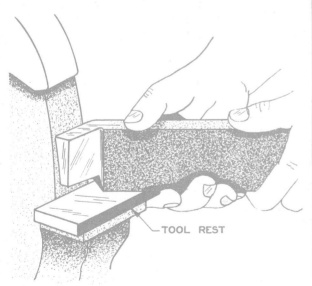

Fig. 864. Use of Tool Rest

Fig. 865. Reinforced Glass Eye Shield for a Grinder
(Courtesy U. S. Electrical Mfg. Co.)

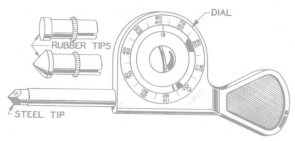

Fig. 866. Speed Indicator

1045. Speeds of Grinding Wheels

Grinding wheels are usually run at a *surface speed* of 4000′ to 6500′ *per minute* (fpm). Surface speed is the speed of the rim of the wheel, the distance it would travel if rolled on the floor for one minute. Note that this is about a mile (5280 feet) a minute or about 33 revolutions per second for a 10″ wheel. The surface speed of the wheel gets slower as the diameter gets smaller. Make sure that the speed of the wheel is right before grinding.

The *revolutions per minute* (rpm) of the wheel may be found with a *speed indicator* (see § *1046*).

1046. Speed Indicator

The *revolutions per minute* (rpm) of a grinding wheel may be found with an instrument called a *speed indicator*, Fig. 866. The point of the instrument is pressed against the *centerdrilled holes* (see § *1191*) in the end of the shaft; the number of revolutions made by the shaft and grinding wheel shows on the *dial* of the indicator, Fig. 867. One hundred revolutions of the shaft make one revolution on the dial. The revolutions per minute can be found by timing with a watch. Rubber tips, which may be used on different shafts, are furnished with the speed indicator.

Review Questions

1. What is a hand grinder?
2. Describe a portable hand grinder.

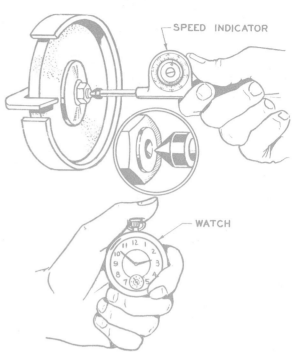

Fig. 867. Finding Speed with Speed Indicator

3. Describe a portable electric grinder.
4. Describe a bench grinder.
5. Describe a pedestal grinder.
6. Describe a wet grinder.
7. What kind of a foundation should a grinder have?
8. Why do grinding wheels break?
9. What is a wheel guard?
10. What is a wheel flange?
11. What is a safety washer?
12. How should a wheel be inspected for cracks?
13. Of what use is the tool rest?
14. How close should the tool rest be to the wheel?
15. What is a grinding wheel coolant?
16. What is meant by surface speed?
17. What is meant by rpm?
18. What is a speed indicator?

Coordination

Words to Know

bench grinder
dial
electric motor
floor-type grinder
glass eye shield
grinding wheel
   dresser
hand grinder
keyed
loaded wheel

mounting
pedestal grinder
portable electric
   grinder
portable hand
   grinder
recessed
revolutions per
   minute
safety flange

safety washer
speed indicator
surface speed
tool rest

trued
water pot
wet grinder
wheel guard

Mathematics

1. What is the surface speed, in feet per minute, of a 10″ grinding wheel at 1800 rpm? (The circumference of a circle is 3.14 times its diameter.)

2. How many rpm's is a 6″ grinding wheel turning if its surface speed is a mile a minute?

Sharpening Tools

1052. Importance of Tool Sharpening

The worker who sharpens tools must use good judgment and possess *skill*. (See § 16.) A *mechanic* is often judged by the way he sharpens his tools. How long a tool will last and the kind of work it will do often depend upon the way it is sharpened.

The grinding wheel must be made ready before a tool can be sharpened.

1053. Loaded and Glazed Wheels

Bits of metal or other materials often fill up and clog the pores of the wheel and form a *loaded* or *glazed*[1] wheel, just as a file becomes clogged with filings, Fig. 873. (See also

Fig. 873. Loaded Grinding Wheel — Before and After Dressing (Courtesy Norton Co.)

§ 254.) This happens when grinding soft materials such as lead, brass, copper, aluminum, rubber, wood, etc. A *loaded wheel* does not cut and must be *dressed* with a *grinding wheel dresser*.

If the wheel glazes or loads often, it is probably too hard for that kind of work. A loaded wheel does not cut and causes unnecessary heat which often *burns the temper* out of a tool. (See § 954.)

1054. Grinding Wheel Dressers

The little cutting edges and points on a grinding wheel are dulled by use and the pores become clogged with bits of metal. Thus the wheel becomes useless until it is sharpened, or *dressed*. A tool known as a *grinding wheel dresser*, Fig. 874, is used for this purpose. There are four kinds of grinding wheel dressers that are commonly used:

(1) *Diamo-carbo dresser.*
(2) *Diamond dresser.*
(3) *Huntington dresser.*
(4) *Abrasive stick.*

These tools remove the old surface of the wheel and make a new surface with new, sharp cutting edges and points.

1055. Diamo-Carbo Dresser

The diamo-carbo dresser is a tube filled with a very hard *abrasive*. (See Fig. 874.)

---

[1]*Glazing* means making a smooth, bright, shiny, and hard surface like glass.

When held against the wheel, it knocks off small bits of the wheel and in this way sharpens it.

1056. Diamond Dresser

The diamond dresser is a *diamond* set in the end of a holder (see Fig. 874). It is the best but the most expensive of all dressers. It lasts much longer than the others and in the long run is the cheapest if it is properly cared for.

1057. Huntington Dresser

The Huntington dresser has a long handle. (See Fig. 874.) One end is shaped like a fork. Between the sides of this fork there are three or four very hard, star-shaped, steel wheels called *cutters*. They turn on a small spindle that extends through the sides of the fork. (See Fig. 876.) When the dresser is held against the grinding wheel, the cutters turn with the grinding wheel and knock off grains of *abrasive*, thus sharpening the wheel.

1058. Dresser Cutters

The star-shaped wheels which are used in *grinding wheel dressers* are made of very hard steel and are called *cutters*, Fig. 876. The points knock off grains of abrasive when the dresser is held against the grinding wheel.

1059. Abrasive Stick

Another way to dress and true a slightly loaded or glazed wheel is with a piece of old grinding wheel or an *abrasive stick*, Fig. 877.

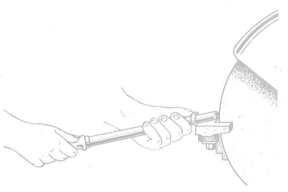

Fig. 875. Dressing and Truing a Grinding Wheel with a Diamo-Carbo Dresser

Fig. 876. Using a Huntington Dresser

Fig. 877. Dressing and Truing Grinding Wheel with an Abrasive Stick (Courtesy Norton Co.)

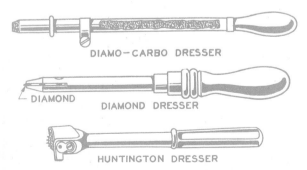

DIAMO-CARBO DRESSER

DIAMOND   DIAMOND DRESSER

HUNTINGTON DRESSER

Fig. 874. Grinding Wheel Dressers

1060. Goggles

Persons working on grinders should wear *goggles* to protect the eyes from flying pieces of metal or grit. (See Fig. 192.) Keep goggles clean. They should fit snugly.

Many people wear eyeglasses while working. Special goggles that fit snugly around the eyes and over the regular glasses should be worn.

Safety glasses that have shatterproof glass, but do not fit properly should not be worn while using the grinder.

1061. Dressing and Truing a Grinding Wheel

When the grinding wheel becomes dull, *loaded* (see § 1053), or out of shape, it must be *dressed* and *trued*. *Dressing* means to sharpen a wheel. *Truing* means to cut the wheel so that there will be no high spots when the wheel is running. Every new wheel should be trued after *mounting*.

Wear *goggles* while dressing or truing a grinding wheel. Dressing or truing is done by moving the *diamo-carbo dresser* or the *diamond dresser* across the face of the wheel as shown in Fig. 875.

It may also be done by moving the *tool rest* (see Fig. 864) away from the wheel, clamping it tightly, and then pressing the *Huntington dresser* (see § 1057) against the grinding wheel as shown in Fig. 876. Every Huntington dresser has a pair of lips which hook over the tool rest to support and guide the dresser. The tool rest should not be too far from the wheel because the dresser may be dragged into the gap between the grinding wheel and the tool rest; this may break the wheel and cause a serious accident. Ask the teacher to show you how to set the tool rest.

The dresser should be moved steadily across the face of the wheel. The appearance of sparks while using the Huntington dresser shows that the teeth of the *dresser cutters* are being ground off. To prevent this, press harder against the face of the wheel. No sparks will appear if the dresser is used correctly.

1062. How to Grind Safely

Wear *goggles* when grinding and grind only on a *guarded wheel* (see § 1033) which is *dressed* and *trued*. The *tool rest* should be as close to the wheel as possible without touching it (see § 1041).

All *cutting tools* should be sharpened *against* the edge. That is, the wheel should turn against the edge of the tool. (See Fig. 881.)

1063. What Does Burning the Temper Mean?

When grinding such tools as chisels, punches, etc., be careful not to *burn* the thin edges or points. The tool is being burnt when it turns to a purple or blue color. Burning a tool causes the steel to lose its *temper*; that is, it loses some of its hardness. Merely grinding off the blue color does not bring back the temper.

Keep the tool cool by dipping it in water often. A *water pot* (see Fig. 858) should be handy for this purpose. The work should be moved across the whole width of the wheel to keep from digging grooves into the wheel and to keep from burning the tool.

1064. Grinding on Sides of the Wheel

All grinding should be done on the face of the wheel. Grinding on the *side* of the wheel spoils its shape and burns the tool quickly. It heats the tool instead of cutting it. Special wheels are made for side grinding.

1065. Grinding High-Speed Steel Tools

Tools made of *high-speed steel* need special care in grinding. (See *high-speed steel* in § 352.) If such a tool is heated by grinding and then dipped in water, it often cracks. Fig. 878 shows a drill that was overheated during grinding and then *chilled* in water that was too cold. Most of the cracks could not be seen until the drill was dipped in acid which ate into the cracks and made them more noticeable. (See § 1129.) A *loaded* or *glazed* wheel will heat the tool quickly and thus help to crack the steel.

Some men think that a fine, hard wheel will last longer than a coarse, soft one. (See §§ 1010-1016.) It will, but they forget that tools cost more than grinding wheels. A coarse, soft wheel will grind the tool with less pressure and with less heat.

The tool can also be kept from heating by continually pouring water on the part of the tool touching the wheel. A *wet grinder* does this to some extent. (See §§ 406 and 1031.) The tool should also be moved back and forth across the *face* of the wheel to prevent overheating.

1066. Hollow Grinding

The hollow or curved-in surface made by the curve of the grinding wheel is called *hollow ground*. The curved sides of a razor are excellent examples of *hollow grinding*, Fig. 879. All *hand tools* and knives should be hollow ground to do their best work (see § 19). The hollow ground surface is made by holding the tool in one position on the grinding wheel, Fig. 880. *Ice skates* should be hollow ground.

1067. Angles of Cutting Edges on Tools, Knives, Etc.

The harder the material to be cut, the larger should be the *angle of the cutting edge;* the softer the material to be cut, the smaller should be the angle of the cutting edge. As examples, compare the *cutting angle* on a *cold chisel* which is used for cutting metal with the angles on a pocket knife or a bread knife which cut softer materials. This rule applies to all cutting and cutting edges.

1068. Sharpening a Cold Chisel

Wear goggles. Hold the chisel in the left hand which should rest on the *tool rest*, Fig. 881. The right hand should hold the head end

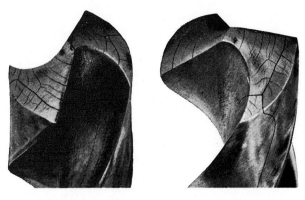

Fig. 878. Cracks in a Steel Drill from Improper Cooling (Courtesy Union Twist Drill Co.)

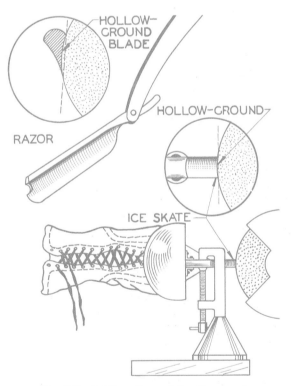

Fig. 879. Hollow-Ground Ice Skate and Sides on Razor

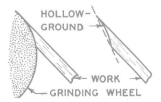

Fig. 880. Hollow-Grinding

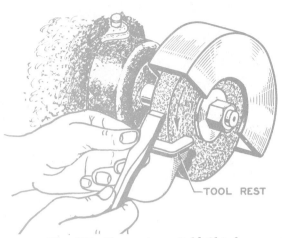

Fig. 881. Sharpening a Cold Chisel

Fig. 882. Oilstone

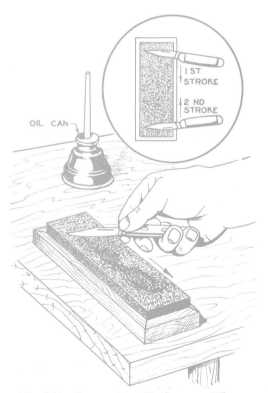

Fig. 883. Sharpening a Knife on an Oilstone

of the chisel and thus guide the cutting edge back and forth slowly and gently over the *face* of the grinding wheel. Use the left hand to hold the tool against the tool rest. Move the cutting edge across the face of the grinding wheel lightly to prevent *burning* which softens the steel.

Keep the chisel cool by dipping it in water often. Examine the chisel often to make sure that the same amount is ground off both sides and that the *cutting angle* is correct. The beginner may use a *center gage* to test the cutting angle. (See Fig. 189.)

1069. Sharpening a Screwdriver

A screwdriver may be ground flat or it may be *hollow ground* and sharpened to a blunt point to fit the slot in the screw as explained in section 689 and Fig. 542.

1070. Drill Sharpening

Some grinders have a *drill grinding attachment* on which drills are sharpened. (See Fig. 402 and Unit 26.)

1071. Snagging

Snagging means the removing of the rough places on *castings* with a grinding wheel. (See § 1000.)

1072. Oilstones

Oilstones, also called *hones*, Fig. 882, are smooth abrasive stones made in many shapes and sizes. They are used for sharpening, chiefly to put the finishing touches on cutting edges of tools, Figs. 883 and 884. When using the oilstone, put oil on it to wash away the bits of metal that are ground off the work.

Oilstones should be kept clean and moist. An oilstone which is kept in a dry place should be kept in a box with a cover; a few drops of clean oil should be left on the stone.

1073. Sharpening Cutting Tools on an Oilstone

The sharpening of *cutting tools* on oilstones is called *honing* or *whetting*. Knives, razors, and wood chisels may be sharpened this way.

The oilstone must lie flat on the bench. Put a few drops of oil on the stone. This will keep the stone from *glazing*. (See § 1053.) All cutting tools should be sharpened with the edge of the tool working against the stone as shown by the arrows in Figs. 883 and 884. Straight strokes as shown by the arrows will sharpen a tool quicker than will circular strokes.

Wipe all oil and grit off the oilstone with a rag when you are finished with it. Dirty oil left on the stone dries and carries the steel dust into the pores of the stone. (See § 1031.)

1074. Sharpening Pointed Tools on an Oilstone

The points of a scriber or a *divider* should be sharpened by rubbing on an oilstone. Both points of the divider should be the same length and should touch each other at the tips, Fig. 885.

1075. Slipstone

A slipstone is a small, wedge-shaped oilstone, Fig. 886. It is used to sharpen cutting edges of irregular shapes which cannot be sharpened on the flat oilstone, Fig. 887.

1076. Steel for Knife Sharpening

Kitchen knives may be sharpened on a *steel*, which is a long, *tapered* rod of steel with a handle on one end, Fig. 888. The cutting edge of the knife should be toward the

handle of the steel. Stroke from the point of the steel toward the handle and from the handle of the knife to the point; first on one side of the steel, then on the other side.

1077. Sharpening Scissors

Scissors may be sharpened with a small *oilstone* or with a fine, *double-cut file*, Fig.

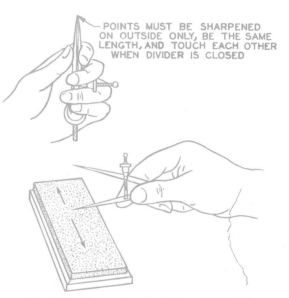

Fig. 885. Sharpening the Points of a Divider

Fig. 886. Slip Stones

Fig. 884. Sharpening a Wood Chisel on an Oilstone

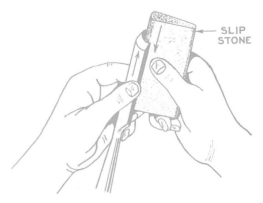

Fig. 887. Using a Slip Stone

889. (See §§ 233-234.) File lightly against the cutting edge of the scissors, beginning at the *heel* of the scissors with the point of the file. After filing, do not close the scissors until the *burr* (see § 262) is removed with an oilstone. (See Fig. 889.)

1078.   Sharpening Scrapers

See sections 262-266.

Review Questions

1. Why is tool sharpening important?
2. What is a loaded wheel?
3. What is a glazed wheel?
4. Describe three grinding wheel dressers.
5. Why should goggles be worn when grinding?
6. What is meant by dressing a wheel?
7. What is meant by truing a wheel?
8. What is meant by burning the temper?
9. How can you avoid burning the temper?
10. Why should wood and soft metals such as lead, copper, and brass not be ground on a grinding wheel?
11. What is meant by hollow grinding?
12. What is meant by snagging?
13. For what are oilstones used?
14. What is a slipstone? For what is it used?

Coordination

Words to Know

abrasive stick	hollow grinding
burning the temper	hone
chill	Huntington dresser
diamo-carbo	knife sharpening
dresser	steel
diamond dresser	oilstone
dresser cutter or	slipstone
cutter	snagging
dressing	tool sharpening
glazed wheel	truing
glazing	whetting

Occupational Information

1. What are some of the dangers when running a grinder?
2. How may grinding cause poor health?
3. In which trades is a knowledge of tool sharpening important? List the tools that are sharpened in each.
4. Describe centerless grinding.

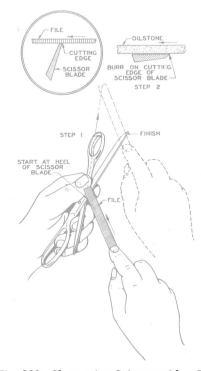

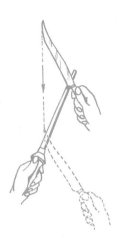

Fig. 888. Using a Knife Sharpening Steel   **Fig. 889. Sharpening Scissors with a File**

Photomicrographs
Photomicrograph of a
Chip Being Cut
by a Grain of a
Grinding Wheel
Diameter of Circle is
.0025")
(Courtesy The
Cincinnati Milling
Machine Co.)

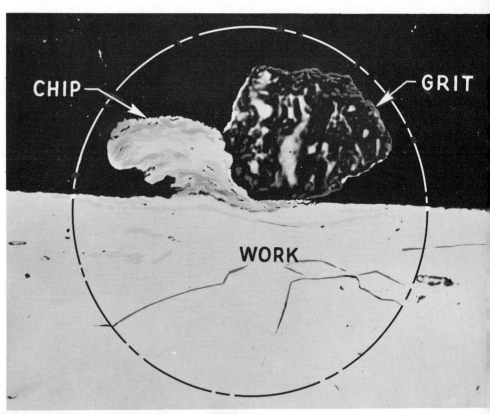

CHIP

GRIT

WORK

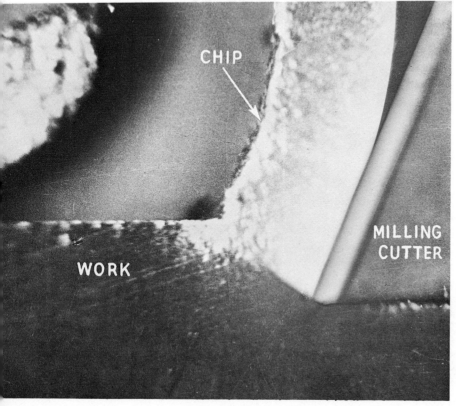

CHIP

WORK

MILLING
CUTTER

Photomicrograph of
Milling Cutter
Making a Chip
(Note the Great
Similarity to the Chip
from a Milling Cutter
and the Chisel in
Fig. 187)
(Courtesy The
Cincinnati Milling
Machine Co.)

417

Inspecting
Tractor Engine
Crankshafts
(Courtesy **Today**,
International Harvester
Co.)

Part *XI*

Finishing and Inspecting

Buffing

1085. What Does Buffing Mean?

Buffing means to polish with a wheel made of cloth or other soft material. Such a wheel is called a *buffing wheel;* it is coated with some kind of polishing material. Buffing gives the metal a bright and shiny surface. (See § 276.)

1086. Buffing Wheels

Buffing is done with wheels made of cloth, felt, or leather. Such wheels are called *buffing wheels,* Fig. 901. Cotton or wool is used for *cloth wheels.* Pieces of cloth are laid one on another until they make up the thickness of the wheel; they are then sewed. *Felt wheels* are made of layers of *felt,* which is wool and hair or fur mixed and pressed together. *Leather wheels* are made of leather from walrus or bull-neck hides. Sheepskin is also used.

Brush wheels are set with *bristles,* thus forming brushes. They are used to polish and finish work and to get various effects in polishing.

1087. Buffing Spindle

The buffing spindle is a *cone-shaped* attachment for the grinder, Fig. 902. It has a *threaded hole* in the large end which is screwed on the end of the grinder shaft. The

Fig. 901. Cloth Buffing Wheel

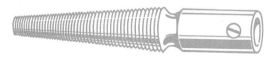

Fig. 902. Buffing Spindle

419

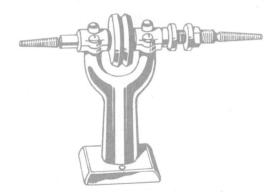

Fig. 903. Polishing Head

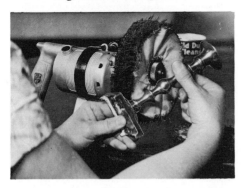

Fig. 904. Buffing (Courtesy Goodell-Pratt Co.)

cone has threads on which to screw the buffing wheel.

1088. Polishing Head

A polishing head looks somewhat like a grinder, Fig. 903. It is run at high speeds and is used for buffing and polishing.

1089. Polishing Compounds

Soft cutting materials are put on buffing wheels for buffing. Some of the cutting materials used are *lime, tripoli,*[1] *crocus* and *rouge,*[2] *emery flour* (see § 282), etc. These are mixed with *tallow* (see § 401) or some other heavy grease and pressed into *cakes*. It is called *polishing compound* or *buffing compound*. Coarse compounds are used for coarse work while fine compounds are used for fine finishing.

[1] *Tripoli* is a weathered, decomposed limestone; also called rottenstone.

[2] *Rouge* is a soft, iron oxide. It comes in different shades of red, the darker the color the harder the rouge; the lighter product is called *rouge* and the darker *crocus.*

Table 33
BUFFING COMPOUNDS AND USES
(See Section 1089)

METAL	COMPOUND	
	ROUGHING	FINISHING
Aluminum	Tripoli	Rouge
Brass	Tripoli	Lime
Copper	Tripoli	Lime
Pewter	Tripoli	Rouge
Steel	400 Silicon Carbide	Rouge

1090. How to Buff

Choose a *polishing compound* according to the kind of finish wanted. (See § *1089.*) Put it on the buffing wheel by holding the cake against the edges of the cloth. It is best to put only a little polishing compound on the wheel at a time. The surface of the buffing wheel thus becomes coated with the compound and is then ready for the buffing.

The work should be held on the underside of the front of the wheel so that if it is pulled out of the hands it will fly *away from the operator,* not toward him, Fig. 904. Again, when the work is held on the underside of the wheel, the dust will also fly away from the operator. The work should also be moved and turned as it is held against the wheel. In this way the cloth rubs every corner and curve of the work.

Change from a wheel with a coarse polishing compound to a wheel with a finer compound until you get the finish you want. If the work comes from the wheel looking greasy and dirty, it means that too much polishing compound has been put on the wheel. Gasoline or benzine will remove most of the grease but hot water and washing soda are better.

Review Questions

1. What is meant by buffing?

2. Of what materials are buffing wheels made?

3. Describe a brush wheel.

4. What is a buffing spindle?

5. For what is a buffing spindle used?

6. What is a polishing head?

7. Name some polishing compounds.

8. How should the work be held when buffing?

9. What is the cause of dirty, greasy looking work that has been buffed? How may it be cleaned?

Coordination

Words to Know

bristle	felt wheel
brush wheel	leather wheel
buffing compound	polishing compound
buffing spindle	polishing head
buffing wheel	rouge
cloth wheel	silicon carbide
emery flour	tripoli

Occupational Information

1. What are the dangers in buffing?

Drawing Tubing — Chain at Left Can Draw 130 Feet (Courtesy Link-Belt Co.)

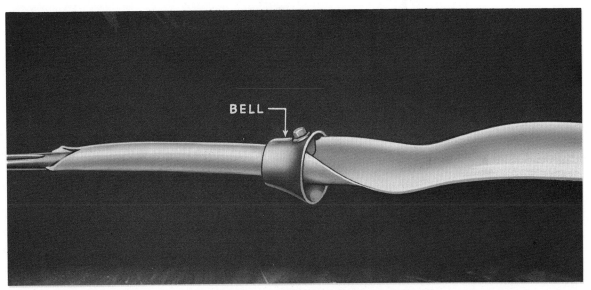

Flat Piece of Steel Passing Through Bell in Which It Is Formed into Pipe
(Courtesy Youngstown Sheet and Tube Co.)

Metal Finishing

1095. What Is Meant by Metal Finishing?

Metal finishing is the last operation or finishing touch that is given to a metal surface to make it look nice, to protect it from rusting, and to make it wear longer. A finish that is lovely to touch and lovely to look at is a beautiful finish. When you see a nicely finished surface, you want to touch it, feel it, look at it. (See § 277.)

A *planed surface* is described in section 90. *Filing* is explained in Unit 15, *drawfiling* in section 250, and *scraping* in sections 260-261. *Frosted, spotted* or *flaked* finishes are explained in sections 264-266, *hand polishing* in Unit 17. *Galvanizing* is described in section 371, *tinplate* in section 376, *bright finish* in section 740, *hammered finishes* and *planishing* in sections 834, 835, and 838. *Grinding* is explained in sections 1006, 1007, and Unit 61, and *buffing* in Unit 52. Other metal finishes are described in this unit.

1096. Cleaning Old and Greasy Metal

Before the metal finishes described in this unit can be used, the metal must be well cleaned.

Rusty metal, which is to be painted, may be cleaned with a wire brush. (See §§ 856 and 1097.) Rust on tools should be removed at once by rubbing with an oily cloth. If rust still remains, rub with a fine abrasive cloth; then wipe thoroughly with an oily cloth again.

Old and dirty metal, covered with hard grease or paint, can be cleaned by boiling it in:

Water .... 1 gal.
Caustic soda[1] or *sal soda*.... ½ gal.

Boil in a cast iron kettle. This is called *pickling*. (See § 330.) If the solution is boiled first and the parts then put into it, they will dry quickly afterward and will not rust. Remove the parts with a piece of wire, pliers, or tongs so that the solution will not get on the fingers; rinse the parts with clean, cold water. The cleaned parts must not be touched with the fingers.

1097. Cleaning Copper or Brass

The darkened surface formed on copper or brass by heating is *oxide*. (See § 856.) Copper may be cleaned by putting it in this *solution*, called a *pickle* (see §§ 330 and 1096):

Water .... 5 parts
Sulfuric acid .... 1 part
(See section 101.)

The acid should be added slowly to the water or an explosion will result. When the work is

[1]*Caustic soda* is lye or sodium hydroxide. Like strong acids (sulfuric, nitric) it is very poisonous. Even small spatters of it causes burns and eats holes in cloth.

bright and clean, wash the acid off in clear water and dry the metal in clean *sawdust*.

Brass may be cleaned the same way, except that *nitric acid* (see section *658*) should be used instead of sulfuric acid.

1098. Cleaning Pewter

Old *pewter* (see § *378*) that looks dull can be made bright and cheerful by washing it in warm, soapy water, then rinsing well in clear water. Articles with a rough finish can be rubbed with fine, wet sand or very fine abrasive cloth, but powdered *pumice*[2] gives a much better finish. This rubbing must be done carefully; always rub in the same direction and along the lines of the object.

The brightness of polished pewter may be preserved by coating it with *clear lacquer;* then it will not need washing or polishing and will not show fingerprints.

1099. Painting

Flat paint, which is paint without *gloss,* is often used to decorate or improve the appearance of metal. It is sold in many colors and may be put on with a brush, or it may be *sprayed* on. (See § *1103.*) If the paint is too thick add a little *turpentine.* (See § *405.*) Read about *red lead* in the next section.

1100. Red Lead Keeps Metal From Rusting

Red lead is made by mixing *oxygen* (see section *321*) with melted *lead.* When cooled it turns to a reddish orange color, hence the name. It is made into a powder. This powder is mixed with *linseed oil* (see § *403*) to make *red lead paint.*

Red lead paint is the best paint for iron, steel, and other metal surfaces; it keeps the metal from rusting. Water does not affect red lead paint. It is used to paint and protect machinery, fire escapes, railroad cars, bridges, metal boats, ships, oil tanks, gas tanks, and the steel in skyscrapers.

Around the home, red lead may be used to paint eave troughs, metal on roofs, metal windows, pipes, iron fences, and railings. Metal surfaces to be painted must be clean, dry and free from rust and grease. Other uses of red lead are explained in sections *268* and *777.*

1101. Enameling

Enamel is paint mixed with *varnish.* It. makes a hard and *glossy* surface when dry. Enamels of many colors for decorating metal are sold. They may be put on with a brush or *sprayed* on. (See § *1103.*)

Quick drying enamels will dry in about four hours. Some enamels can be baked onto the metal, as is the *enamel* on automobiles and many machines.

1102. Lacquering

Lacquering means to put lacquer on something. *Lacquer* is *alcohol* and thin *shellac varnish.* (See footnote, p. 48.) Lacquer is harder and tougher than *enamel.* (See § *1101.*) It keeps metal from rusting. Lacquered metal can be washed without removing any of the lacquer. It must be put on thin or it will look streaky and sticky. Lacquer dries as quickly as the alcohol evaporates and, therefore, must be put on as quickly as possible. Thick lacquer can be thinned with alcohol.

Lacquer catches fire easily and must be kept away from flames. Keep container closed when not in use. *Clear lacquer* or *transparent lacquer* is colorless and consequently the metal underneath can be seen. *Flat lacquer* has no *gloss.* Lacquer is sold in many colors.

Small parts may be coated by dipping them into lacquer. Some lacquer can be put on with a soft *hair brush* and is called *brushing lacquer* while other lacquer is *sprayed* on and is known as *spraying lacquer.* (See § *1103.*)

Banana oil[3] is another type of lacquer.

---

[2] *Pumice* is *lava* which is the scum thrown up by a *volcano.* This scum hardens into a rock which is ground into powder and used for polishing.

[3] *Banana oil* is a kind of lacquer that gets its name from the banana-like odor. It is used for finishing wood and metal.

Fig. 910. Spraying Wheel on Truck Assembly Line (Courtesy *World*, International Harvester Co.)

1103. Spraying

Paint, enamel, or lacquer may be put on metal by spraying with a tool called a *spray gun*, Fig. 910. Automobile bodies and fenders are usually sprayed. If possible, the sprayed surface should be in a vertical position and the spraying should be done back and forth from side to side.

1104. Bronzing

When an article is given a bronze color it is known as *bronzing*. *Bronze powder*, which is powdered *brass* or *bronze* (see §§ 369-370), is often used for bronzing. If the entire surface is to be a bronze color, the bronze powder may be made into a *bronze paint* by mixing it with *banana oil*. The bronze paint can then be put on with a brush.

If the article is to be only partly bronzed, or *spotted*, it can first be coated with paint, enamel, or lacquer. While still sticky, a very small amount of bronzing powder may be dusted on with a pepper shaker or it may be blown on from the end of a screwdriver. Colored bronzing powders can also be bought.

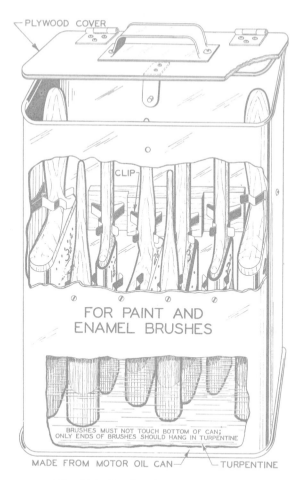

Fig. 911. Brushes Hung in Solvent

1105. "Rusty" Color for Iron and Steel

An object made of iron or steel may be made to look old and rusty. Put on two coats of black *flat paint* (see § 1099). Then give it a coat of shellac and quickly dust *burnt umber*[4] over it freely. Before this is dry, wipe some of the umber and shellac off in places; this will show black metal underneath and the "rusty" metal in the unwiped places.

1106. Keep Brushes Clean

Brushes that are cleaned after each time they are used will give good service. Clean well any brush that will not be used for a

---

[4] *Umber* is a brown earth naturally colored by iron rust; this is *raw umber*. When heated, it turns to a darker, reddish-brown color and is called *burnt umber*. Both are used by artists and for colorings in paints.

long time; then shake it out well, lay it down flat, and let it dry.

A *paint brush* or *enamel brush* may be cleaned in *turpentine.* (See § *405.*) Of course, if it is to be used again the next day, it may be put in a can of turpentine. But it should not rest on its hair, or *bristles.* Drill a hole through the handle, stick a stiff wire through it, and hang the brush in the can so that the bristles do not touch the bottom. Or, a special can may be made as in Fig. 911.

Alcohol will clean a brush that has been used in *shellac.* (See section *61.*) A brush that has been used in *lacquer* (see § *1102*) and is still wet may be cleaned with lacquer thinner. If it is hard, soaking in lacquer thinner will soften it for cleaning.

1107. Hammered Finish

See section *834.*

1108. Green Color for Brass (Antique Finish)

Brass and bronze turn green when left in the air, especially if left in the moisture of salt water. Brass can be given a rust green or *antique*[5] green finish that will make it look as if it were very old. Make a solution of:

Water	1 gallon
Common salt	2 ounces
Household ammonia[6]	4 ounces
Sal ammoniac	2 ounces

(See § *852.*)

Large work can be brushed with the solution. Small work may be dipped into the solution. It may have to be painted or dipped several times to get the desired color. The work may then be *stippled*[7] with a soft, round brush moistened with the solution. It should then be rinsed with clear water, dried, and lacquered. (See § *1102.*)

[5] *Antique* means old, ancient.

[6] *Household ammonia* is ammonia mixed with water, also called *ammonia water, aqua ammonia,* and *ammonium hydroxide* (NH_4OH). It is the common ammonia which your mother uses in washing and cleaning.

[7] *Stipple* means to apply by repeated touches, usually with a straight up-and-down motion.

1109. Antique Green Finish for Copper

You can make copper look very old by placing it in an airtight box in which there is placed a saucer of water and another saucer of *hydrochloric acid.* (See § *852.*) Now and then add small pieces of marble or *chalk*[8] to the acid. The water keeps the air moist; the acid with the marble or chalk forms *carbonic acid gas* which turns the copper to a rich green color in a few days.

Another way to put a green color on copper is to make this solution:

Salt	2 ounces
Vinegar	½ gallon

Let it stand for one day. Then dip the work into the solution or put it on the work with a brush. Let it stand until the next day. Then sprinkle on just enough clear water to moisten the copper.

1110. Coloring Copper

Copper is easier to color than any other metal. It can be colored yellow, brown, red, blue, purple, or black. The beginner can get good results by the method known as *oxidizing.* Make a solution:

Ammonium sulfide	1 ounce
Cold water	1 gallon

The work is dipped into this solution. The color produced depends on the length of time the work is left in the solution. Then dry the work in sawdust and give it a coat of *lacquer* (see § *1102*).

Ammonium sulphide must be handled with great care because it stains the fingers and has a bad odor. It should be kept in a dark bottle with a glass cover. Ammonium sulfide is only good for coloring copper; it is not good for brass. *Potassium sulfide (liver of sulfur)* may be used instead of ammonium sulfide.

[8] *Chalk* is *calcium carbonate* and the chemical is $CaCO_3$. *Blackboard crayon* is usually made of *gypsum* and not of chalk.

1111. Smoke Finish on Iron or Steel

Smoke finish, also called *oil blackening,* is a cheap and simple way of blackening iron or steel. Heat the metal a little and coat it with *lubricating oil.* (See § 394.) Then heat the metal until the oil burns off. The metal will turn to a black color and be protected against rusting. (See § 834.)

1112. Coloring Iron or Steel with Heat

Polished iron or steel can be colored yellow, brown, purple, violet, or blue by cleaning it, then simply heating it until it turns to the desired color, and quickly cooling it by dipping it in oil. Iron or steel can also be given a blue color by heating it in hot sand or wood ashes in an iron container. Look at the pieces now and then until you have obtained the desired color. Then remove and dip in oil.

Another way to color steel a dark blue color is to hold it in melted lead. When using melted lead, wear *goggles* and be sure that the steel and the tools used for handling the steel are dry or an explosion will result.

1113. Wax Finish on Metal

Warm the metal just enough to allow the wax to flow on. Use *beeswax,* if possible. Then let it cool; polish with a soft cloth.

1114. Frosting or Flowering

See section 266.

1115. Spot Finishing

An ornamental finish, called *spotting,* or *spot finishing,* can be put on flat metal surfaces in the following manner: Make a round piece of wood, about ⁵⁄₁₆″ to ½″ in diameter and about 2″ long, to fit the drill chuck in the drill press. Put *abrasive flour* (see § 282) and oil on the surface to be spotted. As the wood spins at highest speed, press lightly on the surface covered with the emery and oil. Round, polished spots are thus made on the surface, Fig. 912.

1116. Burnishing

Burnishing means to make smooth and bright by rubbing with something hard and smooth, without removing any metal; instead, the pressure flattens the points or roughness on the surface.

1117. Electroplating

Electroplating, or *plating* for short, is covering metal with a thin coat or film of another metal by the use of *electricity.* This is done to make the metal look or wear better, or both. If a *direct current* (see § 469) is passed between two *copper plates* which are hung in a *copper sulfate solution* (see § 101), some of the copper is taken off one plate and placed on the other, Fig. 913.

Note that it must be *direct current,* not *alternating current,* because the current must flow only in one direction. The plate from which the metal is removed is called the *anode* and the plate upon which the metal is placed is called the *cathode.*

Metals such as nickel, copper, gold, and silver are used to coat, or plate, cheaper metals. The thickness of the plating depends upon how strong a current is used and how

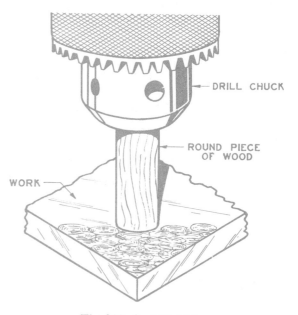

Fig. 912. Spot Finishing

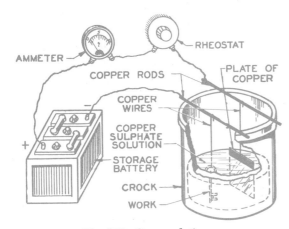

Fig. 913. Copperplating

long the article is left in the solution. (See also *electroplater* in § *19.*)

There are three steps in plating:

(1) Metal must be clean (see § *1096*).
(2) Actual plating is done (see § *1118*).
(3) Final polishing.

1118. Copperplating

Copperplating is the coating of a metal article with *copper*. Read section *1117*. To do good plating, the metal must be very clean and bright. Even handling with the bare hands is enough to spoil its surface for good plating. (See § *1096*.)

A cheap and simple way to copperplate iron and steel is explained in sections *101-102*. This copper coat, however, soon wears off.

The equipment and materials needed for better copperplating in a school shop are:

1 5-gallon *crock* or *polyethylene container.*
2 *dry cells* or 1 *auto battery, battery charger* or *eliminator* (see §§ *465*).
1 small sheet of the purest copper.
1 gallon *copper sulfate solution* (see § *101*).
1 *ammeter* (see § *466*).
1 *rheostat.*[9]

The sheet of copper should be about half again as large in surface area as the article to be plated. (See Fig. 913.) The *positive* (+)

___
[9] A *rheostat* is an instrument for regulating the amount of electricity passing through a circuit.

side of the *dry cells* or *battery* should be connected with copper wire to the sheet of copper. The *negative* (—) side of the dry cells or battery should be connected with copper wire to the object to be plated. Dip the object to be plated and the sheet of copper into the crock of *copper sulfate solution.* Connect an *ammeter* and a *rheostat* in the *circuit* (see § *461*).

The current should be one *ampere* or less. (See § *466*.) If the current is too strong, the deposit will be soft and coarse and will come off. A small current gives a good, hard, fine deposit. Fifteen to twenty minutes is enough for ordinary copperplating. The work should then be washed with clear water, dried in sawdust, polished, and *lacquered* (see § *1102*).

Review Questions

1. What does metal finishing mean?
2. What is meant by pickling?
3. How can old and greasy metal be cleaned?
4. What is flat paint?
5. How can enamel be put on metal?
6. What is lacquer?
7. What is meant by spraying?
8. What does bronzing mean? How is it done?
9. What is meant by antique finish?
10. How is smoke finish put on iron or steel?
11. How can iron or steel be colored brown, purple, or blue?
12. What is meant by spot finishing? How is it done?
13. What is the difference between hand polishing, buffing, and burnishing?
14. What is meant by electroplating?
15. What is meant by copperplating?

Coordination

Words to Know

abrasive flour	ammonium
alcohol	hydroxide
ammonia water	ammonium sulfate

anode
antique finish
aqua ammonia
banana oil
bronze paint
bronze powder
bronzing
brushing lacquer
burnishing
burnt umber
calcium carbonate
carbonic acid gas
cathode
caustic soda
chalk
copperplating
crock
electroplating or
   plating
enamel
flat lacquer

flat paint
glossy
greasy
gypsum
household ammonia
lacquer
lacquering
lava
negative
oxidizing
paintbrush
painting
pickle
positive
potassium sulfate
   or liver of sulfur
quick drying
   enamel
raw umber
red lead paint
rheostat

smoke finish or
   oil blackening
spot finishing
   or spotting
spray gun
spraying
spraying lacquer

stipple
transparent lacquer
umber
varnish
volcano
wax finish

Drafting

1. Design a spray gun for the school shop.

Occupational Information

1. Of what value is electroplating?

2. What are some of the dangers of electroplating in industry?

3. Name and describe some of the occupational diseases related to various kinds of metal finishing. How must these diseases be guarded against?

4. What are the steps in finishing automobile bodies?

Hand Grinding Operation to Dress a Weld on a Dozer Blade on Earth-Moving Equipment (Courtesy International Harvester Co.)

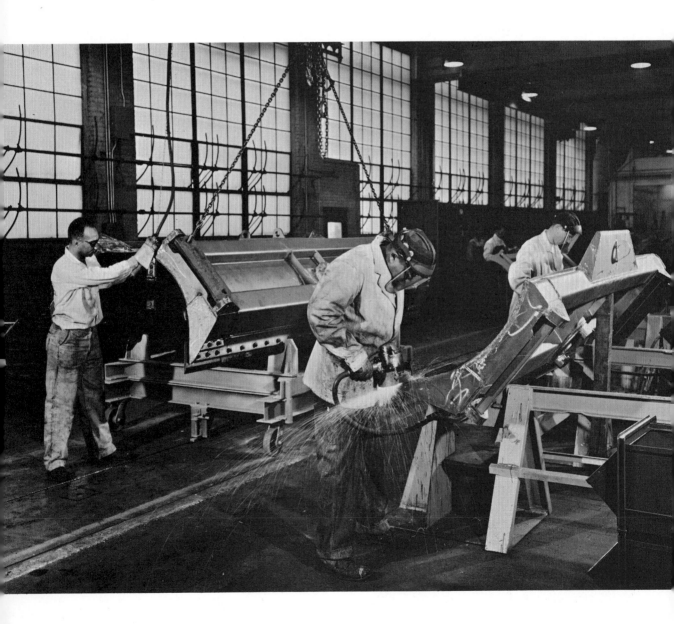

Stamping, Stenciling, and Etching

1125. Reasons for Marking Tools, Materials, and Jobs

Tools often have to be *marked*. Sometimes, the name of the firm or the name or number of the department to which the tool belongs is marked on it. It is often necessary to mark the size and other information on the tool. For example, see the sizes and other information on drills, reamers, taps, threading dies, gages, etc. Materials that are made of metal often have to be marked to tell what kind, grade, or size they are. Manufactured parts are often marked with the name or *trademark* of the manufacturer or with a part number. Watches and cars have *serial numbers*.

Interchangeable manufacture is made easier if the parts are marked or if they have *part numbers*. (See § 1140.)

The name or *initials* and date should be put on each job a pupil makes. These will make the job more valuable in the years to come. Indeed, many such articles are kept from generation to generation. The marking of tools, materials, and jobs is done by *stamping*, *stenciling*, or *etching*; these are explained in this unit.

1126. Steel Letters and Figures

Stamps for stamping letters and numbers are made of steel and are called *steel letters*

and figures, Fig. 918. A letter or number is cut in the end of a piece of steel which is then *hardened and tempered*. (See §§ *951* and *954*.) These stamps come in sets in sizes from $\frac{1}{64}''$ to $1''$. They are used to mark tools, materials, and jobs made of soft steel, copper, brass, aluminum, and other soft metals. Do not use them on *hardened steel*. The cutting tool must be harder than the material to be cut.

1127. Stamping

Use *guide lines* to do a neat job. Fig. 919 shows the layout for $\frac{1}{8}''$ letters and figures.

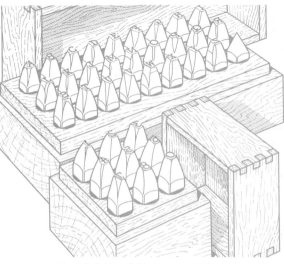

Fig. 918. Steel Letters and Figures

431

The guide lines may be drawn with a pencil. The stamp is held in the left hand and struck with a hammer. Try out the position of the stamp on a wooden block before marking the metal; unless this is done the letter or figure is often stamped upside down on the metal.

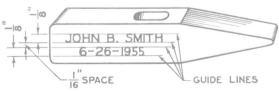
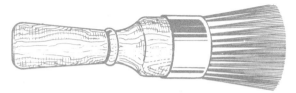

Fig. 919. Use Guide Lines when Stamping

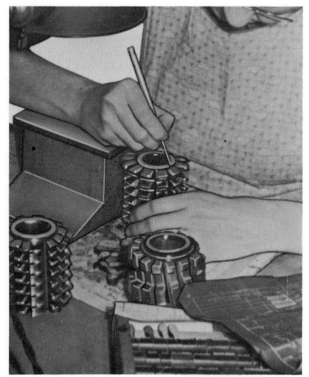

Fig. 920. Stencil Brush

Fig. 921. Scratching Lines for Etching
(Courtesy Barber-Colman Co.)

One part is often lighter than another part after striking the stamp. Carefully reset the stamp, lean it toward the direction where the stamping is lighter, and strike it again. Repeat until you have an evenly stamped marking.

A *prick punch* (see Fig. 41) is often used for marking *periods;* a *cape chisel* (see Fig. 186) is often used for marking *dashes.*

1128. Stencils

A stencil is a thin sheet of metal or a piece of stiff paper in which a figure, letter, or *pattern* is cut. This stencil is laid upon the surface to be marked; color is then rubbed or stripped on with a *stencil brush,* Fig. 920. Thus the figure, letter, or pattern is marked on the surface underneath.

1129. Etching

Etching is a way of marking or decorating by allowing acid to eat into the metal. It is the best way to mark *hardened steel.* (See § 951.) Beautiful designs may be etched on things made of steel, copper, brass, and other metals.

Etching is done as follows:

Step 1: Clean the metal surface.

Step 2: Cover surface with melted *wax* or *asphaltum*[1] and allow to dry.

Step 3: Scratch the lines with a needle or *scriber* (see Fig. 40) so that the metal shows, Fig. 921.

Step 4: Place drops of *hydrochloric acid* (see § 852) or *nitric acid* (see section 658) on the scratched parts with a wooden stick or a *glass dropper.*[2]

Or, if you wish, add one part of *nitric acid* to two parts of water in a crock, and dip the whole article into this solution. Be sure to put the water in the crock first, and then add the

---

[1] *Asphaltum* is a mineral pitch that is black or brown in color. It is another name for *asphalt.*

[2] A *glass dropper* is a glass rod or tube for applying a liquid in drops.

acid; otherwise it will explode. If the solution is too strong, add more water; it is too strong if it bubbles a lot and gives off heavy greenish-yellow fumes. These acids are poisonous. They eat holes in cloth and should, therefore, not be spilled on clothing. The acid eats the metal only where the wax or asphaltum has been removed. After the acid has eaten deep enough, it should be washed off with water. All the remaining wax or asphaltum should then be cleaned off with *gasoline* or *kerosine*. (See §§ *390-391*.)

1130. Electric Marker

The electric marker, Fig. 922, marks tools *electrically*. It may be connected to any electric light socket. The marking is done with a *carbon point*. (See § *319*.) This tool is especially useful for marking *hardened steel*. (See § *951*.)

Review Questions

1. Give the reasons for marking tools, materials and jobs.

2. What are steel letters and figures? For what are they used?

3. How can you avoid marking upside down with steel letters and figures?

4. Should steel letters and figures be used on hardened steel? Why?

5. How can a period be made?

6. How can a dash be made?

7. What is a stencil? How is it used?

8. What is etching?

9. Etching is especially suitable for marking what kind of steel?

10. With what kind of a tool are the lines scratched for etching?

11. Name the acids used for etching.

12. How can the asphaltum be cleaned off after etching?

13. Tell what you know about the electric marking machine.

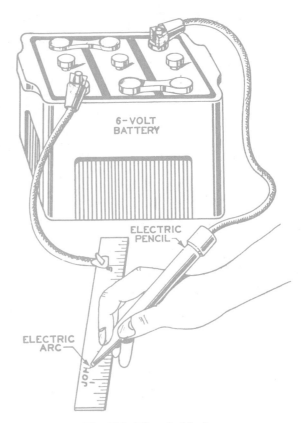

Fig. 922. Electric Marker

Coordination

Words to Know

asphaltum	marking
carbon point	part number
dash	period
electric marker	serial number
etching	stamping
glass dropper	steel letter
guide line	stencil
initial	stencil brush
interchangeable	trademark
manufacture	

Occupational Information

1. Tell about the dangers involved in handling acids.

Quality Control:

Inspection, Measurement, and Gaging Tools

1133. Meaning and Reasons for Inspection

The *quality* of manufactured products is controlled through inspection at various times. *Inspection* is the official checking or examination of materials, parts, or articles at different times while they are being made, or immediately after they are made. The following are thus inspected:

Materials (see § 1134)
Performance (see § 1135)
Finish (see §§ 1095 and 1136)
Measurements (see § 1137)
Interchangeability (see § 1140)

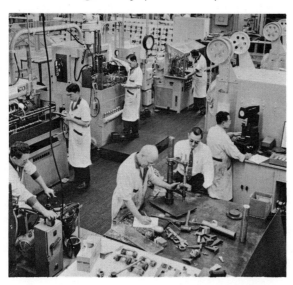

Fig. 924. Inspection Room (Courtesy *Today,* International Harvester Co.)

Parts which do not pass inspection are scrapped. Measuring instruments have to be inspected regularly by *inspectors* in the *inspection department,* Fig. 924. (See *inspector* in § 19.)

1134. Inspecting Materials

Metals, leather, cloth, lumber, paints, and thousands of materials are inspected for strength, appearance, colors, cracks, quality of material, etc. (See § 1038.)

1135. Inspecting Performance

Automobiles are often tested on different kinds of roads, in all kinds of weather, and at different speeds before they are sold to the customer. Such testing is usually called the *final inspection.* All machinery and appliances are given such an inspection.

1136. Inspecting Finish

Metal finishes (see § 1095) are often inspected, Fig. 925. Surfaces which have been cleaned, scraped, polished, or ground are inspected.

1137. Inspecting Measurements

Measurements must be accurate, which means that they must be exact or correct. The measurements on automobile parts, for example, are inspected after every operation during their manufacture.

Fig. 926 shows an automobile *chassis* (pronounced *shassy* or *chassy*) being inspected.

The *surface plate* is 8′ wide, 18′ long and is perfectly level and accurate to within 0.005″ from one end to the other.

1138. Principles of Linear Measurement

Linear measurement means measurement along a straight line, such as the distance between two points or between two surfaces. In the United States, Great Britain, and Canada the *English* system of linear (straight line) measurement generally is used. The standard unit of measurement for the English system is the *inch*. Most other countries use the *metric* system of linear measure. The standard unit of measurement for the metric system is the *meter*. One meter equals 39.37″.

English System

With the English system, the inch is divided into smaller parts for finer measurement. It may be divided into fractional parts such as ½″, ¼″, ⅛″, ¹⁄₁₆″, ¹⁄₃₂″, or ¹⁄₆₄″. It may also be divided into decimal fractions such as 0.1″, 0.01″, and 0.001″. Decimal fractions are expressed in the following manner:

One-tenth inch = 1/10″ = 0.1″
One-hundredth inch = 1/100″ = 0.01″
One-thousandth inch = 1/1000″ = 0.001″
One ten-thousandth inch = 1/10,000″ = 0.0001″
One hundred-thousandth inch = 1/100,000″ = 0.00001″
One-millionth inch = 1/1,000,000″ = 0.000001″
One-millionth inch = 1 microinch

Common fractions also may be expressed as decimal fractions in the following manner:

½″ = 0.500″	¹⁄₁₆″ = 0.0625″
¼″ = 0.250″	¹⁄₃₂″ = 0.03125″
⅛″ = 0.125″	¹⁄₆₄″ = 0.015626″

Metric System

With the metric system, the meter is divided into smaller parts for finer measurements in the following manner:

1 meter = 10 decimeters (dm)
1 decimeter = 10 centimeters (cm)
1 centimeter = 10 millimeters (mm)

Therefore, one decimeter is one-tenth meter, one centimeter is one-hundredth meter, and one millimeter is one-thousandth meter. The metric system also includes units of linear measurement which are larger than the meter.

Fig. 925. Inspecting Finish on Automobile Bumpers
(Courtesy Oldsmobile Div., General Motors Corp.)

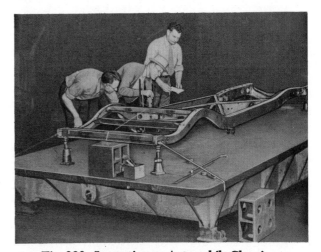

Fig. 926. Inspecting an Automobile Chassis
(See Section 1140)
(Courtesy Pontiac Div., General Motors Corp.)

It is sometimes necessary for mechanics or machinists to convert measurements from the English system to the metric system, or vice versa. Tables for converting measurements from one measuring system to the other are included in handbooks. The following are common metric and inch equivalents:

1 millimeter (mm) = 0.03937079″ (about 1/25″)

10 millimeters = 1 centimeter (cm) = 0.3937079″

10 centimeters = 1 decimeter (dm) = 3.937079″

10 decimeters = 1 meter (m) = 39.37079″

1 inch = 25.4 millimeters (mm)

1 inch = 2.54 centimeters (cm)

1139.   Standards for Measurement

Without a standard for linear (straight line) measurement, parts such as automobile parts could not be produced to fit interchangeably on the same make and model automobile. Replacement parts for the same make and model must fit interchangeably anywhere in the world (see § 1140). A *standard* is necessary so that an inch or a meter is the same length in all parts of the world. (See § 616.)

The International Bureau of Weights and Measures, established in 1875 near Paris, France, represents most nations of the world, including the United States and Canada. It keeps standards for metric measurement, including a standard for the meter. The international standard for the meter is the distance between two finely scribed lines on a platin-iridium alloy metal bar at a temperature of 32° F. (0° centigrade). This metal bar was declared the *International Prototype Meter,* and the various member nations received an exact duplicate copy of it. The United States received its copy in 1889 which is now at the Bureau of Standards at Washington, D. C.

In 1893 the U.S. Bureau of Standards adopted the metric system as a *standard* for

legally defining the pound and the yard. The length of the U.S. yard was defined as $\dfrac{3600}{3937}$ meter. One inch was defined as 2.54 centimeters, exactly. Therefore, the units of linear measurement in the English system are defined in terms of equivalent metric units.

In 1959, the English speaking countries, including the United States, Great Britain, and Canada, accepted the *International Inch* by general agreement, without specific legislation. Before that date, the inch in Great Britain was defined in terms of the British Imperial Yard which was several millionths of a millimeter shorter than the U.S. yard.

The International Bureau of Weights and Measures also defined the length of the meter in terms of light wavelengths. One meter equals 1,650,763.73 wavelengths of orange light emitted by Krypton-86 atoms in an electrical discharge. Since no standard of length is maintained for the English system, the International Inch, as defined in terms of metric units (2.54 centimeters), can be stated in terms of wavelengths of Krypton light as follows:

1″ = 0.0254 meters × 1,650,763.73 wavelengths per meter

1″ = 41,929.3987 wavelengths

1 wavelength = 0.0000238″

Light waves do not vary significantly with temperature changes and changes in atmospheric conditions. Therefore, measurement by this exact method may be duplicated in any part of the world.

Precision *gage blocks,* as shown in Fig. 960, are used as a practical standard for measurement in machine shops and industrial plants the world over. Gage blocks are used for checking the accuracy of many kinds of measuring tools, measuring instruments, and inspection gages. They are also used for making very accurate measurements.

Precision gage blocks are available which are manufactured with tolerances of plus or minus 0.000002″ (2-millionths). In their manufacture, they are measured to light-wave accuracy with optical measuring instruments. Gage blocks are described further in § 1156.

1140. Interchangeability

Automobile parts are often made hundreds and even thousands of miles apart. Bodies are made in one factory, engines in another, wheels in another, tires in another. Spark plugs for the engine are made in one factory, carburetors in another, electrical parts in another, and so on. It is, therefore, necessary to make each part very exactly like the next part. (See § 665.) Fine measuring tools and instruments insure exact measurements when making *interchangeable parts*. (See §§ 27 and 1125.)

Parts of one automobile must fit other automobiles of the same model. Wornout or broken parts of your automobile, washing machine, vacuum sweeper, or typewriter can be replaced by new parts easily even when they are a number of years old. This is made possible by a system of *interchangeable parts*. If a new part fits an old machine, the part is said to be *interchangeable*.

1141. Dimension Limits

Suppose that a dimension on a drawing is 1″. It is impossible to make the size on the object *exactly* 1″. It may be 1″ when measuring with a *steel rule* (see § 103), but when measuring with a *micrometer* (see Figs. 131-132) it would be found that it is a little over or under 1″. Now suppose it is made so that it will be 1″ when measured with a micrometer, which measures to the nearest 0.001 inch. Yet when it is measured with a *vernier micrometer* (see Fig. 139), which measures to the nearest 0.0001 inch, it is again a little over or under 1″ because of finer calibrations to 1/10,000ths.

[1]*Tolerance* comes from the word *tolerate*, to endure, put up with, or to allow a certain amount oversize or undersize.
[2]The *difference* is found by subtraction.

Then suppose again it is made so that it will be 1″ when measured with a vernier micrometer, but when it is measured with a still finer measuring instrument it is found to be a little over or under 1″. Each time that a finer measuring instrument is used, it is found that the dimension is either oversize or undersize instead of being *exactly 1″*. Hence, no two parts can be made *exactly* the same size. For this reason, *working drawings* (see § 27) often give *double dimensions,* Fig. 927. The double dimensions specify the limits of size, including the upper and lower limits.

One dimension is sometimes placed above the other as (A) in Fig. 927. Thus, the article can be made any size between 1.999″ and 2.001″. If the size is under 1.999″ or over 2.001″, the article cannot be used.

Another way is to use a *plus sign* and a *minus sign* as (B) in Fig. 927. Sometimes the plus and minus signs are joined into one sign, as $\pm$. If 0.001″ over or under were allowed, it would appear on the drawing as (C) in Fig. 927.

This small amount oversize and undersize is called the *limit*. (See § 671.) It tells the *mechanic* at the bench or machine and the *inspector* just how exact the dimension on the work must be. Read also section 1144.

1142. Tolerance

Tolerance[1] is the *difference*[2] between the largest and lowest *limits* of a dimension. Thus:

The tolerance of $\dfrac{1.999}{2.001}$ is .002″.

It may be necessary to make the tolerance as small as 0.0001″ or as much as ⅛″, depend-

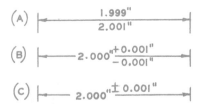

Fig. 927. Dimension Limits
(In each instance the tolerance is 0.002″)

ing on the use of the part. The smaller the tolerance the greater must be the care in making the article and the greater the cost of making it. It is a waste of time, money, tools, and energy to make the tolerance any smaller than necessary.

Also study *allowance* in sections 671 and 1143.

1143.   Allowance

An *allowance* is an intentional difference between the maximum material size limits of mating parts. An allowance may be either positive or it may be negative. A *positive allowance* is the minimum clearance between mating parts, Fig. 928. A *negative allowance* is the maximum interference between mating parts, Fig. 929. A *positive allowance* provides clearance for a running or sliding fit, see Fig.

928. (Also see §§ 667-668.) In Fig. 928, the difference between the maximum material size of the tongue (1.997″) and the maximum material size of the groove (2.000″) provides 0.003″ positive allowance.

A *negative allowance* provides interference between mating parts, thus producing a force fit. Parts which fit together with a force fit must be assembled by driving, pressing, or shrinking them together. (See § 670.) The shaft and hole in Fig. 929 are designed with a negative allowance. This causes interference between the parts, and they must be forced together. The tightest possible fit (shaft size 1.503″ and hole size 1.500″) provides 0.003″ interference. The loosest possible fit (shaft size 1.502″ and hole size 1.501″) provides 0.001″ interference.

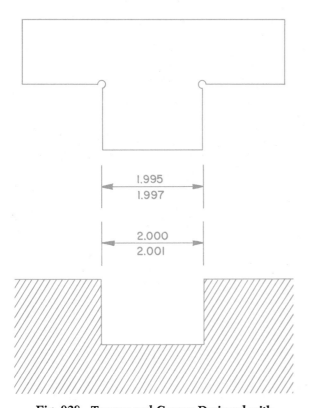

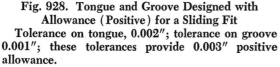

Fig. 928. Tongue and Groove Designed with Allowance (Positive) for a Sliding Fit
Tolerance on tongue, 0.002″; tolerance on groove 0.001″; these tolerances provide 0.003″ positive allowance.

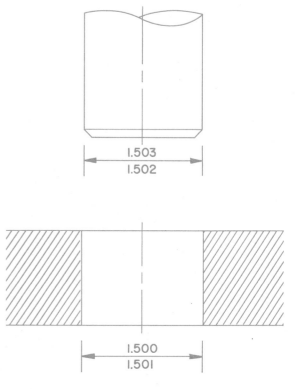

Fig. 929. Shaft and Hole Designed with Allowance (Negative) for Force Fit
Loosest fit is 0.001″ interference; tightest fit is 0.003″ interference.

1144. Gages for Measuring Different Materials

Gaging is done to determine whether a part or piece of material is produced within specified size limits. The primary purpose of gaging is not to determine the actual size of a part but to determine whether the part is inside specified dimension limits. (See § 1141.) The tools, instruments, or devices used to do gaging are called *gages* (also spelled gauge).

In metalwork, a gage is used to test or check one or more dimensions on a manufactured part or piece of material. A *double gage* is used to check two dimensions to see if they are inside dimension limits. A gage such as the *limits snap gage* in Fig. 931 is a double gage. It is used for inspecting the dimension limits of large numbers of parts rapidly. The parts must pass inspection, or they are not accepted.

Any part which can be gaged can also be measured with conventional measuring tools such as micrometers. However, dimension limits on parts may be inspected more rapidly with gages than with conventional measuring tools. Generally, less training and skill are required for inspecting parts or materials with gages, and there is less possibility for human error.

Gage numbers are used to indicate sizes of wires, drill rod (see § 328), small drills (see § 494), *machine screws* (see § 737), wood screws, the wall thicknesses of seamless tubing (see § 780), and the thickness of sheet metal and plates. Each size is given a certain number. (See Figs. 379, 380, 590, and 635.) There are, however, different gages for different materials, and the gage numbers are different for different materials.

Table 34 gives the thicknesses of the gage numbers for different materials. For example, No. 10 sheet steel is 0.1345″ thick, No. 10 sheet copper is .1019″ thick, No. 10 steel wire is .1350″ in diameter, a No. 10 drill is .1935″ in diameter, and a No. 10 machine screw is .1900″ in diameter.

Each *gage system* has a different name. When buying any of these materials, the name or kind of material should be given in addition to the name of the gage, the gage number, and the size in *thousandths of an inch* so that mistakes cannot be made.

1145. Inspection Tools and Gages

At some time, *inspectors* use most of the *layout tools* described in Unit 6 and the micrometers described in Unit 10. Gages of all kinds are used by inspectors to check or examine parts and materials that are being made or that have been finished. (See Figs. 924, 926, 932-942.) Gages are made of hardened steel so that there will be little wear and they will be as accurate as possible.

Many kinds of inspection gages are available for a variety of purposes. Some are designed for general use and can be used for a number of measuring and gaging purposes within a broad range of sizes; some are designed for special gaging purposes within a very narrow size range; while others are designed to gage only one size.

Adjustable-type gages are designed for general use. They generally can be adjusted for gaging different materials or parts within a certain range of sizes. Several gages of this type include the dial indicating-type gages in Figs. 942, 943, 948, 949, and 950. The snap gage in Fig. 932 can be adjusted for gaging various dimensions within its size range.

Fixed-type gages are designed for special measuring applications involving specific size limits. Some are used for gaging only one size. A few of the common fixed-type gages include caliper-type snap gages, Fig. 931; ring gages, Fig. 934; plug gages, Fig. 935; thread gages, Fig. 937; and reference gages, Fig. 962. Gages are generally named after their most distinguishing feature, such as their shape, form, or use. Inspection workers and machinists should

Table 34
GAGES, MATERIALS, GAGE NUMBERS, AND SIZE IN DECIMALS
(See Section 1144)

	Manufacturer's Standard Gage[3]	U.S. Standard[4] Gage	Galvanized Sheet Gage	American Standard Wire Gage or Brown & Sharpe Gage	U.S. Steel Wire Gage or American Steel & Wire Co.	Twist Drill and Steel Wire Gage	Am. Steel and Wire Co.	Birmingham or Stubs' Iron Wire Gage	American (National) Standard Screw Gage	
	1	2	3	4	5	6	7	8	9	10
Gage Number	For Iron and Steel Sheets	For Iron and Steel Sheets and Plates	For Galvanized Steel Sheets	For Wire & Sheet Metal Except Iron, Steel & Zinc[5]	For Steel Wire (Not Music Wire or Drill Rod)	For Twist Drills and Drill Rod	For Music (or Piano) Wire[6]	For Iron Telephone and Telegraph Wire & Tubing Walls	For Machine Screws	For Wood Screws
0	....	.3125	....	.3249	.3065	....	.009	.340	.060	.060
1	....	.2813	....	.2893	.2830	.2280	.010	.300	.073	.073
2	....	.2656	....	.2576	.2625	.2210	.011	.284	.086	.086
3	0.2391	.2500	....	.2294	.2437	.2130	.012	.259	.099	.099
4	0.2242	.2344	....	.2043	.2253	.2090	.013	.238	.112	.112
5	0.2092	.2188	....	.1819	.2070	.2055	.014	.220	.125	.125
6	0.1943	.2031	....	.1620	.1920	.2040	.016	.203	.138	.138
7	0.1793	.1875	....	.1443	.1770	.2010	.018	.180	...	.151
8	0.1644	.1719	0.1681	.1285	.1620	.1990	.020	.165	.164	.164
9	0.1495	.1563	0.1532	.1144	.1483	.1960	.022	.148	...	.177
10	0.1345	.1406	0.1382	.1019	.1350	.1935	.024	.134	.190	.190
11	0.1196	.1250	0.1233	.0907	.1205	.1910	.026	.120	...	.203
12	0.1046	.1094	0.1084	.0808	.1055	.1890	.029	.109	.216	.216
13	0.0897	.0938	0.0934	.0720	.0915	.1850	.031	.095	...	...
14	0.0747	.0781	0.0785	.0641	.0800	.1820	.033	.083	...	.242
15	0.0673	.0703	0.0710	.0571	.0720	.1800	.035	.072	...	...
16	0.0598	.0625	0.0635	.0508	.0625	.1770	.037	.065	...	.268
17	0.0538	.0563	0.0575	.0453	.0540	.1730	.039	.058	...	...
18	0.0478	.0500	0.0516	.0403	.0475	.1695	.041	.049	...	.294
19	0.0418	.0438	0.0456	.0359	.0410	.1660	.043	.042	...	...
20	0.0359	.0375	0.0396	.0320	.0348	.1610	.045	.035	...	.320
21	0.0329	.0344	0.0366	.0285	.0317	.1590	.047	.032	...	...
22	0.0299	.0313	0.0336	.0253	.0286	.1570	.049	.028	...	...
23	0.0269	.0281	0.0306	.0226	.0258	.1540	.051	.025	...	...
24	0.0239	.0250	0.0276	.0201	.0230	.1520	.055	.022	...	.372
25	0.0209	.0219	0.0247	.0179	.0204	.1495	.059	.020	...	...
26	0.0179	.0188	0.0217	.0159	.0181	.1470	.063	.018	...	...
27	0.0164	.0172	0.0202	.0142	.0173	.1440	.067	.016	...	...
28	0.0149	.0156	0.0187	.0126	.0162	.1405	.071	.014	...	...
29	0.0135	.0141	0.0172	.0113	.0150	.1360	.075	.013	...	...
30	0.0120	.0125	0.0157	.0100	.0140	.1285	.080	.012	...	...

[3]The *Manufacturers' Standard Gage* for steel sheets is now being used for carbon steel and alloy steel sheets.

[4]The *United States Standard Gage* was established by Congress in 1893 for measuring sheet and plate iron and steel. It was the standard gage used for many years.

[5]*Zinc sheets* are measured by a *zinc gage* which is not given in the above table.

[6]The *Music Wire Gage* of the American Steel and Wire Company is used in the United States. It is recommended by the *United States Bureau of Standards*.

be familiar with the common kinds of gages and their applications.

Reference gages, also called *reference disks* (see Fig. 962) or *master gages,* are made of hardened steel and are used to test or check inspection gages. They are checked to determine whether they are worn, damaged, or out of adjustment. Micrometers can also be checked in this manner (see Fig. 130).

The size should always be stamped on fixed-type gages and on reference gages. Gages are available in many sizes. They should be checked from time to time to determine their accuracy.

1146. Drill Gage, Screw-Pitch Gage, Thickness Gage, Sheet Metal and Wire Gages, Center Gage, and Radius Gage

Drill gages are described in section 494.

The *screw-pitch gage* is described in section 611.

The *thickness gage* is described in section 672.

Sheet metal and wire gages are described in section 793.

Two uses of the *center gage* are given in sections 215 and 1183.

The *radius gage,* also known as a *fillet gage,* has a number of blades which fold into a handle like the blades of a pocket knife, Fig. 930. It is marked in *fractions* of an inch, as for example, ¼″, and is used to measure rounded corners, or *radii* (plural of *radius,* explained in section 30).

1147. Go and No-Go Gages

Go and no-go gages are often called *limits gages.* Sometimes they also are called *double gages* because they have two gaging points or surfaces. One tests the upper size limit and the other tests the lower size limit of a part being gaged. The size limits are those which are indicated on the drawing for the part. The sizes generally are stamped on the gage (see Fig. 932). There are several types of go and

no-go gages. The common types include snap gages, ring gages, and plug gages.

The principles involved in testing parts with go and no-go gages can be understood by studying Fig. 931. The figure shows a cylindrical part being tested with a limits *snap gage.* The upper gaging point is the *go* point, while the lower one is the *no-go* or not-go point. If the part is inside the specified size limits on the drawing (the size limits frequently are stamped on the gage also), it will pass through the *go* point or surface, but it will not pass through the *no-go* point or surface. If the part is not within the size limits, it is useless. Go and no-go gages can be used quickly and easily.

1148. Snap Gages

Snap gages are used for checking the outside diameter, length, or thickness of parts. They are used in a manner similar to the way

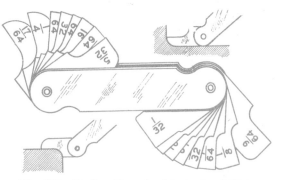

Fig. 930. Radius Gage for Measuring Fillets and Rounded Edges

Too Small
The screw has passed both sets of points

Just Right
Passed upper points —hangs on lower

Too Large
Will not pass upper points

Fig. 931. Limit Gages (Courtesy Greenfield Tap and Die Corp.)

a caliper is used, see Fig. 44. Hence, snap gages are often called *caliper gages*. Snap gages are available in a wide variety of styles and sizes. They may be the fixed-type, Fig. 933; the adjustable-type, Fig. 932; or the indicating-type, Fig. 949.

Snap gages of the adjustable type, Figs. 931 and 932, are widely used limits gages of the go and no-go type. The procedure for using them is explained in section 1147. They have one stationary anvil and two adjustable button anvils, Fig. 932. The outer button is set at the upper-size limit, and the inner one is set at the lower-size limit. The sizes may be tested for accuracy with gage blocks.

Adjustable-type snap gages may be supplied *set* and *sealed* at specific size limits by the manufacturer. The sizes are then stamped on the gage. They are also available *unset* and *unsealed*. They may then be adjusted to the desired size with gage blocks, as in Fig. 932.

Limits-type snap gages are available with gaging rolls, instead of anvils, for testing the pitch diameter of screw threads, see Fig. 940. Dial indicating-type snap gages are also available, see Fig. 949.

1149. Ring Gages

A ring gage is a hardened steel ring or collar. Three kinds of ring gages are used:

(1) Plain ring gages, Fig. 934.
(2) Tapered ring gages, Fig. 935.
(3) Thread ring gages, Fig. 938.

Plain ring gages (see Fig. 934) are used to test the external dimension limits of straight

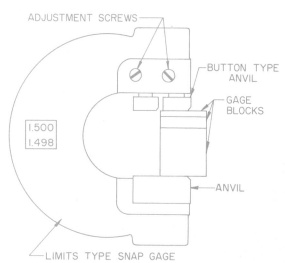

Fig. 932. Testing Size of Adjustable Limits
Snap Gage with Gage Blocks
(Courtesy Greenfield Tap and Die Corp.)

Fig. 934. Plain Ring Gage
(Courtesy Greenfield Tap and Die Corp.)

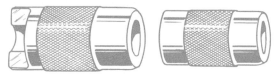

Fig. 935. Tapered Plug Gages and
Tapered Ring Gages

Fig. 933. Fixed-Type Snap Gages

round parts. The *no-go* ring, identified by the groove around the outside diameter, is used to check the minimum size limit. The *go* ring is used to check the maximum size limit. The go ring should pass over a part which is inside specified size limits, with little or no interference. The no-go ring should not pass over the part. If both rings pass over the part, it is undersize. If neither does, it is oversize.

Tapered ring gages (see Fig. 935) have a tapered hole and are used for testing the size and fit of a taper, such as the tapered shank on a drill or reamer. (See Figs. 376 and 459.)

Thread ring gages, of the go and no-go type in Fig. 938, are used for checking the fit and the pitch diameter limits of external screw threads. (See sections 609, 618, 620, and 1151.)

1150. Plug Gages

Three kinds of plug gages are in common use: (1) plain-cylindrical plug gages, Fig. 936; (2) cylindrical-taper plug gages, Fig. 935; and (3) thread plug gages, Fig. 937. Plug gages of special design are also made for checking square holes or holes of special shape.

Plain-cylindrical plug gages, Fig. 936, are accurate cylinders which are used to check the size limits of straight cylindrical holes. The go gage should enter the hole with little or no interference. If great pressure is necessary, the hole is too small. The no-go gage should not enter the hole. If it does, the hole is too large.

Cylindrical-taper plug gages, Fig. 935, are used for checking the size, amount of taper, and the fit of tapered holes. This type of gage is used to test the tapered hole in drill sleeves (Fig. 382), in machine tool spindles, and in various kinds of tool adaptors.

Thread plug gages, Fig. 937, are used for checking the size limits and the fit of internal screw threads. (See § 1151.)

1151. Thread Measurement and Thread Gages

The emphasis in screw thread measurement is always on the pitch diameter, explained in section 609. The tolerances and the limits on the pitch diameter largely determine the class (see § 620) or fit (see § 618) of the thread. The size and accuracy of screw

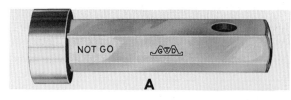
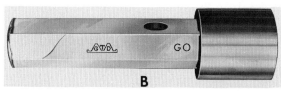

Fig. 936. Plain Cylindrical Plug Gages
(Courtesy Greenfield Tap and Die Corp.)
    A. No-Go Gage
    B. Go Gages
    C. Double-End Gage

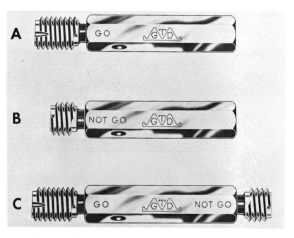

Fig. 937. Thread Plug Gages
(Courtesy Greenfield Tap and Die Corp.)
    A. Go Gage
    B. No-Go Gage
    C. Double-End Gage

threads usually are measured or tested with the following:

(1) Screw-pitch gage (see Fig. 478 and § 611).
(2) Thread micrometer (see Fig. 126).
(3) Thread plug gage (see Fig. 937).
(4) Thread ring gage (see Fig. 938).
(5) Roll-thread snap gage (see Fig. 939).
(6) Other methods.

Thread Micrometer

The pitch diameter (§ 609) of external 60° V-threads, including Unified and American (National) form threads, can be measured directly with a thread micrometer, Fig. 126. The micrometer spindle has a 60° conical

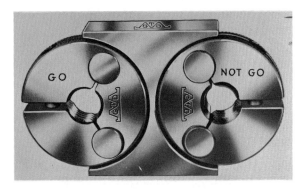

Fig. 938. Thread Ring Gages
Go and No-Go Gage with Holder
(Courtesy Greenfield Tap and Die Corp.)

Fig. 939. Inspecting Threads with a Ring Gage
(Courtesy Taft-Pierce Mfg. Co.)

point. The anvil has a 60° V-groove. The anvil swivels so that it can be held at a convenient angle for reading the micrometer. The micrometer should always be checked for a zero reading in the closed position before using it. (See inset in Fig. 126.)

The number of threads per inch which can be measured with a specific thread micrometer is limited. One inch capacity thread micrometers are designed for each of the following ranges of threads per inch: 8 to 13, 14 to 20, 22 to 30, and 32 to 40. Larger capacity thread micrometers also are available. Hence, care should be taken to select the right thread micrometer for the thread to be measured. For example, a 1″ capacity micrometer designed for the thread range from 8 to 13 threads per inch should be selected for measuring the pitch diameter of a ¾-10 UNC thread (¾″ diameter Unified National Coarse Thread with 10 threads per inch).

The pitch diameter for each diameter, pitch (see § 612), and fit (see § 618) or class (see § 620) of thread may vary within certain size limits. The size limits are listed in handbooks for machinists. For example, the pitch diameter for an external ¾-10 UNC class 2A thread may range from 0.6773 to 0.6832″. Hence, if the pitch diameter is found to be inside this size range, the thread will fit properly.

Thread Plug Gage

Limits type thread plug gages, Fig. 937, are used for checking internal threads for the proper fit or class of thread. (See §§ 618 and 620.) The gages include a *go* gage and a *no-go* gage. The go gage is the longer gage, and it has a chip groove for cleaning the threads. The go gage is the minimum pitch diameter, and the no-go gage is the maximum pitch diameter of the internal thread.

In using thread plug gages, the go gage should enter the tapped hole for the entire length of the gage. The no-go gage may or may not enter. If it enters the hole, it should fit snugly on or before the third thread, thus showing that the thread has the maximum pitch diameter for the specified fit or class of thread. If the gage enters farther, the thread is oversize and will fit too loosely.

Thread plug gages are made for each size, pitch, and fit or class of thread. They are made for all standard Unified and American (National) form threads. They are also made for pipe threads.

Thread Ring Gage

The accuracy and the fit of external threads may be tested with thread ring gages, Figs. 938 and 939. These are limits-type gages which include both *go* and *no-go* gages. The *go* gage checks the maximum pitch diameter, flank angle, lead, and clearance at the minor diameter, simultaneously. (See Figs. 473, 475, and 479.) The *no-go* gage checks only the pitch diameter to determine whether it is below minimum size limits.

Both ring gages are used in checking a thread. The *go* gage should turn on freely, or one of the thread elements is inaccurate, and the thread will not fit the mating internal thread properly. The *no-go* gage should not turn on. If it does, the pitch diameter is under the specified minimum size limits and the thread will not fit properly with the mating thread. Thread ring gages are made for each size, pitch, and fit or class of thread.

Roll-Thread Snap Gage

External Unified and American (National) screw threads can be tested rapidly and accurately with a roll-thread snap gage of the limits type, shown in Fig. 940. The gage in Fig. 940 is the open-face type which can be used close to shoulders.

The outer or *go rolls* check all thread elements simultaneously. They are set at the maximum pitch diameter limit. The inner or *no-go rolls* are set at the minimum pitch diameter limit. They check only the pitch diameter to determine whether it is below the minimum pitch diameter specified. Threads which are accurate and within the proper pitch di-

ameter limits will pass through the go rolls and are stopped by the no-go rolls. Roll-thread snap gages are made for each size, pitch, and fit or class of thread.

Other Methods

Screw threads may be inspected or measured by other methods. A method called the *three-wire method* may be used for measuring the pitch diameter of external screw threads. This method is more complex and is explained in handbooks for machinists. Thread measur-

Fig. 940. Roll-Thread Snap Gage (Courtesy Greenfield Tap and Die Corp.)

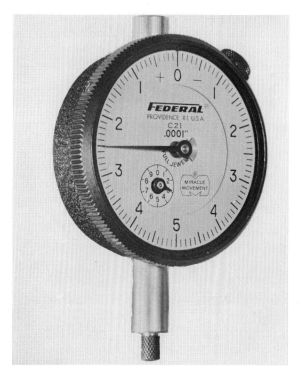

Fig. 941. Dial Indicator (Balanced Type) (Courtesy Federal Products)

ing and inspection instruments of special design are also available for checking threads.

1152. Dial Test-Indicator Gages

Inspectors, machinists, and toolmakers use a variety of dial-indicating gages and measuring instruments. A *dial indicator*, also called a *dial gage*, looks somewhat like a watch, Fig. 941. The dial indicator shows visually the

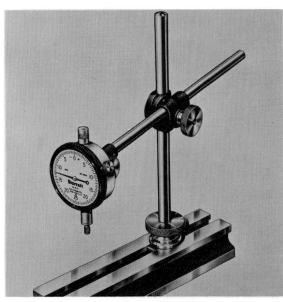

Fig. 942. Dial Test-Indicator Set
(Courtesy L. S. Starrett Co.)

Fig. 943. Checking Height of Machined Part with Dial Test-Indicator
(Courtesy L. S. Starrett Co.)

amount of error, in size or alignment, for a part being measured or gaged, see Fig. 943.

The graduations on dial gages vary in size. They may be indicated in thousandths (0.001), in ten-thousandths (0.0001), or to the nearest 0.00005″. The dial indicator in Fig. 941 has 0.0001″ graduations. The numbered graduations are in thousandths, and the shorter graduations between are ten-thousandths.

Two types of dial gages are in common use. The *balanced type,* as in Fig. 941, is numbered in both directions starting with zero. This type is most common on inspection-type gages. The *continuous-reading* type, as in Fig. 945, is numbered clockwise, continuously starting at zero. The range of graduations on small gages may vary from 0.010″ to 0.050″.

Dial Test-Indicator Set

The dial test-indicator set shown in Fig. 942 is mounted on a column which is clamped in the T-slot in the steel base. It may be used as a gage for checking the thickness of parts at an inspection bench. The gage also may be swiveled on its column to test the thickness of a workpiece mounted on a machine tool table, see Fig. 943. A dial test-indicator gage can be mounted on a surface-gage base, Fig. 64, for checking the straightness or alignment of machine parts as shown in Fig. 944.

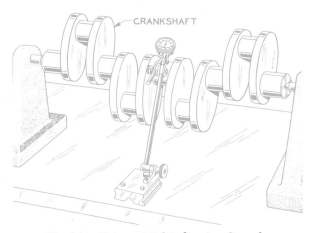

Fig. 944. Using a Dial-Indicating Gage for Testing the Straightness of a Part

In using a dial indicator set, the indicator must first be set to *gaging height* or *gaging thickness;* this is the basic thickness of the part to be gaged or tested. The gaging height may be set with a planer gage (see § 1154 and Fig. 956), with gage blocks (Fig. 960), or with other available gaging tools or devices.

The gaging height is established between the dial indicator contact point and the surface on which the part rests. For testing the thickness of parts on a machine tool table, the gaging height is between the dial contact point and the table surface, see Fig. 943. For checking whether small parts are within minimum and maximum size limits, the gaging height is established between the dial contact point and the steel base of the gage, as shown in Fig. 942. In setting the gaging height the dial should be set at *zero*, and it should be under enough spring tension to enable the dial hand to rotate in either direction through the desired measuring or gaging range.

A *universal dial-indicator set,* Fig. 945, may be used for many kinds of testing and measuring applications. With the variety of accessories provided, it may be mounted on a surface-gage base. It may then be used on a machine table or on a surface plate, see Fig. 944. It may be mounted in the tool post on a lathe, as shown in Fig. 946. With the hole attachment, holes can be accurately aligned or tested in a lathe chuck or on other machine tools, see Fig. 947.

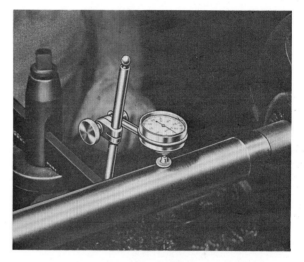

Fig. 946. Checking Runout on a Lathe
(Courtesy L. S. Starrett Co.)

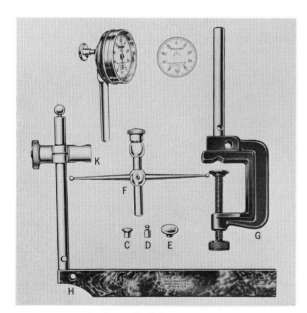

Fig. 945. Universal Dial-Indicator Set
(Courtesy L. S. Starrett Co.)
  C. D. & E. Contact Points
  F. Hole Attachment
  G. Clamp
  H. Tool Post
  K. Sleeve

Fig. 947. Hole Attachment Permits Accurate Internal Tests with Dial Indicator
(Courtesy L. S. Starrett Co.)

Dial-indicating depth gages, Fig. 948, are used for gaging the depth of grooves, shoulders, keyways, holes, and similar recesses. Extension points make it possible to increase the measuring depths.

Dial-indicating snap gages, Fig. 949, are used for gaging the diameters of parts. The gage shows whether the parts are within the size limits specified. The gage may be set for

any *basic size* within its capacity, and it shows the amount which the part is over or under the basic size. These gages are available in several sizes. Thus a gage with a capacity from 0″ to 1″ can be set to gage the thickness of any part within this size range. The gage is set by adjusting the frame and indicator point simultaneously with the knurled adjustment wheel. A dial-indicating snap gage may be used for measuring parts at a bench. It also may be used for measuring parts which are mounted in a machine such as a lathe or cylindrical grinding machine.

Dial Comparator

A dial comparator, Fig. 950, is used for measuring thicknesses. It also may be used for gaging thickness to determine whether parts are within the limits specified. The dial in Fig. 950 has 0.001″ graduations and a dial range of 0.100″. It is also equipped with a revolutions counter. The sliding table on the column may be raised or lowered for parts of various thicknesses. The contact point is raised or lowered through its range with the lifting

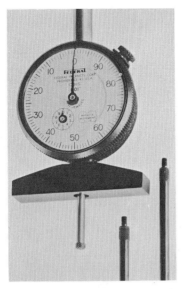

Fig. 948. Dial-Indicating Depth Gage with Extension Points (Courtesy Federal Products)

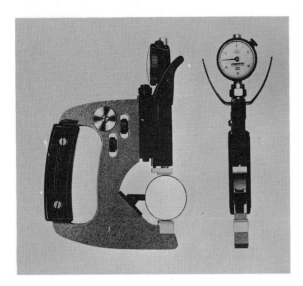

Fig. 949. Dial-Indicating Snap Gage (Courtesy Federal Products)

Fig. 950. Dial Comparator (Courtesy Federal Products)

lever at the top. The gaging height is established between the dial-contact point with either a planer gage (Fig. 954) or with gage blocks (Fig. 960).

1153. Universal Indicator

A *universal indicator,* Fig. 951, may be used for many measuring and gaging purposes. It is equipped with an indicator hand which is actuated by a contact point. When the contact point touches a surface, the indicator hand is actuated through its range of 0.010″. The hand swings plus or minus 0.005″ from the zero point.

A universal indicator can be mounted on a surface gage for gaging the height of parts on a surface plate, see Fig. 252. It can be mounted in a lathe tool post for checking alignment of workpieces in a lathe chuck. It

can also be mounted in a drill press or other machine spindle to check the alignment of the spindle with a hole in a part, as shown in Fig. 353.

1154. Planer and Shaper Gage

A *master planer and shaper gage,* Fig. 954, is very often used for setting the height of the cutting tools on machines such as planers and

Fig. 953. Universal Indicator Used to Test Alignment of Hole for Machining Setup

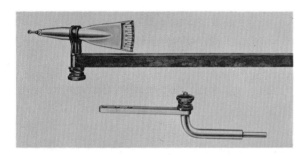

Fig. 951. Universal Indicator and Attachment

Fig. 952. Universal Indicator Used with Surface Gage on Surface Plate

Fig. 954. Master Planer and Shaper Gage Used to Set Height of Cutting Tools

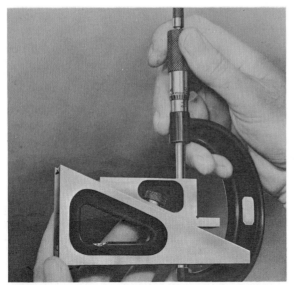

Fig. 955. Gage Height or Width is Measured and Set to Micrometer Accuracy

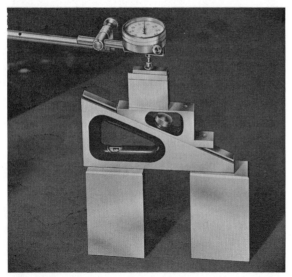

Fig. 956. Master Planer and Shaper Gage Used with Gage Blocks for Setting Up Work on Surface Plate

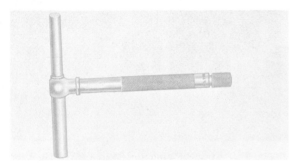

Fig. 957. Telescoping Gage

shapers (see Fig. 954). It also may be used for setting the tool height on milling machines, surface grinding machines, and other machine tools.

The height or width of the gage may be adjusted and set to micrometer accuracy, as shown in Fig. 955. Cylindrical extension parts can be screwed into the gage for added length (see Fig. 954).

Other uses of a planer and shaper gage include the following: use in conjunction with gage block for establishing height on a surface plate (see Fig. 956); use for establishing gaging heights for gaging tools such as dial-indicating snap gages (Fig. 949), dial-test indicators (Fig. 942), and dial-indicating comparators (Fig. 950).

1155. Telescoping Gage

A *telescoping gage*, Fig. 957, is used for measuring or gaging the size of holes. The end of the gage has a plunger which is under spring tension when retracted. The gage is used by retracting the plunger and inserting the gage in a hole as in Fig. 958; the knurled nut on the handle is then tightened, thus locking the plunger in position. The gage is then removed from the hole, and the distance across the ends of the gage is measured with a micrometer. The telescoping gage may be used for measuring grooves as well as holes. These gages are available in sizes with measuring distances from $5/16''$ to $6''$.

Fig. 958. Using a Telescoping Gage

Small-hole gages, Fig. 959, as the name implies, are used for measuring small holes, grooves, and recesses from ⅛″ to ½″ width. When the gage is used, the ball end is inserted in the hole or groove to be measured. The knurled screw on the handle is turned until the ball end expands enough to cause a slight dragging pressure. The gage is then extracted from the hole, and the distance across the ball end is measured with a micrometer.

1156. Gage Blocks

Gage blocks are solid, simple-looking *hardened steel* blocks, Fig. 960. They are ground and finished to different sizes and have extremely flat, precision ground, lapped, and polished surfaces. Gage blocks are exact within a few *millionths of an inch*. Very thin tissue paper is one thousandth of an inch (0.001″) thick; dividing this thickness into a thousand parts gives one millionth of an inch (0.000001″). (See § 134.)

The best known gage blocks were invented by Carl E. Johansson in Sweden in 1895. They became known the world over as *Johansson gage blocks* or *Jo-blocks*. Today similar gage blocks are manufactured by several companies.

Gage blocks are used to test or check the sizes and exactness of *inspection gages, measuring machines,* and other measuring instruments, Figs. 932 and 950. They must be used in a temperature of 68° F. for most accuracy.

Gage blocks are *wrung* together by sliding one block over the other in various combinations to get the desired combined size. It is wonderful how these blocks stick together as if magnetized when wrung together with a little pressure. This sticking together is called *adhesion.* Two blocks held up 200 pounds in a demonstration, Fig. 961.

1157. Master Gages

Master gages are gages that are used to check or inspect other gages. All other gages are compared with them. Thus, *reference gages*, Fig. 962, and *gage blocks* are master gages (see §§ 1145 and 1156). There are many other kinds.

1158. Magnifying Glass

A magnifying glass is often used to inspect work, Fig. 963. Cracks and scratches can thus be found. Measurements can also be made more exactly with a magnifying glass. (See § 246.)

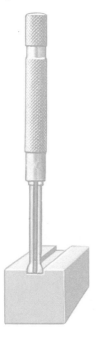

Fig. 959. Small Hole Gage

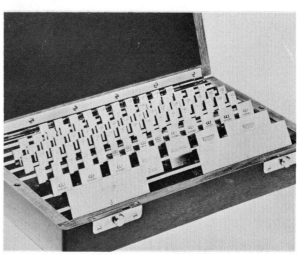

Fig. 960. Gage Blocks
(Courtesy C. E. Johansson Gage Co.)

1159. Care of Inspection Tools and Gages

Gages are very expensive. They should be kept very clean and handled and stored away with the greatest of care and skill.

Many gages have to be protected from heat and cold. For example, the warmth of the hand will *expand* or warp the gage and thus change its size. (See § 721.) The change in size may be only .0001″ to .0002″, more or less. The size of a gage lying in the sunlight will change the same way. Rubber or wooden handles are often put on gages to protect them from the warmth of the hand while *gaging* a piece of work. Rooms in which gaging is done and in which gages are stored (see Fig. 924) should be kept at 68° F.

A gage which has been dropped on the floor or otherwise bumped, should be checked or inspected before using it again. Gages become worn after they have been used to inspect many pieces and should, therefore, be inspected from time to time. (See § 145.)

Fig. 962. Reference Disks
(Courtesy Brown & Sharpe Mfg. Co.)

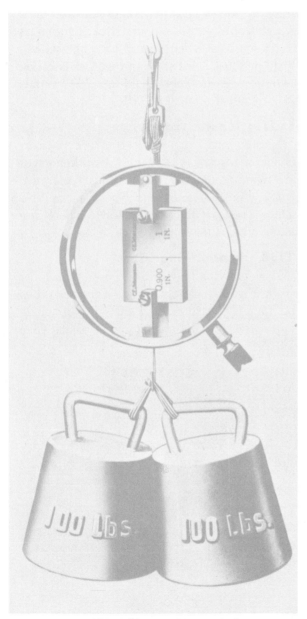

Fig. 961. Adhesion of Gage Blocks
(Courtesy C. E. Johansson Gage Co.)

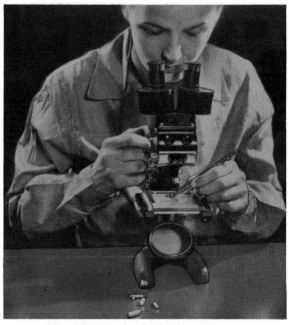

Fig. 963. Toolmaker's Microscope
(Courtesy George Scherr Co.)

Review Questions

1. How is the quality of manufactured products controlled?

2. What factors are inspected for the purpose of controlling the quality of manufactured metal products?

3. List two systems of linear measurement, and list the standard unit of measurement for each.

4. What is the international standard for the meter?

5. What is the length of the International Inch, in terms of metric units? Also, in terms of wavelengths of krypton light?

6. How can the length of 1″ be measured accurately, to plus or minus 2-millionths inch, in machine shops or industrial plants all over the world?

7. What is meant by the interchangeability of parts?

8. What is meant by dimension limits?

9. What is meant by tolerance on parts?

10. What is meant by allowance on mating parts?

11. Explain the difference between negative and positive allowance.

12. What is the primary purpose of gaging?

13. What is a double gage, and what is it used for?

14. Why should one indicate the kind of material and also indicate the thickness in thousandths of an inch when ordering sheet metal?

15. What is the principal difference between adjustable gages and fixed gages?

16. For what purpose are reference gages used?

17. What are *go and no-go* gages used for? List several types.

18. What is a snap gage?

19. What is a ring gage?

20. List three kinds of ring gages.

21. List three kinds of plug gages.

22. List three kinds of gages which may be used to inspect the pitch-diameter limits or the class and fit of external screw threads.

23. Explain how a thread micrometer is selected and used to measure a screw thread.

24. List two types of dial gages, and explain how their graduations are numbered.

25. List several uses for a dial-test indicator set.

26. List two ways in which the gaging height may be established for a dial indicator.

27. Name several kinds of dial-indicating gages.

28. For what purpose is a dial comparator used?

29. What is a universal indicator?

30. List several uses for a planer and shaper gage.

31. For what purpose is a telescoping gage used?

32. What is a small-hole gage?

33. What are gage blocks, and how are they used?

34. What are master gages?

35. How do changes in temperature affect precision gage blocks and gages?

Coordination

Words to Know

accurate	dial-test indicator
adhesion	difference
allowance	dimension limit
American (National)	double dimension
Standard Screw	double gage
Gage	English system of
American Standard	measurement
Wire Gage or	final inspection
Brown & Sharpe	gage or gauge
Gage	gage blocks
Bureau of Standards	gage system
caliper gage	gaging
centimeter	go or no-go gage
chassis	inspecting
cylinder gage	inspection
decimeter	department
dial comparator	inspector
dial indicator	interchangeable part

International Bureau of Weights and Measures
International Inch
International Prototype Meter
Johannson gage block
limit
limit gage
linear measurement
magnifying glass
master gage
master planer and shaper gage
material
metal finish
meter
metric system
millimeter
millionth of an inch
minus sign
music wire gage
negative allowance
performance
plus gage
plus sign
positive allowance
radii (plural of radius)
radius gage or fillet gage
reference disk
reference gage
ring gage
roll-thread snap gage
scleroscope
sheet metal and wire gage
small-hole gage
snap gage
standard of measurement
taper cylinder gage
tapered hole
tapered-plug gage
tapered-ring gage
telescoping gage
thread gage
thread micrometer
tolerance
universal-dial indicator
universal indicator
zinc gage

Occupational Information

1. What does accuracy mean?
2. Write a biography of Carl E. Johansson.

Testing Hardness of Metal

1165. How Hardness of Metal Is Determined

The *hardness* of metals can be determined with several different types of hardness testing instruments. The hardness is designated by a *hardness number,* from a *hardness scale,* which is based on the kind of hardness testing instrument used. The following are three of the most common types of hardness testing instruments:

(1) Rockwell Hardness Tester. (See Figs. 974 and 975.)

(2) Brinell Hardness Tester. (See Figs. 976 and 977.)

(3) Scleroscope Hardness Tester. (See Fig. 978.)

Some hardness testers are equipped with a penetrator which may be a tiny hardened steel ball, carbide ball, or a diamond point. On these kinds of hardness testers, a load is applied to the ball or point, and it penetrates and dents the metal, see Figs. 974 and 976. The depth of penetration produced by one tester, or the size of the dent produced by the other, is measured and indicates the hardness of the metal. The deeper the dent, or the larger the dent, the softer the metal.

Since some metals are softer than others, a lighter load must be applied to the penetrator on soft metals than on hard metals. Otherwise, a deep dent may appear on the surface

Fig. 974. Rockwell Hardness Tester
(Courtesy The Hole-Krome Screw Corp.)

of the tested part. Therefore, several different hardness scales may be used with one kind of testing instrument. The scale used depends on the type of penetrator and the amount of load applied to the penetrator while making the test. For soft metals, a smaller load is applied. The loads applied for making tests according to several different hardness scales are shown in Table 35.

The hardness for a part generally is specified on the drawing for the part. For example, the hardness may be designated RC-40 to 45 (Rockwell-C, 40 to 45). If a Rockwell Hardness Tester is not at hand, the hardness may be tested with another kind of tester, such as the Brinell Tester or the Scleroscope

Tester. The hardness values obtained according to one hardness scale may be converted to equivalent hardness values on another scale. This is done by reading horizontally across Table 35. For example, RC-40 (with 150-kg load) is equivalent to Brinell-371 (with carbide ball and 3000-kg load) or Shore Scleroscope No. 54.

Manufacturers of hardness testing instruments generally supply instructions for their use. The instructions should be followed carefully. For best results, three tests generally should be made when testing the hardness of a part. Sometimes the hardness values vary slightly for each test. The hardness value is an average of the three hardness number values.

1166.   Rockwell Hardness Test

Rockwell hardness tests are based on the depth of penetration made in metal by a specific kind of penetrator point under a specific load. The hardness is indicated directly by a hardness number which is read on a dial, see Fig. 975. The hardness number is based on the difference in depth of penetration caused by a *minor* load and a *major* load applied to the penetrator. Deep penetration indicates a softer metal. The hardness numbers may be indicated in either red or black. The red numbers indicate the RB Scale, while the black numbers indicate the RC Scale.

Rockwell hardness testers of several types are available. They may be the stationary-type, Fig. 974, or the portable-type, Fig. 975. The load generally is applied through a system of weights, levers, screws, or a combination of these devices. Testers are available for testing according to the *standard Rockwell Hardness Scales* only or for testing according to the *Rockwell Superficial Hardness Scales* only. Some testers can be used for testing hardness according to either scale.

The *Rockwell-C* (RC) Scale requires use of a diamond-point penetrator, called a *brale*. A minor load of 10 kilograms (22 lbs.) and a major load of 150 kilograms (330.8 lbs.) is

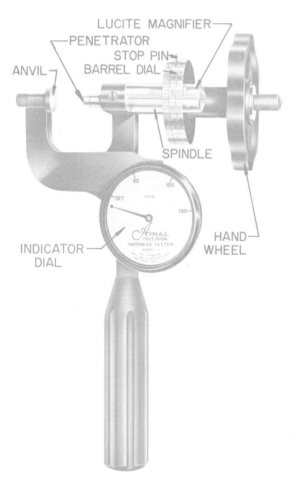

Fig. 975. Portable Hardness Tester
(Courtesy Ames Precision Machine Works)

Table 35

HARDNESS NUMBERS FOR STEEL APPROXIMATELY EQUIVALENT TO ROCKWELL C SCALE

Rockwell C-Scale Hardness No.	Diamond Pyramid Hardness No.	Brinell Hardness No. (10-mm Ball, 3000-kg load)			Rockwell Hardness No.			Rockwell Superficial Hardness No. (Superficial Brale Penetrator)			Shore Scleroscope Hardness No.	Tensile Strength (Approx.) 1000 psi
		Standard Ball	Hultgren Ball	Carbide Ball	A Scale (60-kg Brale)	B Scale (100-kg 1/16" Ball)	D Scale (100-kg Brale)	15-N Scale (15 kg)	30-N Scale (30 kg)	45-N Scale (45 kg)		
68	940	...	...	...	85.6	...	76.9	93.2	84.4	75.4	97	...
67	900	...	...	...	85.0	...	76.1	92.9	83.6	74.2	95	...
66	865	...	...	...	84.5	...	75.4	92.5	82.8	73.3	92	...
65	832	...	...	(739)	83.9	...	74.5	92.2	81.9	72.0	91	...
64	800	...	...	(722)	83.4	...	73.8	91.8	81.1	71.0	88	...
63	772	...	...	(705)	82.8	...	73.0	91.4	80.1	69.9	87	...
62	746	...	...	(688)	82.3	...	72.2	91.1	79.3	68.8	85	...
61	720	...	...	(670)	81.8	...	71.5	90.7	78.4	67.7	83	...
60	697	...	(613)	(654)	81.2	...	70.7	90.2	77.5	66.6	81	...
59	674	...	(599)	(634)	80.7	...	69.9	89.8	76.6	65.5	80	326
58	653	...	(587)	615	80.1	...	69.2	89.3	75.7	64.3	78	315
57	633	...	(575)	595	79.6	...	68.5	88.9	74.8	63.2	76	305
56	613	...	(561)	577	79.0	...	67.7	88.3	73.9	62.0	75	295
55	595	...	(546)	560	78.5	...	66.9	87.9	73.0	60.9	74	287
54	577	...	(534)	543	78.0	...	66.1	87.4	72.0	59.8	72	278
53	560	...	(519)	525	77.4	...	65.4	86.9	71.2	58.6	71	269
52	544	(500)	(508)	512	76.8	...	64.6	86.4	70.2	57.4	69	262
51	528	(487)	494	496	76.3	...	63.8	85.9	69.4	56.1	68	253
50	513	(475)	481	481	75.9	...	63.1	85.5	68.5	55.0	67	245
49	498	(464)	469	469	75.2	...	62.1	85.0	67.6	53.8	66	239
48	484	451	455	455	74.7	...	61.4	84.5	66.7	52.5	64	232
47	471	442	443	443	74.1	...	60.8	83.9	65.8	51.4	63	225
46	458	432	432	432	73.6	...	60.0	83.5	64.8	50.3	62	219
45	446	421	421	421	73.1	...	59.2	83.0	64.0	49.0	60	212
44	434	409	409	409	72.5	...	58.5	82.5	63.1	47.8	58	206
43	423	400	400	400	72.0	...	57.7	82.0	62.2	46.7	57	201
42	412	390	390	390	71.5	...	56.9	81.5	61.3	45.5	56	196
41	402	381	381	381	70.9	...	56.2	80.9	60.4	44.3	55	191
40	392	371	371	371	70.4	...	55.4	80.4	59.5	43.1	54	186
39	382	362	362	362	69.9	...	54.6	79.9	58.6	41.9	52	181
38	372	353	353	353	69.4	...	53.8	79.4	57.7	40.8	51	176
37	363	344	344	344	68.9	...	53.1	78.8	56.8	39.6	50	172
36	354	336	336	336	68.4	(190.0)	52.3	78.3	55.9	38.4	49	168
35	345	327	327	327	67.9	(108.5)	51.5	77.7	55.0	37.2	48	163
34	336	319	319	319	67.4	(108.0)	50.8	77.2	54.2	36.1	47	159
33	327	311	311	311	66.8	(107.5)	50.0	76.6	53.3	34.9	46	154
32	318	301	301	301	66.3	(107.0)	49.2	76.1	52.1	33.7	44	150
31	310	294	294	294	65.8	(106.0)	48.4	75.6	51.3	32.5	43	146
30	302	286	286	286	65.3	(105.5)	47.7	75.0	50.4	31.3	42	142
29	294	279	279	279	64.7	(104.5)	47.0	74.5	49.5	30.1	41	138
28	286	271	271	271	64.3	(104.0)	46.1	73.9	48.6	28.9	41	134
27	279	264	264	264	63.8	(103.0)	45.2	73.3	47.7	27.8	40	131
26	272	258	258	258	63.3	(102.5)	44.6	72.8	46.8	26.7	38	127
25	266	253	253	253	62.8	(101.5)	43.8	72.2	45.9	25.5	38	124
24	260	247	247	247	62.4	(101.0)	43.1	71.6	45.0	24.3	37	121
23	254	243	243	243	62.0	100.0	42.1	71.0	44.0	23.1	36	118
22	248	237	237	237	61.5	99.0	41.6	70.5	43.2	22.0	35	115
21	243	231	231	231	61.0	98.5	40.9	69.9	42.3	20.7	35	113
20	238	226	226	226	60.5	97.8	40.1	69.4	41.5	19.6	34	110
(18)	230	219	219	219	...	96.7	...	...	...	...	33	106
(16)	222	212	212	212	...	95.5	...	...	...	...	32	102
(14)	213	203	203	203	...	93.9	...	...	...	...	31	98
(12)	204	194	194	194	...	92.3	...	...	...	...	29	94
(10)	196	187	187	187	...	90.7	...	...	...	...	28	90
(8)	188	179	179	179	...	89.5	...	...	...	...	27	87
(6)	180	171	171	171	...	87.1	...	...	...	...	26	84
(4)	173	165	165	165	...	85.5	...	...	...	...	25	80
(2)	166	158	158	158	...	83.5	...	...	...	...	24	77
(0)	160	152	152	152	...	81.7	...	...	...	...	24	75

The values in boldface type correspond to the values in the joint SAE-ASM-ASTM hardness conversions as printed in ASTM E140-65, Table 2. Values in parentheses are beyond normal range and are given for information only. Data from Metals Handbook 8th Edition, American Society for Metals. (Reprinted with permission.)

used. The RC Scale is used for testing the hardness of heat-treated or hardened steels which are harder than Rockwell-B 100.

The *Rockwell-B* (RB) Scale requires use of a ¹⁄₁₆″ diameter hardened-steel ball penetrator. It is used with a minor load of 10-kg and a major load of 100-kg (220.5 lbs.). The RB Scale is used for testing hardness of unhardened steel, cast iron, and nonferrous metals.

Of the various Rockwell Hardness Scales, see Table 35, the RC and RB are standard and are the most widely used. With the Rockwell Superficial Hardness Scales, lighter loads are applied and a smaller dent is made in the surface of metal being tested. However, these tests generally are not as accurate as the RC or RB tests.

1167. Brinell Hardness Test

Brinell Hardness Tests are made with a testing machine, Fig. 976, which forces a hard ball of a specific diameter under a specific load into a smooth metal surface. The ball is 10 millimeters (mm) in diameter, and it may be made of hardened steel, hultgren, or carbide. For standard Brinell (BHN) Hardness Tests on steel, a load of 3000-kg (6600 lbs.) is applied. The load is applied steadily and is maintained for a minimum period of 15 seconds for steel and 30 seconds for nonferrous metals.

The width of the dent made by the ball determines the Brinell Hardness Number. The width of the dent is measured with a microscope, Fig. 977, which has a special calibrated measuring lens. The width of the dent is con-

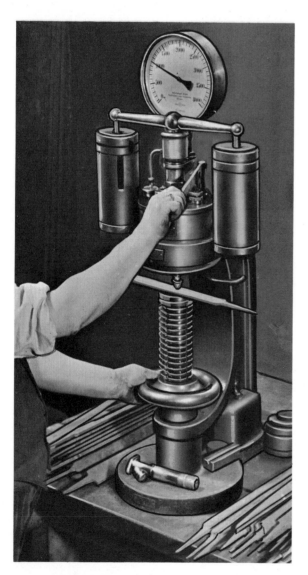

Fig. 976. Brinell Hardness Tester
(Courtesy Henry Disston & Sons, Inc.)

Fig. 977. Brinell Microscope for Measuring
Diameter of Impression Made by Brinnel Hardness
Tester (Courtesy Bausch & Lomb)

verted to a hardness number by using a comparison chart which is supplied with the testing machine. Wider dents are produced in softer metals which have lower hardness numbers.

Brinell testers generally work best on metals which are not extremely hard. These include nonferrous metals, soft steels, and medium-hard steels. The Brinell hardness of steel generally ranges from about BHN 150 for soft, low-carbon steel to BHN 739 for hardened, high-carbon steel. On very hard steels, the dent is so narrow that it is difficult to see or measure. The following are the maximum hardness values which can be determined with each kind of ball penetrator used on a Brinell tester: BHN 630 with carbide ball, BHN 500 with Hultgren ball, and BHN 450 with steel ball.

1168. Shore Scleroscope Test

Hardness tests made according to the *Shore Scleroscope Hardness Scale* are made with a *Scleroscope Tester*, Fig. 978. The Scleroscope Tester operates on the rebound principle. It measures the height to which a diamond-tipped hammer rebounds after being dropped on a metal surface to be tested. Harder metals cause the hammer to rebound higher, thus indicating higher hardness values.

Scleroscope Testers are essentially *nonmarring*, particularly on harder metals. A small dent may appear on softer metals. The hardness number is read directly on the vertical column, Fig. 978. On some Scleroscope Testers, the hardness numbers are read directly on a dial instead. Small parts may be held in a clamping stand for testing.

1169. Testing Hardness with a File

The hardness of steel may be tested with the *arris* of a file, see Fig. 979. If the file cuts, the steel is soft. If the file does not cut but slips over the steel, it is hard. Do not attempt to test the hardness of hardened steel with the flat surface of the file, or you will dull and

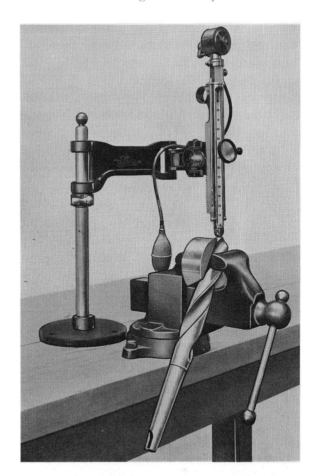

Fig. 978. Testing Hardness with Scleroscope (Courtesy The Shore Instrument and Manufacturing Co.)

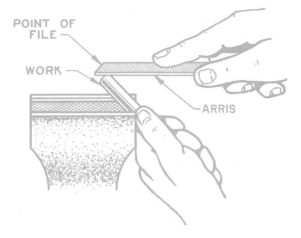

Fig. 979. Testing the Hardness of Steel with the Arris of a File

ruin the teeth. By studying Table 36 carefully you can make a rough estimate of the hardness of steel by using the arris of a file.

Table 36
DATA FOR ESTIMATING HARDNESS OF STEEL WITH A FILE

ROCKWELL C HARDNESS NUMBER	ACTION OF FILE ON STEEL
20	File removes metal easily with slight pressure
30	File starts to resist cutting metal
40	File cuts metal with difficulty
50	File barely cuts metal with great difficulty
57	File glides over metal without cutting

Review Questions

1. How is the hardness of metals generally designated?

2. List three common types of hardness testing instruments or machines.

3. Explain how you can convert a hardness value on one hardness scale to an equivalent hardness value on another scale.

4. List two common types of Rockwell Hardness Testers.

5. On what kinds of metal are Rockwell-C tests generally made?

6. What kinds of metal are generally tested according to the Rockwell-B Scale?

7. List one advantage and one disadvantage in using the Rockwell Superficial Hardness Scales.

8. Explain how a Brinell Hardness Test is made.

9. On what kinds of metal do Brinell Hardness Testers work best?

10. List the maximum hardness values which should be tested with each of the following kinds of ball penetrators on a Brinell Hardness Tester:
(a) Carbide Ball
(b) Hultgren Ball
(c) Hardened Steel Ball

11. Explain how a Scleroscope Hardness Tester operates.

12. What is the major advantage in using a Scleroscope Tester?

13. Explain how the hardness of steel can be tested or estimated with a file.

14. How many different hardness scales are listed on Table 35?

Coordination

Words to Know

arris	penetrator
Brinell Hardness Number	Rockwell-B number
Brinell Hardness Tester	Rockwell-C number
carbide ball	Rockwell Hardness Number
diamond point	Rockwell Hardness Tester
hardened steel ball	Rockwell Superficial Hardness
hardness	
hardness number	Scleroscope Hardness Tester
hardness scale	
Hultgren ball	Shore Scleroscope Hardness Number
kilogram	
major load	standard hardness number scales
minor load	
nonmarring	

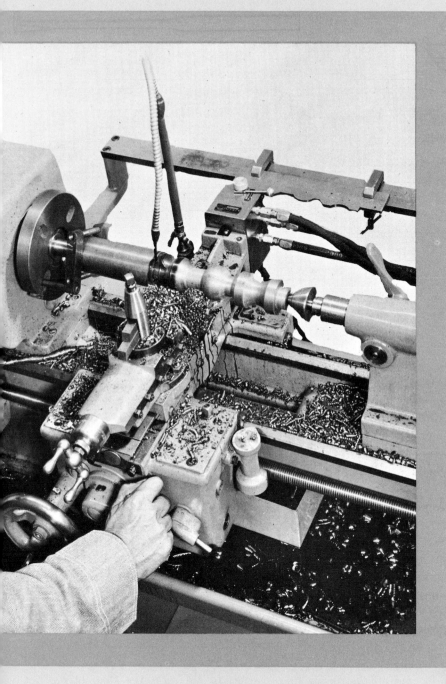

Turning from a Template
— Note Tracing Attach-
ment at Rear
(Courtesy Clausing Div.,
Atlas Press Co.)

Machine Tools

Part *XII*

The Lathe and Lathe Operations

1175. The Lathe as a Machine Tool

The metalworking lathe, Fig. 990[1], is a *machine tool*. A *machine tool* is a machine which is used for cutting metal; it holds both the workpiece and the cutting tool. There are many kinds of machine tools. The most common kinds of machine tools are often called *basic machine tools*. Five of the most basic kinds of machine tools include drill presses, lathes, shapers and planers (Fig. 1105), milling machines (Fig. 1151), and grinding machines (Figs. 1246, 1256, and 1267).

Most of the many other kinds of machine tools are specialized, mass production type machine tools. These are modifications or adaptations of one or more of the basic machine tools listed above. For example, specialized production machine tools which are adapted from the lathe include turret lathes, hand screw machines, automatic screw machines, and chucking machines. Each of these machines can perform some of the operations which can be performed on a lathe. However, the specialized production machines perform these operations more rapidly and efficiently.

It is important that you learn about the basic kinds of machine tools, including the drill presses, lathes, shapers, milling machines,

[1]Many of the illustrations in this unit are reprinted by arrangement with South Bend Lathe, Inc. from *How to Run a Lathe*. (copyrighted, all rights reserved)

and grinding machines. When you understand the kinds of setups, the kinds of cutting tools, and the kinds of operations which can be performed on these machines, you can apply this knowledge and experience to specialized production machine tools. The principles involved in performing operations on the basic kinds of machine tools also apply to performing these same operations on modern, specialized mass-production machine tools.

1176. Why the Lathe Is Important

We are living in the age of the machine. The airplane, steamship, locomotive, electric motor, computer, transfer machine, and automobile are, indeed, among the outstanding inventions. All these wonders were made possible through the development of the lathe. It is the oldest and most important machine tool in industry.

The modern lathe can perform many different operations. In studying the history of other machines, we find that the idea of their operation comes from the lathe. There are more lathes in this country than any other kind of metalworking machine tool.

The lathe, Fig. 990, performs many kinds of external and internal machining operations. *Turning*, Fig. 1040, is the most common external machining operation performed on a lathe. Turning can produce either straight, curved, or irregular cylindrical shapes. (Also see Fig. 1021.) Other external, machining operations performed on a lathe include knurling, Fig. 1054, and thread cutting, Fig. 1066. The lathe can also perform most of the internal hole-machining operations which are normally performed on a drill press. These include drilling, centerdrilling, countersinking, counterboring, boring, and reaming. (See Figs. 457, 1032, 1050, and 1052.)

Only a few of the most common turning, boring, hole machining, and thread machining operations are explained in this unit.

1177.   Who Runs the Lathe?

A person who earns his living by doing different operations on a lathe is a *lathe operator*. The *machinist* makes parts for machines on the lathe. The *toolmaker* makes parts of tools on the lathe. The *jeweler* makes small parts of jewelry on a small lathe which is called a *jeweler's lathe*. The *metal spinner* (Fig. 1090) and *pewterer* spin bowls, trays, saucers, etc., on the lathe. (See § 1215.) The *metal pattern-maker* makes parts for metal patterns on a lathe. (See § 962.)

1178.   Lathe and Its Parts

Before attempting to operate a lathe you should become familiar with the principal component parts, units, and controls on the lathe. These are named in Figs. 990 and 993. By studying Fig. 993 carefully, you can understand the function of each major assembly unit in relation to other major parts on the

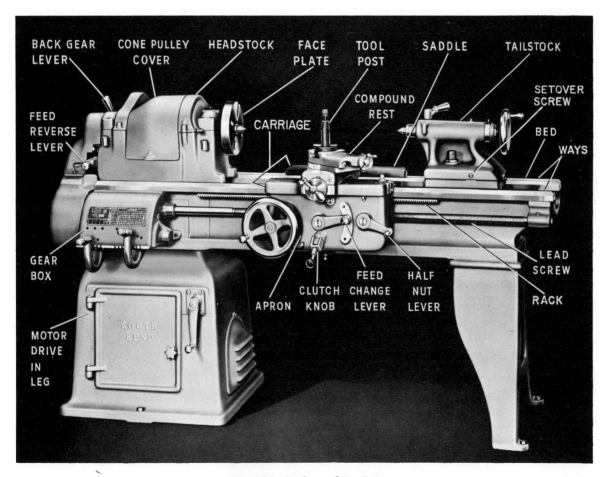

Fig. 990.   Lathe and Its Parts
(Courtesy South Bend Lathe, Inc.)

lathe. The major parts may be designed somewhat differently on different lathes; however, the basic principles which apply to their function are much the same for all lathes.

The controls on different lathes may also be designed somewhat differently. However, all lathes are equipped with similar controls, and these controls perform similar functions. When you have learned the names of the principal parts, parts units, and controls, you can learn to operate the lathe without damaging the machine or injuring yourself.

The *lathe bed* is the long part which rests on four legs. The *headstock* is fastened to the left end of the bed, and the *tailstock* can be clamped at any point along the bed. The *carri-*

age is the part which slides back and forth on the bed between the headstock and the tailstock. The V-shaped tracks of the bed upon which the carriage and tailstock slide are called *ways*.

1179. Size of Lathe

Lathes range in size from tiny *jewelers' lathes* to large machines. A small lathe that sets on a bench is a *bench lathe*.

Fig. 992 shows that the size of a lathe is measured by:

(1) *Swing.*

(2) *Length of bed.*

The *swing* is measured by the largest diameter of work that can be turned in the lathe.

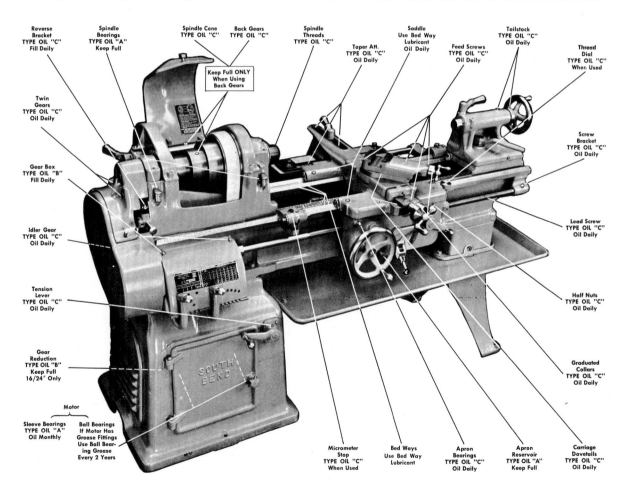

Fig. 991. Oiling the Lathe
(Courtesy South Bend Lathe, Inc.)

For example, a piece 10″ in diameter is the largest work that can be turned in a 10″ lathe. Thus a 10″ × 5′ lathe has a 10″ swing and a bed 5′ long.

1180. Getting Acquainted with the Lathe

Get acquainted with the lathe by first cleaning it thoroughly and then oiling it. The power should be turned off before this is done so there will be no danger of getting caught in a running lathe.

Move the different handles and levers without power to find out what happens. Parts should move easily, without force. Slide the tailstock to the end of the *lathe bed*. Then move the carriage by hand to about the center of the bed. Next, turn the lathe spindle, Fig. 991, by hand to see if any part of the lathe is locked. CAUTION: *If the lathe is turned on while the spindle or any part of the lathe is locked, the lathe may be damaged.* The spindle may have been locked by the previous operator in order to install or remove a face plate or chuck. Ask your instructor to explain how to unlock the spindle, or free any other part of the lathe which is locked, before you start the lathe.

Next, request permission from your instructor to turn on the power. Then, carefully put the lathe through its movements. CAUTION: *Most lathes must be stopped while shifting, adjusting, or changing any of the controls on the headstock end of the machine.* Check with your instructor to see if any of the controls on the headstock end of your lathe may be changed while the lathe is running. The controls on the apron or carriage generally can be moved while the machine is turned on and running. The proper methods for determining the cutting speed, determining the rpm, and setting the rpm of the spindle are explained in section 1182. The depth of cut, suggested feeds, and the procedures for using automatic feeds are explained in section 1183.

1181. Oiling the Lathe

The lathe should be oiled every day with good *lubricating oil*. (See § 394 and Table 14 for grades and comparative brands.) The places where the lathe should be oiled are shown in Fig. 991. Consult the chart for your lathe as requirements may vary. Some lathes have lubrication charts mounted on the machine. Only a drop or two of oil in each *oil hole* is necessary. Keep the *ways* clean and oiled. (See § 1178.) Wipe off all wasted oil.

1182. Cutting Speed and RPM

Cutting speed on a lathe is the speed at which the circumference of the work passes the tool bit. It is expressed as surface feet per minute (sfm). If a continuous chip were cut on a lathe for one minute, the length of the chip would be the cutting speed.

Cutting speed is related to *rpm* (revolutions per minute). On a lathe, rpm means the number of revolutions of the work in one minute. For a stated cutting speed, work of large diameter should run at a lower rpm than work of small diameter.

Soft metal generally should be machined at a higher cutting speed than hard metal. A *rough cut* is made at a lower cutting speed

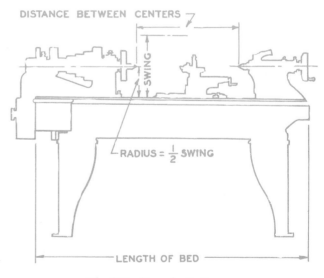

Fig. 992. Size of a Lathe

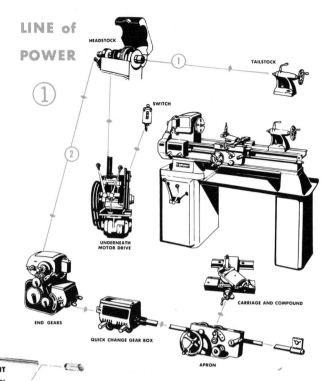

LINE of POWER ▶ ▶

Electrical energy is turned into working power by the motor, then transferred efficiently through the V-belt drive to

(**1**) Rotate work

(**2**) Move the cutting tool

LINE of POWER ①

② SWITCH

① HEADSTOCK

TAILSTOCK

UNDERNEATH MOTOR DRIVE

END GEARS

QUICK CHANGE GEAR BOX

APRON

CARRIAGE AND COMPOUND

② **HEADSTOCK**

Headstock supports spindle which rotates on "Zero Precision" tapered roller bearings. Work holders are mounted on spindle nose.

COLLET ATTACHMENT

Collet attachment passes through the hole through entire length of the spindle. Special jaws on collet, release or grip small diameter work at the spindle nose.

LATHE DOG, DOG PLATE AND CENTERS

The lathe dog clamps around the work piece. The dog plate mounts on the spindle. As work piece is placed on the spindle nose center, the tail of the lathe dog is slipped into a slot in the dog plate so that when dog plate revolves it turns the work piece.

TAILSTOCK

Tailstock center supports right end of work held "between centers." It can be offset to cut tapers, locked in any position along lathe bed, and has handwheel feed for tailstock tools.

CHUCK

Chuck mounts on spindle nose. Adjustable jaws permit holding of larger diameter, odd-shaped or stub-end work.

HOLDING and ROTATING WORK

CARRIAGE AND COMPOUND

Carriage provides rigid support for cross-slide and travels — either to the right or left along the bed. Cross slide moves compound in or out with power feed or handwheel. Compound swivels to provide angular feeds.

DETAIL FROM APRON (REAR VIEW)

Lead screw transmits power through apron by (1) spline drive for power feeds and (2) by half nuts for thread cutting. Precision lead screw threads are used only for thread cutting.

③ **END GEARS**

Outboard gear on spindle drives end gear train which operates lead screw through gear box.

QUICK CHANGE GEAR BOX

Double tumbler levers permit rapid selection of desired ratio (Pitch and feed) between spindle r.p.m. and lead screw r.p.m.

APRON (FRONT VIEW)

Apron controls are centrally grouped with selector lever for power longitudinal and cross feeds, friction clutch for engaging feeds, half-nut lever for thread cutting, and hand wheel for hand traverse of carriage. Built-in safety mechanisms prevent engaging half-nuts and power feeds at the same time.

HOLDING and MOVING TOOL

Fig. 993. How a Modern Lathe Operates
(Courtesy Sheldon Machine Co.)

than a *finish cut*. Different metals are cut at different cutting speeds. Suggested cutting speeds for various metals are listed in Table 37.

The cutting speed or rpm for lathe work can be determined with the following formulas:

D = Diameter of work in inches

Pi = Constant 3.1416 (Round off Pi to 3 for quicker calculations)

CS = Cutting speed in surface feet per minute

rpm = Revolutions per minute

$$CS = \frac{D'' \times Pi \times rpm}{12}$$

$$rpm = \frac{CS' \times 12}{D'' \times Pi}$$

Recommended cutting speeds for each kind of steel are included within a range. For example, a recommended cutting speed for turning ordinary low-carbon steel is from about 90′ to 100′ per minute, see Table 37. Hence, it is not necessary to calculate cutting speeds or rpm to exact decimal figures. Therefore, most mechanics substitute the figure 3 instead of 3.1416 for Pi when calculating approximate cutting speeds or rpm for machining metals.

Example: Calculate the approximate cutting speed for stock 1″ diameter in a lathe, revolving at 344 rpm.

$$CS = \frac{1 \times \overset{1}{\cancel{3}} \times 344}{\underset{4}{\cancel{12}}} = \frac{\overset{86}{\cancel{344}}}{\underset{1}{\cancel{4}}}$$

CS = 86 feet per minute

Example: Calculate the approximate rpm for a piece of steel 1¼″ diameter which is to be machined at 90 feet per minute.

$$rpm = \frac{90 \times \overset{4}{\cancel{12}}}{1.25 \times \cancel{3}} = \frac{360}{1.25}$$

rpm = 288

The above formulas also may be used for calculating the cutting speeds for drilling and milling. In these cases, *D* is the diameter of the drill or the milling cutter.

The cutting speed or rpm may also be determined by consulting a *table of cutting speeds*. (See Table 40, p. 550.) These tables are available in technical handbooks and wall charts.

The *cone pulley* and *back gears*, Fig. 994, on the headstock make it possible to run the lathe at different speeds. The back gears are fastened to a shaft behind the cone pulley. A lathe with a *4-step cone pulley* and back gears has eight different speeds. (See Fig. 996.) Each of the four steps of the cone pulley gives a different speed, making four speeds; by using the back gears four slower speeds are obtained, making eight different speeds in all. When the back gears are not used, the *bull-gear pin* (see Fig. 994) must be engaged. When the back gears are used, the bull-gear pin must be disengaged. The back gears can be connected with the cone pulley by shifting the *back-gear lever* while the lathe is stopped.

Some lathes have V-type step pulleys which are driven by a V-belt instead of a flat belt,

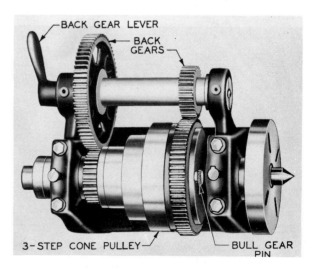

Fig. 994. Cone Pulley and Back Gears
(Courtesy South Bend Lathe, Inc.)

Fig. 997. When spindle speeds are changed with this type of pulley, the tension on the belt is first released with a release lever provided for this purpose. The belt then is moved manually to the desired step on the pulley.

The lathe in Fig. 993 has a lever-shift V-belt drive system. Speed changes with this drive are made by shifting either or both of the speed change levers to the desired position. This system provides four speeds in direct drive and four speeds in back-geared drive.

Some lathes have a *variable-speed drive* system. This kind of belt drive system also is used on drill presses and some other kinds of machines. (See Fig. 326 and § 422). Drive systems of this type are infinitely variable. This means that any desired rpm, within the speed range of the lathe, may be selected.

CAUTION: *With most V-belt variable speed-drive systems changes in speed can be made only while the lathe is running.*

With a *geared-head drive* system, as on the lathe in Fig. 998, changes in speed are made by shifting the speed-change levers. This involves shifting gears, not belts, see Fig. 999. On most head-geared drive systems, however, the lathe must be stopped in order to change speeds. CAUTION: *If the gears are shifted while the lathe is running, serious gear damage may result.*

1183. Carriage Feed, Depth of Cut, and Threading Mechanism

The lathe is designed so that the cutting tool may be fed manually or automatically along the work while machining. The feed is called *longitudinal feed* when the tool is fed

Table 37
SUGGESTED LATHE TOOL DATA FOR MACHINING VARIOUS METALS WITH HIGH-SPEED STEEL TOOL BITS[2]

MATERIAL	SIDE RELIEF	END RELIEF	TRUE BACK RAKE	SIDE RAKE	SUGGESTED CUTTING SPEEDS IN FEET PER MINUTE[3]
Aluminum	10°	10°	35°	15°	200-1500
Brass	10°	8°	0°	0°	150- 300
Bronze	10°	8°	0°	0°	90- 100
Cast Iron, Hard	8°	8°	5°	8°	30- 50
Cast Iron, Malleable	8°	8°	8°	10°	80- 100
Cast Iron, Soft	8°	8°	8°	10°	50- 80
Fiber	15°	15°	0°	0°	80- 100
Free Machining Steel	10°	10°	16°	10°	150- 350
High-Carbon Steel	8°	8°	8°	8°	50- 70
Low-Carbon Steel	10°	10°	16°	10°	90- 100
Medium-Carbon Steel	10°	10°	12°	10°	70- 90
Plastics, Acrylics	15°	15°	0°	0°	60- 70
Plastics, Molded	10°	12°	0°	0°	150- 300

[2]All angles are true working angles measured from horizontal and vertical planes.

[3]Use the lower speeds on roughing cuts and when machining dry. Use higher speeds when using cutting fluids and for finishing cuts. See Table 15 for selection of cutting fluids.

along the work, parallel to the lathe bed. The longitudinal feed is used for operations such as *turning*, Fig. 1040, and boring, Fig. 1052. The feed is called *cross feed* when the tool is fed across the end of the workpiece, as in facing operations, Fig. 1030.

The amount of longitudinal feed is the distance that the tool moves along the workpiece during one revolution of the work. The amount of cross feed is the distance the tool moves across the end of the workpiece (in or out) during one revolution of the work.

The amount of feed, including both longitudinal and cross feed, is controlled through the use of the feeding and threading mechanisms on the lathe. These mechanisms include the end gears, Fig. 1000; the quick-change gear box, Fig. 1001; and the *carriage and apron assembly,* as shown in Fig. 1003.

The *end gears* transmit power from the lathe spindle to the lead screw through the *gear box.* The lead screw transmits power to

Fig. 996. Lathe with Flat-Belt Drive
(Courtesy South Bend Lathe, Inc.)

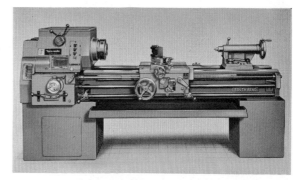

Fig. 998. Modern-Geared Head Lathe
(Courtesy South Bend Lathe, Inc.)

Fig. 997. Manual-Shift V-Belt Drive
(Courtesy Sheldon Machine Co.)

Fig. 999. Headstock with All-Geared Drive
(Courtesy South Bend Lathe, Inc.)

Fig. 1000. End-Gear Train
(Courtesy South Bend Lathe, Inc.)

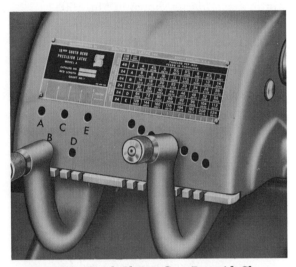

Fig. 1001. Quick-Change Gear Box with Chart
(Courtesy South Bend Lathe, Inc.)

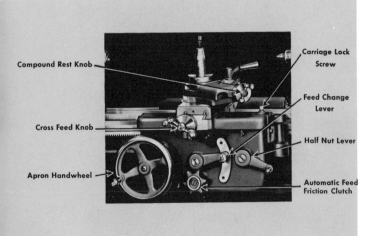

Fig. 1003. Parts of Lathe Carriage and Apron
Assembly (Courtesy South Bend Lathe, Inc.)

the carriage and apron assembly. (See Fig. 993.)

The controls on the carriage and apron affect all movements of the tool and the carriage. The *apron handwheel* is used for manual, longitudinal movement of the carriage. The *cross-feed knob* is used for manual cross feed of the tool. The *compound-rest knob* is used to feed the tool manually with the compound rest. The *carriage-lock screw* may be tightened to lock the carriage and thus prevent longitudinal movement for operations such as facing. (See Fig. 1030.)

The compound rest is normally set at an angle of about 29° from the crosswise position, as in Fig. 1003. This is the angle at which it is set for cutting Unified and American (National) Screw threads (Fig. 1071). It also is a convenient angle for performing a majority of other lathe operations. The compound rest may be swiveled and set at any desired angle for turning or boring tapers. (See Fig. 1048.)

The *feed-change lever* is used to select any of the following feeds: longitudinal feed, cross feed, and feeds for threading. For longitudinal or cross feeding, the lever is moved to the upper or lower position as desired. For thread-cutting feeds, the feed change lever is located at the center position as shown in Fig. 1003.

The *clutch knob*, Fig. 990, (also called the *automatic-feed knob*, Fig. 1003) is used to engage or disengage automatic longitudinal or cross feed. The *half-nut lever*, Fig. 1003, is used to engage the feed for thread-cutting

SOUTH BEND LATHE WORKS				SOUTH BEND, IND. U.S.A.					
	STUD GEAR	LEFT HAND TUMBLER	THREADS PER INCH FEEDS IN THOUSANDTHS						
POWER CROSS FEED .375 TIMES LONGITUDINAL FEED	48	A	4 .0841	4½ .0748	5 .0673	5¼ .0612	5½ .0585	6 .0561	6½ .0518	7 .0481
	24	A	8 .0421	9 .0374	10 .0337	11 .0306	11½ .0293	12 .0280	13 .0259	14 .0240
	24	B	16 .0210	18 .0187	20 .0168	22 .0153	23 .0146	24 .0140	26 .0129	28 .0120
	24	C	32 .0105	36 .0093	40 .0084	44 .0076	46 .0073	48 .0070	52 .0065	56 .0060
	24	D	64 .0053	72 .0047	80 .0042	88 .0038	92 .0037	96 .0035	104 .0032	112 .0030
	24	E	128 .0026	144 .023	160 .0021	176 .0019	184 .0018	192 .0017	208 .016	224 .0015

Fig. 1002. Index Chart for Quick-Change Gear
Lathe (Courtesy South Bend Lathe, Inc.)

operations only. The *feed-reverse lever,* Fig. 990, is used to reverse the direction of the lead screw, and thus reverse the direction of either longitudinal or cross feeds.

The levers on the quick-change gear box, Fig. 1001, are used for the selection of feeds. An *index plate,* Fig. 1002, is located on the quick-change gear box, Fig. 1001. Note that there are large numbers and small decimal numbers on the index plate. The large numbers indicate the pitch or number of threads per inch for threading operations only. Hence, if the large number 16 were selected, the lathe would feed longitudinally $\frac{1}{16}''$ for each revolution of the workpiece. The carriage would travel 1″ while the workpiece revolved 16 times. Thus 16 threads would be cut for 1″ of length. The *half-nut lever* must be used for threading operations, and it will function only when the *feed-change lever* is in the center position.

The small decimal numbers on the index plate indicate the amount of feed per revolution for longitudinal and cross feeds. It should be noted that the amount of cross feed is not always the same as the amount of longitudinal feed. This varies on different lathes. For the lathe represented in Fig. 1001, the cross feed is equal to 0.375 times the longitudinal feed. Thus, if a coarse feed of 0.0105″ were selected, the cross feed would equal 0.375 × 0.0105″, or 0.004″ per revolution of the workpiece. The ratio of cross feed to longitudinal feed generally is indicated on the index plate located on the quick-change gear box, Fig. 1002.

The wheels, levers, and knobs used for the selection and control of feeds and speeds are designed somewhat differently for different lathes. Therefore, it is always best to have your instructor show you how these controls work before operating the lathe. This information is often available in the *maintenance manual* which generally is delivered by the manufacturer with each new lathe.

Feed Selection

The amount of feed varies with the type of metal and the *depth of cut.* Soft metals are generally cut with coarser feeds than hard metals. Finishing cuts are made with finer feeds than roughing cuts. Suggested feeds for machining steel would be .010″ for a rough cut and .005″ for a finish cut.

Depth of cut means the distance the tool is advanced into the work at a right angle to the work. It is the depth measured between the machined surface and the work surface, Fig. 1004. This definition is true for all machine tools. A deeper cut may be taken on soft metals than on hard metals. The depth of a finishing cut is less than the depth of a roughing cut. On small lathes a common rough cut depth in steel would be .060″ to .125″. Finishing cuts are usually .010″ to .020″ on any lathe. Cuts less than .010″ deep generally are too small to be accurate. A .010″ cut removes .020″ from the diameter. A $\frac{1}{16}''$ cut removes $\frac{1}{8}''$ from the diameter, see Fig. 1004.

1184. Lathe Chucks

A lathe chuck is used to hold work. It should be screwed on or off the *headstock spindle* (see Fig. 1035) while the lathe is stopped. There are three principal kinds of

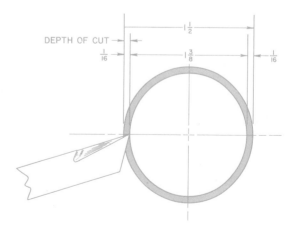

DEPTH OF CUT

$1\frac{1}{2}$

$\frac{1}{16}$

$\frac{3}{8}$

$\frac{1}{16}$

Fig. 1004. The Diameter is Reduced Twice the Depth of the Cut When Turning

lathe chucks: the *four-jaw independent chuck,* Fig. 1005; the *three-jaw universal chuck,* Fig. 1006; and *collet chucks,* Figs. 1007 and 1008.

The *four-jaw independent chuck* has four *jaws* and each must be moved separately with

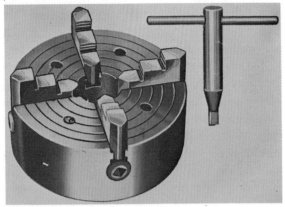

Fig. 1005. Four-Jaw Independent Chuck
(Courtesy South Bend Lathe, Inc.)

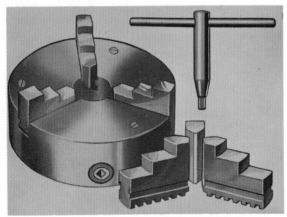

Fig. 1006. Three-Jaw Universal Chuck
(Courtesy South Bend Lathe, Inc.)

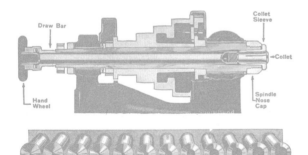

Fig. 1007. Cross Section of Collet Chuck and Set of Collets (Courtesy South Bend Lathe, Inc.)

a *chuck key,* also called a *chuck wrench;* it is used chiefly to hold work that is not perfectly round. It may be used to hold work which is round, square, rectangular, or irregular in shape. The jaws on this kind of a chuck are *reversible;* that is, they can be taken off and put on again in the opposite direction. They have steps so that different sizes of work can be held as shown in Figs. 1012 and 1052.

The four-jaw chuck is more accurate than a three-jaw chuck because the work can be centered in the chuck exactly with a dial indicator. (See Figs. 946 and 947.) However, even with considerable experience, it takes much more time to center work accurately in a four-jaw chuck than in a three-jaw universal chuck.

The *three-jaw universal chuck* has three jaws that work at the same time. Thus when one jaw is screwed down upon the work with the chuck key, the other two jaws move also. This kind of chuck usually has two sets of jaws; one set holds the larger work while the

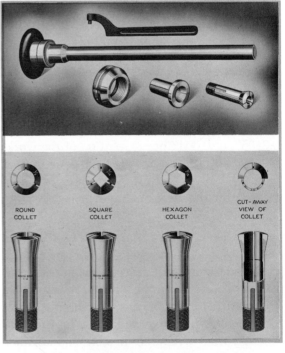

Fig. 1008. Collet Chuck and Types of Collets
(Courtesy South Bend Lathe, Inc.)

other set holds rings and small work (see Figs. 1030, 1032, and 1054). Three-jaw universal chucks center work accurately to within 0.002″ to 0.003″. Generally, they retain this accuracy until either the jaws become worn or the threads on the spindle nose become nicked or damaged.

Collet chucks of the spring collet-type, Fig. 1008, are made to hold work which is close to a specific diameter. A spring collet should be used only for holding work which is within about 0.005″ of the designated size of the collet. They are commonly used for work smaller than 1″ in diameter.

There are several types available. A common one is the *draw-in type* which fits into the nose of the lathe spindle with a hand-wheel draw bar. Collets are available in sizes by ¼₄ths, up to 1⅟₁₆″ diameter. Collet chucks are very accurate, save time in mounting work, and speed up production.

There are two other kinds of spindles: the long, taper-key drive spindle shown in Fig. 1009 and the cam-lock type spindle shown in Fig. 1010. Each is removed differently.

Chucks should be handled carefully. They should be oiled regularly, kept clean, and not overloaded or abused. The threads in threaded nose chucks should be cleaned with a thread cleaning tool as in Fig. 1011.

1185. Chucking

Chucking means to fasten work in a *lathe chuck* (see Figs. 1005 and 1006) so that it will not wobble when turning. This is called *truing.*

A *four-jaw independent chuck* will hold work that is not perfectly round. Each jaw works separately. Place the work in the center of the chuck between the four jaws and tighten them. The circles on the chuck (see Fig. 1012) help to locate the work in the center. Then run the lathe at a medium speed, rest the hand on the *carriage* or on the *compound rest,* and hold a piece of chalk so that it touches only the high spots of the work as

Fig. 1009. **Spindle Nose with Long-Taper Key Drive**
(Courtesy South Bend Lathe, Inc.)

Fig. 1010. **Cam-Lock Spindle**
(Courtesy South Bend Lathe, Inc.)

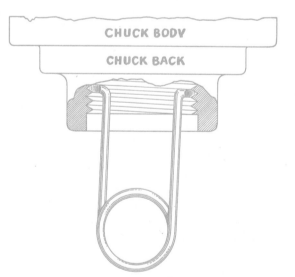

Fig. 1011. **Cleaning Threads in Chuck**

it turns, Fig. 1012. The *chalk mark* tells which jaws have to be reset. It usually takes a few trials of marking with chalk to get the work to turn without wobbling.

The *chalk method* of centering work in a four-jaw chuck is accurate enough for many lathe operations. It is satisfactory for jobs which can be completed in one setup. For operations requiring more accurate centering,

a dial indicator is used. (See Figs. 945, 946, and 947.) However, the workpiece should always be centered as close as possible by the chalking method described above, before using the dial indicator. The workpiece then can be centered exactly with the dial indicator, see Figs. 1013 and 1014.

When centering work in a four-jaw chuck with the use of the dial indicator, it is best to center the work between one pair of jaws at a time. For example, center the work between the jaws numbered 1 and 3, and test with the dial indicator until a zero reading is obtained at these locations on the workpiece. When the workpiece has been centered accurately between the first pair of jaws, it can be centered between the second pair easily and rapidly. To put work in a *three-jaw universal chuck*, place it between the jaws and tighten (see § 1184).

1186.   Lathe Cutting Tools

Cutting in the lathe is done with *cutting tools*, also called lathe tools. The *cutting edges* are shaped differently depending on the type of toolholder in which they will be mounted, the type of metal to be machined, and the type of cut to be made, Fig. 1021.

Lathe cutting tools are made of small pieces of cutting-tool material called *tool bits* and

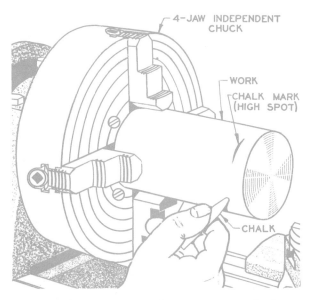

Fig. 1012. Truing Work in a Four-Jaw Chuck

Fig. 1013. Centering Work with a Dial-Test Indicator (Courtesy South Bend Lathe, Inc.)

Fig. 1014. Testing Face of Work with a Dial Indicator (Courtesy South Bend Lathe, Inc.)

held in a toolholder (see Fig. 1024). Cutting tools commonly are made of the following cutting-tool materials:

High-speed steel (see § 352).
Cemented-tungsten carbide (see § 350).
Cast alloys (see § 353).

The cutting edge of any cutting tool splits the metal like a *cold chisel* or a *wedge.* (See Fig. 187 and § 61.)

1187. Toolholders

The toolholder supports the *tool bits.* There are two common classes of turning tool-

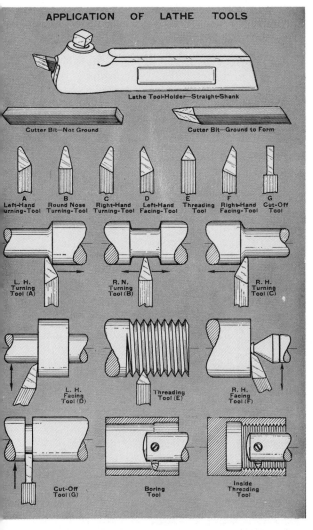

Fig. 1021. Lathe Tool Bits and Their Applications with Various Lathe Operations (Courtesy South Bend Lathe, Inc.)

holders: *16½° toolholders* and *zero-degree toolholders.* When the tool bit is mounted in a 16½° toolholder, it is tilted upward 16½°, increasing the back rake angle as in Fig. 1022. When a tool bit is mounted in the zero-degree toolholder, no back rake is provided by the holder, and any necessary back rake must be ground on the tool bit, as in Fig. 1023.

The zero-degree toolholder is designed for mounting tungsten carbide-tipped tools. See Fig. 1023. As the carbide tip is brittle, it must have a minimum *grinding angle.* This type of toolholder also may be used for tool bits made of high-speed steel or cast alloys, as in Fig. 1023. The grinding angle for tools in the 16½° toolholder is greater than for zero-degree toolholders. Compare Figs. 1022 and 1023.

The toolholder is mounted in the tool post, see Fig. 1027. There are three types of turning tool bit holders in each class: the *left-hand,* the *straight,* and the *right-hand* toolholders, see Fig. 1024.

The *left-hand toolholder* is bent so that cutting can be done close to the *chuck,* Fig. 1041, without the chuck striking the *carriage* or *compound rest.*

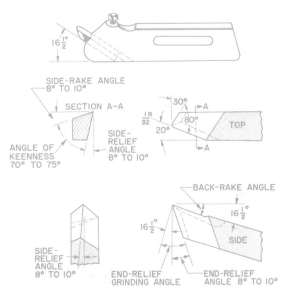

Fig. 1022. (Top) Standard 16½° Toolholder for High-Speed Steel Tool Bits; (Below) R. H. General-Purpose Turning Tool with Angles Given

The *right-hand toolholder* is bent so that cutting can be done close to the *tailstock.*

The *straight toolholder* is straight and is used for most *straight turning* on long work-pieces. (See § 1196 and Figs. 1022 and 1040.)

In addition to turning toolholders, the following kinds of toolholders with cutting tools also are used: cut-off tools, boring tools, knurling tools, and threading tools (see Fig. 1024).

1188. Grinding Lathe Turning Tools

Tool bits may be ground to many different shapes (see Fig. 1021) with good machining results. However, the basic relief angles and rake angles must be provided.

Locate each of the terms below in Fig. 1025. Also, locate some of these terms in Figs. 1022 and 1023.

Face: The face is the top ground portion of the tool from which the chips slide off.

Flank: The flank is the ground surface below the cutting edge of the tool.

Nose angle: The angle formed by the side-cutting edge and the end-cutting edge.

Nose radius: The rounded portion of the nose of the tool. The nose radius for a finishing tool is greater than for a roughing tool (see Fig. 1026).

Side-relief (formerly side clearance) is the angle formed between the flank and a vertical plane or the work being cut.

End-relief (formerly front clearance) *angle* is the angle formed at the nose of the tool bit between the ground end of the tool and the work.

End-relief grinding angle is the angle which must be ground on the end of the tool bit in order to produce the actual end relief when the tool is mounted in the lathe. For tools

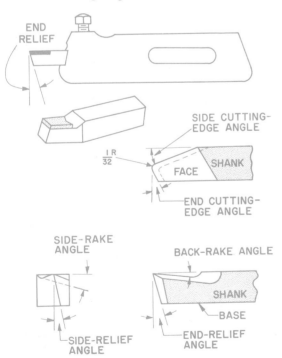

Fig. 1023. (Top) Zero-Degree Toolholder;
(Below) L. H. General-Purpose Turning Tool
(Note grinding angles are the same as relief angles.)

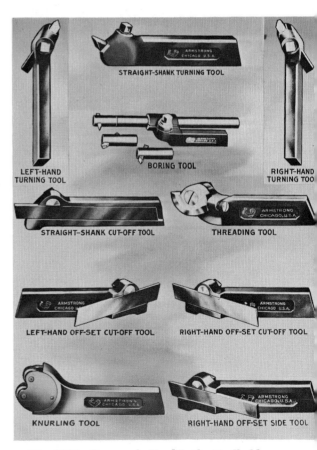

Fig. 1024. **Commonly Used Lathe Toolholders and Cutting Tools**
(Courtesy Armstrong Bros. Tool Co.)

mounted at the level of the lathe center in a zero-degree toolholder, as in Fig. 1028, the end grinding angle is the same as the end relief. Carbide-tipped tools, Fig. 1023, generally are set at the level of the center line of the work, as in Fig. 1028. For tools mounted in a 16½° toolholder, the end-grinding angle is greater than the actual end-relief angle (see Fig. 1022). The end-relief angle is checked with the tool mounted in the toolholder, as shown in Fig. 1029.

Side-rake angle is the angle formed between the face of the tool and a horizontal plane. When a continuous, long wirelike chip is formed, a decreased side-rake angle will frequently cause the chip to coil up and break off.

Back-rake angle is the angle formed between a horizontal plane and a line sloping back from the cutting edge at the end of the tool. A back-rake angle of 16½° is automatically provided for tools mounted in a 16½° toolholder. Tools mounted in a zero-degree toolholder have no back rake provided and any required back rake must be ground on the tool. The back-rake angle influences the direction in which the chip leaves the nose of the tool. A decreased back rake frequently

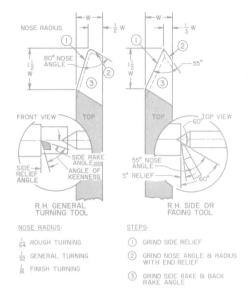

Fig. 1026. Grinding the Two Most-Used Tool Bits

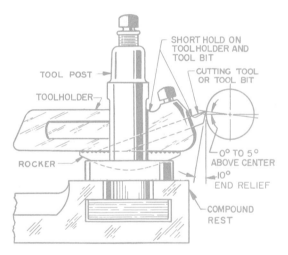

Fig. 1027. Setting the Cutting Tool

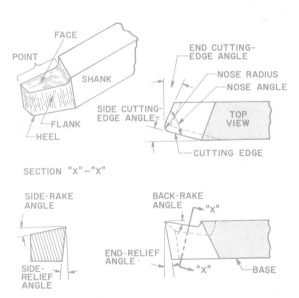

Fig. 1025. Cutting Tool Terms Applied to Single Point Tools Used on Lathes, Shapers, and Planers

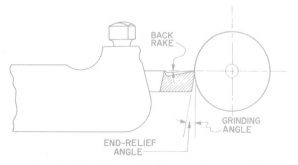

Fig. 1028. Cutting Tool Set on Center with Zero-Degree Toolholder

Fig. 1029. Checking Relief (Clearance) Angles on Tool Bit (Courtesy South Bend Lathe, Inc.)

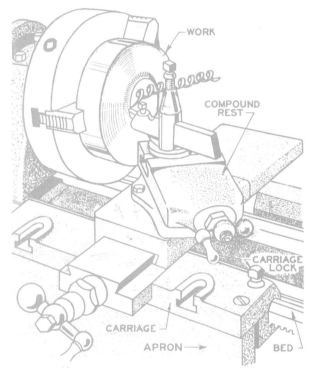

Fig. 1030. Facing Work Mounted in Chuck

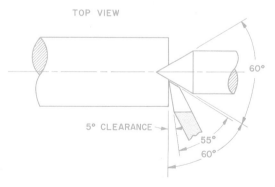

Fig. 1031. Right-Hand Side Facing Tool, Facing End of Work Between Centers of a Lathe

causes the chip to break off more readily. The *side-cutting edge angle* and the *end-cutting edge angle* are shown in Fig. 1025.

A *right-hand* (*RH*) *lathe tool bit* has the cutting edge on the left side. The tool cuts from right to left, or from the tailstock toward the headstock of the lathe (see Fig. 1022).

A *left-hand* (*LH*) *lathe tool bit* has the cutting edge on the right side. The tool cuts from left to right, or from the headstock toward the tailstock (see Fig. 1023).

In sharpening a lathe tool bit, first determine the grinding angles (see Table 37) for the type of tool bit desired. The steps for grinding a RH general turning tool and a RH facing tool are indicated in Fig. 1026. The angles should be checked carefully with a tool-angle gage at the angle the tool will be held in a holder, Fig. 1029. A tool-angle gage can be made very simply from a strip of sheet metal 2″ × 3″. The required side-relief angle and end-relief angle may be laid out with a bevel protractor (see Fig. 78) and cut off. Finally, the ground surfaces should be whetted on an oilstone to remove any roughness on the cutting edges or nose radius. Keep the tool cool while grinding by dipping it frequently in water.

1189. Setting the Cutting Tool

The *toolholder* should have a short hold on the *tool bit,* and the *tool post* should have a short hold on the toolholder, Fig. 1027. If the toolholder extends too far out of the tool post or if the tool bit extends too far out of the toolholder, the springing or vibrating of the cutting edge will cause *chatter marks.*

The tool post should be set to the left on the *compound rest* (see Fig. 1041).

The *cutting edge* of the tool should pass through the center of the work. A good way is to set the cutting edge of the tool at the height of the *lathe center.* High-speed steel tools may be set a little above as in Fig. 1027, if desired. Modern carbide-tipped tools (or those ground similarly) are set at the height of the lathe center, as in Fig. 1028.

1190. Facing

Facing is the cutting or *squaring* of the end of a piece of work, Fig. 1030. Set the cutting tool so that the cutting edge passes through the center and is the only part that touches the work. (See § 1189.) Then lock the *carriage* to the *bed* by tightening the *carriage lock,* Fig. 1030. This keeps the tool against the work.

When ready to start cutting, always turn the machine by hand to make sure that everything is set properly before turning on the power.

The type of tool and its setting for facing long work between centers of the lathe are

shown in Fig. 1031 and at the right in Fig. 1026.

1191. Centerdrilling

A piece of metal that is to be *turned* in the lathe must have small, *centerdrilled* holes in both ends. (See §§ 588-589 and 1196.) The small holes form *bearing* surfaces so that the work can be held between *lathe centers*, called *centers* for short. (See Fig. 1039.)

Locate the centers of the work first. (See § 115.) The drilled part of the hole must be deeper than the *countersunk* part to make room for the sharp point of the lathe center. It also holds a small amount of center lubricant to prevent the dead center from overheating. Centerdrilling is done with a combination drill and countersink, Fig. 1032. The

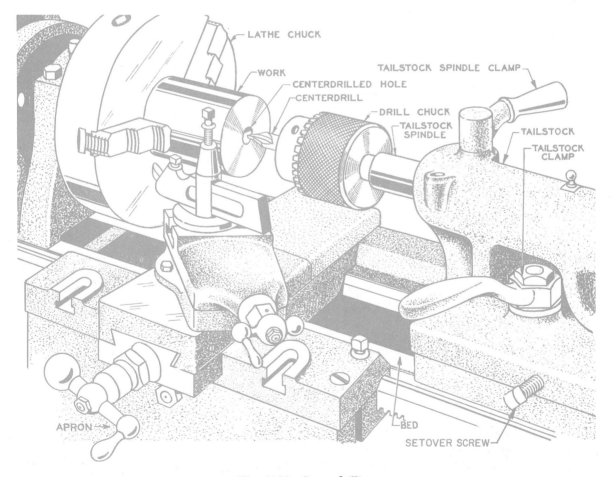

Fig. 1032. Centerdrilling

centerdrilled hole must be drilled to the proper depth, as shown at the top on Fig. 1033. If the hole is either too shallow or too deep, grooves will be worn in the lathe center, thus damaging it.

The centerdrilling may then be done on the drill press or on the lathe as in Fig. 1032. CAUTION: *Before centerdrilling on a lathe, the headstock and tailstock must be in accurate alignment.* The alignment may be checked by aligning the centers as shown in Fig. 1035. If the centers are not accurately aligned, the point of the centerdrill will break off.

To centerdrill on the lathe, fasten the *centerdrill* in a *drill chuck* which is held in the *tailstock*. Fasten the work in the *lathe chuck*. Then, slide the tailstock so that the centerdrill is near the work, and clamp the tailstock to the *bed*. The centerdrilling is then done by turning the *handwheel* of the tailstock while the work is turning.

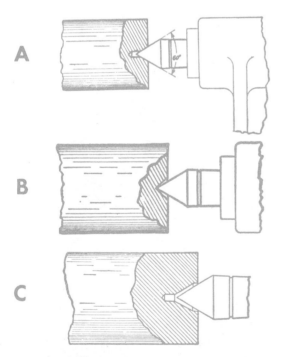

Fig. 1033. Good and Poor Center Drilled Holes
(Courtesy South Bend Lathe, Inc.)
  A. Good
  B. Hole too Shallow and Wrong Angle
  C. Hole too Deep

To save the time of chucking the work, especially when many pieces must be centerdrilled, the centerdrill and drill chuck may be held in the headstock and the work held firmly against the tailstock center with the left hand. The tailstock handwheel is then turned with the right hand to move the work against the centerdrill.

Use oil when drilling steel. *Cast iron* should be drilled dry.

1192.   Faceplate

The faceplate (see Figs. 1039 and 1041) is used instead of the lathe chuck on some work such as *straight turning.* (See § 1196.)

1193.   Lathe Centers
and Setover Screws

The two lathe centers, called *centers* for short, are used to support the work (see Fig. 1039). The one in the headstock is called the *headstock center* or *live center* because it turns with the *headstock spindle.* The center in the *tailstock spindle* is called the *tailstock center* or *dead center* because it does not turn. Both centers have a *Morse taper* (see Fig. 1034 and § 492).

The point of the dead center must be *hardened* (see § 951) to make it tough so that when the work rubs on it and causes heat, the point will not wear off.

The tailstock center may be removed from the tailstock spindle by turning the *handwheel.* This screws the spindle into the tailstock and knocks out the center. To loosen the center in the headstock spindle, put a rod called a *knockout rod* in the hole at the other end of the spindle. Hold the center with the right hand, and with the left hand tap lightly with the bar.

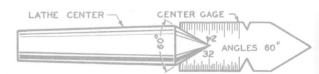

Fig. 1034. Testing the Angle of a Lathe Center

Good work depends to a great extent upon the condition of the lathe centers. Each point must have an angle of 60° which may be tested with a *center gage*, Fig. 1034. The lathe centers and the *spindle holes* must be very clean because the smallest nick or speck of dirt will cause trouble with the work at a later time. They must fit the spindle holes exactly so that there will be no looseness.

The centers must also be tested for *alignment* which means that the two points must meet when the tailstock with its center is slid up to the headstock center, Fig. 1035. Run the lathe at a medium speed to see if the live center wobbles. If it wobbles, a new point must be cut or ground on it.

For straight turning, the centers must be perfectly aligned. For taper turning, the tailstock may be intentionally moved off center a calculated amount. If the dead center is to one side of the live center, it is aligned by turning the *setover screws* on the tailstock, Fig. 1036. The alignment of the centers can best be tested by taking a straight cut (see § 1196) and then measuring the diameter at both ends of the work with a micrometer. If both measurements are the same, the centers are *aligned* and the turning may go on. If the measurements are not the same, the setover screws have to be set again and another cut must be made for another test. This must be repeated until both measurements are the same. Small movements can be determined with a dial indicator (see Figs. 945 and 946.)

1194. Lathe Dogs

A lathe dog, Fig. 1037, is used to keep work which is to be turned between centers from slipping (see Fig. 1039). It is clamped on the end of the work, Fig. 1038, which is then placed between centers. The *tail* of the dog slips into the slot in the faceplate.

There are many sizes of dogs. Use the smallest one that will slip over the work. The *clamp dog* is used for large work.

1195. Mounting Work Between Lathe Centers

To place work between centers for *straight turning* as in Fig. 1040:

Step 1: *Face* and *centerdrill* the work (see §§ 1190-1191).

Step 2: Screw the *faceplate* on the headstock spindle.

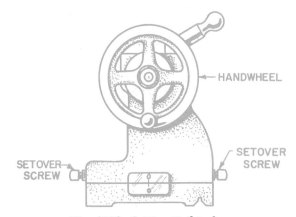

Fig. 1036. Setting Tailstock

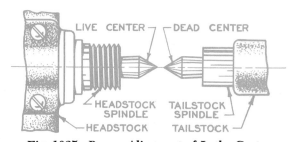

Fig. 1035. Proper Alignment of Lathe Centers, Viewed from Above

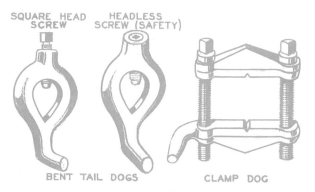

Fig. 1037. Lathe Dogs

Step 3: Clamp a *lathe dog* on the work (see Fig. 1038).

Step 4: Be sure the lathe centers are in good condition (see § 1193) and the centerdrilled holes in the ends of the work are clean. The center holes must be the proper depth, see Fig. 1033.

Step 5: Put a drop of center lubricant or a mixture of oil and *white lead* (see § 397) in the centerdrilled hole which goes on the tailstock center.

Step 6: Place the work between the lathe centers, Fig 1039, by sliding the *tailstock* up to the work.

Step 7: Clamp the tailstock to the *bed*.

Step 8: Turning the *handwheel* on the tailstock will set the *dead center* so that the work will move freely on the centers, yet be tight enough to allow no looseness endwise. The *tail* of the dog must fit loosely in the slot of the faceplate

when the work is set on centers, ready for straight turning.

Step 9: Clamp the *tailstock spindle clamp*. (See Fig. 1040.)

1196.   Straight Turning

For straight turning, Fig. 1040, the work is first placed on *centers,* and the cutting tool is set for cutting. (See §§ 1189 and 1195.) The tool should be set on the left side on the *compound rest* so that the *lathe dog* will not strike it, Fig. 1041. The compound rest is attached to the cross slide (see Fig. 1040). For most turning, the compound rest is set at an angle of about 29° or 30° from the crosswise position, as shown in Fig. 1040. However, when it is necessary to turn very close to the lathe dog or chuck, the compound rest may be set at the crosswise position, as shown in Fig. 1041.

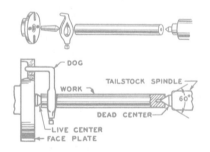

Fig. 1039. Work Held Between Lathe Centers

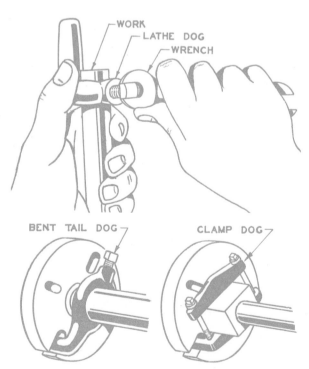

Fig. 1038. Fastening Lathe Dogs to the Work

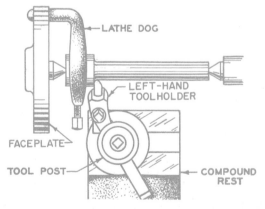

Fig. 1041. Setting the Tool Post and Toolholder to Cut Close to Faceplate

The cutting should be from the tailstock toward the headstock. The reason for this is that when the cutting is toward the headstock, the pressure is on the headstock center which turns with the work. Should the tool feed toward the tailstock, then the pressure is on the dead center. This increases the rubbing, and the point of the dead center may be damaged.

A squeak is a sign that something is wrong. Either the centers are too tight against the work or the dead center needs oiling.

1197.   Taper Turning

The machining of tapers is an important operation on the lathe.

There are three methods of turning tapers. The one chosen depends on the angle of the taper, the length of the taper, and the number of pieces to be turned. The *offset tailstock method* is most commonly used. In this method, the right end of the turning will be smaller when the tailstock is moved toward the operator and larger when moved away from the operator. Tapers can also be turned by using a *taper attachment* as in Fig. 1047. If the taper is short and the angle of taper is known, the taper can be turned by setting the compound rest for this angle and turning the compound rest feed screw by hand. Both internal and external tapers can be turned by the *compound rest method*. An internal taper can be bored as shown in Fig. 1048.

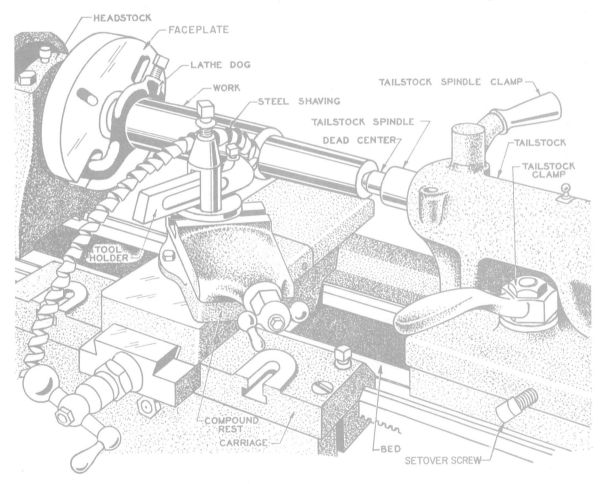

Fig. 1040. Straight Turning

The amount of taper may be specified either by the taper in inches per foot or by the length of the taper and the diameters at the ends of the taper. Two formulas will enable you to calculate the tailstock offset for either specification. In these formulas, the following symbols are used:

T = Total length of stock in inches

t = Length of portion to be tapered in inches

D = Large diameter

d = Small diameter

Offset = Setover of tailstock in inches

tpf = Taper per foot

Fig. 1047. Turning a Taper with a Taper Attachment (Courtesy South Bend Lathe, Inc.)

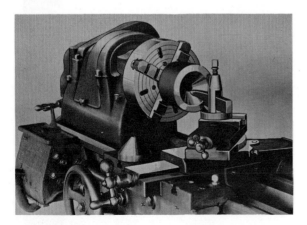

Fig. 1048. Boring an Internal Taper with Compound Rest-Set at Desired Angle (Courtesy South Bend Lathe, Inc.)

Taper given in inches per foot: Divide the total length of the stock in inches by 12 and multiply this quotient by one-half the taper per foot specified. The result is the offset in inches:

$$\text{Offset} = \frac{T}{12} \times \text{½ tpf}$$

For example, to calculate the amount of tailstock offset for turning work 4″ long with a taper of .600″ per foot:

$$\text{Offset} = \frac{4}{12} \times \text{½} \times .600''$$
$$= \frac{1}{3} \times .300''$$
$$= .100''$$

Diameters given at ends of taper: Divide the total length of the stock by the length of the portion to be tapered and multiply this quotient by one-half the difference in diameters. The result is the offset in inches:

$$\text{Offset} = \frac{T}{t} \times \text{½} \, (D - d)$$

For example, to calculate the amount of tailstock offset for turning work with a length of 6″, a tapered length of 3″, a large diameter of ½″ and a small diameter of ¼″:

$$\text{Offset} = \frac{6}{3} \times \text{½} \, (.500 - .250)$$
$$= .250''$$

To move the tailstock, use the setover screws shown in Fig. 1036. The most accurate way to determine the amount of the setover is to measure the offset between the live and dead centers, Fig. 1049. A dial indicator (see Fig. 945) may be used to observe accurately

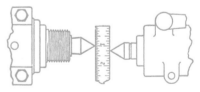

Fig. 1049. Checking Amount of Tailstock Setover

the amount of setover. The cutting edge of the tool must be exactly at the level of the center of the work when cutting tapers. (See Fig. 1028.)

1198. Drilling, Reaming, and Counterboring

Hole-machining operations such as drilling, reaming, countersinking, and counterboring are commonly performed with a drill press, see Fig. 457. These hole-machining operations can also be performed readily in a lathe. When they are performed in a lathe, the workpiece is held in an appropriate lathe chuck. The drill, reamer, countersink, or counterboring tool is held in the tailstock. The tailstock should always be accurately aligned with the headstock for all hole-machining operations, see Fig. 1035.

For drilling and reaming with small diameter, straight-shank drills, countersinks, and reamers, the tool is held in a drill chuck. The drill chuck is mounted in the tailstock, as in Fig. 1032. The tailstock is clamped to the lathe bed so that it does not move. The tool is then fed to the desired depth with the tailstock handwheel.

Larger drills with taper shanks are mounted directly into the tailstock, as shown in Fig. 1050. Taper-shank reamers, counterbores, and other special taper-shank cutting tools also may be mounted directly in the tailstock for hole-machining operations. Use a cutting fluid (Table 15) for hole-machining operations on steel. Cast iron may be machined dry.

The various kinds of reamers, countersinks, and counterboring tools are explained in Unit 30. The care and use of these tools are also explained in these sections. Hence, if you have not studied these sections previously, you should read them before using these tools.

1199. Boring in a Lathe

It is impossible to make an exact or perfect hole with a drill. This is explained in section 564. Also, a hole that is too large to be made

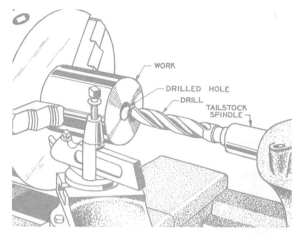

Fig. 1050. Drilling

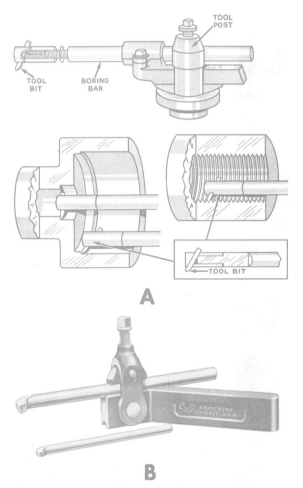

Fig. 1051. Internal Boring
(Courtesy Armstrong Bros. Tool Co.)
A. Boring Tool
B. Forged Boring Tool in Boring Toolholder

by a drill or a hole that must be made exactly round (*true*) is made by *boring.*

Boring is the cutting and enlarging of a round hole to make:

(1)   A more exact size.

(2)   A hole that will not wobble.

(3)   The hole accurate with its *axis.*

Boring is done with a *boring tool.* There are two kinds of boring tools: the kind that is shown in Figs. 1051-A and 1052 and the smaller, *forged* boring tools shown in Fig. 1051-B. The *tool bit* is held in a *boring bar* which is held in the *tool post* of a lathe, and the cutting is done as shown in Fig. 1052. The work turns, and the tool is held in a fixed position by the tool post and the carriage moves parallel to the axis of the hole.

Boring can also be done on a *drill press, milling machine* (see Fig. 1223), or on a specially built *boring machine;* in these machines the work is held still and the boring tool turns. (See § 597 and Figs. 457 and 468.)

1200.   Knurling

Handles on some tools and screws are made rough in order to give a better grip as the handles on *scribers* in Fig. 40. This is called *knurling*[4] and is done with a *knurling tool* in the lathe, Figs. 1053 and 1054. Two small hardened steel wheels or rolls, called *knurls,* turn in the knurling tool when pressed into the rotating work. There are coarse, medium, and fine knurls.

Procedure

1.   Set the knurling tool at a right angle to the work, Fig. 1054.

2.   Set the lathe for a slow back geared speed, see section 1182.

[4]Pronounced *nurling*; also spelled nurling.

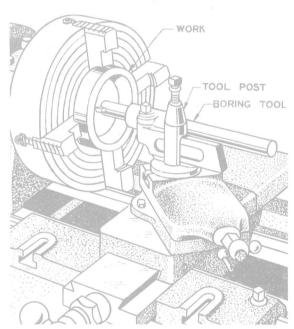

Fig. 1052. Boring

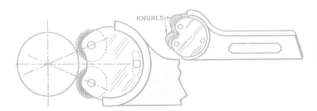

Fig. 1053. Knurling Tool

Fig. 1054. Knurling (Courtesy Armstrong Bros. Co.)

3. Set the lathe for a feed of about 0.020″ to 0.035″, see section 1183.

4. Force the tool slowly and firmly into the workpiece, starting at the right end.

5. Start lathe and apply cutting fluid liberally.

6. Engage the longitudinal feed, and let the tool feed across the workpiece to the desired length.

7. When the tool reaches the left end, disengage the longitudinal feed and stop the lathe. Without withdrawing the tool, reverse the direction of longitudinal feed. Cross feed the tool into the work about 0.010″ to 0.015″ more. Start the lathe, engage the longitudinal feed, and allow the tool to travel back to the right end. Repeat this procedure until the knurl is cut to the desired depth.

1201. Mounting Work on Mandrel

A *mandrel,* Fig. 1055, is a solid steel bar with a slight taper. Sometimes it is necessary to machine cylindrical parts accurately in relation to a drilled or bored hole which is in the part. Gear blanks, V-pulleys, and collars are parts of this type. When these kinds of parts are machined, a tapered mandrel is pressed into the hole in the part. A lathe dog is clamped on the mandrel and it is mounted between centers in the lathe, as shown in Fig. 1056. The outside diameter and the faces of the part are then machined accurately in relation to the hole.

1202. Cutoff Tool

Cutoff tools, Fig. 1057, are held in a cutoff-toolholder. Three kinds of cutoff-toolholders are shown in Fig. 1024; these include straight, right-hand and left-hand toolholders. The cutoff-tool blade should be ground as shown in Fig. 1057. An end relief of about 5° is adequate. Since the tool is provided with tapered sides which provide side relief, the sides should not be ground. A back rake of 0° to 5° is adequate.

Cutoff operations are performed on workpieces which are mounted in a chuck. CAU-

TION: *Never attempt to cut off stock mounted between centers.* To do so will cause the workpiece to bend or break and fly out of the lathe. The cutoff tool may be used for cutting grooves, cutting to a shoulder, or for cutting off stock. The cutoff tool should be mounted at the height of the centerline of the work, see Fig. 1028. If chatter or vibration develops, it generally can be reduced by reducing the cutting speed.

1203. Steady Rest and Follower Rest

A *steady rest* is used to hold long bars rigid or steady while turning, threading, or boring in a lathe. The steady rest can be used to sup-

Fig. 1055. Mandrel (Courtesy South Bend Lathe, Inc.)

Fig. 1056. Work Mounted on a Mandrel (Courtesy South Bend Lathe, Inc.)

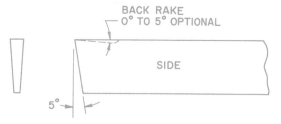

Fig. 1057. Cutoff Tool Blade

port work mounted in the chuck, as in Fig. 1058. It also can be used to support workpieces mounted between centers, as shown in Fig. 1059. The steady rest is clamped to the lathe bed. The jaws in the steady rest are adjusted so that they rub the work lightly. Machining operations can be performed with the carriage being used on either side of the steady rest.

A *follower rest* is a supporting device which is attached to the saddle of the lathe, as shown in Fig. 1059. It is used for either turning or cutting threads on long workpieces.

Fig. 1058. Using Steady Rest for Boring or Internal Threading (Courtesy South Bend Lathe, Inc.)

Fig. 1059. Using Both Steady Rest and Follower Rest for Cutting Threads in a Long Bar

The jaws on the follower rest are adjusted so they touch the work lightly. The follower rest follows along the work, thus holding it steady while the piece is being machined. The follower rest may be used alone, or it may be used in conjunction with the steady rest, as shown in Fig. 1059.

1204. Cutting Threads on a Lathe

Screw threads can be cut on work mounted in a lathe, as shown in Fig. 1066. The workpiece may be mounted in a chuck, or it may be mounted between centers. The threads may be right-hand, left-hand, internal or external threads.

Before cutting screw threads on a lathe, you should be familiar with the kinds of threads, thread fits, classes of threads, and the calculations necessary for cutting threads. This information is included in Unit 31.

The American (National) Form Thread is illustrated in Fig. 480. Information, concerning this kind of thread is included in section 615. Fits for this thread are explained in section 618.

The Unified (National) Form Thread is illustrated in Fig. 481. Information concerning this kind of thread is included in section 619. Formulas used for making thread calculations for this thread are included in section

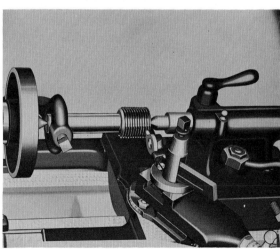

Fig. 1066. Cutting Thread on a Lathe

615. The thread classes(formerly called fits) for Unified Threads are explained in section 620. The devices for measuring screw threads for the proper fit or for the proper class of thread are explained in section 1151.

Thread-Cutting Tools

Two kinds of single-point, thread-cutting tools commonly are used for cutting threads on a lathe. An ordinary lathe tool bit may be ground as shown in Fig. 1067 for cutting either National Form Threads or Unified (National) Form Threads. If the tool is ground with a relatively sharp point, it may be used for cutting threads with a wide variety of pitches. The tool is set on the centerline of the work, Fig. 1069, for cutting threads. The tool also is set square with the work, Fig. 1070.

Another kind of thread-cutting tool is shown in Fig. 1068. The top face of this tool should always be in line with the shank of the tool-holder as shown. The tool is then set on the centerline, Fig. 1069, and is set square with

the work, Fig. 1070. This kind of threading tool also may be used for cutting either National Form Threads or Unified (National) Form Threads. The sides of the threading tool are designed so that there is always adequate side relief. Hence, the tool may be resharpened by grinding the top face only. The face is ground flat across the top so the tool may be used for cutting either right-hand or left-hand threads. When the cutting tool is worn out, a new one can be installed on the tool-holder.

When right-hand external Unified and American (National) Form Threads are cut, the compound rest should be set at a 29° angle to the right, as in Fig. 1071. The tool travels from the right toward the left for right-hand external threads. A thread with the desired 60° V-form is thus produced. Several cuts are required. The tool is fed into the work with the compound rest for each additional cut until the thread is cut to the desired pitch diameter. (See §§ 609 and 1151.)

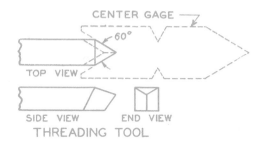

Fig. 1067. Threading-Tool Bit

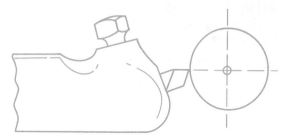

Fig. 1069. Top of Tool Bit Set on Center for Cutting Screw Threads

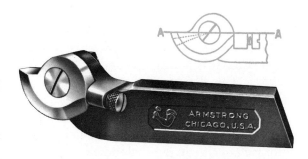

Fig. 1068. Threading Tool (Courtesy Armstrong Bros. Tool Co.)

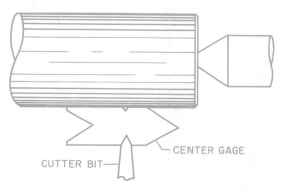

Fig. 1070. Threading-Tool Set Square with Work

When left-hand external threads are cut, the compound rest is swung 29° to the left. The feed is then reversed, and the carriage and the tool travel from the left toward the right.

The procedure for cutting external Unified and American (National) Form Threads is included in this section. An internal thread is cut with a threading tool bit inserted in a boring toolholder as shown in Fig. 1051. If you wish to cut internal threads, acme threads, or any other kind of special thread on a lathe, ask your instructor to show you the correct procedure. Procedures for cutting these kinds of threads are included in more advanced machine tool technology books.

Procedure:

The following is the procedure for cutting right-hand external Unified and American (National) screw threads on a lathe:

1. Determine the number of threads per inch to be cut. Set the quick-change gear levers to the desired pitch. (See Figs. 1001 and 1002.)

2. Determine the depth of the thread. (See §§ 607 and 615.)

3. Mount the stock in the lathe. It may be mounted in the chuck or between centers, depending on the length and design of the part to be threaded.

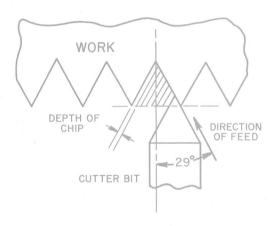

Fig. 1071. Action of Threading Tool with Compound-Rest Set at 29° Angle

4. Lay out the length to be threaded, and mark it with a lead pencil or with the point of a tool bit. If desired, a groove may be cut at the end of the thread, using a cutoff tool. The width of the groove should be equal to the width of the cutoff-tool blade. The depth of the groove should be equal to the depth of the thread. The groove makes it easier to avoid breaking off the point of the cutting tool when the tool is withdrawn after each cut.

5. Set the compound rest at a 29° angle to the right. (See Fig. 1071.)

6. Set the point of the tool bit on the centerline of the work, Fig. 1069, square with the work, as in Fig. 1070.

7. Set the lathe at a low, back-geared rpm when cutting your first threads. With experience, you can cut threads at higher speeds.

8. Set the feed-change lever, Fig. 1003, to the *threading position*. On most lathes this is located in the center position.

9. Advance the tool until it just touches the work. Then set the micrometer collar on the *cross-feed knob* to *zero*, Fig. 1003. Also set the micrometer collar on the *compound-rest feed knob* to zero, Fig. 1003.

10. Bring the carriage to the right end of the work, clear of the work.

11. Advance the tool 0.005″ with the *compound-rest feed knob*. NOTE: The depth for each additional cut is set with the *compound-rest feed knob*. As the depth of thread increases with succeeding cuts, reduce the depth of cut to 0.003″ then to 0.002″. The last several cuts should not be deeper than 0.001″.

12. If the *thread-dial indicator* is not engaged, Fig. 1072, engage it and tighten it in position. The dial should revolve when the carriage is moved.

13. Start the lathe. When a *numbered line on the dial* is in line with the *index line* on the outer ring of the thread-dial indicator, engage the *half-nut lever*, Fig. 1003.

14. Apply cutting oil to the threads.

15. At the end of the thread, disengage the *half-nut lever,* and at the same time, turn the *cross-feed knob* one complete turn to the left to withdraw the tool.

16. Bring the carriage back to the right end of the thread in position to start the next cut.

17. Turn the *cross-feed knob* one revolution to the right to the original *zero* starting position.

18. Repeat steps 12 through 17 until the thread is cut to the desired depth. As the depth of thread is increased, the pitch diameter should be measured with a *thread micrometer* (see § 1151) to avoid cutting the thread too deeply. Another way to determine when the thread is cut to approximately the right depth is to test it with a standard-threaded nut with the same kind of thread which is being cut. The nut should turn on the external thread without excess looseness.

19. When the thread has been cut to the desired depth, chamfer the end of the thread at a 45° angle to a depth equal to the thread depth. (See Fig. 1073.)

Review Questions

1. What is a machine tool?
2. List five of the most basic kinds of machine tools.
3. List several specialized mass-production machine tools which are adapted from the lathe.
4. What kinds of operations can be performed on a lathe?
5. What kinds of workers run lathes?
6. Name the main parts of the lathe.
7. Name the main parts of the headstock.
8. Name the main parts of the tailstock.
9. Where is the leadscrew located?
10. Where is the half nut located?
11. Where is the rack located?
12. Where are the back gears located?
13. How is the size of a lathe measured?
14. Why should one avoid turning the lathe on when the spindle is locked?
15. Why should most lathes be stopped before shifting or changing the controls on the headstock end of the lathe?
16. Can the controls on the carriage and apron generally be adjusted while the lathe is running?
17. How often should a lathe be oiled?
18. Define the meaning of *cutting speed* as it applies to lathes.
19. Define the meaning of *rpm.*
20. List the formula for calculating the approximate cutting speed for lathe work.
21. List the formula for calculating the approximate rpm for lathe work.

Fig. 1072. Thread Dial Indicator
(Courtesy South Bend Lathe, Inc.)

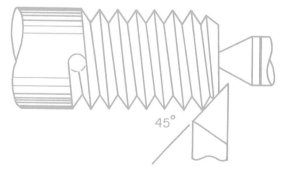

Fig. 1073. Chamfer End of Thread
with 45° Chamfer

22. List the recommended cutting speed range for turning low-carbon steel on a lathe.

23. For what purposes are back gears used on a lathe?

24. How is the speed changed on lathes equipped with a V-belt type variable-speed drive?

25. Can speed changes be made on most geared-head lathes while the lathe is running?

26. What is meant by *longitudinal feed* on a lathe?

27. What is meant by *cross feed?*

28. For what purpose is the carriage lock screw used?

29. At what angle is the compound rest set for normal turning operations?

30. What are automatic feeds?

31. What control is used to engage the automatic feed?

32. What control is used to engage the feed for thread cutting?

33. What purpose do the levers on the quick-change gear box serve?

34. Explain the purpose of the large numbers and the small numbers on the index plate on the quick-change gear box on the lathe.

35. Is the amount of cross feed and longitudinal feed per revolution always the same? Explain.

36. How much is the diameter reduced when turning with a $\frac{1}{16}''$ deep cut?

37. For what purpose is a lathe chuck used?

38. List three types of lathe chucks and explain their uses.

39. What kinds of workpieces can be held in a four-jaw chuck?

40. Why should the lathe chuck be screwed on or off the headstock spindle while the lathe is stopped?

41. Explain how a workpiece is centered in a four-jaw chuck?

42. Of what materials are lathe cutting tools commonly made?

43. For what are lathe toolholders used?

44. List several different kinds of lathe toolholders.

45. What type of toolholder is used for holding carbide cutting tools?

46. What type of toolholder is used for holding high-speed steel tool bits?

47. What is meant by *end relief* and *side relief* on a tool bit?

48. What is meant by side rake on a tool bit?

49. What is meant by back rake on a lathe tool?

50. What is meant by *nose radius* on a lathe-tool bit?

51. At what height should the cutting edge of the tool be set?

52. What is meant by *facing?*

53. How can centerdrilling be done on a lathe?

54. Why must the tailstock center be in accurate alignment with the headstock center before centerdrilling work mounted in the chuck on the lathe?

55. For what purpose is the faceplate used on a lathe?

56. What is the angle of the point on a lathe center?

57. For what purpose are the *setover screws* on the tailstock used?

58. For what purpose are lathe dogs used?

59. Why should turning generally be done in the direction from the tailstock toward the headstock?

60. When turning between centers, what does a "squeak" indicate?

61. List three methods which can be used for turning tapers on a lathe.

62. How should the center be removed from the headstock?

63. How should the center be removed from the tailstock?

64. Why should the lathe centers be free from dirt before installing them in the lathe?

65. List several hole-machining operations which can be performed on a lathe.

66. How are the hole-machining tools generally mounted in the lathe?

67. Why are holes bored rather than just drilling them to the desired size?

68. What purpose does knurling serve?

69. What is a lathe mandrel and for what purpose is it used?

70. Explain three kinds of operations which can be performed with cutoff tools.

71. Why should you *avoid* cutting off a workpiece which is mounted between centers on a lathe?

72. How can you generally avoid chatter on cutoff operations?

73. For what purpose is a steady rest used on a lathe?

74. For what purpose is a follower rest used on a lathe?

75. Explain, briefly, how threads can be cut on a lathe.

76. Explain two kinds of thread-cutting tools which can be used to cut external threads on a lathe.

77. What kind of cutting tool is used for cutting internal threads on a lathe?

Coordination

Words to Know

alignment	compound rest
apron	countershaft
back-gear lever	cross slide
bench lathe	cutting speed
boring bar	dead center
boring tool	depth of cut
bull-gear pin	faceplate
carriage	facing
carriage lock	feed
centerdrilled hole	four-jaw inde-
or centerdrilling	pendent chuck
chalk mark	gib
chatter mark	handwheel
chuck wrench	headstock
chucking	headstock center or
clamp dog	live center
collet	headstock spindle

jewelers' lathe	tailstock
knockout rod	tailstock center
knurling	or dead center
knurling tool	tailstock offset
lathe chuck	tailstock spindle
lathe dog	clamp
lathe tool	taper turning
leadscrew	threading tool
left-hand tool-	three-jaw universal
holder	chuck
power feed	tool bit
rake	back-rake angle
reversible	end relief
right-hand tool-	end-relief
holder	grinding angle
rpm	face
setover screw	flank
sfm	left-hand tool
spindle hole	nose angle
squaring	right-hand tool
straight tool-	side-rake angle
holder	toolholder
straight turning	tool post
swing	way

Mathematics

1. What is the total cost of all the lathes in your school?

2. Calculate the tailstock offset for turning cylindrical work 10″ in length, 6″ to be tapered with a taper of .350″ per foot.

3. Calculate the tailstock offset for a spindle 15″ long, tapered the entire length, large diameter 1⅛″, small diameter ⁹⁄₁₆″.

4. Using the large diameter above and a cutting speed of 80′ per minute, what should the rpm of the lathe be for the piece being cut in problem 3?

5. Calculate the tailstock offset of a center punch having a total length of 6¹⁄₁₆″, 3″ to be tapered, large diameter of ⅝″, and small diameter of ¼″.

6. Using the large diameter, and an rpm of 650, what would the cutting speed be in problem 5 above? Would this be a satisfactory speed for cutting medium-carbon steel?

Spinning a 50-inch Disk
of One-Half Inch Aluminum
(Courtesy Aluminum Company of America)

Metal Spinning

1215.   What is Metal Spinning?

Many beautiful, artistic, and useful articles, such as bowls, trays, saucers, vases, and pitchers can be made from flat pieces of soft *sheet metal* by pressing them over forms which turn in the lathe. This is called *metal spinning*. It can be done easily and quickly.

Copper, brass, aluminum, pewter, and monel metal make beautiful articles at very little cost. In fact, you can probably find some scrap pieces of copper, brass, or aluminum lying around at home. The articles make excellent Christmas presents. (See also *metal spinner* in § 19.)

1216.   Chucks

The forms, made of steel, maple or birch wood, on which the spinning is done, are called *chucks*, Fig. 1085. A chuck is first made on the lathe and then screwed to a small *faceplate* which is then screwed on the headstock spindle.

1217.   Follow Block

It is necessary to have a *follow block* to *press* against the sheet metal and hold it in place against the *chuck*. The follow block is made of hardwood about ⅛″ or ¼″ smaller in diameter than the end of the chuck. It must turn with the work, Fig. 1087.

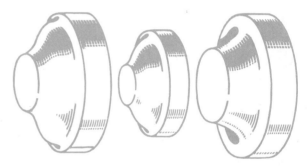

Fig. 1085.   Spinning Chucks

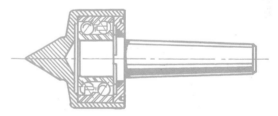

Fig. 1086.   Ball Bearing Back Center

1218.   Back Center

A tailstock center with a *ball bearing*[1] is needed. Such a center, Fig. 1086, is called a *back center*. The sheet metal, cut to a circular shape, is placed between the *chuck* and the *follow block*, Fig. 1087. Thus the chuck, sheet metal, follow block, and the point of

[1] A *ball bearing* is a hardened steel ball placed between two pieces of metal to give a rolling action thus avoiding the friction of one piece of metal sliding on the other.

the back center turn when the lathe is running. If the metal slips, put on a little powdered *rosin*. (See § 852.)

1219.   Tool Rest

A tool rest for metal spinning may be made for a metalworking lathe as shown in Fig. 1088. Another type could fit the slot in the compound rest.

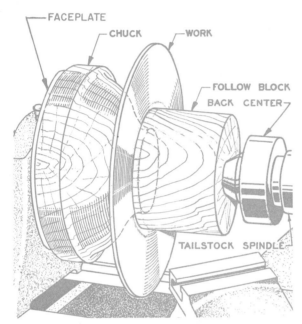

Fig. 1087. **Work Chucked, Ready for Spinning**

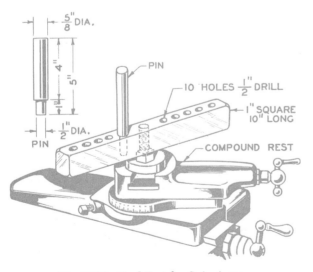

Fig. 1088. **Tool Rest for Spinning on Metalworking Lathe**

1220.   Speed

The speed for spinning depends upon the kind and thickness of the metal. Generally, the thinner the metal the slower should be the speed — sometimes as low as 300 revolutions per minute. On some work the speed may be increased to 1500 revolutions per minute.

1221.   Spinning Tools

Spinning tools, Fig. 1089, are made of hardened steel in many shapes and sizes. They are used to press the metal against the *chuck*. The ends are dull and very smooth.

The handles are about a foot and a half long; broken baseball bats can be used. The total length of the tool may be 30″. Most spinning can be done with a tool made from ¾″ round *tool steel* (see § 328) with the end shaped like an acorn.

The end of a broomstick, cut to about 3 feet in length can be used until a metal spinning tool is made; the metal one is better.

1222.   Holding and Using Spinning Tools

The metal and the ends of the spinning tools should be greased with lard, soap, *tallow* or *cup grease*. (See § 401.) This makes the spinning tool smooth and slippery, allows it to slide easily over the metal, and results in a polished finish.

The spinning tool should be held as shown in Fig. 1090. Hold the handle of the spinning tool under the right arm. Then stretch, press,

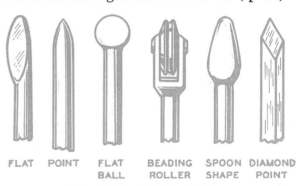

Fig. 1089. **Spinning Tools**

and bend the metal over the chuck, Fig. 1091. If the edge of the metal wrinkles, flatten it immediately before going ahead. This may be done with a *back stick* made from a broom stick or hammer handle about 12" long and flattened at one end. By pressing the back stick behind the metal with the left hand while at the same time pressing in front with

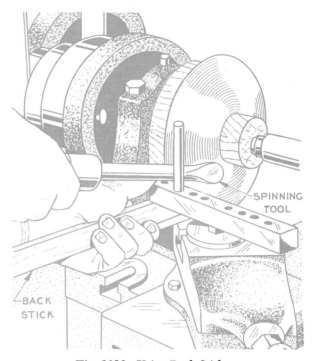

Fig. 1092. Using Back Stick

Fig. 1090. Holding Spinning Tool
(Courtesy Oliver Machinery Co.)

Fig. 1091. Spinning

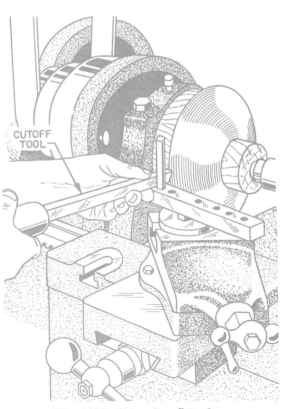

Fig. 1093. Using Cutoff Tool

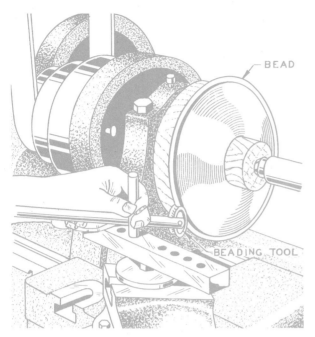

Fig. 1094. Using Beading Roller

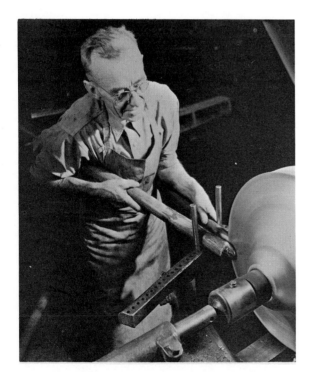

Fig. 1095. Spinning a Large Piece with
Wood Tool and Backing Stick
(Courtesy Aluminum Co. of America)

the spinning tool in the right hand, the wrinkles can be removed, Fig. 1092.

Copper and brass become hard and stiff from stretching, pressing and bending and, therefore, must be softened, or *annealed*. (See § 837.) Aluminum hardens a little; pewter does not harden.

The *diamond-point cutoff tool* is used to cut off and trim the ragged edges, Fig. 1093. The *beading roller* is used to roll a *bead*, as on the edge of a dish, Fig. 1094.

Review Questions

1. What is metal spinning?

2. What is a spinning chuck?

3. What is a follow block?

4. What is a back center?

5. How can you keep the metal from slipping?

6. What should be the speed for spinning?

7. Name some spinning tools. Describe each.

8. How should spinning tools be held?

9. What should be put on the metal and spinning tools to make them smooth and slippery?

10. What is a back stick?

Coordination

Words to Know

back center
back stick
ball bearing
beading roller
diamond-point
  cutoff tool

follow block
metal spinning
spinning chuck
spinning tool

Occupational Information

1. Write a story telling what you know about the metal spinning trade.

2. Is metal spinning a good trade for a young man to enter? Why?

The Shaper and Shaper Operations

1230. The Shaper

The shaper, Fig. 1105, is one of the common basic machine tools. It uses a single-point cutting tool which is very similar to a lathe tool bit, see Figs. 1106 and 1023. Shapers are used primarily for machining flat surfaces. The flat surfaces may be horizontal as in Fig. 1114 or vertical as in Fig. 1136. Grooves, slots, or keyways can be machined with a shaper as shown in Figs. 1123, 1125, and 1120. Curved surfaces also can be laid out and machined by handfeeding the tool along the layout line as shown in Figs. 1039 and 1040.

The workpiece is held tightly in a machine vise, Fig. 1108, or it may be bolted directly to the table, as in Fig. 1132. The cutting tool is held in a toolholder which is moved back and forth in a straight line by a *ram*. The cutting tool *peels* off a chip each time the ram moves forward on a *cutting stroke*. As the ram returns, the table feeds crosswise, an amount equal to the *feed* selected. The cutting tool then makes a new cut on the next cutting stroke, see Fig. 1106 CAUTION: *You should always wear approved safety goggles while operating a shaper, since hot metal chips fly off the work at high speeds.*

The shaper can be found in almost every school shop, tool room, and maintenance machine shop. Its *single-point cutting tool* can easily be ground to another shape. Compare this with the work that is required to re-sharpen each tooth of the *multiple-point cutting tool* used on the milling machine, Fig. 1152. The ease in grinding a shaper tool makes the shaper a very flexible machine.

One disadvantage of the shaper is that its *rate of metal removal* is slow in comparison with the use of a *milling machine*, Fig. 1151. Milling machines use *multiple-tooth* cutters which remove metal more rapidly than the *single-point* tool on a shaper. However, the cutting tool on a milling machine, called a *milling cutter*, is much more expensive than a shaper tool bit. And a tool and cutter grinding machine, or other special grinding equipment, is required for grinding milling cutters, see Fig. 1211. The shaper tool bit is ground on an ordinary bench grinder or pedestal grinder, see Figs. 857 and 858.

Either a shaper or a milling machine may be used for machining flat, vertical, or angular surfaces. Either machine also may be used for machining grooves. Because of a more rapid rate of metal removal, milling machines are rapidly replacing shapers and planers (see Fig. 1141) in production machine shops. However, because of the ease of grinding and maintaining shaper tools, the shaper is frequently used in maintenance machine shops, tool and die shops, and school shops.

Two basic types of shapers are available: the *horizontal-type*, as illustrated in this unit, and the *vertical-type*. The horizontal-type is

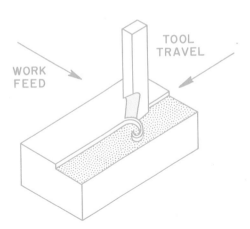

**Fig. 1106. Tool in Relation to Workpiece
When Shaping**

most common and is most widely used. On the vertical-type, the ram moves up and down in a vertical position, instead of the horizontal position.

The basic procedures used and the principles involved in machining with a shaper also apply to operations performed on a planer, Figs. 1141 and 1142. Single-point cutting tools, similar to shaper tools, are also used on planers. Planers and their use are explained in section 1253.

1231.   Shaper Size

The size of a shaper generally is designated by the maximum length of *stroke*. The com-

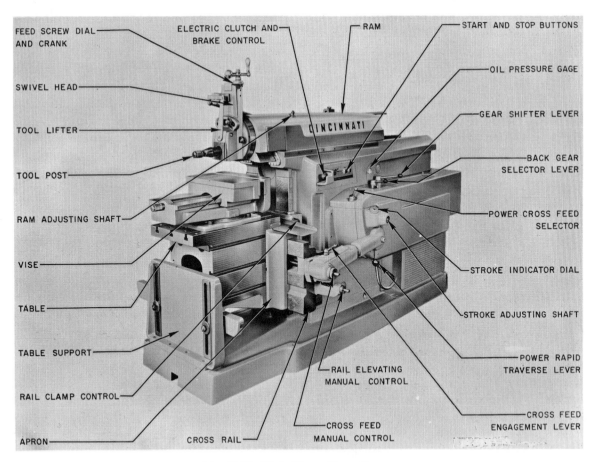

**Fig. 1105. Plain Heavy-Duty Shaper,
Showing Principal Parts
(Courtesy The Cincinnati Shaper Co.)**

mon maximum stroke lengths for shapers of various sizes are 7″, 12″, 14″, 16″, 18″, 24″, and 36″. In each case, the length of stroke may be adjusted for any length from 0″ to the maximum length for the machine.

The maximum stroke length, however, is not the only factor used in designating the physical size and work capacity of shapers. They are sometimes designated for light-duty, medium- or standard-duty, or heavy-duty work. Heavy-duty shapers are heavier and more rigid than the light- or medium-duty types. For example, shapers with a 16″ stroke may range from about 2000 to 6000 pounds in weight.

Heavy-duty shapers of the type shown in Fig. 1105 are available with maximum stroke lengths ranging from 16″ to 36″. The shaper in Fig. 1107, although classified as a 12″ shaper, has a maximum stroke length of 13½″. The shaper in Fig. 1108 has a maximum stroke of 7″ and is designed for relatively light-duty work. The heavy-duty shaper in Fig. 1109 is equipped with a universal table. A *universal table* may be swiveled at any de-

sired angle for making angular cuts, see Fig. 1112.

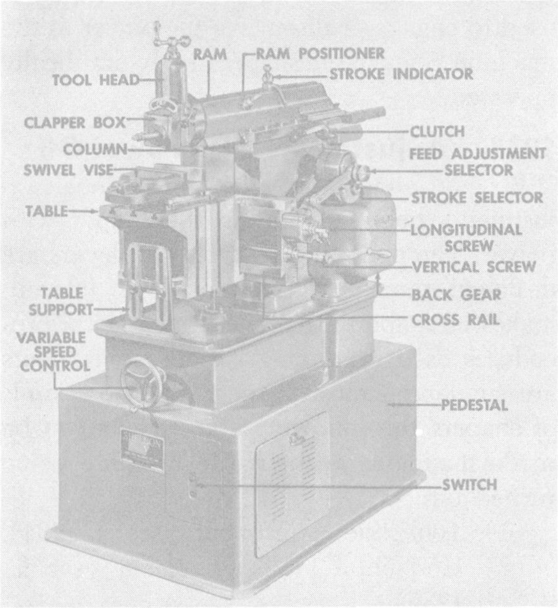

1232. Parts of Shaper

The principal parts of the shaper are identified in Figs. 1105, 1107, and 1110. The names of the principal parts should be learned before attempting to operate the machine. It is always best to have your instructor show you how the various controls are used before op-

Fig. 1108. Bench Shaper with 7″ Stroke
(Courtesy South Bend Lathe, Inc.)

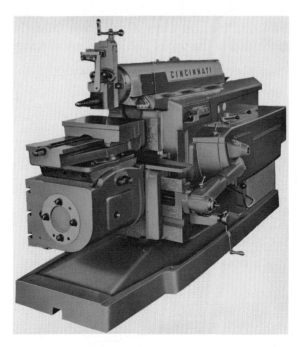

Fig. 1107. 12″ Plain Shaper, Showing Principal Parts (Courtesy Sheldon Machine Co.)

Fig. 1109. Heavy-Duty Shaper with Universal Table (Courtesy The Cincinnati Shaper Co.)

erating the shaper. The following are some of the most important parts on a shaper:

Base
The *base* is the large casting which supports the machine. The base of large shapers rests on the floor. The base of smaller shapers often rests on a pedestal, Fig. 1107, or on a bench, Fig. 1108.

Column
The *column* is an accurately machined vertical surface on the front of the large *base casting* which houses the internal parts of the machine. The complete, large base casting also is sometimes called the column. The accurately machined vertical column provides a bearing surface for the *cross rail*.

Cross Rail
The cross rail supports the *table* at one end. A *table support leg* supports the table at the opposite end. A *swivel vise* is bolted to the table for mounting workpieces to be machined.

Ram
The ram is a heavy casting which slides back and forth in *ways* which are accurately machined in the top of the large base casting.

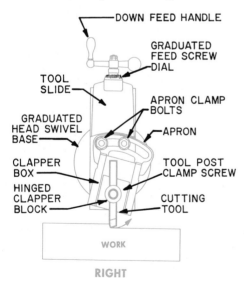

Fig. 1110. Tool Head Assembly
(Courtesy The Cincinnati Shaper Co.)

Tool Head Assembly
The tool head assembly, Fig. 1110, is mounted on the end of the ram. The *cutting tool* may be mounted in a *toolholder,* or it may be clamped directly in the *tool post* as shown in Fig. 1110. The tool post is mounted on a hinged *clapper block,* which is mounted in the *clapper box,* which in turn forms part of the *apron.* During the cut, the clapper block is forced back solidly into the base of the clapper box. On the return stroke, the clapper block swings freely, thus preventing damage to the point of the cutting tool.

The apron is swiveled to the desired angle and is clamped to the *tool slide* with *apron-clamp bolts.* The depth of the cut is established with the *down-feed handle,* and it may be read directly to 0.001″ on the graduated *feed-screw dial.* The *tool head* may be swiveled at any desired angle for making angular cuts, as shown in Fig. 1137.

Drive System
Most shapers are driven by an electric motor. The drive system uses a system of belts, gears, and levers to change speeds and the length of the cutting stroke. A *clutch* is used to engage or disengage the power to the machine. Some large shapers are hydraulically operated.

1233. Adjustments with Power Off
Become acquainted with the manual adjustments before operating the shaper with power. The operating controls and levers are designed somewhat differently on different makes of shapers. However, the general procedures used in making various adjustments are similar on most shapers. On most kinds of shapers the following adjustments can be made manually, without the machine being turned on:

   (1) Tool-slide adjustment (see § 1234).
   (2) Horizontal table movement (see § 1235).
   (3) Table elevation (see § 1236).
   (4) Length of stroke (see § 1237).

(5) Position of stroke (see § 1238).

(6) Cutting speed (see § 1239).

(7) Feed adjustment (see § 1240).

1234. Tool-Slide Adjustment

Move the tool slide, Fig. 1110, up or down with the *down-feed handle*. This handle turns the tool-slide feed screw, thus establishing the depth of cut desired. Use the down-feed handle, also, for feeding the tool manually when making vertical cuts, Fig. 1136, and for making angular cuts, Fig. 1137. Some shapers are equipped with a *tool-slide lock screw* or *lever*, as shown in Fig. 1107. The locking device prevents the tool from *digging in*, due to backlash in the down-feed screw, while making heavy horizontal cuts.

When horizontal cuts are made, both the tool and the tool slide should have as little overhang as possible, see Fig. 1111. Check to see that the tool and the toolholder are clamped tightly. Also check to see that the apron is swiveled in a direction opposite to the direction in which the tool is feeding, see Fig. 1110. This will enable the tool and clapper block to swing up and away from the work on the *return* or backward stroke. When possible, the tool should be in a vertical position, as shown in Fig. 1111, so that it cannot dig further into the work if it becomes loosened. When the depth of cut has been established and set, the tool-slide locking lever or device should be tightened just enough to hold snugly.

1235. Horizontal Table Movement

Place a hand crank on the *longitudinal-* or *cross-feed screw*, Figs. 1105 and 1107, and move the table crosswise in either direction. In order to do this the *cross-feed engagement lever* or knob must be disengaged. The table then slides freely in either direction.

The *table assembly* on a shaper consists of several major parts, see Fig. 1105. The parts include the *table*, the *apron* to which the table is attached, and the *table support*. A heavy-duty swivel vise is generally bolted to the table.

The table on a shaper may be either the *plain*-type or the *universal*-type. A universal table, as shown in Fig. 1112, may be swiveled about its axis for making angular cuts. A plain-type table, as in Figs. 1105, 1107, and 1108, cannot be swiveled.

1236. Table Elevation

The table can be raised or lowered as required for large or small workpieces. The table should be set at an elevation which permits minimum overhang of the tool and tool slide, as in Fig. 1111. On most shapers, the cross rail is equipped with several column *clamping nuts* which are carefully adjusted for proper clearance along the machined vertical column bearing surfaces. These clamping

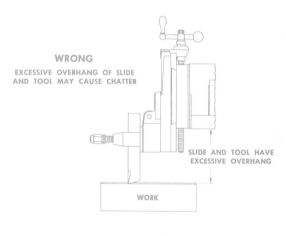

WRONG
EXCESSIVE OVERHANG OF SLIDE AND TOOL MAY CAUSE CHATTER

SLIDE AND TOOL HAVE EXCESSIVE OVERHANG

WORK

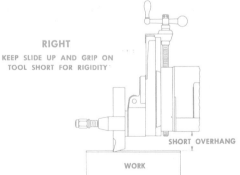

RIGHT
KEEP SLIDE UP AND GRIP ON TOOL SHORT FOR RIGIDITY

SHORT OVERHANG

WORK

Fig. 1111. Use a Short Overhang on Both the Tool and Tool Slide
(Courtesy The Cincinnati Shaper Co.)

nuts may be located on one or both columns. Only *one* of the clamping nuts is designed for clamping the cross rail and table assembly securely to the column while cuts are made. This *clamping nut* must be loosened *slightly*

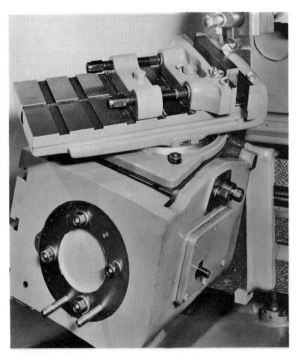

Fig. 1112. Set Up with Both Universal Table and Vise Swiveled (Courtesy The Cincinnati Shaper Co.)

Fig. 1113. Rocker Arm is Graduated for Stroke Adjustment (Courtesy South Bend Lathe, Inc.)

in order to raise or lower the table. Ask your instructor to show you which *column clamping nut* must be loosened in order to raise or lower the table. The clamping nuts on the table support must also be loosened before raising or lowering the table.

The cross rail and table assembly are raised or lowered with a hand crank placed on either the *vertical screw*, Fig. 1107, or on the *rail elevating manual control*, Fig. 1105. When the table is at the proper elevation, lower it and again raise it slightly to take out the backlash in the adjustment screw. Then tighten the *column clamping nut* and the clamping nuts on the table support legs. For many jobs with workpieces of similar size, the table may be left at the same elevation. However, it must be raised or lowered for smaller or larger workpieces.

1237.   Length of Stroke

The stroke should be at least ¾″ longer than the cut. It should start about ½″ before the cut and should continue at least ¼″ beyond the cut. The length of stroke is determined by the position of the crank pin and sliding block. These are located on the *vibrating arm* inside the machine, See Fig. 1113. The vibrating arm is connected to the main-drive gear. The farther the crank pin is located from the axis of the drive gear, the longer the stroke. On the small shaper in Fig. 1113, the graduation marks on the vibrating arm indicate the length of stroke.

The length of stroke is adjusted somewhat differently on different shapers. On the large shaper in Fig. 1105, merely place a hand crank on the stroke adjusting shaft, and turn to the desired stroke length. The length is indicated on the stroke-indicator dial.

On most smaller shapers, first move the ram to the extreme rear position, if the handwheel is provided; if no handwheel is provided, the power must be used. On a small shaper, such as the machine in Fig. 1113, loosen the nut on the crank pin, and move the sliding block to the graduation mark which indicates the desired length of stroke. Then tighten the nut on the crank pin. On shapers of the type shown in Fig. 1107, the stroke is adjusted by turning the stroke selector with a hand crank; the length of the stroke is indicated by a stroke indicator on top of the ram.

Some shapers have a *lock nut* located on the stroke selector shaft. On machines so equipped, the lock nut must be loosened before attempting to adjust the length of stroke. After the length has been adjusted, the lock nut again must be tightened before the machine can be operated.

1238. Position of Stroke

The position of a given stroke, such as a stroke 6″ long, may be moved forward or backward, depending on the location of the workpiece mounted in the vise or bolted to the table. Thus the position of the stroke is always adjusted after the workpiece is mounted. First the length of the stroke must be adjusted before attempting to adjust the position of the stroke.

To adjust the position of the stroke, first move the ram to the extreme rear position and adjust the length of stroke desired. (See § 1237.) Loosen the ram *hand clamp* device on machines so equipped; the ram hand clamp is located on top of the ram, Fig. 1108, or above the stroke indicator in Fig. 1107. The position of the ram is then adjusted by turning the *ram adjusting shaft*, Fig. 1105, with a hand crank. On the machine in Fig. 1107, the *ram positioner* is turned with a hand crank. On small machines, as in Fig. 1108, the ram is pushed manually to the desired position. When the position of the stroke has been adjusted, the ram *hand clamp* again must be tightened before starting the machine. When correctly positioned, the stroke will start at least ½″ before the cut and end ¼″ or more beyond the end of the cut. Therefore, the stroke will be at least ¾″ longer than the cut.

1239. Cutting Speed

The cutting speed is designated in surface feet per minute (sfm). The cutting speed is increased by increasing the number of cutting strokes per minute. The cutting speed for shaper work, like the cutting speed for turning on a lathe, depends upon the following:

(1) Kind of material in the cutting tool.
(2) The kind of material being machined.
(3) The machinability of the material being machined. (See § 358 and Table 9, page 154.)
(4) Depth of cut.
(5) Rigidness of the machine and the workpiece setup.

The cutting speeds for shaping with high-speed steel cutting tools are similar to the cutting speeds used for turning on a lathe. The same recommended cutting speeds may be used, (see Table 37). The following formula may be used for calculating the approximate number of strokes per minute required for a given cutting speed:

$$N = \frac{CS \times 7}{L}$$

N = Number of strokes per minute
CS = Cutting speed for metal being cut (in feet per minute)
7 = Mulitiplier to convert feet to inches (a shaper cuts about two-thirds of the time)
L = Length of cutting stroke in inches

Example: Calculate the approximate number of strokes per minute required for shaping a piece of low-carbon steel with a 6″ stroke at 90 surface feet per minute.

$$N = \frac{90 \times 7}{6}$$

$$N = \frac{630}{6}$$

$$N = 105 \text{ strokes per minute}$$

When the number of strokes per minute is given, the cutting speed can be calculated with the following formula:

$$CS = \frac{N \times L}{7}$$

The method for changing the number of strokes per minute is somewhat different for different makes of machines. On larger machines, of the type in Fig. 1105, the number of strokes desired is selected by shifting the two gear-shaft levers provided. The number of strokes per minute on the machine in Fig. 1107 is changed by turning the variable-speed handwheel while the machine is running. On some shapers, the number of strokes per minute is changed by changing a V-belt to different steps on the drive pulley, see Fig. 328.

1240.   Feed Adjustment

The feed can be adjusted for heavy or light feeds. For horizontal cuts, *feed* is the distance the table moves horizontally along the cross rail for each new cut, see Fig. 1106. The amount of feed depends on the same factors as cutting speed. Lighter feeds generally are used for (1) deep cuts, (2) cuts with light-duty shapers, and (3) producing a smoother surface finish.

For finishing cuts, a feed of 0.010″ to 0.020″ and a depth of 0.005″ to 0.015″ is recommended. A finishing tool with a nose radius of ⅛″ or larger generally is used. Sometimes a finishing tool with a flat nose or a nose with a slightly elliptical shape is used, see Fig. 1124. With finishing tools of this kind, much coarser feeds may be used.

For deep roughing cuts, a fine feed of 0.010″ to 0.020″ is often used. For shallower roughing cuts, a coarser feed may be used. Larger shapers can take much heavier cuts than small shapers, see Fig. 1114. As a general rule, the feed and the depth of the cut should not be greater than the machine, the cutting tool, and the setup can stand. If the workpiece is not held tightly in position, it may be pushed off the machine.

On most smaller shapers the feed is changed by loosening the *feed-adjustment selector*, Fig. 1107, and sliding the feed connecting rod in the *slotted crank disk*. The feed connecting rod operates the longitudinal-feed screw which feeds the table crosswise. To increase the feed rate, move the feed-adjustment selector toward the outside of the slotted crank. CAUTION: *The feed must be set so that the table feeds crosswise on the return or backward stroke.* If the table feeds on the forward or cutting stroke, the feed-adjustment selector should be moved to the opposite side of the slotted crank disk. If the table feeds crosswise during the cutting stroke, the tool will be damaged.

On large shapers, as in Fig. 1105, the feed is changed by manually turning a dial to the desired feed rate. The feed is engaged on most shapers by moving a *feed-engagement lever,* knob, or ratchet in the desired direction of feed.

1241.   Adjustments with Power On

Many smaller shapers are equipped with a *handwheel* which enables the operator to run

Fig. 1114. Making a Heavy Cut with a Large Solid Cutting Tool on a Heavy-Duty Shaper
(Courtesy The Cincinnati Shaper Co.)

the *ram* through the complete stroke without turning on the power; on machines so equipped, this procedure should always be followed before turning on the power. Many newer shapers and larger shapers are not equipped with a handwheel for manual movement of the ram. On these machines the ram can be moved only with power. The power to the ram is controlled with the *clutch lever* or with a *clutch and brake control,* see Figs. 1107 and 1105.

CAUTION: *Never run the ram back into the column with the tool slide set at an angle. The slide will strike the column and cause serious damage to the tool head assembly.* (See Fig. 1115.)

(1) Before starting the machine, observe that the tool slide is in a vertical position (for either horizontal or vertical cuts), and see that the tool will clear the vise, the workpiece, and the setup.

(2) Turn on the motor, engage the clutch, and observe the stroke.

(3) Engage the power automatic cross feed with the *cross-feed engagement lever,* Fig. 1105. When the lever is swiveled to the right, the table feeds to the right along the table cross rail. When the lever is swiveled to the left, the table feeds to the left. The left side of the machine is the side on which most of the controls are located. The operator operates the machine from the left side. Some shapers have a *ratchet knob,* instead of a *cross-feed engagement lever,* for engaging automatic cross feed.

(4) After observing the operation of the stroke and the automatic cross feed, disengage the cross feed, disengage the clutch, and stop the machine.

1242. Vise Alignment

A swivel vise mounted on the shaper table can be used for holding many kinds of workpieces. The vise generally is bolted on the top surface of the table. However, it may also be bolted on the side of the table for special job setups, see Fig. 1133. The base of the vise is provided with a keyway and a key which keep the swivel base aligned with the table. The vise jaws usually can be set accurately enough for most jobs by careful alignment of the degree graduation mark and the index mark on the swivel base.

For very accurate work, either the workpiece or the vise may be aligned more accurately with the use of a dial indicator, see Fig. 1116. The following procedure should be used:

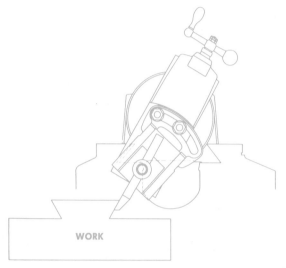

WORK

Fig. 1115. CAUTION: Do Not Run the Ram Back into the Column with the Slide Set at an Angle: Slide Will Strike Column
(Courtesy The Cincinnati Shaper Co.)

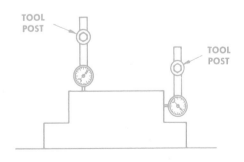

TOOL POST

TOOL POST

Fig. 1116. Using Dial Indicator for Setting Work Level and Parallel
(Courtesy The Cincinnati Shaper Co.)

(1) Set the vise parallel to the ram stroke.

(2) Set the length of the stroke at least 1″ shorter than the length of the vise jaw.

(3) Set the position of the stroke so that it does not travel closer than ½″ from either end of the vise jaw.

(4) Insert a dial indicator in the tool post, with the dial plunger touching the stationary vise jaw. This is done in a manner similar to the dial setup shown at the right in Fig. 1116. Set the dial for a zero reading, with some pressure against the dial plunger.

(5) Run the ram back and forth with the *handwheel*, and observe any error in angular setting. Adjust the vise by swiveling it as necessary for a zero reading on the dial indicator.

A similar procedure can be used to check the alignment of the jaws of the vise for a

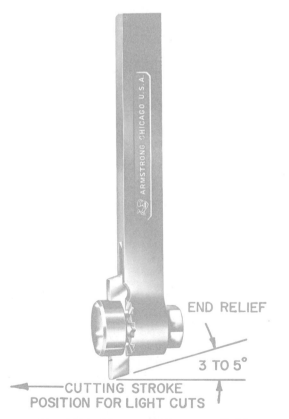

Fig. 1117. Planer and Shaper Toolholder
(Courtesy Armstrong Bros. Tool Co.)

position at a right-angle (90°) to the stroke. The vise is first set at a right angle to the stroke. However, in this case, the table is fed crosswise, back and forth, by manual cross feed.

1243. Safety with the Shaper

(1) Always wear approved safety goggles or a safety face shield.

(2) Be certain that the vise and the workpiece are fastened securely.

(3) Use the right cutting tool for the job.

(4) Remove all wrenches or other needless tools from the machine table before starting the machine.

(5) Select the proper speed, feed, and depth of cut for the kind of material being machined.

(6) Do not run the ram back into the column when the tool slide is set at an angle. To do so will cause serious damage to the tool head assembly. (See Fig. 1115.) On machines equipped with a *handwheel*, run the ram through its full stroke manually before turning on the power to start the machine. This will help determine that the tool clears the work, and the tool slide does not strike the column.

(7) Be sure that no one is inside the safety zone for the machine.

(8) Check to see that the back of the ram will not strike some object or some person.

(9) Stand to the left of the machine, parallel to the stroke of the machine, while operating it. Do not reach across the work or the machine table while the machine is running.

(10) Do not touch the tool or the work while the machine is running.

(11) Remove chips with a brush only when the machine is stopped.

(12) Make adjustments on the machine only while it is stopped.

(13) Stop the machine before leaving it.

(14) Clean the machine and the area when you complete the job.

(15) Remove sharp burrs or edges from machined parts to avoid being cut.

1244. Tools and Toolholders

Shapers use *single-point* cutting tools which are very similar to single-point lathe tools. The shaper tool generally is held in a standard *planer and shaper toolholder,* as shown in Figs. 1117 and 1118. The terms which apply to single-point cutting tools on a shaper or planer are essentially the same as the terms which apply to lathe tools. Thus, cutting-tool terminology for many kinds of single-point cutting tools has been standardized. Cutting-tool terms are shown in Figs. 1025 and 1023 and are explained in section 1188. These terms should be understood before attempting to grind a shaper tool bit.

Shaper Toolholder

A standard planer and shaper toolholder, Fig. 1117, holds the cutting tool parallel to the shank of the toolholder and perpendicular

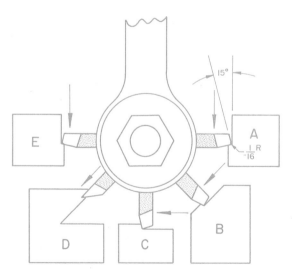

Fig. 1118. Various Tool Positions in Swivel
Head of Planer and Shaper Toolholder
  A. Vertical Cut
  B. Angular Cut
  C. Horizontal Cut
  D. Angular Dovetail Cut
  E. Vertical Cut

to the surface of the work. Note that no rocker block is provided under the tool; therefore, no back-rake angle is provided by the toolholder. The desired back-rake angle must be ground on the tool bit. With the planer and shaper toolholder, the tool may be rotated to five different positions for various kinds of cuts, as shown in Fig. 1118. The toolholder and tool may be swiveled to various other positions for machining other kinds of surfaces, as in Fig. 1119.

The position of the tool in relation to tool travel is important when using the planer and shaper toolholder. For *light cuts,* the tool is clamped in the front of the toolholder as shown in Fig. 1117. For *moderate or heavy cuts,* the toolholder and the tool generally are reversed as shown in Fig. 1120. This procedure brings the point of the tool back to the shank of the toolholder, causing an effect similar to using a *gooseneck tool.* This reduces the possibility of *tool chatter* or *digging in.* (See Fig. 1121.)

Lathe Toolholder

A *zero-degree* (straight) lathe toolholder, Fig. 1023, may also be used in a shaper. It holds the tool bit parallel to the shank of the toolholder and perpendicular to the work in the same manner as the shaper and planer toolholder. However, a 16½° toolholder, Fig. 1022, should not be used in a shaper since the

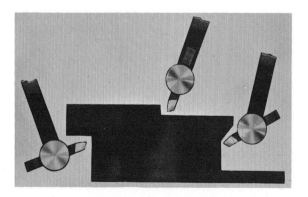

Fig. 1119. Using Planer and Shaper
Toolholder in Close Corners
(Courtesy Armstrong Bros. Tool Co.)

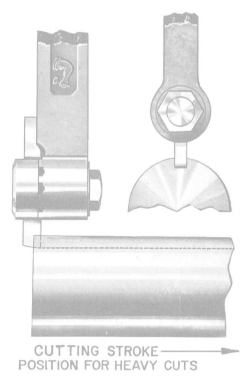

CUTTING STROKE ——————
POSITION FOR HEAVY CUTS

Fig. 1120. Tool and Toolholder Reversed for Cutting Keyways and for Making Heavy Cuts
(Courtesy Armstrong Bros. Tool Co.)

Note: When the tool bit is reversed and the toolholder is turned around, the tendency to vibrate, chatter, and dig in are reduced.

tool will have more tendency to *dig in,* as in Fig. 1121.

Extension Toolholder

Extension toolholders, Fig. 1122, are used for internal machining operations such as cutting keyways, Fig. 1123, or for machining holes of various shapes. The toolholder holds a bar which is similar to a boring bar used on a lathe, Fig. 1051(A). A tool bit of the shape desired is clamped into the bar.

Shaper Tools

Shaper tool bits are ground in a manner similar to lathe tool bits. On shaper tools, however, smaller relief (formerly called clearance) angles are used. An end-relief angle of 3° to 5° and a side-relief angle of 3° to 5° are appropriate for most shaping operations, see Fig. 1117. The small relief angles provide greater strength at the cutting edge where high-impact forces are applied during the cutting stroke, also Table 37 on page 468.

Side-rake and back-rake angles vary with the kind of material being machined. *Side-rake* angles similar to those for lathe tools, Table 37, may be used. An average side-rake

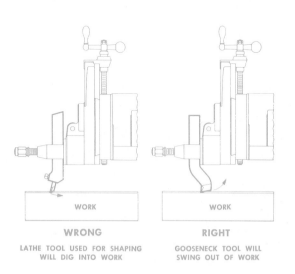

WORK   WORK

WRONG   RIGHT

LATHE TOOL USED FOR SHAPING   GOOSENECK TOOL WILL
WILL DIG INTO WORK   SWING OUT OF WORK

Fig. 1121. Position of Tool and Angle at Which Tool is Held Affects Cutting Angle
(Courtesy The Cincinnati Shaper Co.)

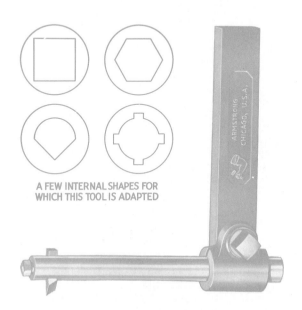

A FEW INTERNAL SHAPES FOR
WHICH THIS TOOL IS ADAPTED

Fig. 1122. Extension Shaper Tool
(Courtesy Armstrong Bros. Tool Co.)

angle of 10° is satisfactory for many general-purpose shaping operations on steel or cast iron. Little or no *back-rake* angle is necessary for most shaping operations. However, a back-rake angle of 2° to 5° is often used for shaping soft steel or soft cast iron. Certain special finishing tools are sometimes given a back-rake angle to increase the keenness of the cutting edge.

The following ranges of angles are recommended for a general-purpose shaper tool:

End relief, 3° to 5°
Side relief, 3° to 5°
Side rake, 10°
Back rake, 0° to 5°

Large solid-shank cutting tools are often used for heavy-duty shaping operations, as in Fig. 1114. For the majority of shaping operations, however, tool bits made of high-speed steel are used.

On shapers, a *left-hand* or *left-cut* tool is most often used. The definition of a *right-hand* or *left-hand* single-point tool is the same for all single-point tools, whether they are used on a lathe, shaper, or planer. When the tool is viewed from the point end face up, a left-cut tool has the cutting edge at the left side. Hence, when looking at the cutting tool from the front of the shaper, the cutting edge of the tool is at the left side, and the table and the work feed from the left toward the right. On a lathe, however, a right-cut tool is most often used.

Some of the common shapes of cutting tools used on the shaper include the following:

(1) *Roughing Tools*: A left-cut roughing tool is shown in Fig. 1118 at *A*, *B*, and *C*. Note the 1/16″ nose radius on the tool. A right-cut roughing tool is shown at *E* in Fig. 1118. A round-nose tool with a flat face (no side-rake angle) may be fed in either direction for roughing cuts, Fig. 1126.

(2) *Finishing Tools*: Several kinds of finishing tools may be used for finishing cuts. The tool shown in Fig. 1118 at *A*, *B*, and *C*, but with a nose radius of 1/8″ or larger, will produce good results with feeds of 0.010″ to 0.020″. For finishing cuts with coarser feeds, a

Fig. 1123. Shaping an Internal Keyway
(Courtesy The Cincinnati Shaper Co.)

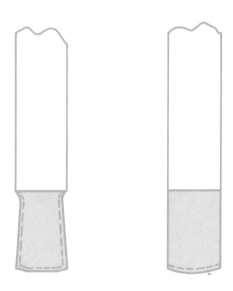

SQUARE-NOSE   ELLIPTICAL-NOSE
FINISHING TOOL   FINISHING TOOL

Fig. 1124. Tools for Finishing Cuts on the Shaper

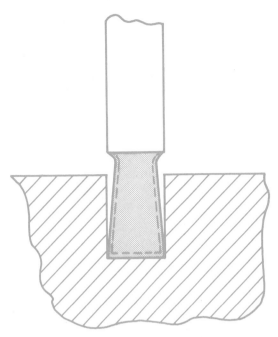

Fig. 1125. Square-Nose Tool for Cutting Grooves or Keyways

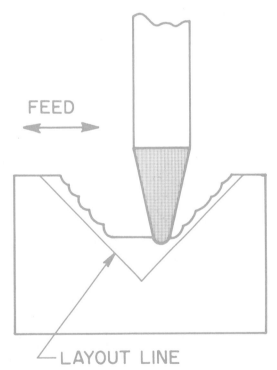

FEED

LAYOUT LINE

Fig. 1126. Roughing Out a V-Shaped Area with a Round-Nose Tool

square-nose tool or a tool with a slight elliptical shaped nose is recommended, (see Fig. 1124). A side-rake angle of about 10° to 15° generally is used on the elliptical-nose tool for finishing cuts on steel. The side-rake angle causes a shearing effect which produces an improved surface finish on many kinds of steel.

(3) *Square-nose Tool:* A square-nose tool Fig. 1125, is used for operations such as cutting grooves, shoulders, or keyways.

(4) *Dovetail Tool:* A dovetail tool is shown at D in Fig. 1118. This kind of tool is used for shaping dovetail angles, as shown in Fig. 1138.

1245. Holding the Work

The workpiece must be held securely in position for machining.

Machine Vise

Many kinds of workpieces can be held in the vise provided with the machine (see Figs. 1123, 1127, 1128, 1129, 1131, and 1133). The vise may be bolted to the top of the machine table or to the side of the table as in Fig. 1133. Other kinds of workpieces can be bolted directly to the machine table as in Fig. 1132. A wide variety of work-holding tools may be used for bolting workpieces directly to the machine table. Examples are shown and explained in Unit 28.

The machine table and the vise should be free from nicks or dirt before the vise is bolted to the table. The vise jaws should also be free of dirt or nicks before the work is clamped in the vise. The workpiece should extend above the hardened vise jaws far enough for the cutting tool to avoid striking the jaws. (See Fig. 1128.)

Emery cloth or soft aluminum sheet may be placed against the rough surface of rough castings to aid in holding them securely in the hardened vise jaws, Fig. 1127. Sometimes it is necessary to place sheet metal or paper shims underneath a workpiece to raise it to the proper level. (See Fig. 1131.)

Parallels

Precision parallels are used to raise and seat the workpiece at the proper elevation in the vise, Fig. 1128. They also hold the workpiece parallel to the bottom of the vise. A round aluminum, brass, or soft steel bar sometimes is used between the movable jaw and the workpiece, as in Fig. 1129. The round bar holds the finished surface of the workpiece firmly against the stationary vise jaw. This procedure causes the surface being machined to be square with the finished surface which is against the stationary jaw.

Hold-Downs

Hold-downs are wedge-shaped, hardened steel bars with the thick edge beveled at an angle of 2° or 3°, Fig. 1130. This causes the thin edge of the hold-downs to press the workpiece downward, thus seating it parallel to the bottom of the vise, see Fig. 1131. Hold-downs will hold the work securely for light and moderate cuts.

Indexing Attachment

Flat surfaces can be machined on round shafts by mounting the shaft between centers on an *indexing attachment,* see Fig. 1134. Any number of surfaces may be equally spaced or spaced at any desired interval, by using this attachment.

1246. Horizontal Cuts

Shapers are most frequently used for machining plane, flat , true surfaces. One or more

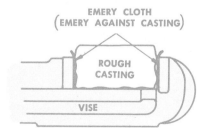

Fig. 1127. Mounting a Rough Casting in a Vise (Courtesy The Cincinnati Shaper Co.)

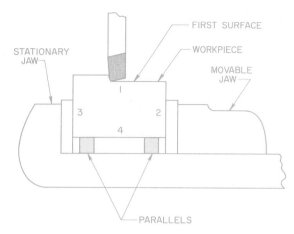

Fig. 1128. Workpiece Mounted on Parallels in Vise; Machining the First Surface of a Block to be Shaped Square and Parallel

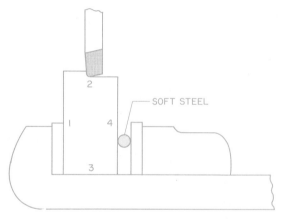

Fig. 1129. Machining the Second Surface of a Block to be Shaped Square and Parallel; The Finished Surface Number 1 is Placed Against the Stationary Jaw

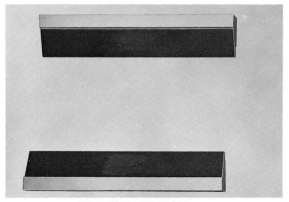

Fig. 1130. Hold-Downs

roughing cuts, as necessary, are made first. The final cut generally is a light finishing cut which produces a smooth finish. Be certain that you understand the safety practices recommended in section 1243 before starting the machine. Wear approved safety goggles or an eye shield.

Procedure for Roughing Cut

(1) Select the workpiece and remove burrs or bumps. Burrs may be filed off.

Larger bumps on castings may be ground off. Make layout lines which indicate the amount of material to be removed.

(2) Remove dirt or chips from the vise. See that the vise is bolted securely to its swivel base and to the table.

(3) Mount the workpiece in the vise as explained in section 1245. A large workpiece may be bolted to the table, as shown in Fig. 1132.

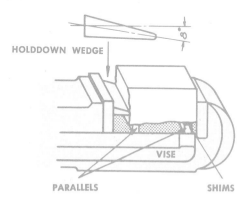

Fig. 1131. Using Hold-Downs
(Courtesy The Cincinnati Shaper Co.)

Fig. 1133. Vise Mounted on Side of Table
(Courtesy South Bend Lathe, Inc.)

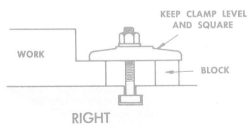

RIGHT
CLAMPING EFFECT IS ON WORK

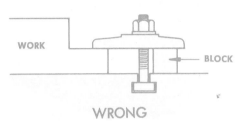

WRONG
CLAMPING EFFECT IS ON BLOCK

Fig. 1132. Clamping Work to Table
(Courtesy The Cincinnati Shaper Co.)

Fig. 1134. Flat Surfaces Being Machined on Shaft with Indexing Head
(Courtesy South Bend Lathe, Inc.)

(4) Select a left-cut roughing tool and clamp it in the toolholder as shown at *C* in Fig. 1118. Clamp the toolholder in the tool post with short-tool overhang and with short-tool slide overhang, shown in Fig. 1111.

(5) The clapper box may be clamped in the vertical position for horizontal cuts. However, some operators prefer to swivel the clapper box to the right, shown in Fig. 1110, for horizontal cuts. With the clapper box swiveled, the tool swings *up and away* from the work on the return stroke. Tighten the apron clamp bolts. Adjust the cutting tool and toolholder so that the tool is in a vertical position or slightly to the right, shown at the right in Fig. 1110.

(6) Adjust the table elevation so that the top of the workpiece is just below and clear of the cutting tool. (See § 1236.)

(7) Adjust the length of the stroke. The stroke should be at least ¾″ longer than the length of the workpiece. The procedure for adjusting the length of the stroke is explained in § 1237.

(8) Adjust the position of the stroke. The stroke should start about ½″ before the cut, and it should end with the cutting tool at least ¼″ beyond the workpiece at the end of the cutting stroke. The procedure for adjusting the position of the stroke is explained in § 1238.

(9) Set the machine for the number of strokes necessary for the desired cutting speed. A cutting speed of 90 to 100 surface feet per minute may be used for machining low-carbon steel. Cutting speeds for other metals are indicated in Table 37. The method for calculating the number of strokes per minute, for a given cutting speed, is explained in § 1239.

(10) Adjust the tool for the desired depth of cut. To do this, feed the work crosswise under the tool with the left hand. With the right hand on the down-feed screw, feed the tool down until it nearly touches the work. With the left hand, feed the work crosswise away from the tool, and with the right hand, feed the tool down to the desired depth of cut.

On cast iron the depth should be deep enough to cut well under the hard surface scale, usually a minimum of ¹⁄₁₆″ deep. In general, a roughing cut may be as deep as the sturdiness of the machine and setup will permit. On most medium-duty shapers, a cut from 0.060″ to 0.125″ depth is recommended. Always allow enough material for a finishing cut of 0.005″ to 0.015″ depth. The finishing cut follows after roughing cuts are made.

(11) Adjust the machine to the desired feed rate. A feed of 0.020″ to 0.030″ is suggested for average roughing cuts. Recommended feeds and the procedure for feed adjustment are explained in § 1240.

(12) With the use of the handwheel, on shapers so equipped, run the ram through the complete stroke without turning on the power. Check to see that the stroke length and position are correct. Be sure that the tool slide does not strike the vertical column. (See Fig. 1115.)

(13) Turn on the machine, engage the clutch, and observe the stroke for proper clearance of the work.

(14) Engage the automatic cross feed and make a horizontal roughing cut. (See § 1241.) Be sure that the table feeds during the return stroke.

(15) When the roughing cut has been completed, disengage the clutch and the

automatic cross feed. With a hand crank on the cross-feed screw, feed the table back to the original position, ready for the next cut.

(16) If more roughing cuts are required, make them by repeating steps 13, 14, and 15.

Procedure for Finishing Cut

(17) Select a finishing tool and mount it in the toolholder, as in step 4 above. Suggested finishing tools are shown in Fig. 1124 and explained in § 1244.

(18) Set the finishing tool for the desired depth of cut. With a square-nose tool or an elliptical-nose tool, a cut from 0.005″ to 0.015″ depth is recommended.

(19) Set the machine for the desired feed rate. Feed rates of 0.020″ to 0.060″ may be used with square-nose or elliptical-nose finishing tools. With a round-nose tool which has a nose radi-

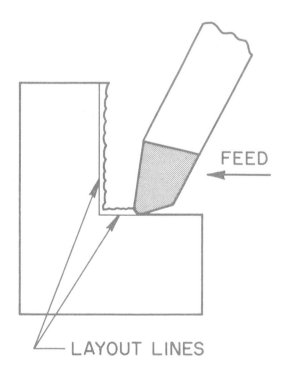

FEED

LAYOUT LINES

Fig. 1135. Machining the Horizontal Surface on a Shoulder

us of ⅛″ or larger, a feed of 0.010″ to 0.020″ should be used for best results.

(20) Start the machine and make the cut as in steps 12 through 15 above.

1247. Vertical Cuts

Vertical cuts are made when machining the ends of stock square. They are also used for machining shoulders square, as in Fig. 1136. Vertical cuts are made by feeding the tool downward with the down-feed handle.

Procedure for Roughing Cut

(1) Do steps 1, 2, and 3 as in making horizontal cuts in § 1246.

(2) Swing the clapper box to the right and clamp tightly, as in Fig. 1110. The tool will then swing *up and away* from the work on the return stroke.

(3) Check to see that the tool slide is in the vertical position, as indicated by the index mark on the graduated swivel base.

(4) Select a tool and toolholder and mount in the tool post.

a. For machining across the end of a workpiece which extends beyond the end of the vise, select a right-cut tool. Position the tool in a shaper toolholder as at *E* in Fig. 1118. The toolholder should have enough overhang so that the tool can cut along the vertical surface without striking the work with the clapper box. Check for clearance of the clapper box by feeding the tool down and up past the surface to be machined.

b. For machining a vertical surface to a shoulder, as in Fig. 1136, select a left-cut tool. The tool with the round nose, Fig. 1135, works best for roughing cuts. The tool with the pointed nose, Fig. 1136, works best for finishing cuts.

Mount the tool in a zero-degree lathe toolholder, the type shown in

Fig. 1023. Mount the toolholder in the tool post at an angle which provides 2° to 5° clearance, as in Fig. 1136. Allow the toolholder to extend far enough below the clapper box to complete the cut without having the clapper box strike the work. This may be checked by feeding the tool down and up, past the surface to be machined.

(5) Adjust the table elevation if necessary. (See § 1236.) See that the tool is clear of the work and located just above the work.

(6) Adjust the length of stroke. (See § 1237.)

(7) Adjust the position of the stroke. (See § 1238.)

(8) Set the machine for the number of strokes required for the desired cutting speed. (See § 1239.)

(9) With the tool above the workpiece, move the table horizontally so that it is in position for the proper *width of cut*. On cast iron, the cut should be wide enough to cut underneath the hard surface scale, usually a minimum 1⁄16″ width.

(10) Turn on the power, engage the clutch, and observe that the stroke clears the work properly.

(11) Make the vertical cut: With the right hand on the down-feed handle, feed the tool down about 0.005″ to 0.010″ on each return or backward stroke. Continue cutting to the desired depth.

(12) Stop the machine, and feed the tool up so it clears the top of the workpiece. Check the machined surface for squareness with a square.

(13) If more than one roughing cut is necessary, repeat steps 9 through 12.

Procedure for Finishing Cut

(14) Select and install a finishing tool of the type shown in Fig. 1136.

(15) Make a fine finishing cut, 0.005″ to 0.015″ depth. Feed the tool down about 0.005″ on each backward or return stroke.

1248. Combination Horizontal and Vertical Cuts

Combination horizontal and vertical cuts are used for machining a shoulder, as shown in Figs. 1135 and 1136. The work is first laid out to show where the finished surface will be. A series of horizontal roughing cuts is made to within 1⁄16″ to 1⁄8″ from the vertical surface, as in Fig. 1135. Material should be allowed for one horizontal finishing cut, which may be made either before or after the vertical cuts. The vertical surface is machined with one or more roughing cuts, and one finishing cut, as in Fig. 1136.

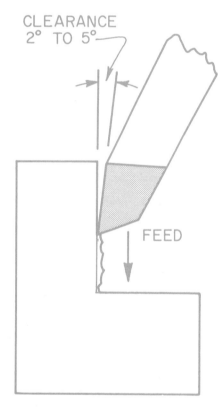

Fig. 1136. Machining the Vertical Surface on a Shoulder

Fig. 1137. Making an Angular Cut with a Shaper
(Courtesy The Cincinnati Shaper Co.)

The procedures for making horizontal cuts are explained in § 1246. The procedures for making vertical cuts are explained in § 1247.

1249. Machining a Block Square

In many machining applications, it is necessary to machine a block or bar of metal square and parallel. The surfaces must be parallel, and the ends must be parallel. When a block is squared with a shaper, the block is machined by using a series of horizontal and vertical cuts. The top, bottom, and both sides of a block or rectangular bar, as in Fig. 1128, are machined with horizontal cuts. (See § 1246.) The work is mounted in the vise with the jaws parallel to the ram. The ends of long blocks are machined with vertical cuts. (See § 1247.)

A short block may be positioned vertically in the shaper vise for machining the ends square. However, when this procedure is used, the vise should be turned at right angles with the direction of the stroke.

Procedure for Shaping a Block Square and Parallel

(1) Machine surface No. 1 with horizontal cuts, as in Figs. 1128 and 1127. Before placing the work in the vise, check the stationary vise jaw with a square to see that it is at a right angle with the bottom of the vise.

(2) Machine surface No. 2 with horizontal cuts, as in Fig. 1129. Place the machined surface No. 1 against the stationary jaw. Insert a round, soft metal rod between the work and the movable jaw, as in Fig. 1129.

(3) Machine surface No. 3 with horizontal cuts, as in Fig. 1129. Place surface No. 1 against the stationary jaw, as in step 2 above.

(4) Machine surface No. 4 with horizontal cuts, as in Fig. 1128. If the work does not seat solidly against both parallels, use a hold-down wedge, as in Fig. 1131.

(5) To machine the ends, swing the vise so the jaws are at right angles to the ram. Check for right angle accuracy with an indicator, as explained in section 1242. Mount the workpiece, on parallels if necessary, with one end extending slightly beyond the jaws. Machine the first end with a vertical cut, as explained in section 1247.

(6) Reverse the ends of the workpiece in the vise, and machine the second end to length with vertical cuts.

1250. Machining an Angle

Angular or bevel cuts may be made on a shaper as shown in Fig. 1137. When the cut is made, the tool head must be swiveled to the desired angle. The angle is indicated by the degree graduation marks on the swivel base. The cut is made by hand feeding the tool with the down-feed handle during each return or backward stroke. Note in Fig. 1137 that the clapper box must be tilted in a direction opposite from the angular surface being machined. Thus the tool swings *up and away* from the cut on the return or backward stroke.

An angular finishing cut is being made in machining a dovetail in Fig. 1138. Note again, that the clapper box is tilted in a direction opposite from the angular surface being machined.

A necessary precaution always must be taken when shaping an angular surface with the tool head swiveled. *Do not run the ram back into the column with the tool slide set at an angle or the slide will strike the column.* (See Fig. 1115.) Thus the length and position of the stroke must be such that the tool head does not go back into the column. Hence, on machines so equipped, the ram should always be run through its complete stroke with the handwheel before turning on the power.

Another way to make angular or bevel cuts is to mount the workpiece in the shaper vise at an angle and make horizontal cuts as in Fig. 1133. The advantage of this method is that automatic cross feed may be used. The vise may be mounted on either the side or top of the table. When making an angular cut by this method, mount the workpiece in the vise so that the layout line for the finished surface is horizontal, parallel with the table top or vise jaws.

Angular cuts must be made when machining the sides of a V-shaped groove, as in Fig. 1126. The material in the V-groove must be roughed out first with horizontal roughing cuts. The round-nose tool, without a side-rake angle, permits making the roughing cuts with either right-hand or left-hand feeds. The sides of the V-groove then are machined at an angle by swiveling the tool head to the desired angle. The tool is fed manually with the down-feed handle, as in Fig. 1137.

1251. Making Irregular Cuts

An irregular or curved surface can be machined with a shaper, as shown in Fig. 1139. The surface to be machined must be laid out

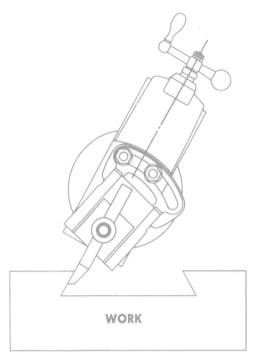

Fig. 1138. Cutting an Angle with Shaper Head Set at an Angle
(Courtesy The Cincinnati Shaper Co.)

Fig. 1139. Shaping an Irregular Surface
(Courtesy The Cincinnati Shaper Co.)

first, as shown in Fig. 1140. If large areas of material are to be removed, they are first removed with horizontal roughing cuts, as in Fig. 1126. Always allow enough material for a final finishing cut. The final finishing cut is made by handfeeding the table horizontally with the left hand, while handfeeding the tool to the desired depth with the right hand. Skilled operators sometimes use a combination of automatic cross feed, while handfeeding the tool to the desired depth.

1252. Cutting Slots or Keyways

Internal slots or keyways may be machined on a shaper by mounting the cutting tool in an extension toolholder as shown in Figs. 1123 and 1122. Square or rectangular keyways, as in Fig. 1123, are cut with a square-nose cutting tool of the type shown in Fig. 1125.

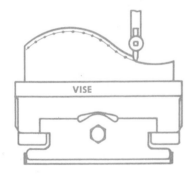

Fig. 1140. Shaping Irregular Surface to Layout Line (Courtesy The Cincinnati Shaper Co.)

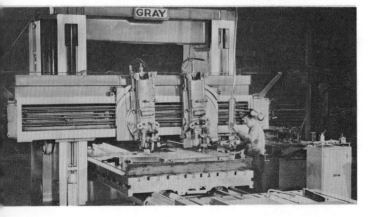

Fig. 1141. Large Industrial Planer with Two Tool Heads (Courtesy G. A. Gary Co.)

When internal keyways are cut, the length and position of the stroke must be adjusted carefully so that the clapper head or tool post does not strike the workpiece.

External slots or keyways are cut with a square-nose tool of the type shown in Fig. 1125. The tool is mounted in a shaper toolholder as shown in Fig. 1120. When a short keyway or slot is machined in a long workpiece, a hole is first drilled at the end of the slot to the depth of the slot. The length and position of the stroke must be carefully adjusted so that the end of the forward stroke stops at the center of the drilled hole.

1253. Planer

The *planer*, Fig. 1141 and 1142, is very much like the shaper, but it is larger and will cut flat surfaces on work that is too large to be handled on the shaper. The work is clamped onto the table, which moves back and forth under the cutting tool. The cutting tools for the planer are single-point tools which have the same general shapes as those for the lathe and shaper, but are usually larger. The cutting tool is held in the *tool head* that is in turn held by the horizontal *cross rail*. The cross rail is attached to vertical *uprights* and can be adjusted up or down.

The cutting tool peels off a new chip on each cutting stroke. At the end of the cutting stroke, the table reverses direction and moves back for another cutting stroke. After the table has returned, the tool head moves the cutting tool over for a new cut.

Since the planer is a large and costly machine tool, it is only found in shops and tool rooms that do a great deal of large work. However, the principles involved in setting up and operating a planer are very similar to those which apply to the shaper.

The size of a planer is determined by the largest size of work that it will machine. For example, a planer 26″ (dimension between uprights) × 26″ (maximum between the table and the cross rail) × 7′ (length of the table) will machine a piece of work up to 26″ wide, 26″ high, and 7′ long. Large planers can machine surfaces more than 20′ in length.

Review Questions

1. What kinds of surfaces can be machined with a shaper?

2. In what ways can workpieces be mounted on the shaper for machining?

3. What is the principal advantage in machining flat surfaces with a shaper, rather than a milling machine?

4. What is the principal disadvantage in machining flat surfaces with a shaper, rather than a milling machine?

5. On what kind of grinder is a single-point shaper tool sharpened?

6. On what kind of grinder is a milling cutter sharpened?

7. In what kinds of machine shops are shapers most frequently used?

8. What is the principal difference between a horizontal- and a vertical-type shaper?

9. How is the size of a shaper generally designated?

10. What is the advantage in having a shaper equipped with a universal table?

11. List the principal parts of a shaper.

12. Name the principal parts of the tool head assembly.

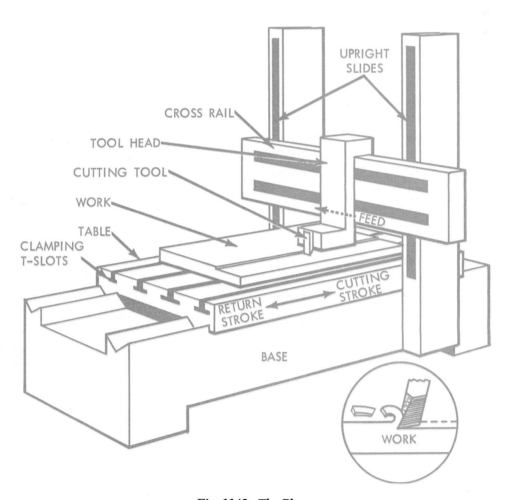

Fig. 1142. The Planer

13. For what purpose is the clutch used on a shaper?

14. List seven different adjustments which generally can be made on a shaper with the power off.

15. What purpose does the tool slide-lock screw serve?

16. Why should the toolholder and cutting tool generally be in a vertical position for making horizontal cuts?

17. Explain the general procedure used for raising or lowering the shaper table.

18. How much longer should the length of stroke be than the length of the surface to be machined?

19. Describe how the length of the stroke can be changed on one kind of shaper.

20. Describe briefly how the position of the stroke is adjusted on one kind of shaper.

21. Describe how the cutting speed for shaping is designated.

22. Explain how the approximate number of cutting strokes per minute can be calculated when you know the cutting speed.

23. Explain how the approximate cutting speed can be calculated for a given number of cutting strokes per minute.

24. What cutting speed is recommended for shaping low-carbon steel with a high-speed steel cutting tool?

25. Explain how the rate of table feed can be adjusted for one kind of shaper.

26. What depth of cut is generally recommended for making finishing cuts on a shaper with a finishing tool?

27. What is the minimum nose radius generally recommended for a finishing tool on a shaper?

28. What rate of feed is often used for very deep, roughing cuts on a shaper?

29. List a general rule which can be used in establishing the maximum feed and depth of cut for a shaper.

30. Does the table feed crosswise during the cutting stroke or during the return stroke?

31. Why should one always run the ram through its complete stroke with the handwheel, if the machine has one, before operating the machine with power?

32. Why should one avoid running the tool head back into the column when the tool slide is swiveled at an angle?

33. On which side of the machine does the operator generally stand when operating the shaper?

34. Explain how the automatic cross feed is engaged on one kind of shaper.

35. Explain how a vise can be accurately aligned with the use of a dial indicator.

36. List several safety practices which should be followed when using a shaper.

37. List three kinds of toolholders which can be used on a shaper.

38. List the following recommended angles for a general-purpose shaper tool: (a) end-relief angle; (b) side-relief angle; (c) side-rake angle; (d) back-rake angle.

39. Which is used more frequently on a shaper, right- or left-hand cutting tools?

40. List two common types of finishing tools used on a shaper.

41. What material can be used as an aid in holding rough castings in a shaper vise?

42. Why are parallels often used under workpieces mounted in the shaper vise?

43. Describe how hold-downs are used to mount workpieces in a machine vise.

44. Explain how vertical cuts are made with a shaper.

45. Describe the kinds of cuts which are made for machining a shoulder.

46. Explain, briefly, the steps to use in machining a block square and parallel.

47. Explain several ways in which an angular cut can be made with a shaper.

48. Explain how an irregular or curved surface can be machined on a shaper.

49. How can an internal keyway be machined with a shaper?

50. In what ways is a planer similar or different from a shaper?

Coordination

Words to Know

apron
apron clamp bolt
back rake
base
base casting
clamping nut
clapper block
clapper box
clutch
column
column clamping nut
cross feed
cross rail
cutting speed
cutting stroke
digging in

dovetail
down-feed handle
drive system
end relief
extension toolholder
feed-adjustment
   lever
feed-adjustment
   selector
feed-screw dial
gooseneck
handwheel
hold-downs
indexing attachment
lathe toolholder
left-cut

milling cutter
milling machine
multiple-point
   cutting tool
multiple-tooth
   cutter
multiplier
parallels
plain table
planer and shaper
   toolholder
ram
ram-adjusting shaft
ram positioner
rate of metal removal
return stroke
right-cut
shaper

side rake
side relief
single-point tool
slotted crank disk
square-nose tool
stroke
strokes per minute
table assembly
table support
tool chatter
tool head assembly
tool post
tool slide
universal table
vertical screw
vibrating arm
vise alignment
width of cut

The Milling
Machine and
Milling Operations

1260.   What is a Milling Machine?

A *milling machine*, Fig. 1151, is a machine tool which cuts metal with a multiple-tooth cutting tool called a *milling cutter,* Fig. 1152. The workpiece is mounted on the milling machine table and is fed against the revolving milling cutter. The speed of the cutting tool and the rate at which the workpiece is fed may be adjusted for each kind of metal being machined.

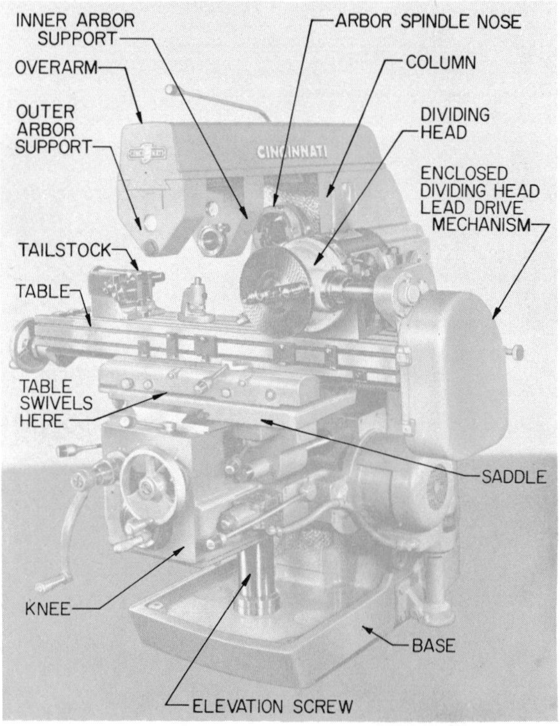

With heavy-duty milling machines, several kinds of milling cutters may be mounted on the machine arbor for milling several surfaces at the same time, Fig. 1152. Of course, on smaller machines, Fig. 1156, lighter cuts must be made. A wide variety of milling cutters is available for use in machining many kinds of surfaces and for performing many kinds of milling operations. (See Figs. 1198 to 1206.)

1261.   Why Milling
Machines Are Important

The milling machine is important because it is one of the basic machine tools, and it performs a wide variety of machining operations. The kinds of operations performed on milling machines are explained in section 1262.

Five of the most basic kinds of machine tools include the drill press, lathe, shaper and planer, grinding machine, and the milling machine. The principles involved in the operation of these five basic machine tools also apply to other specialized mass-production machine tools. Thus, most of the chip-machining operations performed on the many kinds of specialized production machine tools are adapted from the operations performed on the above five basic machine tools.

INNER ARBOR SUPPORT
OVERARM
OUTER ARBOR SUPPORT
TAILSTOCK
TABLE
TABLE SWIVELS HERE
KNEE
ELEVATION SCREW
ARBOR SPINDLE NOSE
COLUMN
DIVIDING HEAD
ENCLOSED DIVIDING HEAD LEAD DRIVE MECHANISM
SADDLE
BASE

Fig. 1151. Universal Milling Machine,
Showing Principal Parts
(Courtesy The Cincinnati Milling Machine Co.)

Milling machines use multiple-point cutting tools. Thus, milling machines cut at a relatively high *rate of metal removal,* as compared with lathes, shapers, and planers which usually cut with a single-point cutting tool. (See Fig. 1152.)

1262.   Kinds of Milling Operations

Milling machines perform a wide variety of machining operations. The variety of milling operations which can be performed on a milling machine depends on the following:

(1) the type of machine
(2) the kind of milling cutter used
(3) the kinds of accessories or attachments available for use with the machine.

Milling machines can machine flat surfaces, including horizontal, vertical, and angular surfaces. (See Figs. 1161, 1162, and 1163.) They machine many kinds of shoulders, grooves, T-slots, dovetails, and keyways. (See Figs. 1194, 1195, and 1198.) Milling machines also machine irregular or curved surfaces with formed-tooth milling cutters. (See Figs. 1199, 1200, 1201, and 1202.)

Milling machines, particularly vertical-type milling machines, Figs. 1154 and 1158, can perform many of the basic hole-machining operations commonly performed on a drill press. These operations include drilling, reaming, countersinking, boring, and counterboring. (See Figs. 457, and 1221-1229.) These operations are described further in section 1266.

Milling machines equipped with a dividing head, Fig. 1151, can machine equally spaced surfaces, grooves, or gear teeth on cylindrical shaped parts, Fig. 1170. By swiveling the table about its axis, universal milling machines can machine spirals, Fig. 1173. Plain milling machines equipped with a universal spiral attachment can also machine spirals, see Fig. 1172.

A wide variety of accessories is available for expanding the variety of operations which can be performed on milling machines. This unit, however, is concerned primarily with the basic kinds of milling operations commonly performed in beginning machine shop classes. Operations of an advanced nature are described very briefly. These descriptions will provide some understanding of the kinds of work which can be done on milling machines.

1263.   Types of Milling Machines

Milling machines can be classified under two basic types. These include *bed-type* and *knee-and-column* type milling machines. Bed-type milling machines usually are specially designed manufacturing milling machines which are used for mass-production purposes. They are explained further in section 1286 and Fig. 1231.

1264.   Knee-and-Column Type Milling Machines

Knee-and-column type milling machines, as the name indicates, are equipped with a *knee* and *column,* see Fig. 1151. The body or frame of the machine is a large casting which includes the *base* and the upright portion called the *column.* The front of the column has an

Fig. 1152. Milling a Casting with Several Cutters Mounted on the Arbor of a Horizontal Milling Machine
(Courtesy The Cincinnati Milling Machine Co.)

accurately machined surface and *V-ways,* which are often called the column. (See Fig. 1151.) The *knee* is mounted on the V-ways of the machined column.

The knee can be raised vertically to any desired elevation. The *saddle* and *table* are mounted on top of the knee. The table can feed *longitudinally* (horizontally to the right or to the left), and it can feed *transversely* (crosswise or cross feed in or out from the column). Bolt workpieces directly to the table as in Fig. 1152, or they can be mounted in a machine vise which is bolted to the table as in Figs. 1161 and 1162. Thus the table on knee-and-column type milling machines can be fed or adjusted in three directions.

The directions are:

(1) vertical
(2) longitudinal
(3) cross feed or transverse.

The table can be fed manually or with automatic power feed.

Knee-and-column type milling machines can be further classified into the following types:

(1) Horizontal-type milling machines (see § 1265).
 a. Plain-type
 b. Universal-type
(2) Vertical-type milling machines (see § 1266).
(3) Combination horizontal- and vertical-type milling machines (see § 1267).

Knee-and-column type milling machines are manufactured in a wide range of sizes and weights. Some school shops have standard, heavy-duty milling machines as shown in Figs. 1151, 1153, and 1154. Many schools have smaller, lighter weight machines such as those shown in Figs. 1156-1159. Regardless of the size of the machine, the principles involved in various milling operations are very similar. Heavy cuts on a milling machine require a heavy-duty, sturdy machine. Hence, lighter cuts and lighter feeds must be taken when using smaller, lightweight machines.

Fig. 1153. Plain Milling Machine, Showing Operating Controls
(Courtesy The Cincinnati Milling Machine Co.)

1265. Horizontal-Type Milling Machine

Horizontal-type milling machines usually have the milling cutter mounted on a horizontal arbor as shown in Fig. 1152. The arbor fits into the spindle nose which is located on the machined face of the vertical column. The

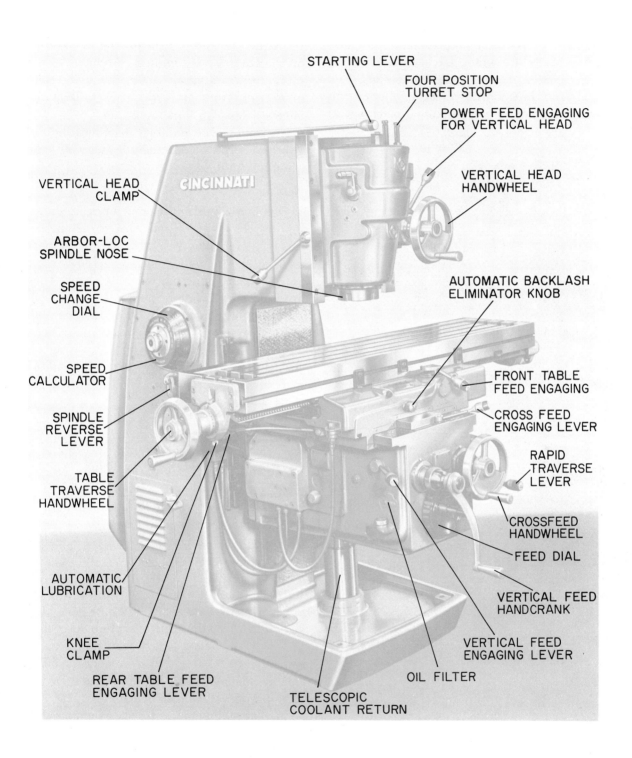

STARTING LEVER

FOUR POSITION
TURRET STOP

POWER FEED ENGAGING
FOR VERTICAL HEAD

VERTICAL HEAD
CLAMP

VERTICAL HEAD
HANDWHEEL

CINCINNATI

ARBOR-LOC
SPINDLE NOSE

AUTOMATIC BACKLASH
ELIMINATOR KNOB

SPEED
CHANGE
DIAL

SPEED
CALCULATOR

FRONT TABLE
FEED ENGAGING

SPINDLE
REVERSE
LEVER

CROSS FEED
ENGAGING LEVER

RAPID
TRAVERSE
LEVER

TABLE
TRAVERSE
HANDWHEEL

CROSSFEED
HANDWHEEL

FEED DIAL

AUTOMATIC
LUBRICATION

VERTICAL FEED
HANDCRANK

KNEE
CLAMP

VERTICAL FEED
ENGAGING LEVER

REAR TABLE FEED
ENGAGING LEVER

OIL FILTER

TELESCOPIC
COOLANT RETURN

Fig. 1154. Vertical Milling Machine,
Showing Operating Controls
(Courtesy The Cincinnati Milling Machine Co.)

arbor is supported rigidly with an *arbor support* or *overarm support*, Figs. 1152 and 1161. Milling cutters used on horizontal milling machine arbors, therefore, have an arbor hole.

End-milling cutters, called *end mills*, Fig. 1203, can be mounted horizontally in the spindle nose of horizontal milling machines as

Fig. 1155. Milling a Dovetail with Vertical Milling Attachments on a Universal Milling Machine
(Courtesy The Cincinnati Milling Machine Co.)

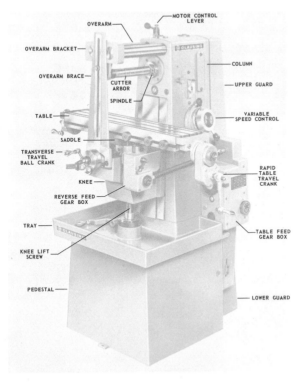

Fig. 1156. Small Plain Milling Machine
(Courtesy Atlas Press)

in Figs. 1179, 1204, and 1169. Thus end-milling operations also can be performed with the cutter operating in a horizontal position on horizontal-type milling machines. End-milling operations, however, are more commonly performed on vertical-type milling machines. (See Figs. 1162 and 1171.)

Horizontal-type milling machines are of two basic types. These include the *plain-* and the *universal-types*.

Plain-Type

Plain horizontal milling machines are shown in Figs. 1153, 1156, and 1157. Machines of this type are in wide use in school shops, tool-and-die shops, maintenance machine shops, and in many industrial machine shops. They are used for all of the common kinds of horizontal milling operations. These include milling flat horizontal surfaces, vertical surfaces, angular surfaces, curved surfaces, irregular surfaces, grooves, and keyways. Plain milling machines can also perform end-milling operations, as explained above.

The table on plain-type milling machines cannot be swiveled for helical milling operations. However, with the use of a dividing head and a universal spiral milling attachment, such operations can be performed. (See Fig. 1172.) A vertical milling attachment, as in Fig. 1155, may be used to perform vertical milling operations on a plain milling machine.

A number of small plain-type milling machines is available. Two kinds are shown in Figs. 1156 and 1157. They are much less expensive than larger machines of the kind shown in Fig. 1153. However, they also have less power, weight, sturdiness, and cutting capacity than the larger machines. The smaller machines are in wide use in many school shops.

Smaller milling machines are available with several choices of table feed:

(1) the table may be entirely handfed,
(2) it may be equipped with power longitudinal feed only, or

(3) it may be equipped with power longitudinal and power transverse or cross feed.

The plain milling machines in Fig. 1156 and 1157 are equipped with power longitudinal table feed. Handfeed is used for transverse (cross) table feed or for changes in table elevation.

Universal-Type

A universal-horizontal milling machine is shown with its principal parts labeled in Fig. 1151. The distinguishing difference between the plain- and the universal-type machines is that the table can be swiveled about its vertical axis on the universal machine. Universal-type machines usually are equipped with a dividing head, tailstock, and a dividing-head lead driving mechanism. These accessories make it possible to perform helical milling operations, as in Fig. 1173. Helical milling is required for cutting helical gears or for making helical cutting tools such as drills, reamers, or milling cutters.

A vertical milling attachment, Fig. 1171, can be used on the universal milling machine

for performing vertical milling operations. In addition to helical milling operations, the universal milling machine can do all of the operations performed on the plain milling machine.

1266. Vertical Milling Machines

Vertical-type milling machines are shown in Figs. 1154, 1158, and 1159. The spindle on vertical milling machines normally is in a vertical position, similar to the spindle on a drill press. However, the head may be swiveled on some machines for angular milling or hole-machining operations, Figs. 1159 and 1163.

Vertical milling machines use cutters called *end mills*, Figs. 1203 and 1204. The end mills are mounted in the nose of the vertical spindle, Figs. 1159 and 1162. Various kinds of spindle adapters are used for mounting the end mills, Fig. 1178.

Except for the position of the spindle, vertical milling machines are very similar to

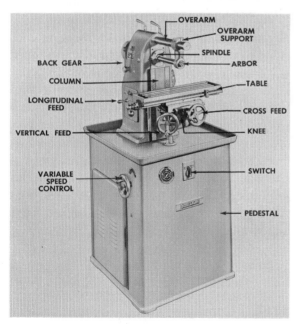

Fig. 1157. Small Plain Milling Machine
(Courtesy Sheldon Co.)

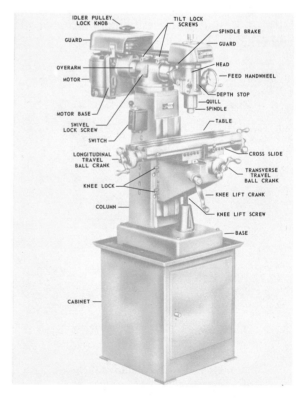

Fig. 1158. Small Vertical Milling Machine
(Courtesy Atlas Press)

plain, horizontal milling machines. Compare the two machines in Figs. 1153 and 1154; notice the similarity of the principal parts and controls. Many of the basic attachments and accessories can be used interchangeably on horizontal and vertical machines. A second difference between the vertical and horizontal machines is that the vertical machines use end-milling cutters; horizontal machines may use either arbor-type milling cutters or end mills. (See Fig. 1169.)

Operations

Vertical milling operations can be performed on vertical milling machines or with a vertical milling attachment on a horizontal milling machine. (See Fig. 1171.) Vertical milling machines can machine horizontal surfaces, angular surfaces, shoulders, grooves, keyways, dovetails, and T-slots. (See Figs. 1221-1229.) In addition, vertical milling machines can perform hole-machining operations such as drilling, countersinking, boring, counterboring, and reaming. (See Fig. 457.)

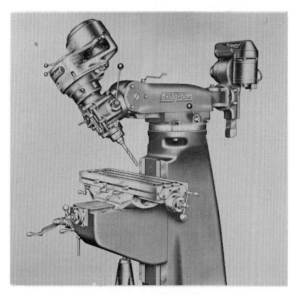

Fig. 1159. Vertical Milling Machine
(Courtesy Bridgeport Machines, Inc.)
The head may be swiveled for drilling or milling at an angle. Vertical shaping attachment is mounted at opposite end of ram.

Heavy-Duty Machines

Heavy-duty vertical milling machines of the type shown in Fig. 1154 are capable of taking very heavy cuts. They are equipped with power longitudinal feed, power cross feed, and power vertical feed for table elevation. The spindle in the head is also provided with power vertical feed.

Light-Duty Machines

A number of light-duty and medium-duty vertical milling machines is available. They are widely used in tool rooms, small industrial machine shops, and in school shops. Several types are shown in Figs. 1158 and 1159. They may be purchased with manual feed only, or with one or more of the following kinds of power feed:

(1) power longitudinal table feed,
(2) power transverse feed (cross feed),
(3) power vertical spindle feed, and
(4) power table elevation.

Light-duty machines produce good results when used for cuts which are within their capacity.

Hole Machining

Vertical milling machines are often used for drilling and other hole-machining operations which require very accurate location of the holes. The 0.001″ graduation marks on the table transverse handwheel and the cross-feed handwheel, Fig. 1154, make it possible to locate the centers of holes accurately. However, always remember to turn the feed wheel or crank in a direction which corrects for wear or backlash in the feed screw before setting the graduated collar at the *zero* index mark. The 0.001″ graduation marks on the vertical head handwheel also make it possible to machine holes accurately to depth. The head may be swiveled for angular hole-machining operations, Fig. 1159.

1267. Combination Horizontal and Vertical Milling Machines

Some milling machines may be classified

as *combination horizontal and vertical milling machines.* The machine in Fig. 1160 is designed for both milling operations. This type of machine normally is available with a standard overarm for use as a horizontal milling machine. However, it is also available with the special overarm which has an independent overhead spindle for vertical milling operations. The vertical spindle is driven by an independent motor. Machines of this type are used for horizontal milling operations, Figs. 1161 and 1169. They also are used for vertical milling operations, Figs. 1162 and 1163. Several manufacturers make light-duty

Fig. 1160. Combination Horizontal and Vertical Milling Machine
(Courtesy The Cincinnati Lathe and Tool Co.)

Fig. 1162. Vertical End Milling with a Combination Horizontal and Vertical Machine
(Courtesy The Cincinnati Lathe and Tool Co.)

Fig. 1161. Horizontal Milling with a Combination Horizontal and Vertical Machine
(Courtesy The Cincinnati Lathe and Tool Co.)

Fig. 1163. Angular-End Milling with a Combination Horizontal and Vertical Milling Machine
(Courtesy The Cincinnati Lathe and Tool Co.)

milling machines which can be used for either horizontal or vertical milling operations.

1268.   Principal Parts

Before attempting to operate a milling machine, you should know the names of the principal parts and the controls on the machine. The parts and controls on most knee-and-column type milling machines, although not exactly alike, are very similar. Many of the basic parts were described in section 1264. The similarities and differences between plain and universal horizontal machines are explained in section 1265. The similarities and differences between vertical and horizontal machines are included in section 1266.

The names of the principal parts and controls of horizontal-type milling machines can be found in Figs. 1151, 1153, 1156, and 1157. The names of the principal parts and controls on vertical-type machines can be found in Figs. 1154 and 1158.

1269.   Milling Machine Controls and Adjustments

Before operating a milling machine, one must know how to make several kinds of ad-

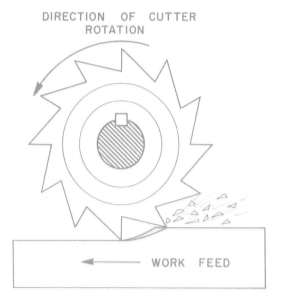

Fig. 1165. Up Milling (or Conventional Milling)
Notice that the chip size increases during the cut.

justments on the machine. These include knee elevation, table adjustments, speed, and feed. It is always best to have your instructor explain the principal parts of the milling machine in your shop. It is also good practice to review the instruction manual provided by the manufacturer of the machine before operating the machine.

Knee Elevation

The knee must be raised or lowered in order to establish the proper elevation of the workpiece under the cutting tool. For *peripheral* (horizontal) milling operations, the knee must be raised to establish the *depth of cut*. For *vertical* milling operations, the depth of cut may be established either by raising the knee or by feeding the tool to depth with the *vertical-head handwheel,* Figs. 1154 and 1158. Generally, it is best to set the depth of cut by raising the knee.

A *knee clamp,* a lever or a locking nut, locks the knee securely to the column during milling operations. The knee clamp must be loosened before raising or lowering the knee. The knee is then raised or lowered with the *vertical-feed hand crank.* Notice that there is a *micrometer collar* with 0.001″ graduations on this control, and also on the longitudinal-feed and cross-feed controls. Some machines are equipped with *power vertical feed* which is engaged with the *vertical-feed engaging lever.* When the knee is located at the proper elevation, the knee clamp must be tightened. If it is not tightened, vibration, chatter, a rough machined surface, and possible cutter damage may result.

A good way to establish the *depth of cut* is to loosen the knee clamp and start the machine. Raise the knee until the cutter just touches the workpiece. Bring the workpiece out from under the cutter. It should be brought to the correct side of the cutter so that the feed is adjusted for *up milling,* Fig. 1165. Set the micrometer collar on the vertical-feed crank at zero, and raise the knee for the desired depth of cut. If you raise the table too high, lower it again by turning the hand-wheel at least ½ turn lower than necessary. Then, raise the table to the desired elevation. This procedure will correct for backlash or wear in the table elevation screw. Lock the knee clamp and the depth of cut is established, ready to make the cut.

Transverse Table Movement

Transverse table movement is cross move-ment of the *saddle* and *table* toward or away from the column. During most milling opera-tions, the saddle is clamped securely to the top of the knee with one or more *saddle-clamp levers*. This reduces table vibration. There-fore, before making transverse table adjust-ments, loosen the saddle clamp. Then the table can be moved toward or away from the column with the *cross-feed handwheel*. After table adjustment, the saddle clamp again must be tightened.

The saddle clamps must be loosened when performing operations which involve trans-verse (cross) table feeding. Some milling ma-chines are equipped with power transverse table feed. On machines so equipped, the feed is engaged with the *cross-feed engaging lever*, Fig. 1154.

Longitudinal Table Movement

Longitudinal table movement is table travel from side to side, either toward the right or the left. The table may be fed manually with the *table traverse handwheel*, also called the *longitudinal feed*. (See Figs. 1153 and 1157.) Most machines are equipped with power longitudinal table feed. The table power feed is engaged with the *power table-feed lever*. (See Figs. 1153 and 1154.)

Most milling machine tables are provided with a *table-clamp lever* which may be tight-ened to prevent longitudinal table movement during certain operations. The table-clamp lever should generally be tightened during hole-machining operations on either hori-zontal or vertical milling machines.

Rapid Traverse

Larger milling machines are equipped with a *rapid-traverse control*. (See Figs. 1053 and 1054.) This control enables the operator to move the knee or table rapidly in either di-rection with power. Beginners should be very careful in using this control. Serious damage can result if the workpiece should strike the cutter or arbor while the knee is raised rapidly or while the table is traversed rapidly. It is best to ask your instructor to show you how to use the rapid-traverse control before at-tempting to use it yourself. Skilled operators are able to speed up production through the use of this control.

Spindle Speed Adjustment

The spindle speed is designated in *rpm* (revolutions per minute). The rpm may be changed in different ways on different kinds of milling machines. On some machines the rpm is selected and set by turning a *speed-change dial* to the desired rpm. (See Figs. 1153 and 1154.) Other machines may be equipped with levers which shift gears for the desired rpm. Machines of the type shown in Figs. 1156 and 1157 are equipped with a variable-speed drive which must be adjusted while the machine is running. (See § 422 and Fig. 326.) On machines with a step pulley and V-belt drive, Fig. 1158, the rpm is changed by shifting the belt to a different step on the pulley. (See Fig. 328.)

The direction of spindle revolution may be changed on most milling machines. This may be done with a spindle-reversing switch, but-ton, or lever. The machine in Fig. 1154 has a spindle-reverse lever on the left side of the machine.

Feed Adjustment

The rate of feed and the method for deter-mining the rate of feed are explained in sec-tion 1279. After the feed rate has been deter-mined, the machine should be adjusted for the proper rate of feed. On most machines, the feed rate is changed through a series of change gears in a feed-change gear box. On some machines, the desired feed rate is changed by turning a *feed dial* directly to the desired feed rate indicated on the dial. The machines in Figs. 1153 and 1154 are equipped with this type of feed dial located on the front of the knee. The feed rate on many machines is changed by shifting one or more feed-change levers located on or near the feed-change gear box.

Longitudinal, transverse or cross feed, and vertical power feeds are engaged or disengaged with levers located at the front of the machine. The table is fed manually on small machines not equipped with power feeds. The operator then must use his best judgment in feeding the table at the proper rate of feed. Too rapid feeding can cause cutter breakage.

1270. Direction of Feed

The direction of feed in relation to the direction of cutter rotation is an important factor in all milling operations. Two methods of feed are possible. When the work is fed against the direction of the milling cutter, Fig. 1165, the method is called *up milling* (formerly

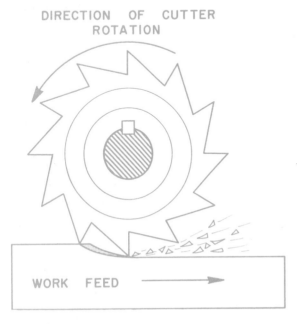

Fig. 1166. Down Milling (or Climb Milling)
Notice that the chip size decreases during the cut.

called conventional milling). When the workpiece is fed with the direction of the milling cutter, Fig. 1166, the method is called *down milling* (formerly called climb milling). CAUTION: *Down milling is done only on machines equipped with anti-backlash devices; check your operator's manual.*

Smaller milling machines, and many older machines, are not equipped with anti-backlash devices. Therefore, only the up-milling method can be used with them. Modern heavy-duty machines of the types shown in Figs. 1151, 1153, and 1154 are equipped with backlash eliminators. Machines so equipped can be used for either up milling or down milling.

Up (Conventional) Milling

With up milling, the cutter tooth starts into the work with a chip of zero thickness and ends with a thick chip. The cutter starts into clean metal and ends by lifting off the rough surface scale. Thus the cutter stays sharp longer. However, the workpiece must be clamped very tightly in the vise or to the table. The cutting forces tend to lift or pull the work out of the vise. The direction of feed forces the work against the cutter, thus compensating for wear or backlash in the table leadscrew and feeding mechanism.

Down (Climb) Milling

With down milling, the cutter tooth starts into the work with a thick chip and ends with a thin chip, Fig. 1166. The scraping action of the cutter tooth at the end of the chip tends to produce a smoother surface. The cutting forces tend to pull the workpiece under the cutter. Thus, any backlash in the leadscrew or feeding mechanism can cause vibration, chatter, and possible cutter breakage. A hard surface scale on the workpiece will dull the cutter more rapidly.

Down milling is gaining wider use today on certain production milling operations. It generally produces a better surface finish on harder steels. Small thin parts and parts which are otherwise difficult to hold can be machined more easily by this method. But remember, to use this method, the machine must be equipped with an anti-backlash device.

The two methods of milling with arbor-type cutters used on horizontal milling machines are shown in Figs. 1165 and 1166. However, the principles involved in these methods of milling also apply to vertical end-milling and face-milling operations. The up-milling method should be used on machines not equipped with anti-backlash devices.

1271. Accessories and Workholding Devices

A variety of attachments or accessories is available for use on plain, universal, and vertical milling machines. Some of the accessories make it possible to hold the work more effectively. Other accessories make it possible to expand the range of operations which can be done with the machine.

Swivel Vise

The swivel vise, Fig. 1167, is bolted to the table with T-slot bolts, Fig. 424. The vise can be swiveled at any desired angle. The angle is indicated by the degree graduations on the swivel base. A majority of the workpieces or projects machined in beginning machine shop classes can be mounted in a swivel vise for milling. Alignment of the vise is explained in section 1282.

Universal Vise

The universal vise, Fig. 1168, can be used for machining workpieces at an angle. The vise can be swiveled at any desired angle on its swivel base. The vise jaws can be tilted at any desired angle, from 0° to the 90° vertical position. This kind of vise is often used for holding workpieces in the vertical position

Fig. 1167. Swivel Vise
(Courtesy The Cincinnati Milling Machine Co.)

Fig. 1168. Universal Vise
(Courtesy The Cincinnati Milling Machine Co.)

Fig. 1169. Milling a Shoulder on Workpiece Mounted on a Swivel Table
(Courtesy The Cincinnati Lathe and Tool Co.)
This shows how horizontal-end milling operations can be performed with a horizontal machine.

for end-milling operations on horizontal milling machines. It can be used in the vertical position for hole-machining operations with a horizontal milling machine. For end-milling and hole-machining operations on horizontal machines, the cutting tool is mounted on an adapter as shown in Figs. 1179 and 1204.

Dividing Head

A dividing head, Figs. 1172 and 1230, is bolted to the milling machine table. It is used for holding a workpiece and for dividing it into a number of equally spaced angular divisions. An *index crank* and an *index plate*, which has many circular rows of holes, are located on the front of the dividing head. By

Fig. 1170. Using the Dividing Head to Cut a Spur Gear
(Courtesy The Cincinnati Milling Machine Co.)

Fig. 1171. Making an Angular Cut with a Vertical Milling Attachment on a Horizontal Milling Machine
(Courtesy The Cincinnati Milling Machine Co.)

indexing, explained in § 1285, a number of equally spaced angular divisions may be machined on a workpiece. (See Fig. 1170.)

A *tailstock* is bolted to the table and is used with the dividing head for holding workpieces between centers, Fig. 1170. Both the tailstock and the dividing head are equipped with 60° centers, the same as lathe centers. The tailstock center can be raised above the center point of the dividing head. This is done when tapered grooves or tapered surfaces are machined on a workpiece.

A workpiece, such as the gear blank in Fig. 1170, is pressed on a *lathe mandrel.* (See Figs. 1055 and 1056.) The mandrel has a driving dog clamped on the driving end and is mounted between the centers of the dividing head and the tailstock. On longer workpieces, center holes are drilled and the workpiece is mounted between centers, Fig. 1172.

A universal 3-jaw chuck may be mounted on the spindle nose of the dividing head for holding short workpieces for many kinds of horizontal or vertical milling operations. One example of its use is shown in Fig. 1171. The dividing head may be swiveled to any desired angular position, from 0° to the 90° vertical position. Thus, with a round workpiece mounted in the chuck in a vertical position, it is possible to mill any number of equally spaced flat surfaces on its circumference. This procedure can be used for machining a square or hexagonal head on a bolt or on the end of a shaft. This kind of setup also can be used for milling screw slots in the head of a screw.

Lead-Drive Mechanism

The lead-drive mechanism is used with a dividing head for milling helical or spiral surfaces or grooves, Fig. 1172. Helical milling is used for milling helical gears, helical milling cutters, helical reamers, drills, and similar items.

Vertical Milling Attachment

This attachment can be mounted to the column and the spindle of horizontal milling machines, Figs. 1155 and 1171. The vertical milling attachment makes it possible to perform a wide variety of vertical milling operations on either plain or universal horizontal machines. The attachment may be used in a vertical position, Fig. 1155, or at an angle for milling angular surfaces, Fig. 1171.

Universal Spiral Attachment

This attachment makes it possible to machine helical or spiral surfaces or grooves with a plain horizontal milling machine. (See Fig. 1172.) The attachment is mounted on the column and is driven by the machine spindle.

On universal milling machines, helical milling is done by swinging the milling machine table on its swivel base, Fig. 1173. The dividing-head lead driving mechanism causes the work to revolve as the table travels longitudinally, thus causing the helical groove to be machined.

Circular Milling Attachment

Several kinds of circular milling attachments are available for use on both horizontal and vertical milling machines. Handfeed- and power feed-types are available. The hand-feed-type, shown in Fig. 1174, is widely used in many shops. A workpiece can be bolted directly to the attachment table, or it may be mounted in a vise which is bolted to the attachment table.

The circular milling attachment makes it possible to machine circular edges, shoulders, or grooves on vertical-type machines. The swivel base of the circular table is provided with degree-graduation marks. Hence this attachment can be used for milling grooves at any desired angle across the top surface of a workpiece. It also permits machining the vertical edges of a workpiece at an angle. (See Fig. 1169.)

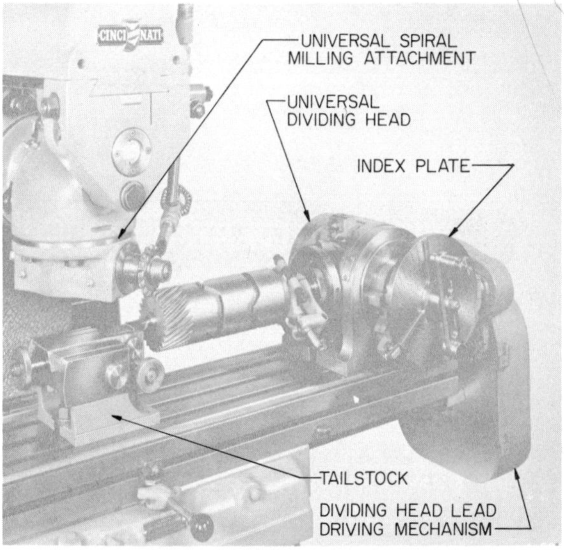

Fig. 1173. Cutting a Left-Hand Helix with the Table Swiveled on a Universal Milling Machine
(Courtesy The Cincinnati Milling Machine Co.)

Fig. 1174. Circular Milling Attachment, Handfeed-Type
(Courtesy The Cincinnati Lathe and Tool Co.)

UNIVERSAL SPIRAL MILLING ATTACHMENT

UNIVERSAL DIVIDING HEAD

INDEX PLATE

TAILSTOCK

DIVIDING HEAD LEAD DRIVING MECHANISM

Fig. 1172. Milling Helical Gear Teeth
(Courtesy The Cincinnati Milling Machine Co.)
This plain milling machine is equipped with a universal spiral milling attachment and a universal dividing head.

Fig. 1175. Arbors, Collets, and Adapters
(Courtesy The Cincinnati Milling Machine Co.)
A. Collet Adapter
B. Shell-End Mill Arbor
C. Arbor, Style A
D. Arbor Adapter
E. Reducing Collet
F. Solid Collet
G. Bushing
H. Split Collet

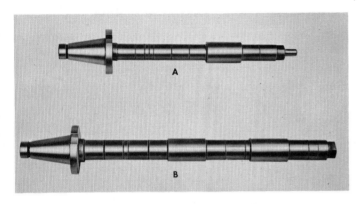

Fig. 1176. Milling Arbors
(Courtesy The Cincinnati Milling Machine Co.)
A. Style A
B. Style B

Fig. 1177. Milling Arbors, Collets, and Adapters
(Courtesy The Cincinnati Milling Machine Co.)
A. Fly cutter arbor
B. Adapter for taper shank-end mill
C. Adapter for small shell-end mill
D. Collet for taper shank-end mill

1272. Arbors, Collets, Adapters, and Holders

A wide variety of milling machine arbors, collets, adapters, and holders is available for holding milling cutters. (See Figs. 1175, 1176, 1177, and 1178.) These devices are used for holding and adapting milling cutters to the spindle of the milling machine. (See Figs. 1179 and 1180.)

Arbor Shanks

Most manufacturers of standard and heavy-duty milling machines have adapted the *national milling machine taper* for the tapered hole in the machine spindle. Arbors for these machines have the same kind of tapered shank. Standard milling machine tapers are steep tapers with 3½″ taper per foot. Because of the steep taper, they are the *self-releasing* type. Hence they must be held in place with a *draw-in bolt* or a locking device or collar, Fig. 1179.

Standard milling machine tapers are made in several sizes, designated by the numbers

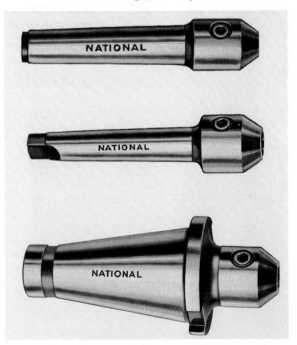

Fig. 1178. Holders for Straight Shank-End Mill
(Courtesy National Twist Drill)

30, 40, 50, and 60. The No. 50 is the most common and is used on machines of the type shown in Figs. 1151, 1153, and 1154. The No. 40 taper is used on smaller machines.

Some milling machine spindles have a standard shallow taper, such as the *Brown & Sharpe taper* or the *Morse taper*. These are *self-holding tapers*. A few manufacturers use a special taper for the spindle hole on their milling machines.

Style-A arbors, as shown at the top in Fig. 1176, have a small pilot at the outer end. The pilot fits in a small bearing in a style-A arbor support, Fig. 1181. The style-A arbor support permits the use of small diameter cutters. This type arbor support easily passes over the vise when using small cutters close to the vise jaws. Style-A arbors generally are used for light-duty milling operations. An additional inner arbor support can also be used with the style-A arbor for more rigid support. (See Fig. 1151.)

Style-B arbors, as shown at the bottom in Fig. 1176, do not have a pilot at the outer end. Instead, they have one or more *bearing sleeves* which are larger in diameter than the arbor *spacing collars*. The bearing sleeves run in the large bearings in the style-B arbor sup-

ports, Fig. 1180. Style-B arbors are used for heavy-duty milling operations. They are desirable for any milling operation so long as the arbor supports clear the vise and the workpiece.

Spacing collars are provided on both style-A and style-B arbors. They hold the arbor rigid and permit spacing the milling cutter at any location along the arbor. The ends of the collars are precision ground to extreme accuracy. This causes the collars to hold the arbor

Fig. 1180. Milling a Crankshaft in a Special Fixture (Courtesy The Cincinnati Milling Machine Co.) The Style-B Arbor is used in this heavy-duty milling operation.

Fig. 1179. Mounting Drills or End Mills in the Spindle Nose of Horizontal Milling Machine (Courtesy The Cincinnati Milling Machine Co.)

Fig. 1181. Straddle Milling (Courtesy The Cincinnati Milling Machine Co.)

straight when the cutter is installed and the arbor nut is tightened. A tiny nick or chip between the collars can cause the arbor to bend and the cutter to run untrue. The arbor, cutter, and collars must be wiped clean before the cutter is installed on the arbor. The cutter must be keyed to the arbor. The key should be long enough so that it extends into one collar on each side of the cutter.

Style-C arbors, as shown at B in Fig. 1175, are used for holding shell-end mills and face mills. (See Fig. 1204.) Thus style-C arbors are often called *shell-end mill arbors.*

Adapters

Adapters are devices which are used to mount cutters of various kinds on the milling machine spindle. An *arbor adapter* (Fig. 1175, D) is used for mounting large face mills directly to the machine spindle. The *collet adapter* (Fig. 1175, A) is used for mounting end mills (Fig. 1203) on the spindle. The tapered hole in the collet adapter is the *self-holding* type. Usually it has either a Morse taper or a Brown & Sharpe taper. Some machines have collets with a special kind of taper. End mills (Fig. 1203) with tapered shanks fit into the tapered hole in the collet adapter. A reducing sleeve (Fig. 1175, E) is inserted in the collet adapter if the tapered hole is larger than the shank on the end mill. Then the end mill is inserted in the reducing sleeve.

Holders

Holders of the types shown in Fig. 1178 are used for holding straight shank-end mills (Fig. 1203). The holders are available with holes of various sizes for end mills of different diameters. The setscrew holds the end mill securely in place. A variety of end-mill holders is available. Some are designed to fit directly into the machine spindle; others are inserted in a collet adapter which is installed in the machine spindle.

The holder at the bottom in Fig. 1178 has a standard milling machine taper and is held in the spindle with a draw bar. The other two holders have self-holding tapers. The one at the top is threaded and is held in the spindle with a draw bar. The holder at the center has a driving tang which prevents it from slipping.

1273.   Removing Standard Arbors

Most milling machines have arbors and collet adapters which have standard, national milling-machine taper shanks. These are held in the machine spindle with either a draw bar or with a locking collar. (See Fig. 1179.) Arbors or adapters which are held with a draw bar are removed in the following manner:

(1) Loosen the nut on the draw bar several turns.
(2) Strike the end of the draw bar with a lead hammer.
(3) While holding the arbor with the left hand, unscrew the draw bar with the right hand.
(4) Remove the arbor from the machine spindle.

1274.   Removing Self-Holding Arbors

Some older milling machines and many smaller vertical milling machines have arbors or adapters with a Brown & Sharpe taper, Morse taper, or with a special taper. These usually are the self-holding type tapers which also are held in the machine spindle with a draw bar. The draw bar should not be turned up too tightly, or it will be very difficult to remove the arbor or adapter.

To remove the arbor or adapter loosen the draw bar by turning it in the proper direction. Some draw bars have left-hand threads while others have right-hand threads. First check to see whether the threads are right- or left-hand. As the draw bar is loosened, it presses against a *retaining collar;* this forces the arbor or adapter out of the spindle at the opposite end. If the arbor does not release when reasonable force is applied to the draw bar with a wrench, request assistance from your instructor.

1275. Milling Cutters

Milling machines use multiple-tooth cutting tools called *milling cutters*. *Standard* types of milling cutters are made in a wide variety of shapes and sizes. They can be used for machining flat surfaces, grooves, angular surfaces, and irregular surfaces. Milling cutters of *special* design, for special kinds of operations or for machining surfaces of special shapes, are also available.

Milling cutters generally are named after the kinds of operations which they perform. Hence, *plain milling cutters* generally are used for machining plain flat surfaces, Fig. 1191. *Angular milling cutters* are used for machining angular V-grooves, dovetails, and similar angular surfaces. (See Figs. 1197 and 1198.)

Cutter Materials

Milling cutters may be the solid-type which is made of one kind of material such as carbon-tool steel (§ 328), high-speed steel (§ 352), or tungsten carbide (§ 350). The majority of the milling cutters used in school shops are the solid-type, made of high-speed steel, Figs. 1191, 1192, and 1203.

Milling cutters are also available with *tungsten-carbide teeth*. The carbide teeth are brazed on the tips of the cutter, as shown at the right in Fig. 1193, and at *G*, *H*, and *J* in Fig. 1203. Very large cutters often have *inserted-type teeth*, Fig. 1231. The inserted teeth may be made of high-speed steel, tungsten carbide, or *cast alloy* (see § 353). The body of the cutter generally is made of a tough grade of alloy steel, thus reducing the cost of the cutter.

High-speed steel cutting tools rank high in impact resistance, wear resistance, and in general toughness. Hence, they are able to withstand the abuse and vibration which often occur on lightweight milling machines frequently used in school shops. High-speed steel also retains its hardness at temperatures up to about 1100° F. without significant softening.

Carbide-tipped cutters should be used on rigid setups and on heavy machines. Vibration or chatter causes them to fracture quite easily. However, they can be used with cutting speeds two to four times greater than high-speed steel cutters. And they retain their

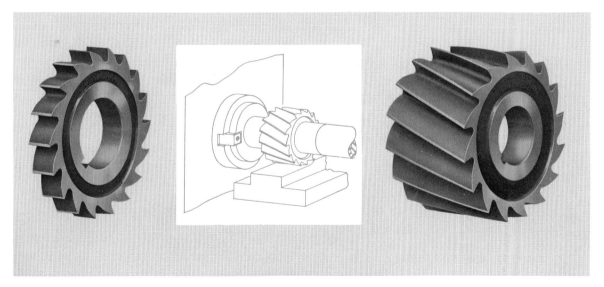

Fig. 1191. Light-Duty Plain Milling Cutters
(Courtesy National Twist Drill)

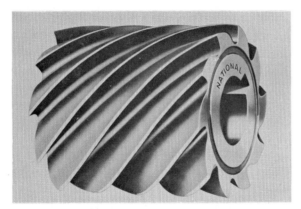

Fig. 1192. Heavy-Duty Plain Milling Cutter
(Courtesy National Twist Drill)

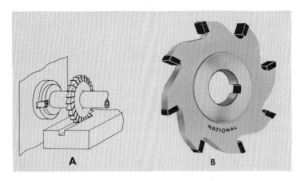

Fig. 1193. Plain-Side Milling Cutters
(Courtesy National Twist Drill)
A. Solid High Speed Cutter
B. Carbide Tipped Cutter

Fig. 1194. Half-Side Milling Cutters
(Courtesy National Twist Drill)
(Right) Single-Sided Plain Mill Cutter
(Center) Straddle Milling Setup
(Left) Single-Sided Plain Mill Cutter

hardness without significant softening at temperatures up to about 1700° F.

Plain-Milling Cutters

Cutters of the plain-milling type are cylindrical in shape and have cutting teeth on the periphery (circumference) only, Fig. 1191. They have an accurately ground hole and are mounted on an arbor for use on horizontal-type milling machines. They are used for machining plain, flat surfaces. Sometimes they are used in combination with other kinds of cutters for milling special kinds of surfaces, Fig. 1152.

Light-duty plain-milling cutters, Fig. 1191, have relatively fine teeth. For example, a 2½″ diameter cutter generally has 14 to 18 teeth. Cutters of this type which are less than ¾″ width have straight teeth parallel to the axis of the cutter. Cutters ¾″ and wider have helical teeth with an 18° helix angle. They are available in a variety of widths and diameters. Light-duty plain-milling cutters generally are used for light and moderate cuts on plain surfaces.

Heavy-duty plain-milling cutters, Fig. 1192, are also called *coarse-tooth milling cutters*. They are similar to the light-duty plain cutters except that they have fewer teeth and a steeper helix angle. For instance, a 2½″ diameter cutter generally has 8 teeth, and the helix angle is 45°. Heavy-duty cutters are recommended for heavy cuts wherever large amounts of metal must be removed. They also work well for light and moderate cuts. In fact, lightweight machines generally can take heavier cuts and produce a better surface finish with coarse-tooth plain cutters than with fine-tooth plain cutters.

Side-Milling Cutters

Side-milling cutters, Figs. 1193, 1194, and 1195, are similar to plain-milling cutters in that they have cutting edges on the periphery. However, they also have cutting edges on the sides. The cutting edges on the periphery do most of the cutting. The cutting edges on the sides finish the sides of the cut to finish size. The teeth may be either *straight* (Fig. 1193), *helical* (Fig. 1194), or *staggered* (Fig. 1195).

Side-milling cutters are used for milling the sides of a workpiece or for cutting slots or grooves. (See Figs. 1193 and 1195.) They also can be used for *straddle milling*. This involves cutting two sides at the same time, Figs. 1181 and 1194. The width between the two cutters is established with spacing collars and shims.

Plain side-milling cutters, Fig. 1193, have straight teeth on the periphery and both sides. They are used for moderate-duty side-milling, slotting, and straddle-milling operations.

Half-side milling cutters, Fig. 1194, have teeth on the periphery and only one side. These cutters are recommended for heavy-duty side-milling and straddle-milling operations.

Staggered-tooth side-milling cutters, Fig. 1195, are narrow cutters with teeth which alternate to either side. This tooth arrangement provides more chip clearance and reduces scoring on the side surfaces being machined. Cutters of this type are recommended for heavy-duty machining of grooves or keyways.

Metal-Slitting Saws

Cutters in the classification of metal-slitting saws, Fig. 1196, are used for ordinary cutoff operations and for cutting narrow slots. They are available with several kinds of teeth.

Plain metal-slitting saws, Fig. 1196, have teeth on the periphery only. They are available in widths from $\frac{1}{32}''$ to $\frac{3}{16}''$ and in diameters from $2\frac{1}{2}''$ to 8''. They have fine teeth, and the sides of the teeth taper toward the hole. The taper prevents the blade from binding in the slots or saw kerf as it rotates. The feed rate should be small (usually about $\frac{1}{4}$ to $\frac{1}{8}$ that used for plain-milling cutters). (See Table 39.)

Staggered-tooth metal-slitting saws, similar to staggered-tooth side-milling cutters, may

be used for wider and deeper cuts. They are available in widths from $\frac{3}{16}''$ to $\frac{1}{4}''$.

Screw-slotting cutters are special, fine-tooth plain-slitting saws. They are used for cutting screw slots and are available in widths from 0.020'' to 0.182''.

Angular-Milling Cutters

Cutters within this classification, Figs. 1197 and 1198, are used for machining V-notches,

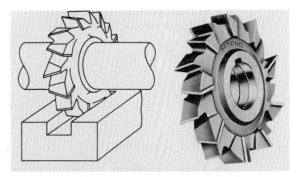

Fig. 1195. Staggered-Tooth Side-Milling Cutter
(Courtesy National Twist Drill)

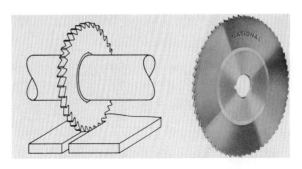

Fig. 1196. Plain Metal Slitting Saw
(Courtesy National Twist Drill)

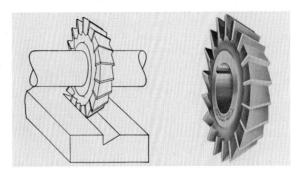

Fig. 1197. Single-Angle Milling Cutter
(Courtesy National Twist Drill)

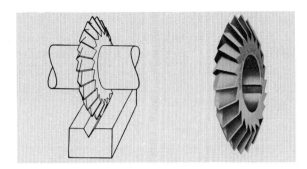

Fig. 1198. Double-Angle Milling Cutter
(Courtesy National Twist Drill)

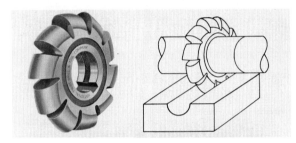

Fig. 1199. Convex Milling Cutter
(Courtesy National Twist Drill)

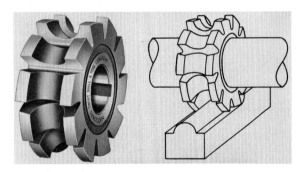

Fig. 1200. Concave Milling Cutter
(Courtesy National Twist Drill)

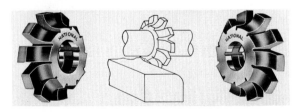

Fig. 1201. Corner-Rounding Milling Cutters
(Courtesy National Twist Drill)

grooves, serrations, dovetails, and reamer teeth.

Single-angle cutters, Fig. 1197, have a single angle with teeth on both sides of the angle. Generally they are available with either 45° or 60° angles.

Double-angle cutters, Fig. 1198, have V-shaped teeth. They usually are available with 45°, 60°, or 90° angles.

Form-Relieved Cutters

Cutters within this classification are used for cutting curved surfaces or surfaces of irregular shape. Several kinds of form-relieved cutters are shown in Figs. 1199-1202. They are used for cutting curved grooves, rounded corners, or flutes in reamers, milling cutters, or gear teeth.

The "Hand" of Milling Cutter

The term *hand* is used to describe the following factors involved in milling:

(1)   Hand of the cutter.
(2)   Hand of the helix.
(3)   Hand of the cut.

Hand of the cutter refers to the direction in which the cutter must rotate to cut. A cutter may be a right-hand cutter or a left-hand cutter. The hand is determined by looking at the front end of the cutter (toward the spindle nose or column) while the cutter is mounted in the machine spindle. A *right-hand* cutter must rotate *counterclockwise* to cut. A *left-*

Fig. 1202. (Left) Spur Gear Milling Cutter
(Right) Fluting Cutter
(Courtesy National Twist Drill,
Cincinnati Milling Machine Co.)

hand cutter must rotate *clockwise* to cut. Thus end mills, reamers, drills, and similar cutting tools are designated right hand (RH) or left hand (LH). All of the end mills in Fig. 1203 are right hand.

Hand of the helix describes the direction of the helical flutes on the milling cutter or on other cutting tools such as drills and reamers. The hand of the helix is determined by looking at either end of the cutting tool and noting the direction in which the helical flutes twist. If they twist away and toward the right, they have right-hand helical flutes, Fig. 1191. If they twist away and toward the left, they have left-hand helical flutes, Fig. 1192.

Hand of the cut refers to the direction of cut. A cut may be a *right-hand cut* or a *left-hand cut*. The hand of the cut is also determined by looking at the front end of the cutter (toward the spindle nose or column)

while the cutter is mounted in the machine spindle. A *right-hand cut* requires *counter-clockwise* rotation of the cutter, Fig. 1214. A *left-hand cut* requires *clockwise* rotation of the spindle. Arbor-type milling cutters with straight teeth can be mounted for cutting with either a right-hand cut or left-hand cut. When the position of the cutter is reversed on the arbor, the direction of cut is changed to the opposite hand.

It is also possible to make either right-hand or left-hand cuts with arbor-type helical cutters. However, when possible, helical cutters should be installed so that side thrust on the cutter tends to force the cutter toward the column, Fig. 1214.

End-Mill Cutters

End-milling cutters commonly are called *end mills*. They are designed for milling slots,

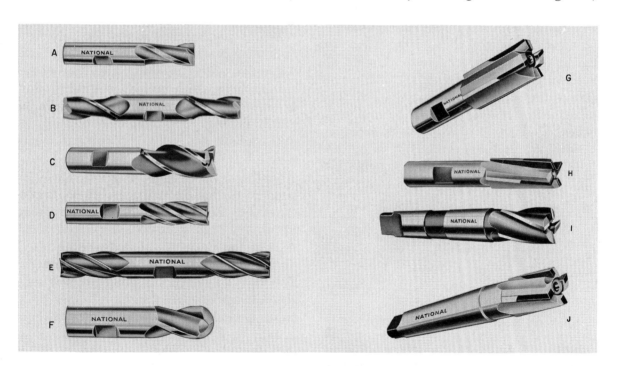

Fig. 1203. End Mills
(Courtesy National Twist Drill)
(A) Two-flute single-end, (B) Two-flute double-end, (C) Three-flute single-end, (D) Multiple-flute single-end, (E) Four-flute double-end, (F) Two-flute ball-end, (G) Carbide-tipped straight flutes, (H) Car-bide-tipped RH helical flutes, (I) Multiple-flute with taper shanks, (J) Carbide-tipped with taper shank and helical flutes.

shoulders, curved edges, keyways, and pockets where ordinary arbor-type cutters cannot be used. However, end mills can also be used for performing many of the same operations performed by arbor-type cutters. Although end mills are most frequently used on vertical-type milling machines, they also can be used on horizontal-type machines, Figs. 1204 and 1179.

End mills include two basic types: the *solid-type* and the *shell-type*. With the solid-type, the teeth and the shank are an integral part. A variety of solid-type end mills is shown in Fig. 1203.

With shell-type end mills, the body and the shank are separate parts, Fig. 1204. Shell-type end mills are mounted on style-C arbors, as shown at *B* in Fig. 1175. Small shell-end mills are mounted on an adapter of the type shown at *C* in Fig. 1177.

End-milling cutters generally have teeth on the circumference and on the end. On *square-nose* cutters, most of the cutting is done by the teeth on the circumference. On *round-nose* cutters (see *F* in Fig. 1203), a large portion of the cutting is done at the end. The teeth on the circumference may be straight or helical.

With the exception of shell-type cutters, the shanks are either *straight* or *tapered*. The flat surface on the shank provides a means for holding the end mill securely in the end-mill adapter with a setscrew, Fig. 1178. The taper-shank end mills have a flat-drive tang which prevents them from turning. They are mounted in the machine spindle with adapters, as shown at *B* and *D* in Fig. 1177.

Two-flute end mills are designed with *end-cutting teeth* for *plunge* and *traverse* milling. Hence, this kind of end mill can be fed to depth like a drill. It then can be fed longitudinally. It may be either the single-end type or the double-end type.

Multiple-flute end mills have three, four, six, or eight flutes. They generally are available in diameters up to about 2″ and may be either the single-end or double-end type. Some types have end-cutting teeth, as at *C* in Fig. 1203. These may be used for plunge milling to depth as well as for longitudinal milling.

Ball-end mills, as at *F* in Fig. 1203, are used for milling pockets in dies. They are also used for milling fillets or slots. They have end-cutting teeth which may be used for drilling to depth (plunge milling) as well as longitudinal milling. *Four-fluted ball-end mills* are also available and are used for similar operations.

Shell-end mills, Fig. 1204, are made in larger sizes than most shank-type end mills. Generally, they are made in diameters from 1¼″ to 6″. They may have either helical or straight teeth. Cutters of this type are used for machining larger shoulders or surfaces. The teeth on all types of milling cutters stay sharp longer if they have a chamfer or a radius ground on the corner of the teeth, Fig. 1204.

T-slot milling cutters, Fig. 1205, are used for milling T-slots such as those on milling machine tables. The narrow portion of the T-slot is machined first with a side-milling cutter or an end mill. The wide portion then is cut with the T-slot cutter.

Fig. 1204. Shell-End Mill
(Courtesy National Twist Drill)

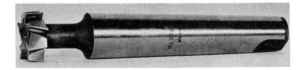

Fig. 1205. T-Slot Cutter
(Courtesy The Cincinnati Milling Machine Co.)

Key-seat cutters, Fig. 1206, are used for cutting seats for woodruff keys. (See Fig. 601.) They are available in sizes for all standard woodruff keys. The end mill-type is made in sizes from ¼″ to 1½″ diameter. The arbor-type is made in diameters from 2⅛″ to 3½″.

Depth of cut is an important factor in preventing end-mill breakage. As a general rule, *the maximum depth of cut should not be greater than one-half the diameter of an end mill.* On hard, tough steel, the maximum depth should not generally exceed ¼ the diameter of the end mill. Suggested feeds for end mills are indicated in Table 39. (Feeds are explained in § 1279.)

1276. Sharpening Milling Cutters

Milling cutters must be sharp to produce a good surface finish and to cut efficiently. When the cutter becomes dull, extreme forces are exerted on the cutter, the arbor, and the machine spindle. These forces can cause cutter breakage. On horizontal-type machines, the extreme forces caused by a dull cutter can bend the arbor, and it will no longer run true.

Milling cutters are sharpened on a *cutter-and-tool grinding machine,* Fig. 1211. Plain-type milling cutters are sharpened by grinding the teeth on the periphery (circumference) of the cutter, as in Fig. 1211. Form-relieved cutters are sharpened by grinding the face of the teeth radially toward the center of the cutter, Fig. 1212. End mills are sharpened by grinding the teeth on the circumference of the cutter, Fig. 1213.

Fig. 1211. Grinding a Plain-Tooth Helical Milling Cutter on a Cutter and Tool Grinder
(Courtesy The Cincinnati Milling Machine Co.)

Fig. 1212. Setup for Grinding Face of Teeth on Form-Relieved Cutters
(Courtesy The Cincinnati Milling Machine Co.)

Fig. 1213. Setup for Grinding an End Mill with Helical Teeth
(Courtesy The Cincinnati Milling Machine Co.)

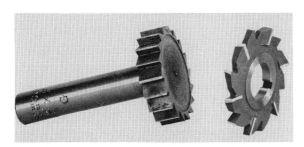

Fig. 1206. Woodruff Key Seat Cutter
(Courtesy The Cincinnati Milling Machine Co.)

Only experienced persons should grind milling cutters. Cutters are expensive and can be damaged if sharpened improperly. This kind of instruction normally is included in advanced machine shop classes. It is not included within the scope of this book. The information and procedures for sharpening milling cutters generally are included in a manual or handbook provided by the manufacturer of cutter-and-tool grinding equipment.

1277.   Using Cutting Fluids

Cutting fluids should be used for all milling operations on steel, aluminum, and copper alloys. Gray cast iron may be machined dry, or an emulsifiable (soluble) oil solution may be used on it. Cutting fluids and their selection are explained in sections 406 and 407. (See Table 15, page 169 for selection of recommended cutting fluids for common metals.)

1278.   Cutting Speeds and RPM

For milling, *cutting speed* refers to the circumferential speed of the milling cutter. It is expressed in *surface feet per minute* (sfm). You can visualize the cutting speed of a milling cutter by imagining it as the distance the cutter could roll across the floor during 1 minute.

Different cutting speeds must be used when machining different metals. If the cutting speed is too fast, the cutter will become overheated and dull rapidly. If the speed is too slow, time will be wasted and production costs will increase.

Factors Affecting Cutting Speeds

One of the most important factors affecting cutting speed is the machinability rating of the metal. (See § 358.) Metals with high-machinability ratings can be machined at higher cutting speeds than those with lower ratings. (See Table 15, page 169.)

When the machinability rating is doubled, the cutting speed may be doubled, provided that proper cutting fluids are used. For example, steel with a rating of 100 may be machined at twice the cutting speed of steel with

a rating of 50. The machinability ratings for various metals are included in handbooks for machinists.

The following factors affect cutting speeds for milling operations:

(1) Kind of metal being machined

(2) Machinability rating of the metal

(3) Hardness of the metal (if heat treated)

(4) Kind of cutting tool material (high-speed steel, cast alloy, or cemented carbide)

(5) Whether proper cutting fluids are used

(6) Depth of cut and rate of feed(roughing or finishing cut)

Table 38
CUTTING SPEEDS FOR MILLING ROUGHING CUTS WITH HIGH-SPEED CUTTERS

Material	Cutting Speed Range in sfm
Low-carbon steel	60-80
Medium-carbon steel, annealed	60-80
High-carbon steel, annealed .	50-70
Tool steel, annealed	50-70
Stainless steel	50-80
Gray cast iron, soft	50-80
Malleable iron	80-100
Aluminum and its alloys	400-1000
Brass	200-300
Bronze	100-200

These suggested speeds may be varied as follows:
    For finishing cuts . . . . .Increase 25-50%
    For carbon-steel cutters . . . . .Decrease about 50%
    For cutters with cast-alloy tips . . . . . . .Increase 50-75%
    For cutters with cemented-carbide
        tips . . . . .Increase 200-400%
Feeds should be as much as the cutter, the setup, and the equipment will safely stand. Recommended cutting fluids should be used, see Table 15, page 169.

Table 39

FEEDS (INCHES PER TOOTH) FOR MILLING ROUGHING CUTS WITH HIGH-SPEED CUTTERS

MATERIAL	PLAIN MILLS (HEAVY-DUTY)	PLAIN MILLS (LIGHT-DUTY)	FACE MILLS	SIDE MILLS	END MILLS	FORM-RELIEVED MILLS	SLITTING SAWS
Low-carbon steel, free machining	.010	.006	.012	.006	.006	.004	.003
Low-carbon steel	.008	.005	.010	.005	.005	.003	.003
Medium-carbon steel	.008	.005	.009	.005	.004	.003	.002
High-carbon steel, annealed	.004	.003	.006	.003	.002	.002	.002
Stainless steel, free machining	.008	.005	.010	.005	.004	.003	.002
Stainless steel	.004	.003	.006	.004	.002	.002	.002
Cast iron, soft	.012	.008	.014	.008	.008	.004	.004
Cast iron, medium	.010	.006	.012	.006	.006	.004	.003
Malleable iron	.010	.006	.012	.006	.006	.004	.003
Brass and bronze, medium hardness	.010	.008	.013	.008	.006	.004	.003
Aluminum and its alloys	.016	.010	.020	.012	.010	.007	.004

These feeds are suggested for roughing cuts on heavy-duty machines, and they may be increased or decreased depending on machining conditions. For average conditions, it may be necessary to reduce these rates by 50%. For finishing cuts the rates generally should be reduced 50%.

Suggested cutting speeds for roughing cuts with high-speed steel milling cutters are given in Table 38. There is no one correct cutting speed for milling one kind of metal. A range of speeds generally will produce good results with a specific kind of metal. It is common practice to select an average cutting speed or a speed which is somewhat less than average. With satisfactory results, the cutting speed may be increased.

Revolutions Per Minute (RPM)

After the cutting speed to be used has been determined, the machine spindle must be set at the proper rpm. Cutting speed and rpm have different meanings, and they should not be confused. *A small diameter milling cutter must turn at a higher rpm than a larger diameter cutter in order for both to cut at the same cutting speed.* An example shows this more clearly: A 1″ diameter end mill and a 2½″ diameter arbor-type cutter are to cut at the same cutting speed. For both to cut at 70 sfm the 1″ diameter cutter must turn at 267 rpm, while the 2½″ diameter cutter must turn at 107 rpm. (See Table 40).

Note that Table 40 can be used for determining the approximate rpm for milling, drilling, turning, and boring operations up to diameters of 3″. It also gives the cutting speeds produced by various rpm when the diameters are given. The machine spindle may be adjusted, as explained in section 1269, for the rpm which is nearest the desired rpm.

Table 40
CUTTING SPEEDS FOR VARIOUS DIAMETERS

Feet per Min.	30'	40'	50'	60'	70'	80'	90'	100'	110'	120'	130'	140'	150'
Diameter Inches						Revolutions per Minute							
1/16	1833	2445	3056	3667	4278	4889	5500	6111	6722	7334	7945	8556	9167
1/8	917	1222	1528	1833	2139	2445	2750	3056	3361	3667	3973	4278	4584
3/16	611	815	1019	1222	1426	1630	1833	2037	2241	2445	2648	2852	3056
1/4	458	611	764	917	1070	1222	1375	1528	1681	1833	1986	2139	2292
5/16	367	489	611	733	856	978	1100	1222	1345	1467	1589	1711	1833
3/8	306	407	509	611	713	815	917	1019	1120	1222	1324	1426	1528
7/16	262	349	437	524	611	698	786	873	960	1048	1135	1222	1310
1/2	229	306	382	458	535	611	688	764	840	917	993	1070	1146
5/8	183	244	306	367	428	489	550	611	672	733	794	856	917
3/4	153	203	255	306	357	407	458	509	560	611	662	713	764
7/8	131	175	218	262	306	349	393	436	480	524	568	611	655
1	115	153	191	229	267	306	344	382	420	458	497	535	573
1 1/8	102	136	170	204	238	272	306	340	373	407	441	475	509
1 1/4	92	122	153	183	214	244	275	306	336	367	397	428	458
1 3/8	83	111	139	167	194	222	250	278	306	333	361	389	417
1 1/2	76	102	127	153	178	204	229	255	280	306	331	357	382
1 5/8	70	94	117	141	165	188	212	235	259	282	306	329	353
1 3/4	65	87	109	131	153	175	196	218	240	262	284	306	327
1 7/8	61	81	102	122	143	163	183	204	224	244	265	285	306
2	57	76	95	115	134	153	172	191	210	229	248	267	287
2 1/4	51	68	85	102	119	136	153	170	187	204	221	238	255
2 1/2	46	61	76	92	107	122	137	153	168	183	199	214	229
2 3/4	42	56	69	83	97	111	125	139	153	167	181	194	208
3	38	51	64	76	89	102	115	127	140	153	166	178	191

This table can be used to determine the approximate rpm for drilling, milling, turning, and boring operations for diameters up to 3 inches. It also gives the cutting speeds produced by various rpm with the diameters given.

(Courtesy The Cleveland Twist Drill Co.)

Calculating RPM

The rpm of a given cutting speed for milling and hole-machining operations can be calculated with the following formula:

$$rpm = \frac{CS \times 12}{D \times \pi}$$

Where:
CS = Cutting speed in sfm
D = Diameter of cutter in inches
π = Pi or 3.1416 (a constant)
rpm = Revolutions per minute

Example: Calculate the rpm for a 3″ diameter cutter which is to mill steel at 90 sfm.

$$rpm = \frac{90 \times 12}{3 \times 3.1416}$$

$$rpm = \frac{1080}{9.4248}$$

$$rpm = 114.5$$

(Compare this to Table 40.)
Or this approach:

$$rpm = \frac{90 \times \overset{4}{\cancel{12}}}{\underset{1}{\cancel{3}} \times \cancel{3.1416}}$$

$$rpm = \frac{360}{3}$$

$$rpm = 120$$

The rpm select on the machine may not be accurate enough to set the speed at exactly 115 or 120, so select the closest arbor speed. The number 3 can be substituted for 3.1416 when calculating the *approximate* cutting speed. This procedure is satisfactory for most applications, thus giving 120 rpm.

Calculating Cutting Speed

The cutting speed for milling and hole-machining operations can be calculated when the diameter of the cutting tool and the rpm are known:

$$CS = \frac{D'' \times \pi \times rpm}{12}$$

Example: Calculate the cutting speed of a ½″ diameter end mill which is milling at a speed of 550 rpm.

$$CS = \frac{0.500 \times 3.1416 \times 550}{12}$$

$$CS = \frac{863.94}{12}$$

$$CS = 72 \text{ sfm}$$

The number 3 may be substituted for 3.1416 for calculating the approximate cutting speed. This procedure is satisfactory for most jobs, thus giving approximately 69 sfm.

1279. Rate of Feed

The *rate of feed* for milling is the rate at which the workpiece advances into the milling cutter. It is the most important factor in determining the rate of metal removal. The feed rate, together with the width and depth of cut, determines the rate of metal removal.

The tendency for beginners is to use too light a feed and a cutting speed which is too high. This dulls the cutter rapidly and shortens tool life. In general, the feed rate should be as great as the cutting tool, the machine, and the work setup can stand without excessive vibration.

Each tooth on the milling cutter should cut a chip of proper size. On cutters with small, fine teeth, the chip should be small. The feed for each tooth on a milling cutter is indicated in *inches per tooth* for each revolution of the cutter. Suggested average feeds, in inches per tooth, for milling roughing cuts with high-speed steel cutters are listed in Table 39. On light-duty milling machines, the indicated feeds should be reduced. For light finishing cuts, the feeds should be reduced by 50%.

Inches Per Minute

The feed rate on most milling machines is set in terms of *inches per minute*. The feed rates may be adjusted for various settings ranging from about ¼″ to 30″ per minute. The feed rates are adjusted with feed-selector dials or levers on the machine. (See § 1269.)

Calculating Rate of Feed

The following procedure generally is used in calculating the rate of feed:

1. Determine the desired cutting speed. For example, 70 sfm for low-carbon steel.

2. Determine the rpm of the cutter. (See § 1278.)

3. Determine the number of teeth on the cutter.

4. Determine the feed in inches per tooth. (See Table 39.)

5. Calculate the feed rate with the following formula:

$$F = R \times T \times rpm$$

Where:
  F = Feed rate in inches per minute
  R = Feed per tooth per revolution
  T = Number of teeth on cutter
  rpm = Revolution per minute of cutter

Example: Determine the feed rate for milling low-carbon steel at 70 sfm, 89 rpm, using a heavy-duty plain-milling cutter 3″ in diameter with 10 teeth and a feed of 0.006″ per tooth.

$$F = 0.006 \times 10 \times 89$$

$$F = 5.34 \text{ inches per minute}$$

With the feed-selector dial or levers, adjust the feed rate to the feed closest to 5.34 inches per minute.

Handfeeding

On machines which are not equipped with automatic table feed, the table must be fed by hand. The operator must feed the table hand crank steadily. Too rapid feeding can cause chatter or cutter breakage.

1280. Safety for Milling

1. Wear approved safety goggles.

2. Wipe up any oil on the floor around the machine.

3. Be certain that the table is clean and dry before making a setup.

4. Always be certain that holding devices such as a vise, angle plate, dividing head, or tailstock are fastened tightly to the table.

5. Select the right kind of cutter for the job.

6. Always be sure that the arbor, cutter, and collars are clean before mounting them in the spindle. Use a rag for handling sharp cutters.

7. When seating workpieces in a vise, use a lead hammer.

8. Be certain that the vise or other holding devices clear the arbor and overarm supports.

9. Select the proper cutting speed, rpm, and rate of feed for the job.

10. Disengage the control handles when using automatic feeds.

11. Be certain that the column clamps, saddle clamps, and table clamps are loosened when making setup adjustments. Be certain to tighten them after the setup.

12. Keep your hands away from the revolving cutter at all times.

13. Clear chips away from the cutter with a brush, such as a paintbrush.

14. Release any automatic feeds after completing the job.

15. Do not allow unauthorized persons within the safety zone of the machine.

16. Clean and wipe the machine when you are finished. Wipe up any oil from the floor.

Remove chips with a small shovel or scoop. Never touch them with the fingers.

1281. Mounting Workpieces

The following methods can be used to mount workpieces on a milling machine.

1. They can be mounted in a vise, as shown in Figs. 1161, 1162, and 1163. The workpiece can be positioned in the vise for milling in the same manner in which it is positioned in the shaper vise for shaping. (See Figs. 1128 and 1129.)

2. Workpieces can be bolted to the milling machine table as shown in Figs. 1152 and 1155. Other methods of clamping workpieces to the table are shown in Fig. 1132. Tools for holding work to the table are shown in Fig. 428.

3. Workpieces can be mounted in a chuck on the dividing head, as shown in Fig. 1171. The head may be swiveled horizontally, vertically, or at any desired angle.

4. Workpieces can be mounted between centers of a dividing head and a tailstock, Figs. 1172, 1170, and 1173.

5. Workpieces can be mounted on a circular milling attachment, Fig. 1174. The part may be bolted to the attachment table. Or a vise can be bolted to the attachment table, and the workpiece can be mounted in the vise.

6. Workpieces can be mounted on special fixtures on the milling machine table, Fig. 1180.

1282. Vise Alignment

When a workpiece is mounted in a milling machine vise, the vise must be properly aligned. Generally the stationary jaw of the vise must be either at *right angles* with the face of the machine column, or it must be *parallel* with the face of the column. For most operations, the stationary vise jaw must be parallel with the machined face of the column.

Before the alignment of the vise on a *universal milling machine* is checked, the table must be swiveled parallel with the face of the column. This can be checked by placing a wide parallel bar between the column and the table. Feed the table transversely (in toward the column), by hand, until it squeezes the parallel lightly against the column. If the table is parallel, no light should show between the parallel and the table or between the parallel and the column. For greater accuracy, a dial indicator can be used to determine if the table is parallel with the face of the column. Correct the alignment of the swivel table if necessary.

Right-angle squareness of the vise with the column can be checked by placing the *blade* of a steel square, Fig. 61, against the stationary jaw of the vise. At the same time, place the *beam* of the square against the machined surface of the column. For greater accuracy, a dial indicator can be clamped on the machine arbor, with the indicator plunger against the stationary vise jaw. The table is then fed transversely (crosswise, in and out) by hand-feeding. If the stationary jaw is properly aligned, the indicator reading will be *zero* for complete cross travel of the vise. Correct the alignment if necessary.

Parallelism of the stationary jaw of the vise, with the surface of the machine column, can be checked with a dial indicator. Clamp the indicator to the arbor with the indicator plunger touching the stationary vise jaw. Handfeed the table longitudinally and note the indicator dial. The indicator dial will read *zero* if the vise jaw is parallel with the face of the column. Correct the vise alignment if necessary.

1283. Milling with a Horizontal Milling Machine

Each kind of operation on a horizontal milling machine requires a different kind of milling cutter. The various kinds of arbor-type milling cutters and their applications are explained in section 1275. Although the cutters are designed differently, the general procedures used are similar for many kinds of horizontal milling operations. It is generally best

for the instructor to explain and demonstrate the use of the milling machine in the shop before it is used.

Procedure

The following basic steps of procedure should be used for milling with a horizontal milling machine.

1. Check alignment of the table.

   This step is necessary with universal milling machines only. The side of the table must be parallel with the machined face of the column. (See § 1282.)

2. Check the alignment of the vise.

   The stationary jaw usually is aligned parallel with the machined face of the column. However, for some operations it should be at right angles with the face of the column. For special angular milling operations, the vise may be swiveled at any desired angle with the face of the column. (See § 1282.)

3. Mount the workpiece securely in the vise.

   The surface to be machined must extend high enough above the hardened vise jaws so that the milling cutter will not cut into the jaws. If the cutter strikes the hardened jaws, it will fracture the cutter teeth and damage the jaws. Seat the workpiece firmly on parallels if it is necessary to elevate the workpiece above the vise jaws. The work should be mounted in a vise for milling in essentially the same way in which it is mounted for shaping. (See Figs. 1127, 1128, and 1129; also review § 1245.)

4. Position the workpiece under the arbor beneath the intended location of the cutter.

   This is done by moving the saddle toward the column with the cross-feed handwheel. The workpiece should be as close as possible to the column.

5. Select the right kind and size of cutter and arbor.

Always handle sharp cutters with a cloth. Also place a clean cloth on the machine table where the cutter, arbor, and collars will be placed.

For plain milling of flat surfaces, the cutter should be a little wider than the surface to be machined. The cutter should be large enough so that the arbor support bearing will clear the vise.

For milling with small diameter cutters, a style-A arbor generally should be used. (See Fig. 1176.) Place the cutter, arbor, and collars on a clean cloth on the machine table.

6. Install the arbor.

Clean the shank and the spindle hole. Use a draw bar to hold the arbor securely in the machine spindle.

7. Mount the cutter on the arbor and position the arbor support.

The arbor, collars, and cutter must be clean and free from nicks before mounting the cutter. When plain heli-

cal cutters are used, the cutter should be installed so that *thrust* tends to push the cutter toward the column, as in Fig. 1214.

Space the cutter at the desired position with spacing collars. The cutter should be as close to the column as the position of the workpiece will permit. Key the cutter to the arbor. The key should extend into the collars on both sides of the cutter. Place the nut on the arbor loosely.

Install the arbor support; allow at least ⅛″ space between the end of the arbor threads and the bearing in the arbor support. Finally, tighten the arbor nut securely against the arbor collars and cutter.

8. Adjust the cross-feed location of the workpiece.

It should be centered or located in the desired position, under the cutter. Tighten the saddle clamp or clamps.

9. Determine the desired cutting speed.
(See Table 38.)

10. Determine the spindle rpm required for the desired cutting speed.
(See Table 40.)

11. Adjust the spindle rpm.
(See § 1269.)

12. Calculate the rate of feed required.
This is explained in section 1279.

13. Adjust the machine for the proper rate of feed.

(See § 1269.) This step is omitted with machines not equipped with automatic table feed.

14. With the workpiece clear of the cutter, start the machine and observe whether the direction of spindle rotation is correct.

(See Fig. 1214.) Direction of rotation is explained in section 1275. Reverse the direction of spindle if the cutter is rotating in the wrong direction.

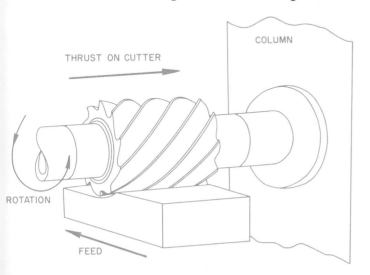

Fig. 1214. Install Helical Cutter so Thrust Forces the Cutter toward the Column
This is a plain milling cutter having a left-hand helix. It is mounted on the arbor for right-hand cutting.

15. Engage the automatic feed and observe whether the direction of feed is correct.

The workpiece should travel against the direction of cutter rotation for *up cutting* or *conventional milling,* as in Figs. 1165 and 1214.

16. Adjust the table elevation for the proper depth of cut.

This is explained under the heading *knee elevation* in section 1269. If a finishing cut is to be made after a roughing cut, allow about 0.010″ to 0.020″ material thickness for the finishing cut. If the surface is to be surface ground after milling, allow at least 0.005″ material thickness, per surface, for grinding.

17. Apply cutting fluid, engage the table feed, and make the roughing cut.

On machines so equipped, cutting fluid may be applied with a pump. On others it may be applied to the cutter with a paintbrush.

If excessive vibration or chatter takes place, stop the machine. It may be caused by one of the following:
(a) depth of cut too deep,
(b) rate of feed too fast,
(c) cutting speed too high,
(d) knee clamp loose,
(e) saddle clamp loose, or
(f) bolts holding the vise may be loose. Make the necessary adjustment.

Machines not equipped with automatic longitudinal table feed must be fed by hand. Feed the table at a steady rate with the table feed handwheel.

Try to avoid stopping the table feed before finishing a cut. If the table feed is stopped and started again, a ridge or irregular surface results at the location where the feed was stopped.

18. At the end of the roughing cut, disengage the table feed, stop the machine, and brush the chips away from the machined surface. *Never move the workpiece back under the revolving cutter.*

It is always good practice to lower the table an amount equal to one turn of the vertical-feed hand crank before bringing the table back to the starting position.

19. If an additional cut must be made, bring the table back to the starting position in preparation for the next cut.

Measure the workpiece. If another roughing cut is needed, raise the table one turn of the vertical-feed hand crank plus the depth of cut desired. Make the roughing cut as in steps 15 through 18.

20. Make a finishing cut if required.

A cut from 0.010″ to 0.020″ deep generally produces a good surface finish. Make the finishing cut as in steps 15 through 18. Measure the workpiece and take an additional cut if necessary.

21. Remove the workpiece from the machine.

22. Clean the machine.

Store tools and other machine accessories in the proper place.

23. Remove the sharp arrises or burrs from the workpiece with a file.

1284. Milling with a Vertical Milling Machine

Vertical milling operations can be performed on vertical milling machines, combination horizontal-and-vertical milling machines, and with vertical milling attachments on horizontal milling machines. A variety of different kinds of end mills, Figs. 1203 and 1204, may be used for vertical milling operations. A variety of holders and adapters also is used for holding the end mills in the machine spindle. (See Figs. 1175 and 1178.)

The principles and procedures involved in most vertical milling operations are similar. This is true, eventhough the particular ma-

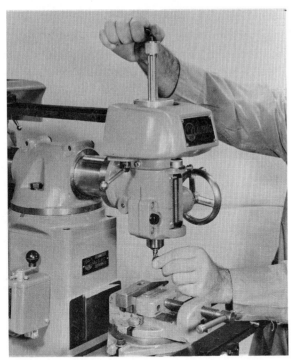

Fig. 1221. Using a Draw Bar to Fasten End Mill
Cutter in the Collet of a Vertical Mill
(Courtesy Clausing Corp.)

Fig. 1222. Machining a Flat Angular Surface
with a Shell-End Mill (Courtesy Clausing Corp.)

chine or the controls on the machine are somewhat different in design. It generally is best to have your instructor explain and demonstrate the use of the vertical milling machine in your shop before it is used.

Procedure

The following are basic steps of procedure for milling a flat surface with a vertical milling machine.

1. Select an end mill for the job.

    For machining a flat surface, the cutter should be slightly wider than the surface to be machined. (See Fig. 1222.) If the surface is wider, several cuts will be required.

2. Mount the milling cutter in the machine spindle. (See Figs. 1221 and 1222.)

    Some machines have collets which hold straight-shank end mills. The cutter should be inserted in the collet, and the collet should be drawn up tightly with the draw bar provided.

    Other kinds of end-mill arbors, collets, adapters, and their uses are explained in section 1272.

3. Check to see that the milling head is perpendicular to the table.

    On some machines, the head may be swiveled for milling angular or beveled surfaces. For machining flat horizontal surfaces, the head must be perpendicular to the table.

4. Mount the vise on the table with T-slot bolts and align the vise.

    For most operations, the stationary jaw should be aligned parallel with the T-slots in the table or parallel with the face of the column. For some operations, the stationary jaw must be aligned at right angles with the table. Occasionally the vise must be swiveled at an angle for milling grooves, shoulders, or vertical surfaces in an angular direction. Procedures for vise alignment are explained in section 1282.

5. Mount the workpiece in the vise.

The surface to be machined must extend high enough above the vise jaws so that the cutter will not cut into the hardened jaws. (See Fig. 1222.) Seat the workpiece firmly on parallels if necessary.

The work should be mounted in the vise for vertical milling in much the same manner as for shaping. (See Figs. 1127, 1128, and 1129. Also review § 1245.)

6. Determine the desired cutting speed. (See Table 38.)

7. Determine the spindle rpm required for the desired cutting speed. (See Table 40.)

8. Adjust the machine for the desired rpm. (See § 1269.)

9. Calculate the rate of feed required. This is explained in section 1279.

10. Adjust the machine for the correct rate of feed.

(See § 1269.) This step is omitted with machines not equipped with automatic table feed.

11. With the workpiece clear of the cutter, start the machine and observe whether the direction of spindle rotation is correct.

(Direction of rotation is explained in § 1275.) Reverse the direction of the spindle if the cutter is rotating in the wrong direction.

When milling shoulders or vertical surfaces with an end mill, use the *up-milling* method. (See Fig. 1165.) By looking at Fig. 1165 and imagining it as the top view of an end mill which is cutting along a vertical surface, you can visualize the up-milling method as it applies to end-milling operations.

12. Adjust the table elevation for the proper depth of cut.

Use the micrometer collar on the knee crank to set the depth of cut ac-

curately. This procedure is explained under the heading, *knee elevation,* in section 1269.

The maximum depth of cut for end mills generally should not exceed ½ the diameter of the cutter. On hard, tough steel the maximum depth of cut should not exceed ¼ the diameter of the cutter. On light-duty machines, the maximum depth of cut must be reduced further.

If a finishing cut is to be made after the roughing cut, allow about 0.010″ to 0.020″ material thickness for the finishing cut. If the surface is to be surface ground after milling, allow at least 0.005″ material thickness, per surface, for grinding.

13. Apply cutting fluid, engage the automatic longitudinal table feed, and make the roughing cut.

On machines so equipped, cutting fluid may be applied with a pump. On others, it may be applied with a paintbrush.

If excessive vibration or chatter takes place, stop the machine. It may be caused by one of the following:

(a) depth of cut too deep,
(b) rate of feed too fast,
(c) cutting speed too high,
(d) knee clamp loose,
(e) saddle clamp loose, or
(f) bolts holding the vise may be loose. Make the necessary adjustment.

Machines not equipped with automatic longitudinal table feed must be fed by hand. Feed the table at a steady rate with the table feed handwheel.

14. At the end of the roughing cut, disengage the table feed and brush the chips away from the machined surfaces, shoulders, or grooves. Measure the workpiece.

15. If additional roughing cuts must be made, bring the table back to the starting position in preparation for the next cut.

16. Use the micrometer collar on the vertical knee crank for setting the depth of cut for additional cuts.

17. Make additional roughing cuts by repeating steps 11 through 16.

18. Make a finishing cut if necessary.

A finishing cut 0.010″ to 0.020″ generally produces good results on horizontal, flat surfaces.

A finishing cut 0.002″ to 0.005″ along vertical surfaces, shoulders, and grooves generally produces good results.

Be certain to use the *up-milling* method of feeding, eventhough the end mill is in a vertical position. (See Fig. 1165.)

19. Remove the workpiece from the vise, clean the machine, and put all tools and accessories in the proper place.

20. Remove sharp arrises and burrs from the workpiece with a file.

Other Vertical Milling Setups

A variety of vertical milling operations and setups is illustrated in Figs. 1223-1229.

1285. Indexing

Indexing is done to move a workpiece so that a series of equally spaced divisions can be machined. Indexing is done with a dividing head. One of the most common types is the *universal-dividing head,* Fig. 1230. Indexing is done to machine square or hexagonal bolt heads, spur gears (Fig. 1170), helical gears (Fig. 1172), flutes in reamers, keyways, and similar items. Other uses of the dividing head are explained in section 1271.

The principal parts of a universal-dividing head are shown in Fig. 1230. Indexing is done in a similar manner on most kinds of dividing

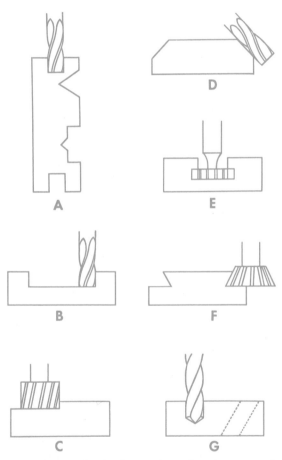

Fig. 1223. Operations Performed with a Vertical Milling Machine (Courtesy Clausing Corp.)

    A. Milling a Groove
    B. Milling a Recessed Area
    C. Milling a Shoulder
    D. Milling a Chamfer
    E. Milling a T-Slot
    F. Milling a Dovetail
    G. Drilling a Hole

Fig. 1224. Milling a Groove with an End Mill (Courtesy Clausing Corp.)

heads. The *index crank* is attached to the *worm shaft* which has a *worm gear* on the end, inside the dividing head. The worm gear drives the *work spindle.* The work spindle has a *40-tooth worm wheel* (sometimes called a worm gear) on the end, inside the dividing head, which meshes with the worm gear on the worm shaft. Hence, when the index crank is turned 40 complete turns, the work spindle turns one complete turn or 360°. Or, one turn of the index crank causes the work spindle to revolve through 9°. (40 × 9° = 360°.)

The *index-plunger pin* holds the crank in position so that the spindle cannot turn. Thus, the index-plunger pin must be withdrawn from the hole in the index plate before the crank can be turned.

The *plate stop* holds the index plate in position so that it cannot turn. It does not turn when the index crank is turned. The index plate does not turn, except for operations involving the machining of a helix or spiral. Thus the index plate must be held in a stationary position while bolt heads, keyways, spur gears, and similar jobs are machined.

Rapid Indexing

The rapid method of indexing is often called *direct indexing* and can be done easily and rapidly. The worm shaft (with index crank on the end) must be disengaged from the work spindle. This is done with a thumbscrew or lever provided for this purpose. Then, by withdrawing the *quick index-plunger pin* from the hole in the back of the *spindle plate,* one can turn the spindle and plate freely by hand.

There are 24 equally spaced holes and spaces in the back of the *spindle plate.* Hence this plate makes it possible to index 24 equal

Fig. 1226. Milling a Bevel with the Head Swiveled (Courtesy Clausing Corp.)

Fig. 1225. Milling the Eye for a Hammer with an End Mill (Courtesy Clausing Corp.)

Fig. 1227. T-Slot Machined with a T-Slot End Mill (Courtesy Clausing Corp.)

Fig. 1228. Boring a Perpendicular Hole at an Angle with Head Swiveled
(Courtesy Clausing Corp.)
The boring tool is mounted in a boring head.

Fig. 1229. Drilling at an Angle
(Courtesy Clausing Corp.)
The holes are equally spaced by indexing with a dividing head.

divisions. The holes are spaced 1/24th of a revolution apart. It is also possible to index 12, 8, 6, 4, and 2 equally spaced divisions by this method. If 12 divisions are desired, every second space or hole is used. For 8 divisions, index 3 holes or spaces. For 6 divisions, index 4 holes or spaces. For 4 divisions, index 6 holes or spaces. For 2 divisions, index 12 holes or spaces.

Procedure for rapid indexing:

(1) Disengage the worm shaft from the work spindle.

(2) Determine the number of holes, or spaces, to index for each equally spaced division to be machined.

(3) Withdraw the quick index-plunger pin from the spindle plate.

(4) Turn the spindle plate by hand for the desired number of holes or spaces to be indexed.

(5) Insert the quick index-plunger pin in the desired hole.

(6) Repeat steps 3 through 5 until all equally spaced divisions have been machined. When the last division has been indexed, the quick index-plunger should be in the same hole in which it was located before indexing the first division. This will check the accuracy of the indexing.

Plain Indexing

The plain method of indexing, sometimes called *simple indexing,* makes it possible to index many numbers of divisions not possible by the rapid-indexing method. Thus 5, 7, 9, 11, 13, and many other numbers of equally spaced divisions can be indexed by the plain-indexing method. This method of indexing generally is required for machining gears.

The *worm shaft* must be engaged with the *work spindle* for plain indexing. Thus the work spindle is turned by withdrawing the *index-plunger pin* and turning the index crank.

The *index plate* has several circles of holes. A different number of holes is equally spaced on each *hole circle*. Some dividing heads have holes on each side of the index plate. The plate may be reversed for the desired hole circle. An index plate of the type in Fig. 1230 has the following numbers of holes in circles and can be considered to be a standard index plate:

One side   24-25-28-30-34-37-38-39-41-42-43

Other side   46-47-49-51-53-54-57-58-59-62-66

Two *sector arms* are located on the front of the index plate. The arms can be swiveled freely around the plate. A *lock screw* is used to lock the two arms securely for a space representing a fraction of a hole circle. Thus it is possible to index a fractional part of a revolution with the index crank.

The following formula can be used to determine the number of revolutions of the index crank for a desired number of equally spaced divisions:

$$T = \frac{N}{D}$$

Where:

T = Number of turns, or fractional part of turns, of index crank

N = Number of turns of index crank for one revolution of work spindle (usually 40 turns)

D = Number of divisions required for workpiece

Example:

Determine the number of revolutions of the index crank for indexing each tooth space for an 18-tooth spur gear.

$$T = \frac{40}{18}$$

$$T = 2\frac{4}{18} = 2\frac{2}{9} \text{ turns}$$

When a fractional part of a revolution of the index crank must be made, the fractional part is established between the two sector arms. To determine a fractional part of a revolution, select a circle with a number of

holes which is divisible by the denominator of the fraction for the number of turns. In the above example, the number 54 is divisible by 9. (54 ÷ 9 = 6) or (1/9 = 6/54). Thus 2/9 = 12/54. The sector arms are then spaced with 12 spaces between holes on the 54-hole circle. (*Note:* This is the space between 13 holes. It is the number of spaces between holes which is important. It is like counting the spaces between the fingers of your hand. You have four spaces between five fingers.)

When indexing for the 18-tooth gear above, each gear is indexed 2 12/54 revolutions. That is 2 complete turns of the index crank, plus the 12/54 revolutions between the sector arms.

It is always a good idea to practice indexing first without actually machining the part. Start indexing by using the *number one* hole in the hole circle. Mark the hole with a pencil;

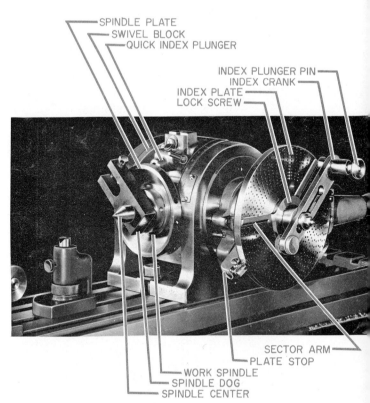

Fig. 1230. Universal Dividing Head,
Showing Principal Parts
(Courtesy The Cincinnati Milling Machine Co.)

then index for each space. In the case of the 18-tooth gear above, index 18 spaces. After indexing 18 spaces, the index-plunger pin should be in the number *one* starting hole.

Other more complex methods of indexing are sometimes necessary. These are described in handbooks for machinists.

1286. Bed Milling Machine

Bed-type milling machines have a heavy base casting which forms a *bed* on which the table travels longitudinally, see Fig. 1231. Bed-type machines very often are heavy-duty mass-production machines. The table does not move transversely (crosswise) toward the column. However, the spindle, on which the cutter is mounted, may be adjusted vertically as well as horizontally.

Bed-type machines may be equipped with one, two, three, or more spindles and cutters. The machine in Fig. 1231 has three spindles and three heavy-duty *face-milling cutters*. Parts are mounted on both sides of the table, and three surfaces are *face milled* at the same time.

Review Questions

1. What is a milling machine?
2. Why are milling machines important?

Fig. 1231. Bed-Type Special Manufacturing Milling Machine
(Courtesy The Cincinnati Milling Machine Co.)

3. What three factors determine the variety of machining operations which can be performed on a milling machine?

4. List several kinds of flat surfaces which can be machined with a milling machine.

5. List several kinds of curved or irregular surfaces which can be machined with a milling machine.

6. List several kinds of hole-machining operations which can be performed with a milling machine.

7. Describe a knee-and-column type milling machine.

8. List the three directions in which the table can be adjusted on knee-and-column type milling machines.

9. List three different classifications or types of knee-and-column type milling machines.

10. List two types of horizontal milling machines.

11. Describe a plain-type horizontal milling machine.

12. What is the distinguishing difference between plain and universal, horizontal milling machines?

13. List the kinds of operations which can be performed on a universal milling machine, but which cannot be performed without special accessories on a plain milling machine.

14. How can vertical milling operations be performed on either plain or universal milling machines?

15. List the kinds of operations which can be performed with vertical milling machines or with vertical milling attachments on horizontal machines.

16. How can holes be accurately spaced and drilled with a vertical milling machine?

17. Explain the features of a combination horizontal and vertical milling machine.

18. Explain how the table elevation may be adjusted.

19. Explain how transverse (crosswise) table position may be adjusted.

20. Why should the knee clamps and saddle clamps be tightened when milling?

21. What is the purpose of a rapid-traverse control on a milling machine?

22. Explain how the spindle rpm can be adjusted or changed on one kind of milling machine.

23. How can the direction of spindle rotation be changed on a milling machine?

24. Explain how the feed rate can be changed on one kind of milling machine.

25. Explain the difference between up-milling and down-milling feeds.

26. For what kinds of operations can a dividing head be used?

27. For what purpose is a dividing-head lead drive mechanism used?

28. For what purpose is a vertical-milling attachment used?

29. For what purpose is a universal-spiral milling attachment used?

30. For what purpose is a circular-milling attachment used?

31. Explain the characteristics of the *national milling-machine taper.*

32. List two kinds of self-holding tapers used on milling-machine spindles.

33. For what kinds of operations are style-A arbors generally used?

34. For what kinds of operations are style-B arbors generally used?

35. What purposes do spacing collars serve on milling arbors?

36. How will nicks on the face of spacing collars affect the straightness of the arbor?

37. For what purpose is a style-C arbor used?

38. For what purpose is a collet adapter used?

39. Explain the steps of procedure used to remove arbors which have a standard milling-machine taper and which are held in the machine spindle with a draw bar.

40. List several kinds of cutting-tool materials from which milling cutters may be made.

41. What are the general characteristics of high-speed steel cutting tools, including milling cutters?

42. For what kinds of operations are plain-milling cutters used?

43. For what kinds of operations are side-milling cutters used?

44. List several kinds of side-milling cutters and explain their uses.

45. For what operations are metal-slitting saws used?

46. List several types of metal-slitting saws.

47. List several types of angular-milling cutters.

48. For what purposes are form-relieved cutters used?

49. How is the *hand* of a milling cutter determined?

50. How is the *hand* of the helix on a cutter determined?

51. For what kinds of operations are end mills used?

52. List two types of shanks on end mills.

53. What type of end mills can be used for plunge milling?

54. List several kinds of end-milling cutters and explain the kinds of operations for which they may be used.

55. Explain how a T-slot can be machined.

56. List a general rule concerning the *maximum* depth of cut for an end mill.

57. How are milling cutters sharpened?

58. On what kinds of milling operations should cutting fluids be used?

59. Explain the meaning of *cutting speed* for milling operations.

60. How does the machineability of metal affect the cutting speed which may be used?

61. List several factors which affect the cutting speed used for milling operations.

62. Explain the difference between cutting speed and rpm.

63. List the formula for calculating the *approximate* cutting speed for milling operations when the rpm is known.

64. List the formula for calculating the approximate rpm for milling when the cutting speed is known.

65. What is meant by the rate of feed for a milling machine?

66. Explain how the *rate of feed per tooth* is selected for a given kind of milling cutter.

67. List several safety precautions to be observed while setting up and operating a milling machine.

68. List six ways in which a workpiece may be mounted on a milling machine.

69. How can the vise be checked for right-angle squareness with the column?

70. How can the vise be checked for parallelism with the column or the T-slots on the table?

71. List several factors which may cause vibration or chatter while milling.

72. What is indexing, and for what kinds of milling operations is it used?

73. Describe a bed-type milling machine.

Coordination
Words to Know

arbor
arbor adapter
bearing sleeves
collets
column
cross feed
cutting speed
dividing head
down milling
end mill
end milling
feed
feed rate
hand of cut
hand of cutter
hand of helix
hole machining
knee clamp
knee elevation
longitudinal
micrometer collar
milling cutter
milling machine
  bed-type
  horizontal-type
  knee-and-column
    type

plain-type
universal-type
vertical-type
parallelism
power vertical feed
rapid traverse
saddle
saddle clamp
spacing collar
spiral milling
straddle milling
swivel vise
taper shanks
  Brown & Sharpe
    taper
  Morse taper
  National milling-
    machine taper
  self-holding taper
  self-releasing taper
transverse
transverse table feed
T-slot
universal vise
up milling
vertical-feed
  engagement lever

Grinding Machines and Grinding Operations

1290. What Is Grinding?

Grinding is a machining operation which removes fine metal chips from a workpiece with a revolving grinding wheel. The grinding wheel is made of many sharp abrasive grains. When the grinding wheel revolves at high speed and rubs against the workpiece, tiny metallic chips are removed from the workpiece, see Figs. 1245-1247.

Because of heat due to friction, grinding chips appear as red hot sparks immediately after leaving the workpiece, but they are cooled immediately by air. Thus grinding wheels remove metallic chips from metal in much the same manner in which metal chips are removed by a lathe tool, saw blade, or milling cutter.

Machines which perform grinding operations are called grinding machines. Many kinds of grinding machines are available. They generally are named according to the kinds of grinding operations which they perform, such as surface grinding machines (Fig. 1254), cylindrical grinding machines (Fig. 1246), and cutter-and-tool grinding machines (Fig. 1211). Some kinds of grinding machines are standard machines which perform a wide variety of grinding operations. Other grinding machines are of special design and can perform only a few kinds of grinding operations.

Grinding operations can be classified under two headings as precision or nonprecision, de-pending on their purpose. *Nonprecision grinding* involves the removal of metal which usually cannot be removed in any other way and which does not require accuracy or close tolerances. Examples include such jobs as grinding cold chisels, center punches, and rough grinding of workpieces. Nonprecision grinding generally is done on a pedestal grinder of the types shown in Figs. 857 and 858.

Precision grinding includes many kinds of grinding operations which require grinding accurately to specified size limits. Precision

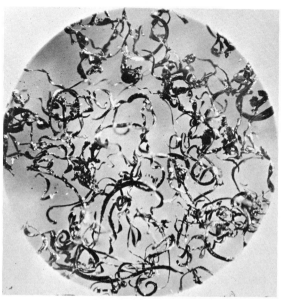

Fig. 1245. Magnified View of Metal Chips Produced by Grinding (Courtesy Norton Co.)

grinding machines are available for many kinds of precision grinding operations. Flat surfaces are ground with surface grinding machines, Fig. 1254. Round surfaces are ground with cylindrical grinding machines, Fig. 1246. Milling cutters are ground with cutter and tool grinding machines. (See Figs. 1211, 1212, and 1213.)

Grinding Tolerances

Modern industrial practice requires grinding many kinds of machine parts to tolerances of plus or minus 0.0001″. Special parts for precision instruments and gages are sometimes ground to tolerances of plus or minus 0.000020″ (20 microinches, or 20 millionths of one inch). Grinding operations, therefore, make it possible to machine to closer tolerances than with other common chip-machining operations. A second advantage of grinding is that it can be used to machine materials which are too hard to be machined by other common chip-machining operations. For example, metal-cutting tools and heat-treated parts may be machined accurately to size by grinding.

1291. Kinds of Grinding Operations

Metal parts of many shapes can be machined accurately to close tolerances by grinding. Many parts are rough machined first on a lathe, shaper, milling machine, or special-production machine tool. Then they are machined to finished size by grinding. Parts which are heat treated generally become warped or distorted during heat-treatment processes. Hence, they must be rough machined to an oversize dimension before heat treatment. After heat treatment, they generally are too hard to be machined by other methods. They must, therefore, be machined to final specified size limits by grinding.

The following are several common basic classifications of precision grinding operations:

(1) Surface Grinding
(2) Cylindrical Grinding
(3) Internal Grinding
(4) Form Grinding
(5) Centerless Grinding
(6) Cutter-and-Tool Grinding

Surface Grinding

This kind of grinding produces a smooth, true, flat surface on parts. Surface grinding is done on surface grinding machines, Figs. 1254 to 1257. Surface grinding machines can grind flat surfaces (Fig. 1254), angular surfaces (Fig. 1283), and grooves (Fig. 1281). By shaping the face of the grinding wheel round, curved, or to some special contour, surfaces

Fig. 1246. Grinding a Part in a Plain Cylindrical Grinding Machine (Safety Goggles Are Recommended) (Courtesy Brown & Sharpe)

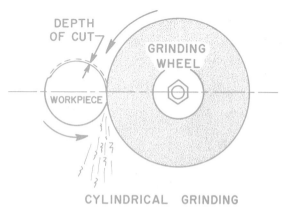

Fig. 1247. Relationships of Grinding Wheel and Workpiece in Cylindrical Grinding

with a special shape can be ground with a surface grinding machine.

Cylindrical Grinding

This classification includes various grinding operations involved in external grinding of round parts with a cylindrical or conical shape. Cylindrical grinding is done on cylindrical grinding machines, Fig. 1246. Several types of cylindrical grinding machines may be used. For cylindrical grinding of long parts, the workpiece is mounted between the headstock and footstock centers, similar to mounting work between centers on a lathe. Short workpieces can be held in either a universal 3-jaw chuck or in a 4-jaw chuck mounted on the headstock as shown in Figs. 1250 and 1251.

The relationship between the grinding wheel and the workpiece for cylindrical grinding operations is shown in Fig. 1247. Roughing cuts vary from 0.001″ to 0.004″ deep, depending upon the shape and size of the work-

piece and upon the size and rigidness of the machine. Finishing cuts generally vary from 0.0002″ to 0.001″ deep.

Cylindrical grinding machines also can grind tapered or conical surfaces. (See Fig. 1248.) The machine table can be swiveled for grinding long tapers, as in Fig. 1249. On universal-type cylindrical grinding machines, the headstock may be swiveled for grinding steep tapers, as in Fig. 1249. On universal cylindrical grinding machines, the headstock also can be swiveled 90° for *face grinding* flat surfaces, as in Fig. 1250.

Fig. 1249. Grinding a Steep Taper with the Head Swiveled on a Universal Cylindrical Grinding Machine (Courtesy Brown & Sharpe)

Fig. 1248. Grinding a Taper with the Table Swiveled on a Universal Cylindrical Grinding Machine (Courtesy Brown & Sharpe)

Fig. 1250. Headstock Swiveled 90° for Face Grinding with a Universal Cylindrical Grinding Machine (Courtesy Brown & Sharpe)

Fig. 1251. Internal Grinding of a Part Mounted in a Chuck on a Universal Grinding Machine (Courtesy Brown & Sharpe)

Fig. 1252. Abrasive Machining a Worm Screw from a Solid Piece (Courtesy Norton Co.)

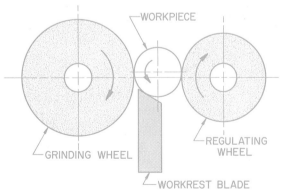

Fig. 1253. Relationship of Grinding Wheel and Workpiece in Centerless Grinding

Internal Grinding

This kind of grinding operation produces a smooth and accurate surface in a cylindrical hole, Fig. 1251. The internal surface may be ground straight or tapered. On special jobs the grinding wheel can be cut to a special form for grinding an internal surface of irregular form.

For industrial production purposes, special internal grinding machines are used. However, in most tool-and-die shops, small machine shops, and school shops, internal-grinding operations are performed with an *internal-grinding attachment* on a universal cylindrical grinding machine, as in Fig. 1251.

Internal-grinding operations also can be performed with a tool post grinder mounted on a lathe. With this setup, the workpiece is mounted in the lathe chuck. The tool post grinder is mounted in the tool post T-slot on the compound rest.

Form Grinding

This refers to grinding surfaces of special form or shape. The face of the grinding wheel must be cut to conform with the shape of the surface to be ground. For example, the grinding wheel in Fig. 1252 is cut to conform with the shape of the screw thread which it is cutting. The grinding of fillets and rounds is another example of form grinding.

Grinding wheels are available with faces having standard shapes for grinding contours which are often used, see Fig. 848. For other nonstandard form grinding operations, the face of a grinding wheel can be cut with a diamond tool to any desired shape. (See Figs. 1273 and 1274.) Form grinding can be done on surface grinding machines, cylindrical grinding machines, and on special grinding machines. (See Fig. 1272.)

Centerless Grinding

This is a form of cylindrical grinding. It is done without using center holes or a chuck for holding the workpiece while grinding. Centerless grinding is done with a *centerless grinding machine.* The relationship of the workpiece, the regulating wheel, and the grinding wheel on centerless grinding machines is shown in Fig. 1253. Straight or tapered objects such as spindles, piston pins, roller bearings, and lathe centers are ground by this method.

Cutter-and-Tool Grinding

This includes the grinding of milling cutters, end mills, counterbores, reamers, and similar metal-cutting tools. Tools of this type generally are ground or sharpened on *cutter-and tool grinding* machines, as in Figs. 1211, 1212, and 1213. Special cutter-and-tool grinding attachments are available for use on some kinds of surface grinding machines for sharpening cutting tools.

1292. Surface Grinding Machines

Surface grinding machines are designed primarily for grinding plain flat surfaces, Fig. 1254. However, by use of special setup tools or accessories, angular and irregular surfaces also can be ground with a surface grinding machine. (See Figs. 1281, 1282, and 1283.) Surface grinding machines can be classified under two principal types, the *horizontal-spindle type* (Figs. 1254 and 1256) and the *vertical-spindle type* (Figs. 1257 and 1258).

Surface grinders of the horizontal-spindle type, Fig. 1254, are most common in small machine shops, tool-and-die shops, maintenance shops, and school shops. With this type machine, the workpiece is mounted on the table, usually on a magnetic chuck (Fig. 1254), in a vise (Fig. 1282), or bolted to the table (Fig. 1284). The table reciprocates back and forth under the grinding wheel which remains in the same position. As the table reciprocates longitudinally (back and forth from right to left), it is fed crosswise under the grinding wheel, Fig. 1255. Thus, the wheel takes a new cut each time the table reciprocates.

Some horizontal-spindle surface grinding machines are equipped for handfeeding only. Machines of this type, Figs. 1265 and 1266, must be fed by hand both longitudinally and crosswise; the *table - hand crank* and the *cross-feed handwheel* provided. Many horizontal-spindle machines are equipped with automatic power feeds for horizontal and cross feeding, as in Fig. 1267. Machines of

Fig. 1254. **Grinding a Part with a Surface Grinding Machine (Courtesy Brown & Sharpe)**

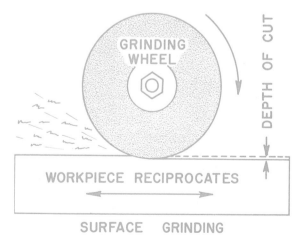

Fig. 1255. **Relationship of Grinding Wheel and Workpiece with Horizontal-Spindle Surface Grinder**

Fig. 1256. Surface Grinder with Horizontal Spindle and Rotary Table (Safety Goggles Are Recommended) (Courtesy Norton Co.)

this type also can be fed manually with the *table handwheel.*

A second kind of horizontal-spindle surface grinder is the *rotary* type, equipped with a rotary table, Fig. 1256. The rotary table is mounted on top of a longitudinal table. The workpiece is mounted on a magnetic chuck which revolves on the rotary table underneath the grinding wheel. As grinding takes place, the longitudinal table is fed in either direction under the grinding wheel. Larger diameter workpieces can be ground on machines of this type.

Surface grinding machines of the vertical-spindle type, Figs. 1257 and 1258, have the grinding wheel mounted on a vertical spindle. Workpieces to be ground are mounted on the table which may be the reciprocating-type, Fig. 1257, or the revolving-type, Fig. 1258. Reciprocating-type tables move back and forth under the revolving grinding wheel. Revolving-type tables rotate underneath the grinding wheel. Vertical-spindle machines provide a larger area of contact between the grinding wheel and the workpiece and, therefore, grind more rapidly than horizontal-spindle machines. Since more heat is also created, a cutting fluid generally must be used while grinding with machines of this type.

Fig. 1257. Surface Grinder with Vertical Spindle and Reciprocating Table

Fig. 1258. Surface Grinding on a Large Vertical-Spindle Type Surface-Grinding Machine with a Rotary Table (Courtesy Norton Co.)

Vertical-spindle surface grinding machines are widely used for production grinding where many parts must be ground rapidly.

1293. Features of Horizontal-Spindle Surface Grinding Machines

Horizontal-spindle surface grinding machines are most commonly used in small commercial shops, tool-and-die shops, and in school shops. Hence this unit is concerned principally with machines of this type. The parts and controls on horizontal-spindle grinding machines may be designed somewhat differently by various machine manufacturers. However, the principles involved in the operation of many machines of this basic type are similar.

Principal Parts

The principal parts and controls of a horizontal-spindle surface grinding machine, equipped for either handfeeding or power feeding, are shown in Fig. 1267. Smaller machines equipped for handfeeding only are shown in Figs. 1265 and 1266.

Size

The size and capacity of surface grinding machines generally is designated by the size of the working area of the table. A *magnetic chuck* with approximately the same working area is often mounted on the table for convenience in holding workpieces, as in Fig. 1254 and 1281. A size 6″ × 18″ machine, as shown in Fig. 1267, has a table with working area of 6″ cross travel and 18″ longitudinal table travel. The smaller machine in Fig. 1265 has a designated size of 5″ × 10″, yet the table work area is 5″ × 11″. The working area of the table is slightly larger than the designated size for some machines. The distance between the center of the grinding wheel and the working surface of the table also is a factor in determining the maximum height of workpieces which may be ground. (See Fig. 1254.)

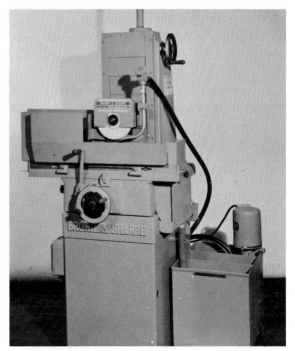

Fig. 1265. Handfeed Surface Grinder with Wet-Grinding Attachment (Courtesy Brown & Sharpe)

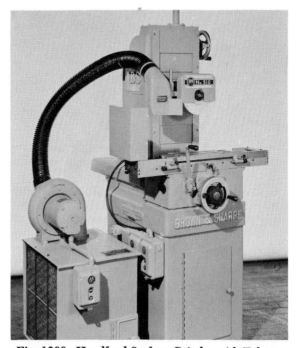

Fig. 1266. Handfeed Surface Grinder with Exhaust Attachment (Courtesy Brown & Sharpe)

Wheel Elevation

The wheel is mounted on a horizontal spindle which may be raised or lowered with the *elevating handwheel,* Fig. 1267. The handwheel generally has 0.0002″ graduations which make it possible to adjust the wheel

Fig. 1267. 6″ x 18″ Surface Grinding Machine with Hydraulic and Hand Feeds
(Courtesy Brown & Sharpe)

(1) Cross-feed handwheel; (2) Dial locknut, Cross-feed handwheel; (3) Table handwheel; (4) Set screw; (5) Throttle adjustment bushing; (6) Table throttle lever; (7) Table reversing lever; (8) Dust deflector; (9) Reversing lever contact roller; (10) Tables; (11) Wheel guard; (12) Upright; (13) Table dog; (14) Carrier locknut; (15) Fine-feed adjustment knob; (16) Dial locknut, elevating handwheel; (17) Elevating handwheel; (18) Fine-feed locknut; (19) Cross-feed directional lever; (20) Cross-feed regulating screw; (21) Wheel truing and rapid positioning lever; (22) Oil lever sight glass; (23) Base; (27) Bed; and (40) Elevating screw guard, upper.

elevation in increments of 0.0002″. Machines of the type shown in Fig. 1268 also have an auxiliary *fine-feed adjusting knob* which makes it possible to adjust the wheel elevation in increments of 0.0001″.

Horizontal-spindle machines may have *direct drive* or *V-belt drive* from an electric motor. With direct drive, the grinding wheel is mounted on the end of the motor spindle.

Wheel RPM

The cutting speed and the rpm of grinding wheels are explained in sections 1045 and 1046. The maximum rpm indicated on the grinding wheel always should be equal to or higher than the rpm of the wheel spindle. If the spindle rpm exceeds the maximum indicated rpm for the wheel, the wheel may fly apart and injure someone. On machines with V-belt drive and a step pulley, the rpm can be changed as necessary for smaller or larger grinding wheels. Most surface grinding machines, however, are designed to operate at one standard speed.

For example, a spindle speed of approximately 3450 rpm is often used on machines which use a 7″ diameter grinding wheel. This gives a cutting speed of about 6319 surface feet per minute. The grinding wheel should be mounted with cardboard disks on each side of the wheel, as shown in Fig. 1270.

Table Feed

The table travels longitudinally (to the right or left), and crosswise (in toward or out from the column). Some machines are available with handfeed only, as in Figs. 1265 and 1266. Other machines are available with power longitudinal and power cross feeds, as in Fig. 1267. Machines with power feed also can be fed by hand.

Table travel may be handfed with the *table hand crank* or *table handwheel.* The table is fed crosswise by hand with the *cross-feed handwheel.*

On machines equipped with power feed, the rate of longitudinal table travel can be adjusted. Table speed should be slower for finishing cuts than for roughing cuts. The amount of cross feed also can be adjusted. Lighter cross feeds are used for finishing cuts than for roughing cuts.

The controls used for changing the rate of longitudinal table feed and the rate of cross feed are somewhat different on each kind of machine. (See Fig. 1268.) Therefore, it is always best to have your instructor explain and show you how to use the various controls before using the machine for the first time. The procedures for using the feed controls and other controls are included in the handbook which generally is provided by the manufacturer of the machine.

Table dogs, Fig. 1268, are provided for setting the length of table travel. As the table travels, the dogs contact the table *reversing lever,* thus causing the table to travel in the opposite direction.

Cross feeds may be set from 0.010″ to 0.250″ on machines equipped with automatic cross-feed mechanisms. However, for average roughing cuts on smaller machines, a cross feed of 0.050″ to 0.100″ is satisfactory. For finishing cuts, the cross feed generally should be less, usually from 0.030″ to 0.050″. *Never use cross feeds in excess of one-half the width of the wheel.* The cross-feed handwheel has 0.0002″ graduations for accurately setting the amount of cross feed, see Fig. 1269.

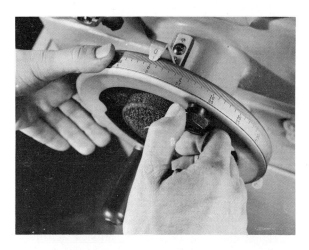

Fig. 1269. Cross-feed Handwheel has 0.0002″ Graduations (Courtesy Brown & Sharpe)

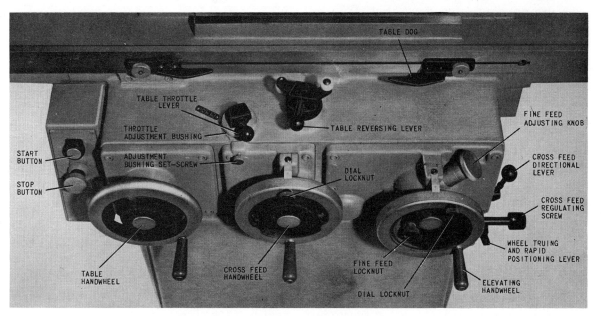

Fig. 1268. Front Operating Controls on a 618-Surface Grinding Machine Equipped with Power and Handfeeds (Courtesy Brown & Sharpe)

Depth of Cut

The depth of cut may vary according to the following:

(1) Whether the cut is a roughing or a finishing cut

(2) Whether grinding is done wet or dry

(3) The rigidness of the machine and the rigidness of the setup

Deep, roughing cuts generally produce a rougher surface than shallow finishing cuts. Surface finish generally is better with wet grinding than with dry grinding. And heavier cuts generally can be made on heavier machines than on lightweight machines. For average conditions, roughing cuts from 0.002″ to 0.003″ should be used. Finishing cuts of 0.001″ or less produce good results.

Wet-or-Dry Grinding

Abrasive grains fracture from the wheel, and fine metal chips are produced while grinding. For dry grinding an *exhaust attachment* is recommended, Fig. 1266. This attachment collects the abrasive grit and dust, and it keeps the machine and the work area clean.

A *wet-grinding attachment,* Fig. 1265, is used for grinding with the use of a cutting fluid. The wet attachment consists of a pump, liquid container, and splash guards. The pump provides cutting fluid at the surface area being ground, thus reducing heat. Hence, heavier cuts generally can be taken. Cutting fluid also improves surface finish, increases grinding-wheel life, and carries grit and grinding dust away.

An emulsifiable (soluble) oil solution is recommended for grinding ferrous metals. A solution composed of 40-parts water and 1-part emulsifiable oil (§ 406) is recommended. Cutting fluids for use with other metals are listed in Table 15, page 169.

1294. Grinding Wheel Selection

Grinding wheels are made of abrasive grains which are held together with a bonding material. Several kinds of abrasive may be used, and the grain size may range from very fine to very coarse. The kinds of abrasive, their properties, and grain sizes are discussed in Unit 17, §§ 278-282.

Grinding wheels can be made very hard or very soft depending on the kind and amount of bonding material used in their manufacture. Complete information concerning grinding wheels is included in Unit 49. Included in Unit 49 are such factors as bond type, grade or hardness of wheels, grain structure of wheels, the grinding-wheel marking system, and the factors to be considered when ordering a grinding wheel.

A standard grinding-wheel marking system (see § 1022 and Fig. 849) is now used by most manufacturers for identifying the characteristics of each grinding wheel. The code number generally is located on the cardboard disk on the side of the wheel.

The following kinds of straight grinding wheels are recommended for surface grinding with horizontal-spindle, reciprocating surface grinders:

MATERIAL	KIND OF GRINDING WHEEL
Soft Steel	23A46 - J8VBE
Cast Iron	32A46 - I8VBE (or)
	37C36 - KVK
Hardened Steel	32A46 - H8VBE
General-Purpose	
Wheel	23A46 - H8VBE
Nonferrous Metals	37C36 - KVK

For more specific grinding wheel recommendations, refer to standard handbooks for machinists or to manufacturers' catalogs.

1295. Truing and Dressing the Wheel

When a grinding wheel becomes dull, loaded, or out of shape, it must be *dressed* and *trued. Dressing* means to sharpen a wheel. *Truing* means to cut the wheel so that there will be no high spots when the wheel is running. Truing also refers to forming a wheel to a particular shape, such as a convex or concave shape. Wheels are trued to special shapes for form-grinding operations. A diamond tool, Figs. 1271 and 874, is used for dressing or truing grinding wheels.

Procedure for Truing

(1) Wear safety goggles.

(2) Mount the grinding wheel on the spindle as shown in Fig. 1270.

(3) Select a wheel truing fixture, and place it on the table or on a magnetic chuck. (See Fig. 1271.) The diamond-point tool should be placed ahead of the vertical center line of the wheel, and it should be inclined slightly in the direction of wheel travel. This procedure will prevent gouging or *digging in.*

(4) Clamp the fixture in position.

(5) Start the machine. With the *elevating handwheel*, lower the wheel until it just touches the diamond-point tool.

(6) With the *cross-feed handwheel,* move the table so that the diamond cuts across the wheel.

(7) Lower the wheel 0.0005″ for each additional cut, as in step 6, until the wheel is true. If the machine is equipped with a wet attachment, a cutting fluid should be used while truing or dressing the wheel.

Procedure for Dressing

When the wheel becomes dull, it should be dressed (sharpened). Wear safety goggles and follow steps 3 through 7 above.

Shaping the Wheel

It is sometimes necessary to grind a special shape or form such as a rounded fillet, a V-groove, or some irregular surface. In such cases, it is necessary to cut or true the grinding wheel to conform to the shape which is to be ground. For example, a V-shaped groove is being ground in Fig. 1272. For this purpose,

Fig. 1271. **Truing a Wheel on a Surface Grinder**
(Courtesy Brown & Sharpe)

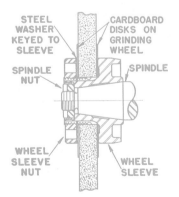

Fig. 1270. **Proper Mounting of Grinding Wheel**
(Courtesy Brown & Sharpe)

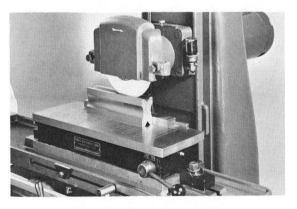

Fig. 1272. **Grinding a V-Shaped Recess**
(Courtesy Brown & Sharpe)

Fig. 1273. Radius and Wheel Truing
(Courtesy Brown & Sharpe)
Note: Tool is mounted at right angles to slide for cutting angular surface on wheel.

Fig. 1274. Shaping Convex Surface on a Grinding Wheel (Courtesy Brown & Sharpe)

the grinding wheel must be ground to the exact shape of the V-groove. A *radius and wheel truing attachment,* Figs. 1273 and 1274, can be used for shaping wheels. In Fig. 1273, the attachment is used for cutting an angular face on the wheel. In Fig. 1274, the attachment can be swiveled for cutting a convex radius on the wheel.

1296. Holding Work for Surface Grinding

Workpieces of various shapes and sizes can be mounted on the surface grinding machine in a variety of ways, depending on the kinds of accessories available. The following methods are suggested for holding work for surface grinding.

1. *By using a magnetic chuck:*

Mount the chuck on the table, and bolt it in position. (See Figs. 1280 and 1281.) Place the workpiece on the surface of the chuck in the desired position. Turn the magnetic control lever 180° toward the *on* position. Workpieces made of magnetic materials can be held securely by this method. If the workpiece has only small areas in contact with the chuck, flat pieces of steel should be

Fig. 1280. Workpiece Held on a Permanent Magnetic Chuck (Courtesy Brown & Sharpe)

placed on the chuck against both ends of the workpiece. The extra-flat pieces help hold the work securely in position.

2. *By using a machine vise:*
Bolt a machine vise on the machine table, as in Fig. 1282 Clamp the workpiece in the vise. An indicator or surface gage may be used to determine whether the surface to be ground is in a horizontal plane.

3. *By using an adjustable-swivel vise:*
Bolt the vise, Fig. 1283, to the table and clamp the work in the vise. Then position the vise at the desired angle, as in Fig. 1283. Angular or beveled surfaces can be ground by using this method. A dial indicator or a surface gage can be used for determining whether the surface to be ground is in a horizontal plane.

4. *By clamping:*
A workpiece can be positioned, aligned, and clamped to the machine table. (See Fig. 1284.) Various work-holding tools may be used for setting up the workpiece on the machine table. (See Unit 28 and Fig. 424.)

Fig. 1282. Workpiece Held in a Vise (Courtesy Brown & Sharpe)

Fig. 1283. Workpiece in an Adjustable Swivel Vise (Courtesy Brown & Sharpe)

Fig. 1281. Grinding a Slot with Workpiece Mounted on Magnetic Chuck (Courtesy Brown & Sharpe)

Fig. 1284. Workpiece Held in Position with Clamps (Courtesy Brown & Sharpe)

5. *By using a precision vise:*

A precision vise, Fig. 1285, can be placed on a magnetic chuck for holding small workpieces securely and accurately. This kind of vise works well for holding parts with a small cross-sectional area. Round parts can be held in the V-groove in the vise jaw.

6. *By using an adjustable vise:*

An adjustable vise, as shown in Fig. 1286, can be placed on a magnetic chuck. The workpiece is then clamped in the vise. The vise can be swiveled at any desired angle, ranging from the horizontal to the 90° vertical position. This method works well for grinding angular or beveled surfaces. It also works well for grinding vertical surfaces on parts of convenient shape, as in Fig. 1286.

7. *By using V-blocks:*

Round workpieces can be clamped on V-blocks for grinding. The V-blocks can be clamped to the table, as in Fig. 1287. They also can be held in position with a magnetic chuck.

1297. Surface-Grinding Procedure

The following are the *preliminary steps of procedure* to be followed in setting up for surface-grinding operations. When the preliminary steps have been completed, the specific procedures for *manual-feed machines,* or for *power-feed machines* should be followed.

1. Select a grinding wheel which is recommended for the kind of material to be ground. (See § 1294.) Test the wheel to see that it is sound. This is done by striking it lightly with a light hammer. A clear ring indicates that the wheel is sound and has no cracks.

2. Mount the grinding wheel on the *wheel sleeve,* as shown in Fig. 1270. Cardboard disks should be placed on each side of the wheel, and the *sleeve nut* should be tightened

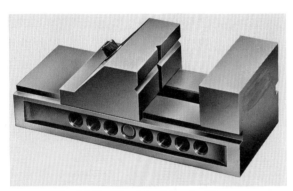

Fig. 1285. Precision Vise for Use on a Magnetic Chuck

Fig. 1286. Workpiece Mounted in an Adjustable Vise (Courtesy Brown & Sharpe)

Fig. 1287. Workpiece Clamped to Machine Table (Courtesy Brown & Sharpe)

snugly. If the sleeve nut is fastened too tightly, the wheel may crack.

3. Mount the wheel and sleeve on the machine spindle. Wipe any dust or dirt from the spindle and from the hole in the sleeve before mounting the unit on the spindle. Tighten the spindle nut snugly. (The spindle nut threads will most likely be LH.) Dress the wheel as explained in § 1295.

4. Remove all burrs or nicks from the workpiece with a file.

5. Wipe dust or dirt from the machine table, magnetic chuck, or other work-holding tools or accessories. Then mount the workpiece on the machine. Suggested methods for holding the work are explained in section 1296.

6. Lubricate the machine with the proper machine oil before using it.

7. *Protect your eyes* by wearing approved safety goggles or face shield.

Procedure for Manual Feeding

8. Complete the *preliminary steps of procedure*, steps 1 through 7, listed above.

9. With the *table hand crank* and the *cross-feed handwheel*, move the workpiece under the grinding wheel. Start the machine spindle. With the *elevating handwheel*, lower the grinding wheel until it just clears the workpiece.

On machines equipped with power feed, the power-feed mechanism should be disengaged for manual operation. The table handwheel must be engaged for manual operation. It automatically becomes disengaged when the power-feed mechanism is used.

10. With the cross-feed handwheel, feed the workpiece outward until the far side of the wheel extends beyond the work a distance equal to ¾ the width of the wheel face. Thus ¼ the width of the wheel is above the work. Move the table to one side until the wheel clears the end of the workpiece.

11. With the elevating handwheel, lower the grinding wheel 0.002″ to 0.003″ for a roughing cut. Allow sufficient material for a

final finishing cut of 0.0005″ to 0.001″ depth. Lock the grinding head in position with the *locking screw*, if the machine is so equipped. Turn on the cutting fluid, or the exhaust, as desired.

12. With the table hand crank or handwheel, feed the table longitudinally under the grinding wheel at a steady rate until the workpiece has passed beyond the grinding wheel at least 1″.

13. With the cross-feed handwheel, feed the work crosswise one complete turn, about 0.100″, for the next cut. On finishing cuts, a cross feed of 0.020″ to 0.050″ is satisfactory.

14. Continue grinding as in steps 12 and 13 until the entire surface has been ground.

15. Measure the thickness of the workpiece. If more roughing cuts are necessary, continue grinding as in steps 11 through 14. However, cross feed each additional cut in the direction opposite to the previous cut. This causes the wheel to wear off more evenly.

16. Make a final finishing cut 0.001″ or less in depth, as desired.

Procedure for Power Feeding

1. Complete the *preliminary steps of procedure*, 1 through 7, listed above.

2. Be sure that the power-feed mechanism is disengaged while setting up work, in preparation for automatic feed. On the machine in Fig. 1267 and 1268, this is done by turning the table throttle lever to the *off* position. The power cross feed also should be disengaged. The table handwheel and the cross-feed handwheel then can be engaged for manual operation while making the setup.

3. With the *table hand crank* and the *cross-feed handwheel*, move the workpiece under the grinding wheel. Start the machine spindle. With the *elevating handwheel*, lower the grinding wheel until it just clears the workpiece.

4. With the cross-feed handwheel, feed the workpiece outward, away from the column, until the far side of the wheel ex-

tends beyond the work a distance equal to ¾ the width of the wheel face. Thus ¼ the width of the wheel is above the work.

5. Move the table to the left until the workpiece has passed the grinding wheel a distance of at least 1″.

6. Bring the right-hand *reversing dog* against the right side of the *table-reversing lever*. Fasten the dog in position by tightening the clamping bolt.

7. Move the table to the right until the end of the workpiece has passed the grinding wheel a distance of at least 1″.

8. Bring the left-hand *reversing dog* against the left side of the *table-reversing lever*. Fasten the dog in position by tightening the clamping bolt.

CAUTION: *When setting the table dogs for automatic longitudinal table feeding, be sure to allow sufficient over-travel of the work in both directions so that cross-feed action can take place before the work travels back under the wheel.*

9. With the elevating handwheel, lower the grinding wheel 0.002″ to 0.003″ for a roughing cut. Allow sufficient material for a final finishing cut of 0.0005″ to 0.001″ depth. Lock the grinding head with the locking screw, if the machine is so equipped. Turn on the cutting fluid, or the exhaust system, as desired.

10. Set the power cross-feed mechanism for a feed of about 0.100″ for roughing cuts. On finishing cuts a feed of 0.020″ to 0.050″ is satisfactory.

11. Engage the automatic longitudinal table-feed mechanism. On the machine in Figs. 1267 and 1268 this is done with the *table throttle lever*.

12. Engage the automatic cross-feed mechanism for automatic feed in the proper direction. On the machine in Figs. 1267 and 1268 this is done with the *cross-feed directional lever*.

13. When the cut has been completed, disengage the automatic longitudinal table feed and the automatic cross feed.

14. Bring the table to one side, against the table dog, so that the end of the workpiece is at least 1″ beyond the grinding wheel.

15. Measure the workpiece. If additional roughing cuts are necessary, proceed as in steps 9 through 14 above. However, for each additional cut, feed the table crosswise in the direction opposite to the direction of feed for the previous cut. This procedure causes the wheel to wear more evenly.

If additional roughing cuts are not necessary, make a finishing cut. Finishing cuts generally should be 0.001″ or less in depth.

16. When the work has been ground to the specified dimension, stop the machine, remove the workpiece, and clean the machine and accessories. Place all tools and accessories in the proper place.

17. Remove sharp burrs or sharp arrises with a file so that you do not get cut by them.

Review Questions

1. Describe the appearance of chips produced by grinding.

2. List several kinds of grinding machines which are named after the kinds of operations which they perform.

3. Explain the difference between non-precision-grinding and precision-grinding operations.

4. To what tolerances or size limits are grinding operations often performed?

5. How can hardened steel parts be machined to size?

6. What is meant by surface grinding?

7. What is meant by cylindrical grinding?

8. How are workpieces held in a cylindrical grinding machine?

9. List several kinds of cylindrical grinding operations.

10. Describe internal grinding, and explain how it is done.

11. Explain how form grinding is done.

12. What is meant by centerless grinding?

13. For what purposes are cutter-and-tool grinding machines used?

14. List several kinds of surfaces which can be ground on a surface grinding machine.

15. Describe how a horizontal-spindle surface grinder operates.

16. Describe the difference between a reciprocating- and rotary-type surface grinding machine.

17. Describe a vertical-spindle surface grinding machine and its use.

18. How is the size of a surface grinding machine usually designated?

19. Why should the spindle rpm of a grinding machine never exceed the maximum recommended rpm for the grinding wheel?

20. For what purpose are table dogs used on surface grinding machines?

21. How much cross feed should be used for roughing cuts on horizontal-spindle surface grinding machines?

22. How much cross feed should be used for finishing cuts on a horizontal-spindle surface grinding machine?

23. List several factors which must be considered in determining the depth of cut for surface grinding.

24. For average conditions, what depth of cut should be taken when surface grinding?

25. What kind of cutting fluid is recommended for wet grinding of ferrous metals?

26. With the use of a code number, according to the standard grinding wheel marking system, list a recommended grinding wheel for surface grinding hardened steel.

27. Explain the difference in meaning between *truing* and *dressing* a grinding wheel.

28. List four kinds of vises which can be used for holding a workpiece on a surface grinder.

29. List several methods, other than using vises, which may be used for holding a workpiece for surface grinding.

Coordination

Words to Know

centerless grinding	longitudinal
conical surface	magnetic chuck
cylindrical grinding	nonprecision grinding
direct drive	precision grinding
dressed wheel	preliminary
dry grinding	reciprocating table
face grinding	rotary table
fillets	surface grinding
form grinding	table dog
grinding	trued wheel
grinding tolerances	vertical spindle
horizontal spindle	wet grinding
internal grinding	wheel elevation

Automation and Numerical Control Machining

Automation and numerical control are inter-related, for numerical control is actually one form of automation. Understanding several basic principles of automation will help you in learning about numerical control.

1300. What Is Automation?

The term automation comes from the word *automatic* which means *self-acting* or *self-adjusting*. Automation now generally applies to machines, equipment, or processes which operate without direct control and adjustment by an operator. Automated machines, processes, or systems of manufacturing generally possess the following characteristics:

(1) They operate with little or no human help.

(2) They detect or sense the need for a corrective adjustment in the process or operation.

(3) They make the required corrective adjustments with little or no human assistance.

The true concept of automation is *continuous automatic production*. This method of production, in some applications, can automatically produce the part(s), inspect, assemble, test, and package the product in one continuous flow.

Feedback

Automated machines, processes, or systems utilize a principle called *feedback* as a basis for self-adjustment. Information about the process or operation is detected and reported (fed back) to an adjusting control. An understanding of the following terms or devices used in automated systems will help in understanding the meaning of feedback.

Output. The work produced by a machine operation or process is output. The output may be either a product or a service, such as a machined part or the opening of a door.

Input. The commands, data, or standards specifying the output is called the input. The commands or data may concern such factors as size dimensions, position location, machine speed, weight, temperature, color, pressure, chemical composition, vibration, resistance, or sound.

Sensors. Electronic, mechanical, or other kinds of instruments or devices which detect (sense) and report conditions of the output products or services are sensors. Sensors may measure size, weight, temperature, color, pressure, or chemical composition. Sensors feed information back to the *control center*.

Control center. The control center compares the output with the input commands or data. With complex automated machines or systems, this device is most often an electronic computer which processes information or mathematical data. On simple automatic machines or processes, the control center may be a simple electrical regulator or a mechanical regulator. The information received from the sensors is compared with the input specifications. The control center gives the necessary instructions to the machine — to stop, continue, or change speed or direction. Thus, the control actually regulates or controls the automated machine or process.

Feedback Control Loop

Engineers use the term "feedback control loop" to describe how an automated machine or process functions. The term *loop* refers to the flow of information through the automated system. A simple automated process utilizing a *closed-loop* system is the heating system in a home. The system includes a furnace, a thermostat, a thermometer and an electrical circuit with a contact switch. See Fig. 1293. The desired temperature (input), for example 72° F., is set on the thermostat. When the temperature falls below 72° F., the thermostat sensor closes a switch in the electrical circuit to the furnace, thus starting the furnace which produces heat (output). When the temperature in the room rises to the desired input temperature setting (feedback), the thermostat sensor opens the switch in the electrical circuit, thus shutting off the furnace. Thus, the heating system is a simple application of a feedback control loop for an automatic process. In this simple system, the thermostat is both sensor and control. The thermometer is included in the system as a "readout" device to show the performance of the heating system to the homeowner. Similar *closed-loop systems* are used for the automatic operation of air-conditioning systems, hot-water heaters, and refrigerators.

A feedback control loop may be either the closed-loop or open-loop system. The closed-loop system is one in which a measurement of the output is fed back and compared with the input for the purpose of reducing their differences. The open-loop system is one in which no corrective adjustment takes place

as a result of the feedback. Instead, a signal such as a light or horn is actuated to warn an operator to make the necessary corrective adjustments. On some open-loop systems, the machine or process is stopped until corrective adjustments are made by the operator. Because closed-loop feedback systems are capable of making required corrective adjustments, they are used on more automated machines or processes.

Automatic Material Handling

Advanced automatic systems involve continuous automatic handling of materials.

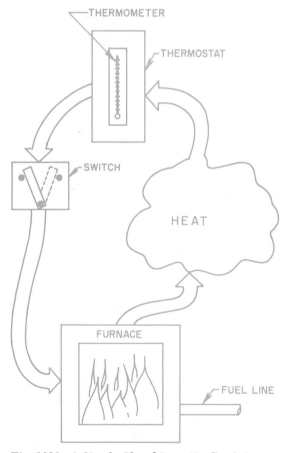

Fig. 1293. A Simple Closed-Loop Feedback System
  The machine (furnace) produces a product (heat) which is measured by the thermostat. The thermostat controls the furnace by activating the switch, as required for starting and stopping the furnace, thereby maintaining a constant temperature.

Such systems have been developed in industries which handle large volumes of materials. These systems are used in such *continuous process* industries as steelmaking, papermaking, chemical processing, and petroleum refining. *Unit-processing* also utilizes automatic material handling as in stamping automobile fenders, machining engine blocks, printing sheets of paper, and filling milk bottles.

Data Processing

Most automated machines or systems must process information in one form or another. Even the simple automatic heating system requires the comparison of input information (the desired temperature setting) with output information (the existing temperature).

Offices, schools, banks, and industrial plants use *electronic computers*, Fig. 1296, for processing mathematical information and many other kinds of data. Computers have complex systems for storing data, or "memory." They store vast amounts of facts, figures, and other information — all in numerical, alphabetical, or symbolic form. When instructed or "programed" properly, they are capable of solving complex problems.

Businesses use electronic computers for such accounting and bookkeeping tasks as keeping records of customer payments, calculating employee wages, printing their checks, and recording bank deposits and withdrawals. Engineers use computers to make the mathematical calculations required in designing roads, bridges, buildings, and dams. Scientists use computers for making necessary calculations in launching and controlling space vehicles. Industrial plants use computers to control materials, machines, and complete manufacturing systems.

Numerical Control

The electronic computer stores numbers, letters, and other symbolic data. It receives numbers as instructions, manipulates numbers to perform calculations, and transmits numbers to indicate results. Number codes are often used for letters and words. With the wide use of the computer for processing *numerical* information, the application of the computer to control the operation of a machine was a very logical development in industry. Since dimensions are given in numbers, other instructions can be coded into numbers. The use of numbers or numerical data to control the operation of production machines and processes came to be called *numerical control*.

Numerically controlled (NC) machine tools machine metals automatically. Sometimes they require the processing of much information in order to guide the cutting tool properly.

NC machine tools which perform point-to-point drilling operations and straight-cut milling operations are shown in Figs. 1294, 1295, 1316, and 1317. These machines are equipped with control systems which can process the numerical information required for automatic operation. In fact the control systems on these machines can be considered as a simple form of computer. The informational data is given to the NC system in code form on a perforated tape. The machine positions the workpiece and actuates the tool. Numerical-control machine tools, therefore, involve the automatic handling of both materials and information.

NC machine tools which have the capability for cutting curved or irregular surfaces or profiles have *continuous-path* NC systems. (See § 1302.) Preparing the tape for NC systems of this type often requires thousands of complex mathematical calculations. Therefore, electronic computers generally are necessary in preparation of the punched tape or punched cards which control the operation of continuous-path NC systems.

Automated machines or processes involve the application of at least one of the following principles in working with materials and information.

(1) Feedback Control.
(2) Automatic Material Handling.
(3) Data Processing.
(4) Numerical Control.

1301.   What Is Numerical Control?

Numerical control, abbreviated NC, is a system of controlling a machine or process through the use of numerically coded information which is the *input* for the machine's control system. The instructions to the machine are in the form of coded numbers punched into a ribbon of paper tape. The function of the tape may be compared to functions performed on jigs or fixtures of conventional machine tools. The tape can be stored for future use in repeating the same job or process. With some numerical-control systems, the coded numerical information is inserted into the control system on punched cards or on magnetic tape instead of punched tape.

NC Applications

Automatic operation by numerical control is readily adaptable to the operation of many metalworking machines or processes. The use of NC is rapidly increasing for automatic operation of machine tools such as drill presses, milling machines, lathes, boring machines, grinding machines, and punch presses. NC also is coming into use for flame-cutting and welding applications. *Point-to-point* NC is used for spot welding while continuous-path NC is used for continuous-path welding. (See § 1302.)

NC is used with inspection machines which take measurements on parts through the use of sensing probes. The machine records the difference between the actual size and the specified size.

NC is being used for assembly operations such as those involved in wiring complex electronic systems. It is also used for tube-forming machines, wire-wrapping machines, and steel-rolling machines.

A more complex system of NC, using various symbols, is also used for making drawings automatically with special drafting machines. This kind of NC system generally requires the use of an electronic computer. Abbreviated information from a sketch is fed into a computer. The computer makes many calculations which locate the coordinate points and provide other required information for drawing lines and curves. When equipped with the proper accessories, a computer can prepare punched tape which is inserted into the NC system of the automated drafting machine. The NC system reads the tape commands and controls the operation of the drafting machine, thus producing the drawing automatically.

Feedback System

NC control systems must locate a cutting tool, or other kind of tool, accurately at specific positions in relation to a workpiece. Center line positions of the tool are specified on the tape as coordinate dimensions, such as the X and Y coordinate dimensions used on a graph. The coordinate dimensioning system is explained in section 1305.

The positioning of the tool generally must be located to tolerances of plus or minus 0.001″ in relation to the workpiece. Some NC systems can maintain positioning accuracy to tolerances of plus or minus 0.0002″. In fact, one of the principal advantages of NC machining is its accuracy. Human error is largely eliminated, and waste is reduced. Other advantages are included in section 1303.

On NC machine tools, the positioning of the tool must take place automatically, in accordance with input commands on the coded tape. Furthermore, the tool must be guided and repositioned continuously as commanded by the tape. This generally requires a positioning system which has a *feedback control loop* designed for automatic corrective adjustments. Most NC systems use a *closed-loop feedback* system called a *servo-*

mechanism. A servomechanism is an automatic feedback control system which controls the mechanical position of the tool in relation to the work.

A servomechanism may use electric motors or hydraulic cylinders for mechanical positioning of the tool in relation to the workpiece. On most NC machine tools, the table is moved while the tool remains stationary. However, on some machines, the tool moves while its table remains stationary. A servomechanism is needed for each control axis, such as X- and Y-axes. On vertical drilling and milling machines, as in Figs. 1294 and 1295, the table is moved along its X- and Y-axes by servomechanisms. The X-axis is the longitudinal table travel. The Y-axis is the transverse or cross-feed travel.

The principle involved in the operation of the servomechanism on a machine tool is similar to the principle involved in the operation of the closed-loop feedback system on the furnace in Fig. 1293 (also see § 1300). The control system processes the numerical

information on the punched tape (input) to create a signal to the servomechanism. A sensing device constantly senses the position of the table or the tool. When the desired position is signaled by the sensor, the computer sends a "stop" signal. This prevents movement from the desired position or tool path. The sensing device in a servomechanism generally is an electronic, mechanical, or optical device.

NC Machining

An example of a simple 2-axis (§ 1306) numerically controlled machine tool is the combination drilling and milling machine called a *machining center.* (See Fig. 1294.) Machines of this type perform drilling, reaming, boring, tapping, and straight-cut milling operations. This multiple-purpose machine tool can replace several machines such as a drilling machine, a tapping machine, and a vertical-type milling machine. The machine is controlled by a 1″ wide ribbon of paper tape which has coded instructions in the form of punched holes, Fig. 1308. The holes are punched into the tape with a tape-punching machine, Fig. 1309, similar to an ordinary typewriter.

The perforated tape includes coded instructions concerning:

(1) The sequence of the operation.
(2) The kind of operation.
(3) The depth of the cut.
(4) The location of the cut.
(5) Tool changes.

Smaller NC machines of the single-spindle type, as in Fig. 1294, require manual tool changes by the machine operator. On most machines of this basic type, the operator also sets spindle speeds and feeds manually after each tool change. After the workpiece has been clamped into position, the speeds and feeds are adjusted by the operator. He then presses the *start button* and the machine performs all the operations for a given tool auto-

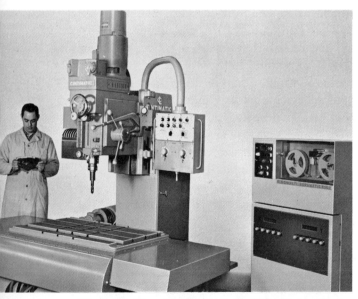

Fig. 1294. Numerically Controlled Machining Center (Courtesy The Cincinnati Lathe and Tool Co.) This 2-axis point-to-point NC machine automatically drills, mills, taps, and bores.

matically and in proper sequence, as instructed by tape commands.

The large console or cabinet to the right of the machine in Fig. 1294 houses the numerical-control system. The system includes a *tape reader* which reads the control tape. The tape is mounted on reels much like moving picture film in a projector. The NC system reads the coded tape, interprets the information on the tape, stores some of the coded information in its *memory* system as necessary, and controls the movements of the machine tool and table as commanded by the tape.

Machines of the type shown in Fig. 1294 also can be operated manually. The X- and Y-coordinate positions of the holes to be drilled, or for other operations to be performed, can be dialed into the control system manually. Remember that X and Y are longitudinal and cross-feed table travel. Thus, the tool can be located accurately to plus or minus 0.001″. The spindle can then be actuated by manual feed or with power feed. Hence, machines of this basic type are versatile and can take the place of several other machines in the shop.

Turret-Type NC Machines

NC machine tools which have more automatically controlled features also are in use. Three-axis (§ 1305) turret-type drilling and milling machines, as in Fig. 1295, can change tools automatically by rotation of the 8-station tool turret, as commanded by the tape. Thus, the machine can automatically perform eight different machining operations in the proper sequence on a given part. Each kind of operation can be repeated automatically up to as many as 999 times. Additional coded information included on the perforated tape for 3-axis turret-type NC machines, as in Fig. 1295, includes:

(1) The Z-axis (tool depth) coordinate dimension (§ 1305).

(2) The feed rate.

(3) The depth for rapid travel of the spindle.

(4) The tool number (turret position).

The operator mounts the work on the machine table. He then presses the start button, and the machine automatically performs all of the programed operations without further supervision. Other examples of numerically controlled machine tools are shown in Figs. 1316 and 1317. These machines are explained in section 1310.

1302. Kinds of NC

There are two principal kinds of NC equipment: (1) point-to-point positioning, and (2) continuous-path contouring equipment. The point-to-point equipment is much simpler than the continuous-path type, both in design and in programing of the input information. The programing of the operations and the preparation of the control tape for point-to-point equipment generally does not require the aid of an electronic computer. However, a computer generally is required for the pro-

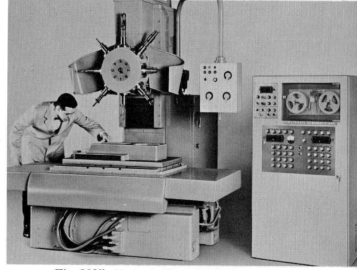

Fig. 1295. Numerically Controlled Turret Drilling Machine
(Courtesy The Cincinnati Lathe and Tool Co.)
This machine has a 3-axis point-to-point positioning system with all axes tape controlled.

graming and tape preparation for contour machining applications on continuous-path equipment.

Continuous-Path NC

Machining operations which require the cutting tool to follow a prescribed path along a contoured edge or surface require continuous-path NC.

An example of continuous-path contour milling is shown in Fig. 1297. The cutting tool must cut, within prescribed tolerances, to the curved line specified on the blueprint for the part being machined. Therefore, the center line path of the cutting tool must be described geometrically in terms of its X- and Y-coordinate dimensions (§ 1305). For 3-axis (§ 1306) contoured edges or surfaces, the Z-axis is the vertical position of the table or tool.

Most NC continuous-path systems are programed in terms of straight-line paths. Therefore, the contour generally is broken down into short straight-line *chords,* or segments. The chords must be short enough that the cutting tool path will produce a reasonably smooth contour within the specified tolerance. In Fig. 1297 the chord lengths are greatly exaggerated so that they can be visualized. Note that curves with a small radius have shorter chord segments than curves with a larger radius. Each chord length must be specified in terms of its X- and Y-coordinates.

Close-tolerance contour machining requires a greater number of straight-line chord segments. Therefore, a greater number of coordinate positions are also required. The example in Fig. 1297 prescribes a tolerance of —0.001″. Tolerances may be designated:

(1) Minus
(2) Plus
(3) Plus or minus

Since the tolerance in Fig. 1297 is designated minus, the contour cannot be oversize, but it may vary as much as 0.001″ undersize.

Fig. 1296. A General-Purpose Electronic Computer System Aids in Preparation of Control Tapes for Continuous-Path Numerical Control Machine Tools (Courtesy IBM)

A. Information is punched at console at right.
B. Details are located in tape storage at rear.
C. Completed information is printed on printer at front.

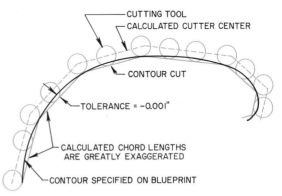

Fig. 1297. Contour Milling with Continuous-Path Numerical Control

The arc is divided into chord segments (exaggerated example) which are within specified tolerances. The cutting tool travels along the straight line chords, thus generating a curve made of these tiny straight line segments.

Some continuous-path NC machine tools, such as vertical milling machines, are of the 2-axis type. (See § 1306.) This type generally cuts continuous-path contours in the X- and Y-plane only. Three-axis machines can cut 3-dimensional contours, such as die cavities, which require cutting movements along the X-, Y-, and Z-axes simultaneously.

Continuous-path NC systems are more expensive and more complex to program. They generally require the aid of an electronic computer for program and tape preparation. Hence, there are fewer systems of this type in use than the point-to-point systems. Continuous-path systems are most widely used in the aerospace industries. Large industrial plants and large tool-and-die shops also use them. You can learn more about continuous-path NC systems by studying more advanced books. Several are listed in the bibliography. The remainder of this unit will be devoted to point-to-point NC and its applications.

Point-to-Point NC

A *point-to-point* numerical-control system is basically a positioning system. Its principal function is to move a tool or workpiece from one specific position point to another point. Generally, the actual machine function, such as a drilling operation on a machine tool, also is activated at each position by commands on the control tape.

Point-to-point NC systems also are often called *discrete positioning* systems. They are used for such hole-machining operations as drilling, countersinking, counterboring, reaming, boring, and tapping. Point-to-point NC systems also are used on hole-punching machines, spot-welding machines, and for wiring complex electronic circuits.

With certain design modifications or accessories, most point-to-point NC systems also can perform *straight-cut* functions such as straight-line milling. The straight-cut function or operation generally is parallel to either the X-axis or the Y-axis, as in the case of drilling and milling machines. Many point-to-point NC drilling machines are designed with a heavy-duty spindle which also can perform straight-cut end-milling operations. The machine tools in Figs. 1294, 1295, 1316, and 1317 have point-to-point NC systems which also include straight-cut milling capabilities. On 2-axis machines, as in Figs. 1294 and 1316, the rate of feed along the axes generally is controlled manually by the machine operator, usually with a hydraulic valve. Some straight-cut systems can make cuts at 45° to either the X- or Y-axis. On 3-axis machines, as in Figs. 1295 and 1317, the rate of feed for straight milling cuts is automatically controlled by the tape.

A variety of point-to-point NC drilling and milling machines is in wide use. They are known by several different terms. They may be called:

(1) drilling machines,
(2) milling machines,
(3) drilling and milling machines, or
(4) machining centers.

A *machining center* is a machine tool which performs a variety of basic machining operations. The machines in Figs. 1294, 1316, and 1317 are called machining centers. All of these point-to-point machine tools perform similar operations.

1303. Advantages of Numerical Controlled Production

Numerically controlled machines and processes employ the principles of feedback control, automatic self-adjustment, and they automatically handle informational data and materials. NC machines and processes are used for many mass-production purposes.

However, NC machine tools make their greatest contributions as mass-production tools when they are used for the production of parts which must be made in small quantity. It is estimated that ¾ of all metal parts are manufactured in lots of fewer than 50 pieces.[1] Because of their close tolerance capability, NC machine tools often can be used at considerable savings in the production of even one part of one kind.

For the production of machined parts in large quantity, mass production with conventional machine tools, dies, and fixtures is frequently more economical and efficient.

An example will illustrate the advantage of conventional mass-production machining methods for parts produced in large lot numbers. Suppose that 10,000 identical parts must be produced, each having 32 drilled holes. These parts can be produced most rapidly with a multiple-spindle drill press which can drill all holes in each part simultaneously. (Drill presses of the types shown in Figs. 415 and 416 can be used for jobs of this kind.) Of course, expensive jigs and fixtures usually would be required before the parts could be set up and machined. If the cost of tooling were $5000, the tool cost per piece would be $0.50. The machining cost per piece might be as low as $0.33 per piece (60 per hour at $20 machine and labor cost). The total cost per piece would be $0.83.

On the other hand, if an NC machine tool with a single-tool spindle were used to drill the required holes, the job would take much longer. It would require many more man-hours of labor costs. The additional labor costs, together with the relatively high cost of NC machines, would probably result in higher cost per part machined. For example, an NC machine and operator may easily cost $30 per hour to employ. Drilling the same 32 holes would typically require 5 minutes of machine time — 12 parts could be produced per hour at a per-piece cost of $30 ÷ 12 or $2.50. Parts produced in small quantity gen-

erally do not justify the high cost of fixtures for each part. Therefore, small quantities of parts generally can be produced at a lower cost per part with NC machines. Also, an NC machine can be set up quickly to produce a different part.

There are several advantages in using NC machine tools. The following is a brief summary.

1. NC machines generally obtain closer tolerances without requiring costly jigs for guiding the tool.

2. NC machines do not require storage space for large quantities of jigs and fixtures.

3. Inserting a tape can be done more quickly than positioning jigs and fixtures — a savings in setup time.

4. One NC machine, as in Figs. 1294 and 1295, can take the place of several conventional machines such as a drill press, tapping machine, and vertical milling machine. This saves required floor space by machines which would perform the same operations.

5. Material handling is reduced with an NC machine, as material would be moved several times when using conventional machines.

6. Tapes can be prepared more rapidly than fixtures can be made, thus saving *lead* time. Lead time is the time required for planning and tooling up for mass production of a product or part.

7. The tape can be easily stored for use at a later time for another small quantity of parts. This reduces storage space of parts and the cost of keeping large inventories.

8. Design changes can be made easily as a new tape can be produced quickly and at low cost.

9. Duplicate tapes can be made for producing parts on similar machines in the same plant or in plants at other locations.

10. NC is more accurate than a machinist working without jigs and fixtures. Since parts

---

[1]U.S. Department of Labor, *Outlook for Numerical Control of Machine Tools,* Bulletin 1437, March, 1965, p. 5. (Bulletin prepared by the U.S. Department of Labor, W. Willard Wirtz, secretary; Bureau of Statistics, Ewan Clague, commissioner; U.S. Government Printing Office.)

are not spoiled because of human error, waste also is reduced.

11. Tape preparation takes the place of template preparation for continuous-path NC machines.

12. Less inspection cost is required with NC since the machine is more consistent than humans in its accuracy.

13. Management can control the rate of production to meet the required quantity, quality, and accuracy of customer demands.

14. Small quantities are produced at lower cost, thus reducing the cost of the finished product. Hence, more people can buy the products and the standard of living can be improved.

1304. Production Steps in NC Machining

The steps involved in manufacturing machined parts with point-to-point and straight-cut NC machine tools are summarized in Fig. 1298. The *designer*, who frequently is an *engineer*, designs and makes a sketch of the part.

The *parts programer* performs tasks which were formerly done by the machine operator. He writes instruction in code form on a *manuscript* instead of machining the part. He programs the sequence of operations, selects tools, determines cutting speeds and feeds, and indicates when to apply coolant. He indicates the location of each operation with coordinate dimensions. An example of a program manuscript for a part to be machined on a simple 2-axis machine is shown in Fig. 1313. The program is for use on machines of the type shown in Figs. 1294 and 1316.

The information on the program manuscript is then punched into a ribbon of 1″ wide paper tape by a typist using a tape-punching machine. (See Fig. 1309.) The typist types the manuscript on a *manuscript form* sheet, thus checking to see that the coded information is the same as that on the hand written *manuscript form* sheet. At the

same time, the machine punches coded holes in the tape which is in the box at the left end of the machine.

The machine-control tape is given to the machine operator who inserts it into the *tape reader* in the NC unit of the machine tool. The machine operator mounts the workpiece on the machine table. On the 2-axis point-to-point machine, he changes tools, adjusts feeds, speeds, tool depth stops, and turns on the coolant. On the more complex 3-axis machines, most of these duties are done automatically according to commands on the control tape. On machines of this type, the operator merely loads the part and starts the machine. The part is machined automatically.

On single-spindle machines, the operator generally must make tool changes manually. On machines with turret tool heads, as in Fig. 1295, tool changes take place automatically by rotation of the turret, as commanded by the tape. Large 3-axis NC machines of the type in Fig. 1317 are equipped with automatic tool changers. The steps for NC machining production are summarized in Fig. 1298. In small job shops and in school shops, one person must perform all of the operations in all of these steps.

1305. Basis for NC Measurement

A system of *rectangular coordinates,* called the *cartesian coordinate* system, Fig. 1299, is the basis for NC measurements. Three-dimensional objects (those with length, width, and thickness) can be described by this rectangular coordinate system. All points of an object are described by imaginary lines perpendicular to the axes. Generally, the horizontal plane includes the X- and Y-axes. In this plane, along the X-axis, all measurements to the right of the origin are in the $+ X$ direction and those to the left are in the $- X$ direction. At exactly 90° to the X-axis, and in the same horizontal plane, is the Y-axis with its plus and minus directions. The

DESIGN ENGINEER

1. Designs part
2. Makes sketch of part

DRAFTSMAN

Makes engineering drawing of part

PARTS PROGRAMER

1. Studies part drawing
2. Describes location of part in relation to zero reference point on machine table. In some plants this is done by the draftsman.
3. Determines sequence of operations
4. Determines tool selection
5. Identifies position points on parts
6. Determines coordinate dimensions for position points in relation to zero reference point on machine table
7. Prepares the program manuscript

TYPIST

1. Punches tape with tape-punching typewriter
2. Verifies tape with tape verifier
3. Produces extra tapes

NC MACHINE OPERATOR

1. Inserts tape in NC unit
2. Mounts workpiece in machine
3. Installs tools in machine spindle
4. Changes tools: as necessary on machines without tool turrets or automatic tool changers.
5. Makes machine adjustments: feeds, speeds, tool depth stops, and coolant. Only on machines where these are not tape controlled.
6. Removes workpiece from machine

Fig. 1298. Steps in NC Production with Point-to-Point Machine Tools

Z-axis, with its plus and minus directions, is perpendicular to both the X- and Y-axes.

The rectangular system of coordinates is used to describe the dimensions of all parts for numerical-control programing. The axes in this coordinate system also are used for machine axis designation. (See Figs. 1301-1304.)

In Fig. 1299 notice that the X- and Y-plane is divided into quadrants. Many NC systems are designed so that all points on an object are located in the *first* quadrant, as shown in Fig. 1300. With systems of this type, all positions are designated positive or plus $(+)$. When the object is so located, the positive sign $(+)$ may be omitted when preparing a program manuscript. The machines in Figs. 1294, 1295, and 1316 use the first quadrant system. Study the positions of points *A* through *H* until you understand the method for describing points in the first quadrant of the coordinate system.

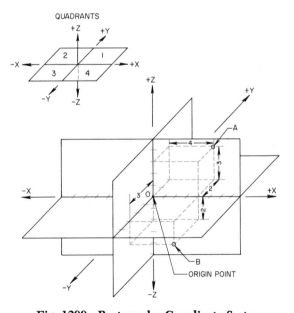

Fig. 1299. Rectangular Coordinate System
(The Cartesian-Coordinate System)
All dimensions are given from the point of origin. Point A has coordinates X = + 4, Y = + 2, Z = + 3. Point B has coordinates X = + 4, Y = − 3, Z = − 2.

1306. Machine Axis Designations and Movements

The axes of a machine tool correspond to the principal machine movements. The axes are designated in accordance with the axes of the rectangular coordinate system. (See Figs. 1299 and 1300.) Generally, the longest axis of machine travel is designated the X-axis. Observe that the X- and Y-axes are in the horizontal plane in Fig. 1299 and the Z-axis in the vertical plane.

Several examples of basic machine tools and their axes designations, according to NAS 983[2], are shown in Figs. 1301 to 1304. Programers, setup men, and operators need to use only the *unprimed* numbers or figures such as X, Y, and Z. The primed numbers, such as X', Y', and Z', are for the machine manufacturer's use for design standardization purposes.

[2]National Aerospace Standard 938, copyright 1966, Aerospace Industries Association of America, Inc. Reprinted by permission.

Some NC machine tools utilize an *incremental* system for dimensioning parts (§ 1307) and for indicating the direction of tool travel in relation to the workpiece. Machines with this type of programing system generally use plus (+) and minus (−) signs

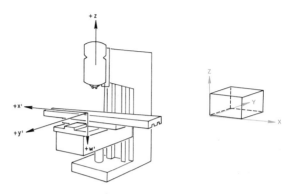

Fig. 1301. Coordinate Axes for Vertical Knee Mill, Drilling Machine, and Jig Boring Machine (Courtesy Aerospace Industries Assn. of America, Inc., Reprinted by permission, Copyright 1966) **Programers, setup men, and operators should think only in terms of unprimed numbers.**

POINT	X	Y	Z
A	5	3	0
B	15	3	0
C	15	7	0
D	5	7	0
E	5	3	4
F	15	3	4
G	15	7	4
H	5	7	4

Fig. 1300. All Coordinate Points are Plus When Located in the First Quadrant with Absolute Dimensioning (The + Sign May Be Omitted)

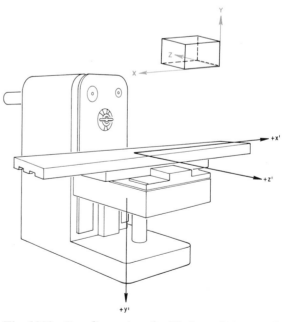

Fig. 1302. Coordinate Axes for Horizontal Knee Mill (Courtesy Aerospace Industries Assn. of America, Inc., Reprinted by permission, Copyright 1966) **Unprimed Numbers Apply for Programers and Operators**

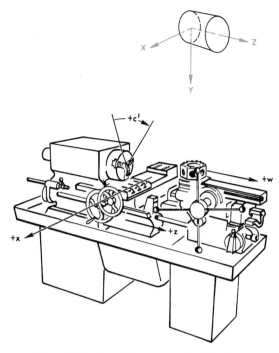

Fig. 1303. Coordinate Axes for Horizontal-Spindle Lathes and Related Machines
(Courtesy Aerospace Industries Assn. of America, Inc., Reprinted by permission, Copyright 1966)
Unprimed Numbers Apply for Programers and Operators

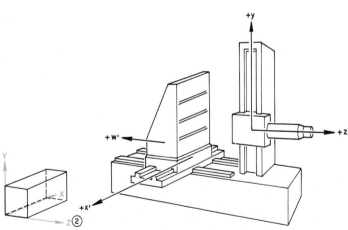

Fig. 1304. Coordinate Axes for a Horizontal Boring Mill
(Courtesy Aerospace Industries Assn. of America, Inc., Reprinted by permission, Copyright 1966)
Unprimed Numbers Apply for Programers and Operators

to indicate direction of tool travel. The + indicates travel in one direction while the − indicates travel in the opposite direction. This programing system is used for a number of NC systems, including the machine in Fig. 1317. An example of the application of incremental dimensioning is illustrated in *programing example No. 2 in § 1309.*

Point-to-point NC systems are in wide use on drilling machines, vertical-spindle drilling and milling machines (Figs. 1294 and 1295), and on multipurpose machines called machining centers (Figs. 1294 and 1317). These machines may be 2-axis machines or 3-axis machines.

On 2-axis machines, the X- and Y-coordinate positions are programed and included on the control tape. There is no Z-axis program to control tool depth, such as the depth of a drilled hole or the depth of a milled slot. Instead, multiple-tool depth stops are set manually by the operator before machining the part. Each depth stop on the multiple-type depth stop device is numbered. On some systems, the operator rotates the appropriate numbered stop during each manual tool change. On other systems, the tool stop number can be programed on the control tape and the machine selects the proper depth stop.

A tool depth stop actually has two stop positions. The first position stops *rapid* Z-axis (tool) travel at *gage height* which is a short distance above the workpiece. A gage height of 0.100″ is satisfactory. The second position stops further Z-axis travel when the tool has fed to depth. If Z-axis stops were not provided, a tool such as a drill would produce a hole in the machine table.

On 3-axis machines, the tool-depth coordinate positions are programed and included with other information on the control tape. Therefore, the depth of tool is controlled automatically by the tape. The machines in Figs. 1295 and 1317 are 3-axis machines with

X-, Y-, and Z-axes travel automatically controlled.

1307. Dimensioning Methods for NC

Drawings for parts which are to be machined on point-to-point NC machines can be dimensioned by the *incremental* (conventional) method or by the *absolute* method.

Incremental Dimensioning

The part illustrated in Fig. 1315 is dimensioned by the *incremental* method. This is the usual or conventional method used for dimensioning. With this method, the distance from one point to a second point on a part is given without reference to a common reference point, such as a *zero point*. (See § 1306 and Problem 2 in § 1309.) Parts which are to be machined on point-to-point NC machines with *incremental control systems* generally are dimensioned by the incremental method.

Absolute Dimensioning

The drawing shown in Fig. 1314 is dimensioned by the *absolute* method. All points are dimensioned from a common reference point. The *part reference point* should not be confused with the *machine-table reference point*. Parts which are to be machined on point-to-point NC machines with *absolute control systems* generally must be dimensioned by the absolute method.

Most absolute NC control systems are designed so that the axis movements of the machine, such as the X- and Y-axes in Fig. 1314, are located in the first quadrant of the coordinate system. On equipment so designed, all coordinate position points are indicated with positive numbers. Thus the position of point A is $+X = 04.000$ and $+Y = 03.000$. When coordinate position points are programed for most NC systems, the plus $(+)$ sign and the decimal points are omitted. The coordinate points generally are indicated with five digits. (See Fig. 1313 and Problems 1 and 2 in § 1309.)

1308. NC Tape

The tape used to control an NC machine is 1″ wide, 8-track tape with Electrical Industries Association (EIA) coding in the form of punched holes, as in Fig. 1308. Each num-

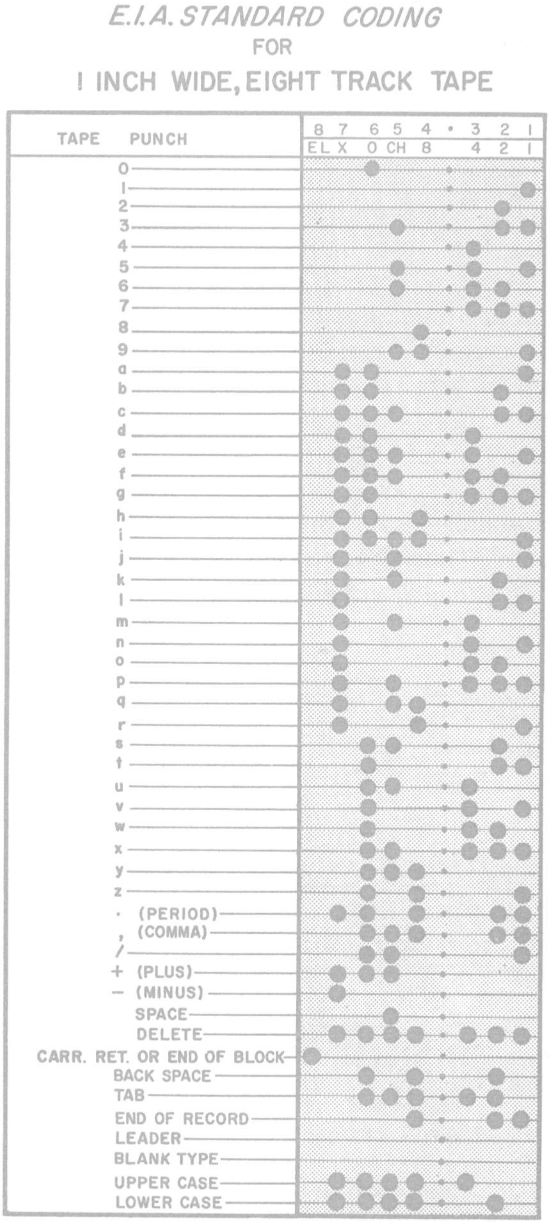

Fig. 1308. EIA (Electrical Industries Association) Standard Code for 1″ Wide, 8-Track Tape (Courtesy The Cincinnati Milling Machine Co.; Cimtrol Div.)

ber, letter, and symbol is called a *character*. The characters include the decimal digits from 0 through 9, the letters of the alphabet, and special characters such as *tab* or *end-of-block*. The characters are punched into the tape with a tape-punching machine, Fig. 1309. The tape generally is made of paper or plastic-laminated paper. The plastic-laminated tape is more durable and therefore is used if many parts are needed.

Binary Numbers

The code system of punched holes in the tape is based on the *binary system of numbers*. The binary number system has only two digits, 0 to 1. (The decimal numbering system has ten digits, 0 to 9.) The binary number system is used in electronic computers and other electronic devices. Electrical circuits can be established on a basis of the two binary numbers, 0 to 1, because these numbers permit only two electrical conditions: (1) *on* or *positive* or (2) *off* or *negative* condition. Thus, when a character is punched in a tape, a hole either *is* or *is not* punched in

each track in the tape. The punched holes, therefore, actuate electrical circuits in the NC system. You can learn more about the binary number system in books with more complete coverage of NC. Several are listed in the bibliography.

Tape Format

The format is the general arrangement of the information on the control tape. (See Fig. 1310). It is the arrangement of the punched holes on a paper tape, or the arrangement of magnetized areas on a magnetic tape. Several different formats are used by the different manufacturers of NC machines. The format and the method for programing a part to be machined by NC are explained in the *Programer's Manual* supplied by the manufacturer of the NC system. Attempts are being made by industry to agree on a standard tape format.

The following formats are used on various point-to-point and straight-cut NC systems:

(1) Fixed-sequential format.
(2) Tab-sequential format.
(3) Word-address format.
(4) Word-address, variable-block format (combines features of the sequential and word-address formats).

Fig. 1309. Tape-Punching Machine and Verifier
(Courtesy Friden, Inc.)
The typist inserts the original tape in the verifier and proceeds to retype the manuscript copy. If the second tape is not identical to the first tape in the verifier, the machine carriage locks to reveal the location of the error. The typist unlocks the keyboard and corrects the error.

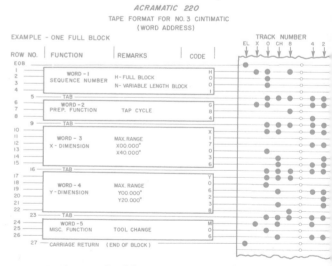

Fig. 1310. Word-Address Tape Format (Courtesy Cincinnati Milling Machine Co.; Cimtrol Div.)

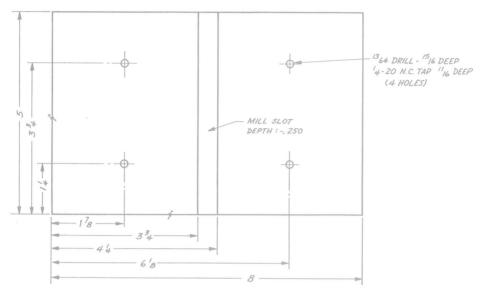

Fig. 1311. Simple Part, Drawing Number 101 (Courtesy Cincinnati Milling Machine Co.; Cimtrol Div.)

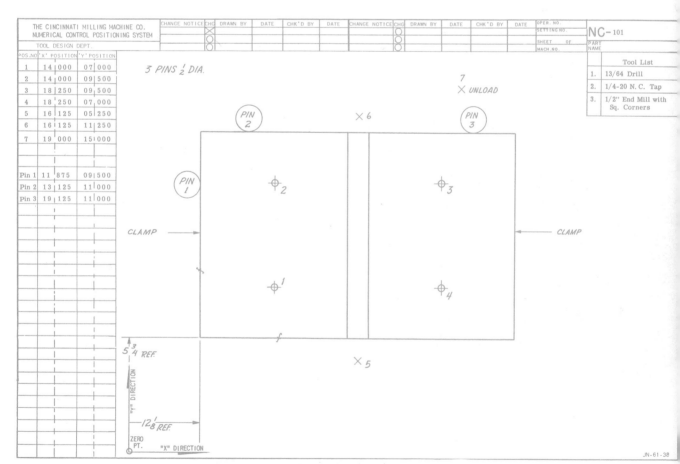

Fig. 1312. Simple Part Number 101, Showing Location on Machine Table
(Courtesy Cincinnati Milling Machine Co.; Cimtrol Div.)
Note stop pins and clamp location. The X and Y coordinate position is included.

An example of the *word-address, variable-block format* is shown in Fig. 1310. A program manuscript is shown in Fig. 1313 for the part shown in Figs. 1311 and 1312. This tape format is used on the machines in Figs. 1294 and 1316. This basic format, with additional information, is used for 3-axis machines of the type shown in Fig. 1295.

Block

An NC manuscript is made of blocks of coded information. A *block* is a word or group of words that forms a unit. On perforated tape, the block must be separated from other similar units by an *end-of-block* character. (See Fig. 1308.) An example of one full block of information is shown in Fig. 1310.

The term *word address* means that each word included in the block is addressed with a letter character identifying the meaning of the word. Thus, the letter character *H* or *N* identifies the sequence number word; the letter *X* identifies the X-dimension word, etc.

Examples of *full-block* and *variable-length blocks* are shown in the program manuscript in Fig. 1313. Sequence numbers 1, 5, 9, and 13 are full blocks; the others are variable-length blocks. NC systems designed for variable-length formats can store information in the *memory storage* unit when the information is the same as that in previous blocks. However, after a miscellaneous function, such as a tool change, it is necessary to use a full block of information, as in Fig. 1313. With

PROGRAM FOR #3 CINTIMATIC

CINCINNATI ACRAMATIC POSITIONING NUMERICAL CONTROL SYSTEM

PART NAME: SAMPLE PART — PART NO.
DRAWING NO.: 101 — REVISION — FIXTURE NO. — PROGRAMMED BY — PAGE OF PAGES
SET UP AND TOOL INFORMATION — DATE

H or N SEQ. NO.	G PREP. FUNCT.	X POSITION		Y POSITION		M MISC. FUNCT.	POS. NO.	TOOL NO.	HEAD POS.	SPINDLE FEED IN./MIN.	SPEED RPM	DEPTH OF CUT	TABLE FEED IN./MIN.	TOOL REMARKS
H001	G81	X14	000	Y07	000	M51	1							13/64 Dia. Drill x 15/16 Deep
N002				Y09	500		2							
N003		X18	250				3							
N004				Y07	000	M06	4							
H005	G84	X18	250	Y07	000	M52	4							1/4-20 NC Tap x 1/16 Deep
N006				Y09	500		3							
N007		X14	000				2							
N008				Y07	000	M06	1							
H009	G78	X16	125	Y05	250	M53	5							1/2 Dia. End mill x 0.250 Deep
N010	G79			Y11	250		6							
N011	G78						6							
N012	G81						6							
H013	G80	X19	000	Y15	000	M02	7							
														Unload

Fig. 1313. Completed Program for Sample Part Number 101 (Courtesy Cincinnati Milling Machine Co.; Cimtrol Div.)

the variable-length block format, the punched tape generally is shorter than tape with fixed-block format.

Information in Blocks

A block of information for a 2-axis point-to-point NC program (Fig. 1313) includes the following information:

(1) Sequence number
(2) Preparatory function
(3) X-dimension
(4) Y-dimension
(5) Miscellaneous function

Sequence Number

The sequence number indicates the relative location of each block of information on the program manuscript and also on the perforated tape. For most NC programing manuscripts, the sequence number is designated with three digits, as in Fig. 1313. Sequence 1 is designated as 001, sequence 12 as 012, and sequence 999 as 999. Many NC systems are equipped with a *sequence-number readout* which shows the X- and Y-coordinate dimensions for each position as a part is being machined. This indicates the sequence number of the operation being performed. A letter character such as *H* or *N* is used as an address for the sequence number, Fig. 1313.

X- and Y-Coordinate Dimensions

The coordinate dimensions are indicated with six characters: the letter address and five digits. The letters X, Y, and Z identify the coordinate-axis dimension. Coordinate dimensions are indicated to the nearest one-thousandth of an inch. Thus, an X-coordinate dimension of 4½″ is converted to 04.500, and the decimal point is omitted on the program on the tape.

Preparatory Functions

Code numbers are used to prepare an NC system for a particular mode of operation. For point-to-point systems, a preparatory function code commands the machine to prepare for a specific machining cycle. Preparatory functions have a cycle code number which identifies the name of the function. Table 45 gives examples of the code used for the program shown in Fig. 1313.

Preparatory function code numbers may be different from manufacturer to manufacturer. The specific code numbers to be used with a given NC system are indicated in the *Programer's Manual* for the machine.

Miscellaneous Functions

Miscellaneous functions are *on-off* functions of an NC machine. Examples of miscellaneous-function codes used for the sample program in Fig. 1313 are given in Table 46.

Table 45
EXAMPLE CODES FOR NC PREPARATORY FUNCTIONS

CYCLE CODE	CYCLE NAME
G78	Mill stop
G79	Mill
G80	Cancel
G81	Drill
G82	Dwell
G84	Tap
G85	Bore

Table 46
EXAMPLE CODES FOR MISCELLANEOUS FUNCTIONS

FUNCTION CODE	NAME OF FUNCTION
M00	Program stop
M02	End of program
M06	Tool change
M26	Full-spindle retract
M50	No cam
M51-59	Select depth cam (nine depth cams available, each with a *rapid* stop and a *feed* stop)

Miscellaneous-function codes also vary from manufacturer to manufacturer. Therefore, it is best to consult the NC system manufacturer's *Programer's Manual* for specific information concerning the codes for the specific machines being programed.

Tool Number

The tool number is designated by code number, such as T1, T2, etc. A tool number may or may not be included in the block of information on the program for a 2-axis machine. The tool number generally is included on programs for 3-axis turret-type machines. The tool number also is programed for 3-axis machines which are capable of automatic selection and installation of different tools.

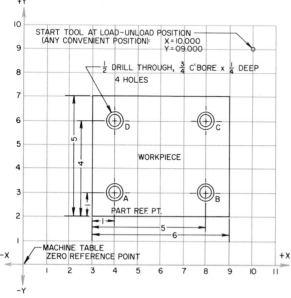

POSITION COORDINATES		
POS. NO	X POSITION	Y POSITION
A	04 ┊ 000	03 ┊ 000
B	08 ┊ 000	03 ┊ 000
C	08 ┊ 000	06 ┊ 000
D	04 ┊ 000	06 ┊ 000
LOAD	10 ┊ 000	09 ┊ 000

Fig. 1314. Workpiece with Absolute Dimensioning Located in First Quadrant on Table of Machine with 2-Axis Absolute NC Positioning System (Fixed-Zero Reference)

The kind of tool for each tool change generally is listed on the program manuscript. This procedure is recommended whether tool changes are made manually or automatically. Since the machine operator is given a copy of the program manuscript, he is able to determine, according to the sequence number, which tool should be in use.

1309. Determining Sequence and Coordinate Dimensions for a Parts Program

In industrial plants, a *parts programer* prepares a *manuscript* called a *parts program* for a part to be machined by NC. Much of the information for the parts program comes from the drawing of the part. The parts program for point-to-point NC systems is much simpler to prepare than one for continuous-path NC systems. And the parts program for a 2-axis point-to-point system requires less programed information than for a 3-axis point-to-point system. An example of the parts program for a 2-axis point-to-point NC system is shown in Fig. 1313. This is the parts program for the part in Fig. 1311, and the program is for a machine of the type shown in Fig. 1294. (See § 1304.)

The first step in the preparation of the parts program is to study the drawing carefully. There is less chance of error in determining coordinate dimensions if the drawing shows the location of the *part reference point* in relation to the *machine-table zero-reference point*, Figs. 1312 and 1314. Parts generally are not located so that the part reference point coincides with the machine-table reference point. However, the X- and Y-coordinate dimensions in the program must be for the actual coordinates of the machine table.

An example of X- and Y-coordinate dimensions for points *A* through *D* is shown in Fig. 1314. The coordinate dimensions show the positions of points on a part which is located on the table of a machine equipped with an absolute NC positioning system. The machine has a *fixed-zero table-reference point*. The table-reference point is the reference point from which all X- and Y-coordinate dimensions must be programed for the machine.

The principles involved in parts programing can be understood more readily by studying the sample programs which follow. The sample programs illustrate the principles involved in determining the *sequence* of operations and the *coordinate dimensions* for the positions at which operations are to be performed. The codes for the *preparatory functions* and for the *miscellaneous functions* are intentionally omitted since these codes vary for different machines. Once again, it must be understood that the *block format* also varies for different machines. Therefore, you should always consult the *Parts Programer's Manual* for a specific NC machine to determine the block format and the code numbers for preparatory functions, miscellaneous functions, and tool numbers.

Programing Example No. 1

Point-to-point positioning to be performed with an *absolute* NC system.

The coordinate positions and tool changes are for machining the holes in the part shown in Fig. 1314 and Table 47. The part is to be machined on a machine with an absolute NC control system with the following characteristics:

Position system —
　Point-to-point (2 axes)
Type of format —
　Word-address, variable-block, (with five digits for X- and Y-dimensions)
Type of dimensioning —
　Absolute, located in the first quadrant
Tools —
　$T_1 = \frac{1}{2}''$ drill; $T_2 = \frac{3}{4}''$ counterbore

Programing Example No. 2

Point-to-point positioning with an incremental NC system.

With incremental NC systems, the *dimension* and the *direction* of tool travel, *in relation to the workpiece*, must be shown for each movement to a new coordinate position. The direction of tool travel is indicated with positive $(+)$ and negative $(-)$ signs, according to the coordinate system. (See Fig. 1299.) On some incremental NC systems, the positive sign $(+)$ may be omitted from the

Table 47
POINT-TO-POINT POSITIONING WITH AN ABSOLUTE NC SYSTEM

SEQUENCE	X INFO.	Y INFO.	TOOL No.	POSITION	NOTES
001	X10.000	Y09.000	T_1	Load	½ dia. drill, four holes
002	X04.000	Y03.000	Mem.*	A	Same tool
003	X08.000	Mem.	Mem.	B	No change in Y-axis, same tool
004	Mem.	Y06.000	Mem.	C	No change in X-axis, same tool
005	X04.000	Mem.	Mem.	D	No change in Y-axis, same tool
006	Mem.	Mem.	T_2	D	Change tool: ¾" c'bore, 4 holes
007	Mem.	Y03.000	Mem.	A	No change in X-axis, same tool
008	X08.000	Mem.	Mem.	B	No change in Y-axis, same tool
009	Mem.	Y06.000	Mem.	C	No change in X-axis, same tool
010	X04.000	Mem.	Mem.	D	No change in Y-axis, same tool
011	X10.000	Y09.000	Mem.	Unload	Return to load-unload position, same tool

*Data is held in memory storage. Machine continues to use the data until new data is inserted in a new block of information.

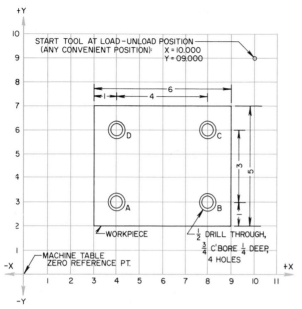

Fig. 1315. Workpiece with Incremental (Conventional) Dimensioning in First Quadrant on Table of Machine Equipped with 2-Axis Incremental NC Positioning System

program and from the tape. When there is no sign, the system assumes that the tool travel is in the positive ($+$) direction.

This program gives the sequence, coordinate positions, and tool changes for machining the holes in the part shown in Fig. 1315 and Table 48. The part is to be machined on a machine with an incremental NC system having the following characteristics:

Position system —
 Point-to-point (2 axes)

Type of format —
 Word-address (with five digits for X- and Y-dimensions)

Type of dimensioning —
 Incremental (conventional) in the first quadrant.

Tools —
 $T_1 = \frac{1}{2}''$ drill; $T_2 = \frac{3}{4}''$ counterbore

Table 48
POINT-TO-POINT POSITIONING WITH AN INCREMENTAL NC SYSTEM

Sequence	X Info.	Y Info.	Tool No.	Position	Notes
001	X10.000	Y09.000	T_1	Load	$\frac{1}{2}''$ dia. drill, four holes
002	− X06.000	− Y06.000	Mem.*	A	Location of pt. A with reference to loading position
003	X04.000	Mem.	Mem.	B	Location of pt. B with ref. to pt. A
004	Mem.	Y03.000	Mem.	C	Location of pt. C with ref. to pt. B
005	− X04.000	Mem.	Mem.	D	Location of pt. D with ref. to pt. C
006	Mem.	Mem.	T_2	D	Tool change: $\frac{3}{4}''$ dia. C' bore, 4 holes, $\frac{1}{4}''$ deep
007	Mem.	− Y03.000	Mem.	A	Location of pt. A with ref. to pt. D
008	X04.000	Mem.	Mem.	B	Location of pt. B with ref. to pt. A
009	Mem.	Y03.000	Mem.	C	Location of pt. C with ref. to pt. B
010	− X04.000	Mem.	Mem.	D	Location of pt. D with ref. to pt. C
011	X06.000	Y03.000	Mem.	Unload	Location of load-unload position with ref. to pt. D

Note: The X and Y positions may be checked for errors by algebraically adding the total of each column. The sum of each column should be equal to the coordinates of the starting position. (In the above problem, the starting position is X10.000 and Y09.000.)

*With this variable-block format, data from the previous block is held in memory storage. The machine continues to use this data until new data is inserted in a new block of information.

1310. NC Machine Tools in Industry

Several point-to-point type NC machine tools and their applications were explained in § 1301: Two-axis machining centers (Fig. 1294) and three-axis turret-type drilling and milling machines (Fig. 1295). In addition to these basic kinds of NC drilling and milling machines, several other types are in wide use. These include *horizontal-spindle* 2-axis machines, Fig. 1316, and also 3-axis machining centers, Fig. 1317.

Horizontal-Spindle
NC Machining Center

The 2-axis point-to-point NC machine shown in Fig. 1316 automatically drills, mills, taps, and bores. Its operation is very similar to the operation of the vertical drilling and milling machine shown in Fig. 1294. However, the horizontal-spindle machine has several distinct advantages. With the horizontal-spindle, the chips fall away from the tool due to gravity. The workpiece may be mounted on an optional revolving index table, so that one setup makes all sides accessible for various machining operations. The workpiece also can be indexed for machining sides with various angles.

The Z-axis spindle of the machine in Fig. 1316 is actuated automatically by the tape. The rapid-approach depth stops and feed-depth stops are preset by the machine operator to put the automatic-spindle depth cycle in operation. After they have been preset, the depth stops are selected automatically by tape command. With automatic cycle operation, the operator simply inserts the tool in the spindle, selects feed and speed, and then presses the start button. Operation proceeds automatically until a tool change is required. When a tool change is required, the cycle stops and the indicator light signals the operator. In addition to selecting the depth stop, the tape specifies the various cycles, such as mill, drill, tap, or bore. For example, after the

tool has completed the cutting sequence to the preset depth, the tool feeds out, and then moves to the next position or cycle.

Three-Axis NC Machining Center

The 3-axis point-to-point NC machining center shown in Fig. 1317 is automatically operated by tape control for all three axes, including the X-, Y-, and Z-axes. The input information on the tape includes (1) the se-

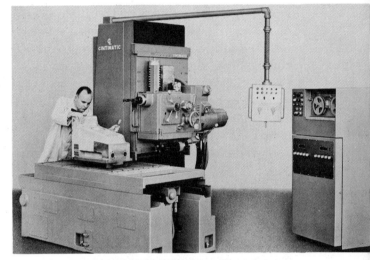

**Fig. 1316. Horizontal-Spindle
NC Machining Center
(Courtesy Cincinnati Lathe and Tool Co.)
This point-to-point NC machine automatically drills, mills, taps, and bores.**

**Fig. 1317. 3-Axis Numerical Control Machining
Center (Courtesy Hughes Aircraft Co.,
Industrial System Div.)**
This machine automatically performs drilling, tapping, boring, and milling operations. It automatically selects and changes tools by tape command.

quence of operations, (2) machining functions, (3) coordinate positions for all three axes, (4) tool-selection number, (5) feed rate, (6) spindle speed, (7) coolant flow, and other miscellaneous functions.

Since the Z-axis tape control includes control of tool depths, it is not necessary for the operator to set the depth stops for each tool. The machine selects the proper tools, as commanded by the tape, and controls the depth.

The 3-axis machining center in Fig. 1317 has a heavy-duty boring head with a capacity of 14 tools. The universal head has a capacity for 30 tools, such as drills, taps, reamers, countersinks, and light milling cutters. Thus, the machine can select and use as many as 44 tools automatically for one job. The various operations that are required can be completed automatically once the operator mounts the workpiece and starts the machine.

Increasing Use of NC Machines

The use of NC machine tools is increasing rapidly, and it is expected to continue to increase. Both point-to-point and continuous-path drilling machines, milling machines, machining centers, and lathes are in wide use.

Persons who are interested in becoming parts programers or NC machine tool operators should have a good understanding of basic machine tool operations and the speeds and feeds of various metals and tools. This kind of experience can be acquired in metalworking and machine shop classes in high schools, vocational schools, and technical schools.

Many employers have programs for training NC machine tool operators and parts programers. NC machine tools are very expensive, and many schools are unable to acquire them. Persons who have acquired a good understanding of basic machining operations in metalworking classes are frequently employed by manufacturers who are willing to provide further training. (See § 19.)

Review Questions

1. What is meant by the term *automation?*

2. List three characteristics which automated machines or systems possess.

3. What is meant by the term *output* as it applies to automated systems?

4. What is meant by the term *input* as it applies to automated systems?

5. What is meant by the term *sensor* as it applies to automated systems?

6. What is the function of a computer in an automated system?

7. What is the meaning of the term *feedback control loop* in an automated system?

8. Explain how the feedback control loop for an automatic heating system functions.

9. Explain the difference between an *open-loop* and a *closed-loop* feedback system.

10. List several industries which utilize automatic materials handling systems.

11. List several applications of electronic computers being used for data processing.

12. What is meant by the term *numerical control?*

13. List three different forms in which the coded information can be inserted into the NC system for a machine tool.

14. List as many applications of NC as you can.

15. What is a *servomechanism* on an NC machine tool?

16. Explain how a servomechanism functions on an NC machine.

17. What is an NC *machining center?*

18. What kinds of coded information must be included on the control tape for a 2-axis NC machining center?

19. Explain the purpose of a *tape reader* in an NC control system.

20. List two principal kinds of NC equipment or systems.

21. Which kind of NC system generally requires the aid of an electronic computer for tape preparation?

22. For what kinds of machining operations are continuous-path NC machines used?

23. Explain how the program for a continuous-path NC system is prepared.

24. What kind of work can be done on a 3-axis continuous-path milling machine which cannot be done on a 2-axis machine?

25. In what industries are 3-axis continuous-path NC machine tools most widely used?

26. What is the principal function of a point-to-point NC system?

27. List six kinds of hole-machining operations which are commonly performed on point-to-point NC machine tools.

28. List several applications, other than machining, for which NC point-to-point systems are used.

29. Most point-to-point NC machine tools also are equipped to perform straight-cut functions. Give an example of a straight-cut operation.

30. List several different types of point-to-point NC machine tools.

31. On what kinds of production lots do NC machine tools make their greatest contribution?

32. On what kinds of production lots are conventional mass-production machine tools more efficient than NC machine tools?

33. List several advantages of NC machine tools for production of machined parts.

34. Outline the basic steps involved in NC production of machined parts.

35. Explain the kind of work which is done by a parts programer.

36. Describe the cartesian coordinate system and explain its three axes.

37. Which quadrant of the coordinate system is the *first* quadrant?

38. How are programed coordinate dimensions designated when all movements of the machine tool NC system are located in the first quadrant?

39. What is meant by the axes of a machine tool and how are they designated?

40. Which axis of a machine tool generally is designated as the X-axis?

41. What type of NC system uses plus $(+)$ and minus $(-)$ signs on programs to indicate the direction of tool travel in relation to the workpiece?

42. What are the principal features or characteristics of 2-axis point-to-point drilling and milling machines?

43. Explain the purpose of the tool depth stops on 2-axis NC drilling and milling machines.

44. Explain the principal features of 3-axis point-to-point drilling and milling machines.

45. Explain the meaning of *incremental* dimensioning.

46. Explain the meaning of *absolute* dimensioning.

47. List two kinds of NC systems.

48. Explain the difference between the *part reference point* and the *machine-table reference point*.

49. Explain the features of the tape which are used to control NC machine tools.

50. What is a *character* on a tape?

51. What is meant by the binary number system?

52. What is meant by the term *tape format*?

53. List four kinds of tape formats used on various point-to-point and straight-cut NC systems.

54. What is meant by *block* on a program manuscript or on a tape?

55. What is meant by the *word address* as it applies to a tape format?

56. List the kinds of information which generally are included in a block of information for a 2-axis point-to-point NC program.

57. Explain the meaning of the sequence number on a program manuscript.

58. Explain how coordinate dimensions are designated on a program manuscript.

59. What is a *preparatory function* and how may it be designated on a program?

60. What is a *miscellaneous function* and how can it be designated on a program?

61. How are different tools designated on a program?

62. What is meant by a *fixed-zero* reference point on an NC machine table?

63. What kinds of experience should one have in order to become a parts programer?

Coordination

Words to Know

absolute dimensioning
absolute NC system
automatic
automation
2-axis machine
3-axis machine
binary number
block
cartesian coordinate
   system
character
closed loop
computer
continuous-path NC
coordinate
   dimensions
data processing
designer
discrete positioning
   system
electronic computer
end-of-block
   character
feedback
feedback control loop
feedback system
fixed-zero reference
   point
fixtures
gage height
horizontal spindle
incremental
   dimensioning
input
loop
lead time
machining center
manuscript
manuscript form
   sheet
memory system
miscellaneous
   function
numerical control
   (NC)
numerical-control
   system
open loop
output
part reference point
parts program
parts programer
point-to-point NC
preparatory function
primed numbers
Programer's Manual
rectangular
   coordinates
sensing device
sensor
sequence number
sequence-number
   readout
servomechanism
straight-cut function
tape format
tape reader
turret-type NC
   machine
unprimed number
verifier
vertical spindle
word address
zero point

References
for Further Study

Machinists Ready Reference. Compiled by C. Weingartner. Ann Arbor, Mich.: Praken Publications.

Metals Handbook, Vol. I: Properties and Selection Eighth Edition. Prepared under the direction of the Handbook Committee. Metals Park, Ohio: American Society for Metals, 1961.

Metals Handbook, Vol. II: Heat Treating, Cleaning, and Finishing Eighth Edition. Prepared under the direction of the Handbook Committee. Metals Park, Ohio: American Society for Metals, 1964.

Metals Properties (ASME Handbook) Samuel L. Hoyt (Ed.), Sponsored by the Metals Engineering Handbook Board of the American Society of Mechanical Engineers. New York: McGraw-Hill Book Co., Inc., 1954.

The New American Machinists Handbook. Edited by Fred H. Colvin and Frank A. Stanley. New York: McGraw-Hill Book Co., Inc., 1955.

Oberg, Erik and F. D. Jones, *Machinery's Handbook* Seventeenth Edition. New York: The Industrial Press, 1964.

Sheet Metal

Anderson, Algot E., *56 Graded Problems in Elementary Sheet Metalwork.* Bloomington, Ill.: McKnight & McKnight Publishing Company, 1959.

Bruce, Leroy F., *Sheet Metal Shop Practice.* American Technical Society, 1959.

Daugherty, James S. and Robert E. Powell, *Sheet Metal Pattern Drafting and Shop Problems.* Peoria, Ill.: Chas. A. Bennett Co., Inc., 1961.

Smith, R. E., *Sheet Metalwork.* Bloomington, Ill.: McKnight & McKnight Publishing Company, 1961.

Art Metal and Spinning

Johnson, Harold V., *Metal Spinning Techniques and Projects.* Milwaukee: The Bruce Publishing Co., 1960.

Siegner, C. V., *Art Metals.* Homewood, Ill.: Goodheart-Willcox Co., Inc., 1961.

Smith, Robert E., *Etching, Spinning, Raising, and Tooling Metal.* Bloomington, Ill.: McKnight & McKnight Publishing Company, 1951.

Foundry and Patternmaking

Cast Metals Handbook. American Foundrymen's Society. DesPlaines, Ill., 1957.

Heine, Richard W., *Principles of Casting.* New York: McGraw-Hill Book Co., Inc., 1955.

Miner, H. D. and J. G. Miller, *Exploring Patternmaking and Foundry.* Princeton, N. J.: D. VanNostrand Co., 1959.

Pattern Maker's Manual. American Foundrymen's Society. DesPlaines, Ill., 1960.

Smith, R. E., *Patternmaking and Founding.* Bloomington, Ill.: McKnight & McKnight Publishing Company, 1954.

Welding

Althouse, Andrew D., Carl H. Turnquist, and W. A. Bowditch, *Modern Welding.* Homewood, Ill.: The Goodheart-Willcox Co., Inc., 1965.

Giachino, J. W., W. R. Weeks, and E. J. Brune, *Welding Skills and Practices.* Chicago: American Technical Society, 1967.

Jennings, R. F., *Gas and A. C. Arc Welding and Cutting.* Bloomington, Ill.: McKnight & McKnight Publishing Company, 1956.

The Oxyacetylene Handbook Second Edition. New York: Linde Division, Union Carbide Corp., 1960.

Smith, R. E., *Forging & Welding.* Bloomington, Ill.: McKnight & McKnight Publishing Company, 1956.

Machining of Metals

Anderson, James and Earl Tatro, *Shop Theory* Fifth Edition. New York: McGraw-Hill Book Co., Inc., 1968.

Burghardt, Henry D., A. Axelrod, and J. Anderson, *Machine Tool Operation, Part I* Fifth Edition. New York: McGraw-Hill Book Co., Inc., 1959.

Burghardt, Henry D., A. Axelrod, and J. Anderson, *Machine Tool Operation, Part II* Fourth Edition. New York: McGraw-Hill Book Co., Inc., 1960.

Childs, James J., *Principles of Numerical Control.* New York: The Industrial Press, 1965.

Cincinnati Milling Machine Co., *A Treatise on Milling and Milling Machines.* 1951.

Feirer, John L., and E. Tatro, *Machine Tool Metalworking.* New York: McGraw-Hill Book Co., Inc., 1961.

Illinois Institute of Technology Research Institute, *APT Part Programing.* New York: McGraw-Hill Book Co., Inc., 1967.

Johnson, Harold V., *General Industrial Machine Shop.* Peoria, Ill.: Chas. A. Bennett Co., Inc., 1963.

Kauffman, H. J., *Machine Shop and Foundry Projects.* Bloomington, Ill.: McKnight & McKnight Publishing Company, 1959.

Knight, Roy E., *Machine Shop Projects.* Bloomington, Ill.: McKnight & McKnight Publishing Company.

McCarthy, Willard J. and R. E. Smith, *Machine Tool Technology*. Bloomington, Ill.: McKnight & McKnight Publishing Company, 1968.

Numerical Control in Manufacturing, American Society of Tool and Manufacturing Engineers, Frank W. Wilson (Ed.). New York: McGraw-Hill Book Co., Inc., 1963.

Porter, H. W., O. D. Lasco, and C. A. Nelson, *Machine Shop Operations and Setups* Third Edition. Chicago: American Technical Society, 1967.

South Bend Lathe Inc., *How to Run a Lathe*. South Bend, Ind.: 1958.

Metallurgy and Heat Treatment

Frier, W. T., *Elementary Metallurgy* Second Edition. New York: McGraw-Hill Book Co., Inc., 1952.

Johnson, Carl G. and W. R. Weeks, *Metallurgy* Fourth Edition. Chicago: American Technical Society, 1956.

Metals Handbook, Vol. II: Heat Treating, Cleaning and Finishing Eighth Edition. Prepared under the direction of the Handbook Committee. Metals Park, Ohio: American Society for Metals, 1964.

Palmer, Frank R. and G. E. Luerssen, *Tool Steel Simplified*. Reading, Pa.: The Carpenter Steel Co., 1960.

Umowski, Joseph S., *Ferrous Metallurgy: Laboratory Manual*. Chicago: American Technical Society, 1960.

Manufacturing Processes and Materials

Ansley, Arthur C., *Manufacturing Methods and Processes*. Philadelphia: Chilton Co., 1957.

Begman, Myron L., *Manufacturing Processes* Fifth Edition. New York: John Wiley & Sons, Inc., 1963.

Campbell, James S., *Principles of Manufacturing Materials and Processes*. New York: McGraw-Hill Book Co., Inc., 1961.

Datsko, Joseph, *Material Properties and Manufacturing Processes*. New York: John Wiley & Sons, Inc., 1966.

DeGarmo, E. Paul, *Materials and Processes in Manufacturing* Second Edition. New York: The Macmillan Co., 1962.

Edgar, Carol, *Fundamentals of Manufacturing Processes and Materials*. Reading, Mass.: Addison-Wesley, Inc., 1965.

Rusinoff, S. E., *Manufacturing Processes*. Chicago: American Technical Society, 1962.

Occupational Information

U. S. Department of Labor, Bureau of Labor Statistics, *Occupational Outlook Handbook*. Washington, D. C.: U. S. Government Printing Office. (A revised edition generally is printed every two years.)

Decimal Equivalents
of Common Fractions

1/64			.01563
	1/32		.03125
3/64			.04688
		1/16	.0625
5/64			.07813
	3/32		.09375
7/64			.10938
		1/8	.125
9/64			.14063
	5/32		.15625
11/64			.17188
		3/16	.1875
13/64			.20313
	7/32		.21875
15/64			.23438
		1/4	.250
17/64			.26563
	9/32		.28125
19/64			.29688
		5/16	.3125
21/64			.32813
	11/32		.34375
23/64			.35938
		3/8	.375
25/64			.39063
	13/32		.40625
27/64			.42188
		7/16	.4375
29/64			.45313
	15/32		.46875
31/64			.48438
		1/2	.500

33/64			.51563
	17/32		.53125
35/64			.54688
		9/16	.5625
37/64			.57813
	19/32		.59375
39/64			.60938
		5/8	.625
41/64			.64063
	21/32		.65625
43/64			.67188
		11/16	.6875
45/64			.70313
	23/32		.71875
47/64			.73438
		3/4	.750
49/64			.76563
	25/32		.78125
51/64			.79688
		13/16	.8125
53/64			.82813
	27/32		.84375
55/64			.85938
		7/8	.875
57/64			.89063
	29/32		.90625
59/64			.92188
		15/16	.9375
61/64			.95313
	31/32		.96875
63/64			.98438
		1	1.0000

Index

Table 12
MELTING POINTS[6] OF METALS

METAL	DEGREES FAHRENHEIT[7]
Solder, 50-50 (See Section 851)	400
Pewter	420
Tin	449
Babbitt	462
Lead	621
Zinc	787
Magnesium	1204
Aluminum	1218
Bronze	1675
Brass	1700
Silver	1761
Gold	1945
Copper	1981
Iron, Cast	2200
Steel	2500
Nickel	2646
Iron, Wrought	2700
Tungsten	6150

Table 38
CUTTING SPEEDS FOR MILLING ROUGHING CUTS WITH HIGH-SPEED CUTTERS

MATERIAL	CUTTING SPEED RANGE IN SFM
Low-carbon steel	60-80
Medium-carbon steel, annealed	60-80
High-carbon steel, annealed	50-70
Tool steel, annealed	50-70
Stainless steel	50-80
Gray cast iron, soft	50-80
Malleable iron	80-100
Aluminum and its alloys	400-1000
Brass	200-300
Bronze	100-200

These suggested speeds may be varied as follows:

For finishing cuts ....Increase 25-50%
For carbon-steel cutters ....Decrease about 50%
For cutters with cast-alloy tips ....Increase 50-75%
For cutters with cemented-carbide
  tips ....Increase 200-400%
Feeds should be as much as the cutter, the setup, and the equipment will safely stand. Recommended cutting fluids should be used, see Table 15, page 169.

Table 17. DRILLING SPEEDS AND FEEDS
For Use with High-Speed Steel Drills
(See sections 557 and 558)

SPEED IN REVOLUTIONS PER MINUTE (RPM) FOR HIGH-SPEED STEEL DRILLS
(REDUCE RPM ONE-HALF FOR CARBON-STEEL DRILLS)

DIAMETER OF DRILL	LOW-CARBON STEEL CAST IRON (SOFT) MALLEABLE IRON	MEDIUM-CARBON STEEL CAST IRON (HARD)	HIGH-CARBON STEEL HIGH-SPEED ALLOY STEEL	ALUMINUM AND ITS ALLOYS ORDINARY BRASS ORDINARY BRONZE	FEED PER REVOLUTION INCHES
	80-100 FT. PER. MIN.	70-80 FT. PER. MIN.	50-60 FT. PER. MIN.	200-300 FT. PER. MIN.	
1/8"	2445-3056	2139- 2445	1528-1833	6112-9168	0.002
1/4"	1222-1528	1070-1222	764-917	3056-4584	0.004
3/8"	815-1019	713-815	509-611	2038- 3057	0.006
1/2"	611-764	534-611	382-458	1528-2292	0.007
3/4"	407-509	357-407	255-306	1018-1527	0.010
1"	306-382	267-306	191-229	764-846	0.015